A Century of
Locomotive Building by
Robert Stephenson & Co
1823–1923

Robert Stephenson

M.P., D.C.L., F.R.S.

A CENTURY OF
LOCOMOTIVE BUILDING BY
ROBERT STEPHENSON & Co.

1823-1923

BY

J. G. H. WARREN

A Reprint with a New Introduction by
W. A. Tuplin DSc MIMechE

DAVID & CHARLES REPRINTS

7153 4378 5

Printed in Great Britain by
A. Wheaton & Company Exeter
for David & Charles (Publishers) Limited
South Devon House Railway Station
Newton Abbot Devon

INTRODUCTION TO THE 1970 EDITION

The 'Table of Contents' shows that for the period 1823 to 1859 this book devotes an average of ten pages to each year. From 1859 to 1923, however, the average is over three years per page. This difference reflects—or perhaps emphasises—the relative importance of the developments that took place in the steam locomotive during those periods. The pioneer, Trevithick in 1804, and his successors in the next twenty years took the momentous first step of discovering how to build a combination of steam-engine and boiler light enough and compact enough to propel itself along rails and moreover to pull (or to push) some pay-load as well. Today when the necessary materials, tools and techniques are readily available to build a steam locomotive for any job by simple routine it is hard to imagine the full extent of the difficulties, doubts and dangers that beset those who, with no experience to go on, produced the first locomotive engines that would work at all. By 1840 or so main principles had been well established, and locomotive designs were merely variations on a theme that was never superseded whilst steam was the motive power.

So it is appropriate in any general history of the steam locomotive to expand on what went on in the early years even at the expense of skimming over the refinements of the succeeding century. Similarly in writing of the work done by the firm of Robert Stephenson & Co it is natural to dwell on its first twenty years because it was during that period that it showed its greatest distinction. Brief mention is made of Trevithick, Blenkinsop, Murray, Hedley and Hackworth but space could hardly be spared for examining the highly vexed questions about the dependence of George Stephenson's work on that done by his predecessors and contemporaries in producing locomotive engines. An interesting detail is that he associated with Losh in carrying locomotives on 'steam springs' before suitable steel springs had become available.

Numerous quotations in this book from Nicholas Wood impress on one that here was a man who, even in those very early days, had acquired a masterly grasp of the fundamental physics and mechanics of the steam locomotive. His record of the Rainhill proceedings and his descriptions of the locomotives are models of careful observation and lucid comment.

The Rainhill Trials are described in satisfying detail and to anyone who has the impression that the steam locomotive originated at that time, it is salutary to be reminded that Stephenson had built fifty-five engines before the *Rocket*. That locomotive was victorious at Rainhill not so much because of excellence in design (although it was very good in that respect), but because it completed the trials without breaking down. The reason for this was the detail 'know-how' acquired by the Stephensons in building and running locomotives during the preceding fifteen years.

It is gratifying to read of the clemency shown by the judges to the unsuccessful competitors in allowing them time to repair breakdowns and to make repeated attempts. Apart from turning out some smoke, Stephenson's *Rocket* alone complied with all requirements and needed no concessions; it was a clear and indisputable winner of the contest.

Braithwaite and Eriesson's engine *Novelty* might well have won if it had stayed the specified course of 70 miles. Twenty trips in each direction over a measured length of $1\frac{3}{4}$ miles must have been fatiguing even for the spectators. It was an early demonstration of the 'push and pull' procedure that some British railways began to use some eighty years later.

Combining for the first time a fire-tube boiler, a double-wall-firebox, blast-induced draught and two outside cylinders, the *Rocket* of 1829 was the first of what became the world-standard type of steam locomotive. Within a single year, however, Stephensons had produced the *Planet* with outside frames, two inside cylinders (nearly horizontal), a smokebox formed as a forward prolongation of the boiler-barrel, which extended backwards in the shape of a double-wall-firebox, whence hot gases reached the smokebox by way of a large number of fire-tubes in the barrel. The quickly-conceived *Planet* with both wheels and cylinders inside the frame introduced a construction widely used in Britain for seventy years or more. But it was the 'Rocket' style, with wheels and cylinders *outside* the frame that eventually prevailed.

The book describes some experimental work in the ten years immediately after the building of the *Planet*. In particular a design produced in about 1832 for piston valves shows very advanced thinking. Even eighty years later some experienced designers had not caught up with it.

The means of moving a valve in a steam engine in appropriately timed relation to the motion of the piston was a mechanism offering scope for ingenuity in design in 1830 and indeed for many years afterwards. The laboured steps by which the seemingly obvious 'link-motion' was reached are typical of development in mechanical engineering. The simplest solution of any problem is the best but it is rarely found quickly. To decide now from the evidence who invented the 'link-motion' is almost impossible but it was certainly neither of the Stephensons. The term 'Stephenson link-motion' means that the mechanism concerned was developed in the Stephenson works and whilst this is a legitimate interpretation of the wording, it is not the natural one and so it is a little misleading.

The opening sentence of the chapter on 'The Blast Pipe' suggests that the author would rather not have mentioned it; he adds that some writers frankly avoided it. The spirited cartoon dated 1876 gives a vivid impression of the violence of the controversy that raged from time to time as to whether the blast-pipe was invented by Hedley, Hackworth or Stephenson in or about 1814. It is hard to see any point in such wrangling as Trevithick's published use of the principle in his locomotive of 1804 invalidated any claim by any successor to be 'the original and true inventor'. The Patent Office would not have been fooled for a moment. In a letter sent to *The Engineer* as late as 1858 Robert Stephenson mentioned that Hackworth's blast-pipe in the *Sans Pareil* (competitor at Rainhill) was so effective as to throw solid fuel from the chimney whereas later (and better) locomotives were so well designed that they 'steamed' with very gentle blast. In other words Trevithick's mild blast-pipe did all that was necessary!

In the experimental three-cylinder double-frame engine built by Stephensons in 1853 for the York, Newcastle & Berwick Railway the two outer cylinders were placed between inner and outer frames and the outer crank-pins were in a common axial plane at right angles to that of the inner crank-pin. The total volume of the outer cylinders was equal to that of the central cylinder. The object of this arrangement was clearly to eliminate the swaying action of the reciprocating parts but the total unbalance and the fluctuation of driving effort were as great as in a two-cylinder engine of the same power. This locomotive seems to be Stephensons' sole lapse from the simplicity of the two-cylinder engine. There was a similar solitary exception in the 999 locomotives built to British Railways' standard designs between 1951 and 1960.

During its later period the firm of Robert Stephenson & Co lost its initial prominence. It had pointed the way and led the way and others were gradually persuaded to see that the best thing they could do was to follow it. So Stephenson's became just one of a group of British competitors expanding in number and size, to build some locomotives for Britain but many more for export. For nearly a century the larger British railways produced most of their own locomotives and only rarely bought any from private builders. The last locomotives to be built for British Railways (90-ton two-cylinder 2-10-0s) had highly-pitched boilers that inspired someone to call the engines 'space-ships' and this was perhaps unwittingly apt, as they were in main principle, just enlarged and extended 'Rockets'.

W. A. TUPLIN

INTRODUCTION

In compiling this Centenary Book our principal difficulty has been to decide what could be included, within reasonable limits, from the mass of material at our disposal, for any full account of the work of Robert Stephenson & Company during the first twenty-five years of the firm's existence, is not only the history of the steam locomotive, but largely involves also the life story of the Stephensons, Father and Son.

Within our present limits however only a sketch of their careers has been possible ; and perhaps nothing more is required if we take into account their world-wide reputations. The best known authorities are still the biographies by Smiles, in his *Lives of the Engineers*, and the *Life of Robert Stephenson*, by Jeaffreson ; there are other memoirs, of which the most valuable is an 'Address on the two late Eminent Engineers,' delivered in 1860 to the North of England Institute of Mining Engineers, by Nicholas Wood, whose own early career was closely connected with that of George Stephenson, and whose pen did valiant service in the cause of the locomotive.

Smiles's biography of George Stephenson has been condemned for its too high lights, and it may be that to satisfy the canons of criticism to-day some toning down would be required ; but to a similar charge made in his own lifetime Smiles replied :—

I wrote the *Life of George Stephenson* simply because I admired the Man—his perseverance his noblemindedness, and his great railway works. I found, from Robert Stephenson, that no other person was likely to write his father's life; and I determined, so far as I could, to supply the defect. The only assistance which I received from him was in information, which was very valuable. He even warned me against writing the life, as he believed that it would probably end in loss of time and labour, as well as of money.

Jeaffreson in some instances contradicts Smiles, and, since unfortunately neither biographer was a trained engineer, the deductions of both on technical matters from the material which they had at their disposal must be received with caution, while some are manifestly incorrect. But Smiles has always been, and will remain, the classic authority, and his portrait of the elder Stephenson will ever be an inspiration to a great public, for whom the technical details of the locomotive, or the difference between an 'exhaust' and a 'blast' pipe, are matters of small moment.

We might with propriety have confined our sketch of early locomotive development by the Stephensons to a full quotation of the 'Narrative of his Father's Inventions,' given to Smiles by Robert Stephenson shortly before his own death ; but we have preferred in disputed cases to rely on earlier and contemporary records and, wherever possible, on the statements of others than those directly interested in the claims made for priority of idea.

In trying to-day to obtain a true perspective of George Stephenson's work it has been impossible to ignore the attempts made from time to time to deny him all credit for the improvement of the locomotive. We can perhaps see in these attempts a justifiable re-action from the inaccuracy of writers who describe Stephenson as the "inventor of locomotives and railroads"; but we cannot fail to notice that some of the later claimants themselves, by ignoring the work of Trevithick and others, are equally open to reproach, and their claims are too frequently found to be based on hearsay or rumour, unsupported by contemporary documents, on mis-statement of dates, and the distortion of recorded facts.

The confusion of the historian by these *ex parte* statements has been worse confounded by the manufacture in later years of drawings, purporting to represent in every detail certain early locomotives, but actually made long after the engines themselves had been scrapped. There have also been published lists giving the numbers and dates of early locomotives made by Robert Stephenson & Company, and statements concerning them, for many of which we are unable to find any evidence; in some cases indeed such evidence as we have is in a contrary sense. It is advisable to state here that the firm's own early records are in some cases incomplete or contradictory, and we must remember that in early days 'as made' drawings were not included in a contract as they are to-day. Moreover, engines ordered for one railway were frequently transferred to another, and makers' order numbers do not necessarily give sequence of construction.

For these reasons we have dealt as far as possible on broad lines with the development of the locomotive, as shown by typical engines of whose identity there can be no question. In our endeavour to support by original contemporary evidence any statement we may make, we have, with the help of many friends, obtained information hitherto unknown to, or ignored by, writers on the locomotive. In one particular instance a two years' search among English, French and German records was rewarded, as we were going to press, by the opportune discovery of a sketch, made by an eye-witness in 1829, which supplied the missing link to a chain of evidence, and has made it possible to reconstruct with certainty an exceptionally interesting locomotive.

To those who have helped us we offer our most grateful thanks, particularly to the following :—

Mr. George Stephenson, a grand-nephew of George Stephenson, for essential information from the first *Minute Book* of Robert Stephenson & Company.

Sir Alfred E. Pease, Bart., great-grandson of Edward Pease, for permission to make use of all the relative valuable material preserved among his family papers, some of it already published in *The Diaries of Edward Pease* (Headley Brothers, 1907).

The Director and Officers of the Science Museum, South Kensington; in particular to Mr. H. W. Dickinson, and Mr. E. A. Forward, for criticism, advice and proof reading. The help of the last named, based on his own studies of early locomotives, has been of special value.

The Chief Librarians of the Darlington, Edinburgh, Glasgow, Liverpool, Manchester, and Newcastle-upon-Tyne Public Libraries, for permission to reproduce many interesting contemporary prints and drawings. We are also particularly indebted to Mr. R. N. Appleby Miller of the latter library for search on our behalf and for valuable material.

The Goldsmith's Librarian, University of London, for permission to reproduce sketches from the Rastrick collection.

The Director of the Conservatoire national des Arts et Métiers, Paris, for permission to photograph models, and to Professeur Édouard Sauvage, Ingénieur en Chef honoraire des Chemins de fer de l'État, for personal help and research.

The Smithsonian Institution, Washington, U.S.A., for information and illustrations, in particular to Mr. Carl W. Mitman.

The Institutions of Civil, and Mechanical, Engineers and their Officials.

The Great Western Railway Company and its Officials, in particular to Mr. G. H. Burrows, and Mr. C. B. Collett, Chief Mechanical Engineer ; the London Midland & Scottish Railway Company and its Officials, in particular to Mr. J. E. Anderson, Mr. G. Hughes, Chief Mechanical Engineer, and Mr. R. C. Irwin, Secretary ; the London & North Eastern Railway Company and its Officials.

The Director of the Belgian State Railways, the Paris Lyons & Mediterranean, and the Paris-Orleans Railway Companies, the Superintendent of Power of the Pennsylvania Railroad, and the Baldwin Locomotive Company.

We are also greatly indebted to the following :—

M. Ferdinand Achard, for search among French records ;—Mr. E. L. Ahrons, whose unique knowledge of particular locomotives has been of special value ;— Mr. J. Snowden Bell, New York, for research and information from American sources ;—Mr. Isaac Briggs ;—Mr. E. M. Bywell, editor of the *North Eastern Magazine* ;—Mr. Waynman Dixon, for important information and illustrations from the papers of the late John Dixon ;—Mr. C. F. Dendy Marshall, for valuable information and many interesting illustrations from his collection ;— Sir David Salomons, Bart., from whose remarkable collection of engravings and prints illustrations have been obtained ; and we have to thank others whose names are recorded by footnotes throughout this book.

Ample acknowledgment has been given throughout to previous authors, but we must record a special debt to the work of the late W. W. Tomlinson, whose well documented *History of the North Eastern Railway*, is both a mine of information and a guide to other sources. The present writer has to acknowledge his personal debt to many whose names do not appear, including members of the staff of Robert Stephenson & Co., and other personal friends who have helped by information, advice and criticism.

Special thanks are due to the Printers, and last, though not least, to the Directors of Messrs. Robert Stephenson & Company, without whose confidence this book could not have assumed its present form.

J. G. H. WARREN

DARLINGTON,
23rd JUNE, 1923

TABLE OF CONTENTS

TABLE OF CONTENTS

————

ADDENDA AND ERRATA

p. 102, for 1844 read 1845.

p. 305, below illustration, read, from a photo of an undated drawing of uncertain origin, presumably in possession. etc.

p. 344, line 22, for 'Great Britain' read 'Great Western.'
last line, footnote (2) read p. xxi, and p. xii, fig. 1.

p. 398, line 2, for 1848, read 1848-9.
line 6, read, 18 by 21 inches in the first, and 16 by 24 inches in the second.

Painted by H. P. Briggs, R.A.   Engraved by C. Turner, A.R.A., 1838.

GEORGE STEPHENSON
1781—1848

A CENTURY OF
LOCOMOTIVE BUILDING

GEORGE STEPHENSON
1781—1848

We have undertaken to discourse here for a little on Great Men, their manner of appearance in our world's business, what ideas men formed of them, what work they did.—*Carlyle.*

La génie n'est autre chose qu'une grande aptitude à la patience —*Buffon.*

GEORGE STEPHENSON was born in 1781 at Wylam-on-Tyne in Northumberland; those who have lived near a colliery pit-head and heard the ceaseless breathing of its pumping engine will best realise the sights and sounds near which the boy grew up. At the age of eight he began his working life, not however at the neighbouring colliery where his father was employed, but in the fields. At fourteen or fifteen he obtained employment as assistant fireman in a colliery near Newburn. At seventeen he was advanced to the office of plugman, and later, after having improved a Newcomen engine, he was promoted 'from the handles of the winding engine to the position of a directing engineer.' Unable up to the age of eighteen to read or write, he had till then depended for his advancement on natural powers of observation which were to stand him in good stead to the end of his life.

From his own evidence, given in 1825 before the Committee on the first Liverpool and Manchester Railway Bill, we learn that in 1803, at the age of 22, he was appointed superintendent engineer at the Killingworth Collieries and continued until 1813 in the service of its proprietors, the Grand Alliance Company. The Grand Allies, as they were commonly known, were at this time Lord Ravensworth, James Archibald Stuart-Wortley, and the Trustees of the deceased Earl of Strathmore; they represented a partnership which had been formed in the eighteenth century for the protection of great mining interests near Newcastle. During this period of Stephenson's service with the Grand Allies the steam engines were placed entirely under his control. In 1813 he became, in his own words, 'a civil engineer generally,' superintending collieries at Killingworth and elsewhere, some of them twenty miles from each other; considerable alterations and improvements were made at his suggestion in the engines and railroads belonging to these collieries. He constructed new engines for most of them, laid down a considerable portion of new railroad, and with the permission of his employers, the Grand Allies, extended his superintendence to other collieries and railroads, in which he similarly introduced alterations and improvements. To these we shall refer later in considering George Stephenson's work in connection with the development of the steam locomotive The full story of his life and of his rise to an honoured eminence is too well known to require repetition in these notes, which are primarily intended to describe his work on the locomotive and his share in the foundation of the Locomotive Building Industry.

George Stephenson lived to see his dreams and prophecies more than fulfilled in a universal adoption of railways and steam locomotion. Small wonder that the Victorians, seeing in the railway an easy road to the millenium of a universal peace and material prosperity, should have counted him among their greatest men; and though Edward Pease, who had found in the born engineer a capable instrument for the fulfilment of his own dreams, was to write later in some disillusionment of high early hopes, he was still able to refer to his choice of Stephenson as a 'marvellously happy one, he being a man of striking self-taught genius and powerful vigorous intellect ; a man of honour, probity and indefatigable perseverance,'—a fitting tribute to a career characterised throughout by the same honesty which led Stephenson in 1821 to urge the use of wrought iron, in place of cast iron, rails for the Stockton and Darlington Railway, honesty to which he sacrificed not only material gain but, for the time at least, his personal friendship with William Losh.

George Stephenson has been erroneously entitled, and will no doubt continue to be widely known, as the 'inventor of the locomotive and railways.' His title to fame rests however not on any such claim, but on the wider grounds of a faith, shared later by his son, which was to tunnel the earth and bridge the sea to smite a path for the iron child of his dreams. Chance threw him in the path of Hedley's Wylam locomotive, but it is due to more than chance that his name is remembered when others are forgotten. The credit for the invention of the steam locomotive in anything foreshadowing its present form is due to another man, Trevithick, a contemporary with whom, as with many others who helped in the early development of the locomotive, Stephenson was on terms of personal friendship; among these, and after Trevithick in point of time, come Blenkinsop, Dodds, Hedley, Hackworth, Kennedy, Losh, Murray, Steele, Wood, and many more. But with perhaps less inventive genius than some, and with less education than many of these men, George Stephenson more than any one helped to establish the practical success of the locomotive and ensure its adoption instead of the fixed engine.

Remarkable too for his civil, as for his mechanical, engineering his greater achievement was perhaps his work in the construction of the Liverpool and Manchester Railway, and his final success as the protagonist in a struggle which would have broken a lesser man. The measure both of the opposition which he faced, and of his actual accomplishment, is to be found in the minutes of evidence before the committee on the proposed Bill ; the measure of his faith in the railroad in his own words—'I mean to make it perfect.'

The traveller crossing Chat Moss may reflect that one of the most remarkable monuments to human perseverance was raised on a bog which might well have been the grave of a career.

Nicholas Wood, speaking after Stephenson's death of the early successes of his career, related how he had 'attached himself to Stephenson and all his nostrums':—

Feeling the advantage as a youth of being in the confidence of such a person it is not to be wondered at that I devoted the whole of my energies, and all my spare time, to improve myself, and to assist him in the various works which he projected from time to time, and in the various experiments connected therewith.

The reputation of a great man, once won, may outrun his worth; but to-day, looking back through more than a hundred years, we may still say that the reputation of George Stephenson is no greater than the strength of character, the integrity of purpose, and the faith through adverse circumstances, which led to an achievement that was to make his name a household word throughout the world. He died in 1848, in his sixty-seventh year, his faculties and reputation undimmed, and time has justified the contemporary judgment of his fellows which placed George Stephenson among the Heroes.

CHAT MOSS

ROBERT STEPHENSON

1803—1859

THE TWO STEPHENSONS

1803–1859

ROBERT STEPHENSON was born at Willington Quay, in Northumberland, in 1803, the year of his father's appointment as engine superintendent to the Grand Allies. With his own profession established George Stephenson determined that his son should be trained to follow him ; so Robert, after four years' schooling in Newcastle, was apprenticed in 1819 at the age of sixteen to Nicholas Wood, his father's friend, then managing engineer and colliery viewer at Killingworth. Robert's three years' apprenticeship was interrupted in 1821 to assist his father, with John Dixon, in a new survey for the Stockton and Darlington Railway, and he afterwards had some further experience as assistant to William James, then surveying a route for a railway from Liverpool to Manchester ; in October 1822, he went to Edinburgh University where he spent six months.

In June 1823, when an engine manufactory was established by his father and others at Newcastle, Robert Stephenson was appointed manager of the concern which through good and ill fortune has borne his name for a century. Though only twenty, and necessarily lacking in practical experience, the young man had so favourably impressed the men of business with whom his father was now firmly associated, that in June of the following year, 1824, he was entrusted with the command of a mining expedition to Columbia, and both the work he did and the letters he wrote during the three years of his engagement, from his twenty-first to his twenty-fourth year, give ample proof of early developed character and ability. After his return, in 1827, from an uncongenial and unsatisfactory enterprise, he not only resumed the management of the works at Newcastle and retrieved the errors which had been committed during his absence, but until the death of his father was intimately connected with him in those railway works which have established the fame of both Stephensons as mechanical and civil engineers.

George Stephenson had not received full recognition until he was over forty, but Robert, thanks to his father, was able to start higher up the ladder to fame. 'I am fully conscious in my own mind,' he said in later years, 'how greatly my civil engineering has been influenced by the mechanical knowledge I derived from my father.'

So early as 1829, in his connection with a proposed line from Warrington to Birmingham, he had to consider whether he might not be brought into opposition to his father as a professional rival ; in 1830 he was engineer-in-chief of the Warrington, and the Leicester and Swannington, Railways, and at the same time directing the Newcastle engine works and improving the locomotive ; in 1833, in his thirtieth year, he was appointed engineer-in-chief of the

London and Birmingham Railway, a vast undertaking, almost four times the length of the Liverpool and Manchester Railway and involving operations of very great difficulty. While so engaged Robert Stephenson had to encounter both the natural difficulties which lay in his path, and the personal antagonism of an influential group of men who had been enraged both by his father's success and by the roughness of tongue with which the stout Northumbrian maintained his views on railways and locomotives in opposition to their own. He had also to meet the jealousy of other locomotive builders, who had now come into the field and maintained that the Stephensons enjoyed an unfair monopoly.

Robert Stephenson's reputation was afterwards carried throughout the world not only by his locomotives but by his bridges, the most famous being those on the tubular system over the Menai Straits, and the River St. Lawrence in Canada, respectively, and the High Level Bridge at Newcastle; notably in the first mentioned he showed that his own conservatism did not prevent his solving a difficult problem by the adoption of a design as bold as it was novel.

'Old George,' as he was known to friends and enemies alike, had been the champion of the railway and the locomotive against those who believed in neither, or at best believed the locomotive to be inferior to the rope; his son was to become the champion of an established system against those who sought to divert the development of railways and locomotives from what the two Stephensons considered to be the lines of sound principle. In the atmospheric railway, which had the support of the younger Brunel and other eminent engineers, the Stephensons saw an attempt to return to the fixed engine system, and they had to combat many even less plausible devices based on what they knew to be fallacies; though neither claimed infallibility, it may be that both men, as they grew older, became less tolerant of opposition. But a century of practice has justified their belief in the suitability and capacity of the steam locomotive for the everyday work of the railway, though with changing conditions the wheel has now come full circle, and the fixed engine controversy has been revived in our own time; not indeed with a 'rope of wind,' but with a rope of electricity. Nicholas Wood, who had known both intimately, and himself rendered valuable service to them and their cause, speaking after both were gone could say with truth of the Two Stephensons:—

It was the indomitable perseverance, and the singular abilities which those two great men possessed, which enabled the elder Stephenson, and afterwards his son, to comprehend and to complete the system of improvements which raised railways and the locomotive engine from a state of comparative inutility to what they at present possess. . . . . . .

It was the lot of the Stephensons, and of men of their time, to be called on to *feel* their way, as it were, slowly and with difficulty towards the conclusions which they should accept. Much of that which is mere routine to you was to them a matter of cautious and patiently pursued experiment. It is yours—my young friends—to scud with flowing sheet along a course on the navigation of which they could only advance by frequent and wearisome casts of the lead line. They had to grope through the shallows and the quicksands of an untried passage where now they have left a clear and well defined chart for the guidance of those who follow them.

The enemies of 'Old George' have denied him genius as an engineer; they have not been able to deny him the 'transcendent capacity of taking trouble,' a characteristic shared by his son. Both men were gifted too with personalities which, though differing in themselves and developed on different lines, inspired not only the confidence but the affection of those with whom they were most intimately connected in their work.

Robert Stephenson in particular by his generous personality endeared himself both to his friends and to his countrymen, and on his untimely death in 1859, in his fifty-sixth year, prematurely aged by a strenuous life, public opinion claimed and mourned him as one of England's representative men and, by the nation's wish, he was buried in Westminster Abbey with every token of respect and regret.

(from an original in the Newcastle Public Library.)

(from a lithograph by J. D. Harding, printed by C. Hullmandel.)

George Stephenson's Locomotives at Hetton
1822

CHAPTER I

THE FIRST RAILROADS

We owe all our railways to the Collieries in the North; and the difficulties which their industry over-
came taught us to make railways and to make locomotives to work them.
Captain J. M. Laws, R.N., before the Gauge Commission, 1845.

The early waggon-ways, whose origin can be traced back to the sixteenth
century[1], and of which there is ample record by the latter half of the seventeenth
century, became generally known as 'Newcastle Roads.'

The manner of the carriage is by laying rails of timber, from the colliery down to the
river, exactly straight and parallel, and bulky carts are made with four rowlets fitting these
rails, whereby the carriage is so easy that one horse will draw four or five chaldron of coals[2]
and is an immense benefit to the coal merchants.[3]

These wooden railways, and the later plateways or tramroads, and finally
the solid cast iron edge-rail, the prototype of the modern rail, were all developed
to meet the needs of collieries and were designed in the first instance for traction by horse-power. In the colliery districts of Wales such railways had
also come into general use by 1810 when a French traveller wrote[4] :—

We crossed several iron rail-ways, leading from founderies and coal mines in the country
to the sea. Four low cast-iron wheels run in an iron groove lying along the road. It is now,
however, the general custom to place the groove on the circumference of the wheel, running upon
the rail, which is a mere edge of iron, upon which no stone or other impediment can lodge.
Five small waggons, and sometimes six, fastened together, each carrying two tons of coal, are
drawn by three horses, that is four tons to each horse, besides the waggons—almost five or six
times as much as they could draw on a common road; on an ascent the waggons are separated.

Men welcome each new means for defeating gravity, time, and space, and
the public enthusiasm for a new means of transport, to be echoed later on the
Stockton and Darlington, the Liverpool and Manchester, and other railways,
is well shown by a contemporary report describing the introduction of rope
haulage by stationary, or fixed, engine power at the opening of a waggon-way
from Bewicke Main to the River Tyne[5] :—

MAY 17TH 1809.
The opening of the waggon-way from Bewicke Main to the river Tyne took place, on
which occasion every road to it was crowded with passengers at an early hour, and before eleven
o'clock about ten thousand people were assembled. About this time, four waggons of small

[1] MSS. of Lord Middleton, Wollaton Hall, Notts. 'Railes' are mentioned in a 'Statement of the delivery
. . . of coals . . .' from Oct. 1597—Oct. 1598. *Hist. MSS. Report Commission* 1911, pp. 169, 177.

[2] The ratio of the London to the Newcastle Chaldron appears to have been constantly in dispute. See
Acts, Henry VIII 1543, and subsequent reigns; the Newcastle Chaldron was declared 53 cwt. by Statute 6 &
7 William III c. 10. Taylor, Archæology of the Coal Trade, *Proc. Arch. Inst. Great Britain and Ireland,* 1852

[3] Roger North, *Life of Francis North, Baron Guildford,* 1676, New ed., 1826, Vol. I., p. 281.

[4] *Journal of a Tour and Residence in Great Britain,* by a French Traveller, 1815, Vol. I., p. 212.

[5] Richardson's *Local Historians' Table Book,* Vol. III. Historical Division p. 80, from local papers.

coals were brought up the first plane by the steam-engine, to the great admiration of the spectators; but owing to some unexplained circumstance, the four waggons of best coals intended for the Tyne did not start till a much later hour.

As soon as the waggons reached the summit of the second and highest plane, up which they went with surprising velocity and regularity, the British flag was hoisted at Ayton cottage; and the event was announced by a discharge of six pieces of cannon, which were answered by an equal number from the Ann and Isabella, His Majesty's armed ship on the Tyne, and from Deptford House, the residence of Mr. Cooke. Immediately on the waggons reaching the first plane, about four hundred gentlemen sat down to dinner, in a tent fitted up for the occasion.

An excellent military band attended. In the evening, in order to prove the excellence of the level railway, six men, without horses, took with the greatest ease four laden waggons, with each ten men on the top, from Ayton cottage to the Tyne; and the first coals being put on board the Ann and Isabella, the discharges of artillery were repeated.

Later the high cost of horses and forage which resulted from the Napoleonic wars drove the colliery proprietors to seek and encourage every means for cheapening the transport of coal, even on the level, where the horse still held its own; the time was ripe for the Steam Locomotive and the men who were to nurse it through its infancy.

CHAPTER II

THE FIRST RAIL LOCOMOTIVES
1804—1814

Every ship that comes to America got its chart from Columbus. Every novel is a debtor to Homer, every carpenter who shaves with a fore plane borrows the genius of a forgotten inventor.
Inventions have all been invented over and over fifty times. Man is the arch machine of which all these shifts drawn from himself are toy models.—Emerson.

We do not know to whom thoughts of locomotion by steam power first occurred, but there is definite record of such thought, and of some practice, during the latter half of the eighteenth century.[1]

TREVITHICK   Within the limits of our present purpose—a just appreciation of George Stephenson's early work—we cannot describe these attempts, but remembering the words of the philosopher we shall hope to avoid the reproach of unfair comparison and undue omission when we state that the first success in heavy haulage on a prepared track was attained by a Cornishman, Richard Trevithick, in 1804, with his high pressure engine; we have his own record of a great event in a letter[2] dated:—

PENYDARRAN, 15th February 1804.

MR. GIDDY,
    SIR,—Last Saturday we lighted the fire in the tram-waggon and worked it without the wheels to try the engine. On Monday we put it on the tramroad. It worked very well, and ran up hill and down with great ease, and was very manageable. We had plenty of steam and power. I expect to work it again to-morrow. Mr. Homfray and the gentlemen I mentioned in my last, will be home to-morrow. The bet will not be determined until the middle of next week, at which time I shall be very happy to see you.
                    I am, Sir,
                            Your humble servant,
                                    RICHARD TREVITHICK.

A few days later, on 20th February, Trevithick writes further to Giddy[3]:—

SIR,—The tram-waggon has been at work several times. It works exceedingly well, and is much more manageable than horses. We have not tried to draw more than 10 tons at a time, but I doubt not we could draw 40 tons at a time very well; 10 tons stand no chance at all with it. We have been but two miles on the road and back again, and shall not go farther until Mr. Homfray comes home. He is to dine at home to-day, and the engine goes down to meet him. The engineer from the Government is with him.
    The engine, with water included, is about 5 tons. It runs up the tramroad of 2 inches in a yard forty strokes per minute with the empty waggons. The engine moves forward 9 feet at every stroke. The public are much taken up with it. The bet of 500 guineas will be decided about the end of this week. Your presence would give me more satisfaction than you can

[1] Cugnot's road locomotive, 1769, is preserved in the Conservatoire des Arts et Métiers, Paris.

[2] *Life of Trevithick*, Vol. I., p. 159 *et seq.*

[3] Davies Giddy, afterwards Sir Davies Gilbert, M.P., 1767-1839, President of the Royal Society; assisted Humphrey Davy, Trevithick, and the two Hornblowers.

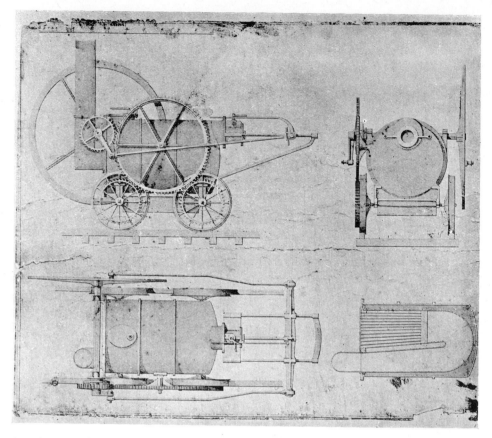

from the original drawing at the Science Museum, South Kensington.

Trevithick's Gateshead Locomotive

from the original in possession of Mr. E. D. Lowy.

Trevithick's Model Locomotive

conceive, and I doubt not you will be fully repaid for the toil of the journey by a sight of the engine.

The steam that is discharged from the engine is turned up the chimney about 3 feet above the fire, and when the engine works forty strokes per minute, $4\frac{1}{2}$ feet stroke, $8\frac{1}{4}$ inches diameter of cylinder, not the smallest particle of steam appears out of the top of the chimney, though it is but 8 feet above where the steam is delivered into it, neither at a distance from it is steam or water found. I think it is made a fixed air by the heat of the chimney. The fire burns much better when the steam goes up the chimney than when the engine is idle. I intend to make a smaller engine for the road, as this has much more power than is wanted here. This engine is to work a hammer.

The engineer from London will try a great many experiments with these engines, as that is his sole business here, and that is my reason for so much wishing you here. He intends to try the strength of the boiler by a force-pump, and has sent down orders to get long steam-gauges and force-pumps ready for that purpose.

We shall continue our journey on the road to-day with the engine, until we meet Mr. Homfray and the London engineer, and intend to take the horses out of the coach, fasten it to the engine, and draw them home. The other end of the road is $9\frac{3}{4}$ miles from here. The coach-axles are the same length as the engine-axles, so the coach will run very easily on the tramroad.

There have been several experiments made by Mr. Homfray and this engineer in London, lately, on these engines. I am very much obliged to you for your offer to assist in making out a publication of the duty and advantages of these engines. As soon as I can get proper specimens at work, and you as an eye-witness of their performance, I shall value your kind offer and assistance far beyond any other to be got, as you have been consulted, and have assisted me from the beginning.

I am, Sir.

Your very humble servant,

RICHARD TREVITHICK.

Writing again, on 22nd February, he says :—

The gentleman that bet 500 guineas against it rode the whole of the journey with us, and is satisfied that he has lost the bet. We shall continue to work on the road, and shall take 40 tons the next journey.

These letters read in conjunction with Trevithick and Vivian's Specification of 1802 show that many of the most important features of the steam locomotive had been anticipated in thought, or actually adopted, by Trevithick, and two facts in particular appear which we shall have to bear in mind later when considering certain claims to priority in invention.

Firstly, the trial of 20th February 1804 proved the sufficiency of smooth wheels for adhesion [1] :—

The periphery of the carriage wheels is sometimes made uneven by projecting heads of nails, or bolts or cross grooves, of fittings to railroads, and, in cases of hard pull, a lever, bolt, or claw is caused to project through the rim of the wheels, so as to take hold of the ground, but, in general, the ordinary structure or figure of the external surface of the wheel is found to answer the intended purpose.

Secondly, the stimulation of combustion by the exhaust, or waste steam passing up the chimney, had been observed and was recorded by Trevithick. But unfortunately there is no definite statement in the contemporary accounts to tell us whether this first successful rail locomotive had the horizontal cylinder

---

[1] Trevithick and Vivian's Specification, 26th March 1802 (No. 2,599).

arrangement with which it is commonly represented, or the vertical cylinder which was the feature of Trevithick's high pressure engine for general purposes. Two early models still preserved [1] show that Trevithick had at least considered such an arrangement for a locomotive, and the illustration on his business card [2] suggests that he may have actually applied it to an engine which is known to have run in 1808 on a circular track laid down on what is now Euston Square, London. [3] In this case also evidence as to the design is inconclusive, but there can be no doubt that before he gave up his work on the locomotive Trevithick had in mind, if not in fact, adopted a direct drive from the cylinder to the crank pin as shown by the model which we illustrate. [4]

A well-known historian of the steam engine, John Farey, writing in 1815 [5] definitely states that the rail locomotive of 1804 had a vertical cylinder, but he was writing eleven years after the event. Another man as well qualified to have given a correct description was prevented by an accident from witnessing the experiments to which Trevithick referred in his letter of 4th March 1804 ; this was Simon Goodrich, chief mechanician to the Navy Board, a trained and keen observer, who left among his papers [6] a letter from Homfray dated :—

PENYDARRAN PLACE,
March 7th 1804.

DEAR SIR,—I am concerned at being obliged to put off your Journey with Lieut. Cunningham for the present—more especially on acct. of the reason.

I have yesterday had a very narrow escape—driving a Gig with a young lady in it—the Horse wd. not hold back going down Hill & run away & throwed us both out—thank God no bones were broke—the Lady escaped wonderfully with only a hurt on the leg—but I have suffered more . . . . . . but as I get better will write to you.

I am, Dr Sir. Yours, &c.,
SAML. HOMFRAY.

Two days later Trevithick writes, on 9th March, to Giddy [7] :—

I am sorry to inform you that the experiments that were to be exhibited before the London gents. are put off on account of an accident which happened to Mr. Homfray on Tuesday last.

Accounts of Trevithick's engine quickly reached the north ; Christopher Blackett the proprietor of Wylam Colliery ordered a locomotive from him and one was actually built to his designs at Gateshead, but it does not appear to have ever run. An original drawing of this engine has been preserved [8] and we have the account of an eye-witness [9] dated 1st May 1805 :—

[1] One at the Science Museum, South Kensington, the other owned by Mr. E. D. Lowy.

[2] Reproduced in *A Cornish Giant*, by Edith K. Harper, E. & F. N. Spon, 1913.

[3] The Mystery of Trevithick's London Locomotives, *Trans. Newcomen.Society*, Vol. I., p. 34.

[4] By permission of Mr. E. D. Lowy, owner of the model and copyright.

[5] Rees' *Cyclopædia*, 1819. Article "Steam Engine." In the preface to his book *The Steam Engine* published in 1827, Farey states that the 'Article' was written in 1815.

[6] Preserved at the Science Museum, South Kensington.

[7] *Life of Trevithick*, Vol. I., p. 168.

[8] At the Science Museum, South Kensington.

[9] Copy of original *MS.* preserved at the Science Museum, South Kensington.

> I saw an Engine this day upon a new plan it is to draw three waggons of Coals upon the Wylam waggon way, the road is nearly leavle, the Engine is to travile with the Waggons each Waggon with the Coals weighs about three-and-a-half tons and the Engine weighs four-and-a-half tons the Engine is to work without a Vacume. The Cylinder is seven inches diameter three feet stroke and is placed inside the Boiler and the fire is inside also the speed they expect to travle at is four miles per houre.

It is much to be regretted that after his initial success Trevithick should have eventually abandoned his work on the steam rail locomotive ; it is clear that he had the opportunity to found what might have been the first locomotive building establishment, but except for his mysterious London engine of 1808, and some road coach locomotives, his versatile genius turned to other work ; he left England for Peru in 1814, and it was left to others to reap the harvest in the vast field opened up by his adoption of high pressure steam. Referring to his struggle against Boulton and Watt, who had consistently opposed the use of high pressure steam, Trevithick had written in 1804 :—

> Let them meet me on fair grounds, and I will soon convince them of the superiority of the 'pressure of steam engine.'

It was indeed only the abandonment of the low pressure engine with its necessary condenser, and consequent great size and weight, which had made the steam locomotive possible.

BLENKINSOP AND MURRAY   The next successful colliery locomotive of which we have ample contemporary evidence was built in 1812 for Charles Brandling, M.P., to the instructions of John Blenkinsop, viewer of the Middleton Colliery, by Fenton, Murray and Wood of Leeds, who are described as 'manufacturers of the most established reputation after Messrs. Boulton and Watt.'

Of this engine we have fortunately both the artistic representation of 1814 and drawings, with a full description, by a French engineer, published in 1815.[1] Except that these drawings show a driving gear wheel on each side they appear to give a generally accurate representation of the locomotive as actually made. This engine cost £380 including a royalty of £30 to Trevithick for his patent rights.[2]   His influence is evident in the design, notably in the use of cocks for distributing the steam, instead of the slide valve which Matthew Murray had patented[3] ; but the boiler had only a single flue, and the adoption of a rack and pinion appears to show that, either the sufficiency of adhesion with smooth wheels as demonstrated by Trevithick had not been appreciated, or that the limitations to engine weight in the case of Blenkinsop's engine made it necessary to depend for haulage capacity on the rack, for which Blenkinsop himself had taken out a patent[4] ; the latter seems the more probable reason for we find Murray writing to Goodrich twelve years later, that the weight of locomotives was the principal obstacle to their wider adoption.

[1] *Bulletin de la Société d'Encouragement d'Industrie*, 1815, No. CXXX.
[2] Tomlinson, *The North Eastern Railway*, p. 21.
[3] Patent Specification, 28th June 1802 (No. 2,632).
[4] Patent Specification, 10th April 1811 (No. 3,431).

from a watercolour by George Walker, published in 'The Costume of Yorkshire in 1814.'

THE COLLIER

The first of Blenkinsop's engines was tried in June 1812, and several others made afterwards on the same principle worked successfully at Leeds for many years, some until 1853, hauling loads in excess of those taken by the locomotives of other designs which immediately followed. They excited the interest of the Grand Duke Nicholas, afterwards Tsar, of Russia who saw one of these engines at work and a model was afterwards sent to Russia by the makers.[1] A Blenkinsop engine was employed for some little time on the Coxlodge waggon-way, near Newcastle-on-Tyne, but owing to the expense of the rack rails engines of this system were not generally adopted for colliery purposes. It was however Blenkinsop's engine which appears to have inspired Thomas Gray of Nottingham with the enthusiasm for railways and locomotives which led him in 1820 to publish his views on the subject[2]; so late as October 1825 unwearied in his advocacy Gray, wrote[3]:—

The man who can *now hesitate* to recommend steam engines instead of horse-power must be pitied for his ignorance or despised for his obstinacy. . . . . . after the demonstration of their utility daily proved by Mr. Blenkinsop these fourteen years.

[1] Letter from Matthew Murray to Simon Goodrich, 21st Nov. 1824, preserved at the Science Museum, South Kensington.

[2] *Observations on a General Iron Railway*, etc., 1820

[3] *Gentleman's Magazine*, Vol. XCV., p. 311.

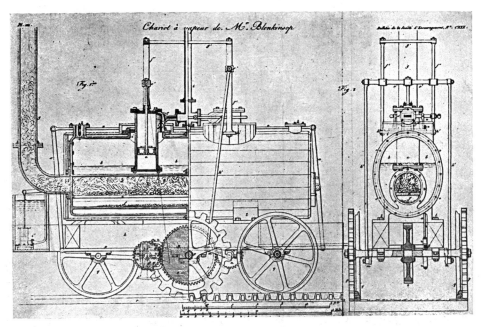

from the Bulletin de la Société d'Encouragement d'Industrie, 1815.

BLENKINSOP'S LOCOMOTIVE.

Unfortunately the writer himself afterwards showed great obstinacy in maintaining the superiority of the rack and pinion locomotive for general railway purposes, long after the sufficiency and desirability of adhesion with smooth wheels had been amply demonstrated, and it is possibly on this account that Gray has not received the credit due to him for his early efforts in the cause of railroads and steam locomotion ; he was one of the first to recognise their great possibilities.

HEDLEY AND HACKWORTH
In 1813 William Hedley, colliery viewer to Christopher Blackett of Wylam-on-Tyne, proved for himself by experiment the truth of Trevithick's theory that 'in general' there was sufficient adhesion with the 'ordinary structure or figure of the external surface of the wheel.' With a full knowledge of Trevithick's and Blenkinsop's engines Hedley, after a first failure, produced successful locomotives differing from either ; he drove through gears, as had both Trevithick and Blenkinsop, but dispensed with the rack rail of the latter, and for the engine mechanism followed generally the lines of the stationary beam engine of the time.

Hedley's engine had not been long at work before one of the proprietors from whom Blackett had obtained wayleaves objected to the passing of the engine as a nuisance, and the circumstances are recorded in the statement of a case for counsel's opinion[1] dated 9th August 1814 :—

[1] Case respecting the use of a steam engine for conveying coals, 9th August 1814. *MS.* preserved at the Science Museum, South Kensington.

Mr. Blackett is Proprietor of a Coalmine at Wylam in Northumberland, and for the purpose of Vending his coals at Lemington he took Wayleaves on various Estates Between these and Wylam especially over the Estate of A for a Term of Years not yet expired whereby A demised a sufficient and convenient Wayleave Liberty and Passage to and for Mr. Blackett his Executors Administrators and Assigns and his and their Agents Servants and Workmen from time to time and at all times during the continuance of the said demise to take lead and carry away with Horses Carts Waggons or any other Carriages whatsoever all and every or any of the Coals to be won wrought and gotten forth and out of the said Colliery and Coalmines in through over and along the lands and closes of A according to the line of way therein described under the yearly certain and contingent rents therein mentioned. When the Lease was granted Mr Blackett led his Coals by the ordinary Coal Waggons drawn by Horses but his agent has recently discovered an invention to draw them by a Steam Engine instead of Horses and for that purpose has obtained His Majesty's Letters Patent as a reward for his Ingenuity and the Steam Engine is now actually at work. In the operation a little noise and Smoak is certainly made which A considers a Nuisance and has requested Mr. Blackett to suspend the use of it, Mr. Blackett is extremely anxious of being upon good Terms with his Landlord and is inclined to yield to his wishes as far as he consistently can but in the first place he is desirous of having the Question of right and wrong established between them.

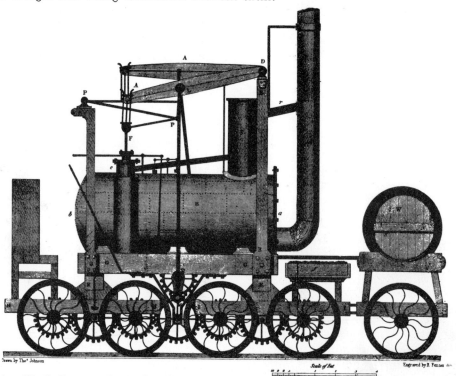

from Wood's Treatise on Rail Roads, 1825, Plate VI.

Hedley's second and subsequent engines were on four wheels, but the earliest contemporary illustration [1] known shows the Wylam engine as in 1825, carried on eight wheels which by that date had been found necessary; the wheels were flangeless, to suit the plate rails then in use, which themselves had flanges on the inside; when the Wylam plate rail was replaced by the stronger

[1] Wood *Treatise on Railroads*, 1st ed., 1825, Plate VI.

edge rail, after 1825, it was possible to return to the use of four wheels, with flanged tyres, and the engines as so altered worked for many years ; two are now preserved[1], the oldest locomotives in the world ; their general appearance when at work in 1844 is well shown by a contemporary etching.[2]

Of the circumstances connected with the inception and construction of the Wylam locomotives the following account was given by Hedley himself some years afterwards in protest against the popular designation of George Stephenson as 'Father of the Locomotive Engine.' Hedley writes under date 10th December 1836[3] :—

In October 1812 I had the direction of Wylam Colliery ; at that period I was requested by the Proprietor (the late Mr. Blackett) to undertake the Construction of a Locomotive Engine. The celebrated Trevithick had previously been applied to for one ; in reply he stated that he had declined the Business. Amongst the many Obstacles to Locomotion at that Period was the Idea entertained by practical Men, and which was acted upon, viz., that an Engine would only draw after it, on a level road, a Weight equal to its own. To obviate this, Trevithick and Vivian proposed to make the Wheels rough or uneven, &c. Mr. Blenkinsop, in 1811, effected the Loco-motion by a Toothed or Rack Rail. In December 1812 W. and E. Chapman by means of a Chain ; and in May 1813 Mr. Brunton, of Butterley, by Movable Legs. I was, however forcibly, impressed with the Idea (and **which** was strengthened by some small preliminary Experiments) that the Weight of an Engine was sufficient for the Purpose of enabling it to draw a Train of loaded Waggons. To determine this important Point I had a Carriage constructed ; this Carriage was placed upon the Railroad and loaded with different Parcels of Iron, the Weight of which had previously been ascertained ; 2, 4, 6, &c., loaded Coal Waggons were attached to it, the Carriage itself was moved by the Application of Men at the four Handles, and, in Order that the Men might not touch the Ground, a Stage was suspended from the Carriage at each Handle for them to stand upon.

I ascertained the proportion between the Weight of the experimental Carriage and the Coal Waggons at that Point when the Wheels of the Carriage would surge or turn round without advancing it. The Weight of the Carriage and the Number of Waggons also were repeatedly varied, but with the same relative Result. This Experiment, which was on a large scale, was decisive of the Fact that the Friction of the Wheels of an Engine Carriage upon the Rails was sufficient to enable it to draw a Train of loaded Coal Waggons. An Engine was then constructed, the Boiler was of Cast Iron, the Tube containing the Fire went longitudinally through the Boiler into the Chimney.

The Engine had one Cylinder and a Fly-wheel ; it went badly, the obvious Defect being want of Steam. Another Engine was then constructed, the Boiler was of Malleable Iron, the Tube containing the Fire was enlarged, and in Place of passing directly through the Boiler into the Chimney, it was made to return again through the Boiler into the Chimney, at the same end of the Boiler as the Fire-place was. This was a most important Improvement. The Engine was placed upon Four wheels and went well ; a short Time after it commenced it regularly drew eight loaded Coal Waggons after it, at the Rate of from four to five miles per Hour on the Wylam Railroad which was in a very bad State ; in Addition to this, there was a great Rise in the Direction of the Load in some Parts of it, the Road itself was of that Kind termed the Plate Rail. It is needless to pursue the Subject further than to state that for a length of Time each new Engine went better and took more Waggons than its Predecessor.

This letter suggests, and there is other evidence to show, that Hedley's first and unsuccessful engine generally resembled Trevithick's Gateshead engine,

---

[1] At the Science Museum, South Kensington, and the Royal Scottish Museum, Edinburgh.
[2] Hair, *A series of views of the Collieries in the Counties of Northumberland and Durham*, 1844.
[3] Hedley's letter to Dr. Lardner, 10th December 1836, *Newcastle Chronicle*, 24th Dec. 1836.

c

except that it had a single flue; that it had a single cylinder is clear. The suggestion that Hedley invented the return flue which he subsequently adopted ignores the fact that Trevithick's Gateshead locomotive had such a flue, which was indeed a feature of all his engines; and as to Hedley's demonstration of the sufficiency of adhesion with smooth wheels it is only fair to remember the clause of Trevithick and Vivian's Specification which we have quoted. It is worth noting too that Hedley describing the improved steaming power of his second engine ascribes this to the return flue, and makes no reference to the steam blast which was afterwards claimed as one of the most important features of his engine, and said to have been invented by him.

from Hair's Views of the Collieries in Northumberland and Durham, 1844.

Much of the credit for these engines has been claimed on behalf of Timothy Hackworth who was, during their construction, foreman smith at Wylam, but into the controversy on the relative merits of Hackworth and Hedley we cannot enter here; the conflicting claims made on behalf of each man respectively have been set forth at length by various writers.[1]

[1] (a) William Hedley, *The Inventor of Railway Locomotion on the present principle*, 3rd ed. 1885; (b) *A Chapter in the History of Railway Locomotion*, 1875, reprinted from the *Practical Mechanics' Journal*, 1850, with a *Memoir of Timothy Hackworth* and *Appendix* by J. W. Hackworth.

CHAPTER III

GEORGE STEPHENSON'S FIRST LOCOMOTIVES
1814—1825

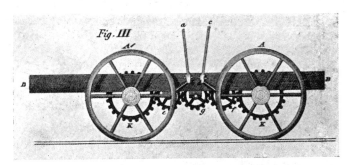

from Wood's Treatise on Rail Roads, 1825, Plate IV.

In 1814 George Stephenson, profiting by the experience of Trevithick, Blenkinsop and Hedley, produced his first locomotive at Killingworth for Sir Thomas Liddell, afterwards Lord Ravensworth, one of the Grand Allies.

We have no contemporary drawing of it but the method of drive has been illustrated, and it is recorded that the engine had two cylinders 8 inches diameter, by 2 feet stroke, with a boiler 8 feet long, 34 inches diameter, having a tube 20 inches diameter passing through it.[1] Stephenson followed Blenkinsop in placing the two cylinders axially along the centre line of the boiler, but he adopted Hedley's method of drive through gears, and his first engine was rather a compromise between the two earlier designs than an improvement on either. His single flue was perhaps in some respects a retrogression, since it provided a smaller total heating surface than was obtained with the return flue, but it was cheaper both to construct and maintain, two important considerations which may possibly have led him to its adoption.

This engine was tried upon the Killingworth Colliery Rail-road, 27th July 1814, upon a piece of road with the edge rail, ascending about one yard in four hundred and fifty, and was found to drag after it, exclusive of its own weight, eight loaded carriages, weighing altogether about thirty tons, at the rate of four miles an hour; and after that time continued regularly at work. The application of the two cylinders rendered the action of the engine regular and secured the continual progressive motion, thus remedying the imperfection caused by the irregular action of the single cylinder and fly-wheel.

Nicholas Wood, the writer of this account, is here evidently making a comparison with Trevithick's Gateshead engine and with Hedley's first and unsuccessful engine, and he distinctly implies that Hedley's second engine also

---

[1] Wood, *Treatise on Rail Roads*, 1st ed., 1825, p 136.

had only one cylinder; from which it would appear that George Stephenson better appreciated the advantages to be obtained by the use of two cylinders as employed by Blenkinsop. It is also to be noted that in his first engine George Stephenson established the sufficiency of adhesion between smooth wheels and edge rails, though this combination afforded less friction than was obtainable with the flanged plate rail which gave contact with the side edges, as well as with the rim, of the wheel.

When the engine had been at work a short time, it was soon found that sufficient adhesion existed upon the edge rail to perform the requisite traction to the load; at first, grooved sheeves were fixed upon the hinder travelling wheels of the engine, and similar grooved sheeves upon the fore-wheels of the convoy-carriage, containing the coal and water, with an endless chain working over each, to procure the adhesion of the wheels of the convoy-carriage, in addition to the adhesion of the engine-wheels; but, on trial, it was found not necessary to resort to the aid of this contrivance, as the adhesion of the engine-wheels alone was found sufficiently adequate to produce the desired effect.

The communication of the pressure upon the piston, through the means of the crank to the cog-wheels, produced great noise, and, in some parts of the stroke considerable jerks; each cylinder alternately propelling, or becoming propelled by the other, as the pressure of the one upon the wheels became greater or less than the pressure of the other, and this when the teeth became at all worn caused a rattling noise.

If any play or space existed between each tooth of the cog-wheels, the transition of this power from one side of the teeth to the other, always occasioned a jerk; and this became greater as the teeth became more worn and the space between each other greater.

DODDS AND STEPHENSON 1815 To obviate this became desirable and Mr. Stephenson, in conjunction with Mr. Dodds took out a patent[1] for a method of communicating the power of the engine directly to the wheels without the aid of these cog-wheels. The patent was dated 28th Feb. 1815, and consisted of the application of a pin upon one of the spokes of the wheels that supported the engine, by which it travelled upon the Rail-road, the lower end of the connecting rod being attached to it by what is termed a ball and socket joint; the other end of the connecting rod being attached to the cross-beam, worked up and down by the piston.

To keep one of the engine crank-pins always at right angles to the other :—

. . . the patentees had two methods, to crank the axle on which each of the wheels was fixed, with a connecting rod between to keep them always at the same angle with respect to each other; or to use a peculiar sort of endless chain passing over a toothed wheel on each axle.

An engine of this construction was tried upon the Killingworth Rail-road on 6th March 1815, and found to work remarkably well.

Ralph Dodds, the co-patentee, was at the time viewer at Killingworth Colliery and appears to have been one of the first men to recognise Stephenson's talents and to have assisted and encouraged him; it seems probable that Dodds' own contribution to the patent was in this direction; but, be that as it may, in the actual application of a direct drive by the connecting rods on to crank-pins in the wheels their engine marks a notable advance upon those which immediately preceded it. The elimination of gears was not the least of the great improvements brought into practical use by George Stephenson, and though the direct drive had been considered by Trevithick, and applied at

---

[1] Dodds and Stephenson's Specification, 28th February 1815 (No. 3,887).

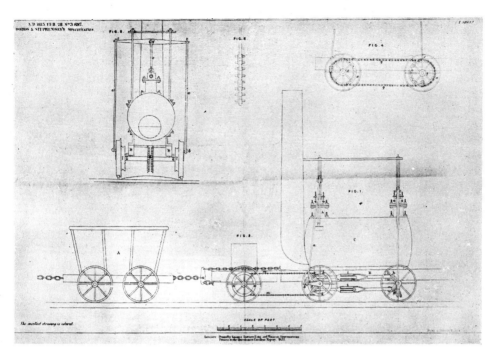

from Dodds & Stephenson's Specification, 1815, No. 3887.

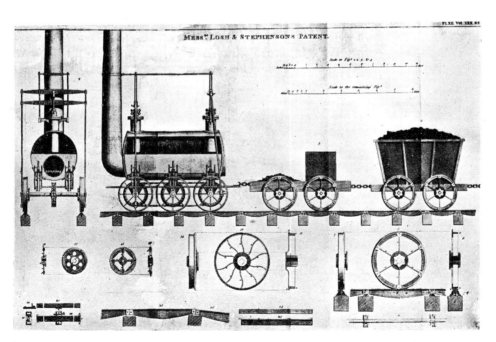

from the Repertory of Arts, No. CLXXX., second series, May 1817.

least to a model, it seems probable, when we consider the mystery which shrouded Trevithick's early locomotives, that the patent of Dodds and Stephenson was the result of independent invention.

Another notable feature is to be seen in the coupling of the wheels by rods connecting the two axles, each of which had two cranks placed at right angles. This, the first recorded, use of cranked axles for locomotives had to be abandoned because at that period 'the mechanical skill of the country was not equal to the task of forging crank axles of the soundness and strength necessary to stand the jars incident to locomotive work.' [1]

LOSH AND STEPHENSON 1816

By this time the waggon-ways were suffering from a usage for which they had not been intended ; it was clear that they too would have to be improved and Stephenson found himself involved in the struggle, which has continued to this day, to make the track keep pace with the locomotive. With the collaboration of William Losh [2], a cultivated and ingenious man, he devoted his attention to improving the fixing and jointing of the rails, and the structure of the wheels, and to finding some means to ensure that the weight of the engine should at all times be carried, in spite of the irregularities of the road, on the four, or if necessary six, wheels on which it was placed. Their invention for this purpose provided for carrying the boiler on cylinders fixed by flanges to the undersides of the barrel and projecting a few inches into it ; these cylinders were open at the top to the water in the boiler and contained solid pistons packed 'in the common way' to render them steam tight ; they were also open at the bottom and fixed by flanges upon the frame of the engine ; the pistons were furnished with rods the lower ends of which passed through holes in the frame and pressed upon chairs which rested upon the axles and were free to move up and down with the piston rod, as the wheels adjusted themselves to inequalities in the road. We have an early reference to this method by Farey who after describing Blenkinsop's engine writes [3] :—

A similar machine has been tried at Newcastle, but they have attempted to employ the wheels alone, without cogs upon the rails. To relieve the weight upon the rails, and obtain a greater re-action to advance the carriage, they applied six wheels for the carriage to run upon; and to make the bearing equal upon all six, the two middle wheels were applied to the piston of a small cylinder beneath the carriage, into which steam was admitted, and by its pressure bore up a portion of the weight of the engine; and accommodated itself to any inequalities of the railway.

A later description by Wood [4] refers to the :—

. . . peculiar and simple contrivance by which the elasticity of the steam within the boiler is made to act upon the axles of the engine in such a manner that the whole weight is always equally distributed upon the four or six wheels of the engine, which ever number it is found necessary on account of the strength of the rails to use. The engine is therefore, as it were, supported upon springs of the most exquisite elasticity by which the various and unavoidable inequalities of the road are never felt.

[1] Robert Stephenson's Narrative of his Father's Inventions. Smiles *Lives of the Engineers*, 1862, Vol. III., p. 487.

[2] Losh and Stephenson's Specification, 26th November 1816 (No. 4067).

[3] Rees' *Cyclopædia*. Article, 'Steam Engines,' 1819, written by Farey in 1815.

[4] Wood, letter to *Newcastle Magazine*, 16th March 1822.

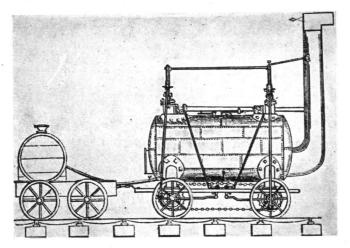

from the cover of James' Report or Essay on a line of Engine Rail Road, 1823.

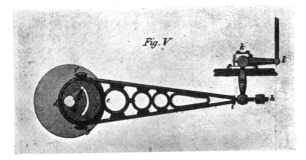

from Wood's Treatise on Rail Roads, 1825, Plate IV.

WOOD'S EXCENTRIC

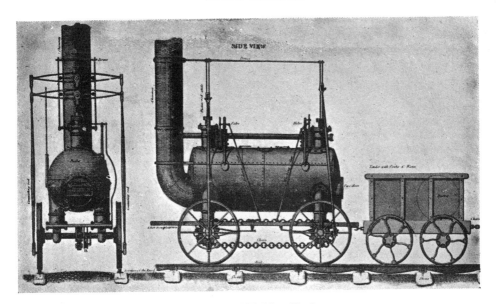

from Strickland's Report on Canals and Rail Roads, 1826 (after Wood).

G. STEPHENSON'S PATENT LOCOMOTIVE ENGINE

in the chimney, to give sufficient intensity to the fire. To effect a greater rapidity, or to increase the draught of the chimney, Mr. Stevenson thought that by causing the steam to escape into the chimney through a pipe with its end turned upwards, the velocity of the current would be accelerated, and such was the effect; but, in remedying one evil, another has been produced, which, though objectionable in some places, was not considered as objectionable on a private Rail-road; the tube through the boiler having been increased, there is now no longer any occasion for the action of the steam to assist the motion of the heated air in the chimney. The steam thrown in this manner into the chimney acts as a trumpet, and certainly makes a very disagreeable noise; nothing, however, is more easy to remedy, and the very act of remedying this defect, will also be the means of economising the fuel.

I have before said, that economy of fuel has not been an object where those engines have hitherto been used; no attempt has, therefore, been made to lessen it; and the steam, after performing its effect in the cylinders, has been allowed to escape into the atmosphere. The water with which the engine is supplied, has generally been heated in a vessel by the side of the road, and carried in a barrel, from which

[from an original, 1st Edition, 1825.]

A

PRACTICAL TREATISE

ON

RAIL-ROADS,

AND

INTERIOR COMMUNICATION IN GENERAL:

WITH

Original Experiments,

AND

TABLES

OF THE COMPARATIVE VALUE OF

CANALS AND RAIL-ROADS.

ILLUSTRATED BY ENGRAVINGS.

By NICHOLAS WOOD,
COLLIERY VIEWER.

" Every accession which Man gains to his knowledge, is also an accession
" to his power; and extends the limits of his empire over the world
" which he inhabit." BACON.

LONDON:

PRINTED FOR KNIGHT AND LACEY,
PATERNOSTER-ROW;

SOLD BY J. AND E. AKENHEAD, NEWCASTLE-UPON-TYNE; AND WESTLEY
AND TYRRELL, DUBLIN.

M.DCCC.XXV.

(George Stephenson's application of Exhaust Steam to promote combustion recorded in 1825)

From these accounts it appears that some of George Stephenson's first locomotives were carried on six wheels, but most of the later ones appear to have been on four wheels only, as shown by the drawings published in 1823 and 1825. Of these later engines, which embodied several improvements, such as the excentrics adopted by him for operating the valve, instead of square tumblers, Wood states :—

The cylinders are placed vertically and partly within the boiler. They are generally nine inches diameter, and lined on the inside with sheet copper; the piston rods work through stuffing boxes in the usual way, and are attached to the cross beams, sometimes formed of a solid piece of wrought iron, and sometimes of more than one as represented. The rectilinear motion of the piston rod is secured by the slides, fastened to the projecting arms cast upon the top of the cylinder, and kept perpendicular by the braces.

The connecting rods are attached to the ends of the cross beams by ball and socket joints, and at the other end by similar joints, to a pin fixed upon one of the spokes of the engine wheels; to strengthen this spoke a circular piece of metal is cast which attaches the two adjoining spokes with it.

The steam is communicated from the boiler to the cylinders through a passage, the area of which is regulated by a sliding lever, or handle, which of course restricts the quantity and regulates the velocity of the engine. The steam is admitted to the top and bottom of the piston by means of a sliding valve which, being moved up and down alternately, opens a communication between the top or bottom of the cylinder and the pipe that is open into the chimney and turns up within it.

The steam, after performing its office within the cylinder, is thus thrown into the chimney and the power with which it issues being proportionate to the degree of elasticity and the exit being directed upwards, accelerates the velocity of the current of heated air accordingly.

Referring to the great objections urged previously against these engines on account of the noise made by the steam escaping into the chimney Wood states that [1] :—

When the engines were first made the steam escaped into the atmosphere and made comparatively little noise; it was found difficult then to produce steam in sufficient quantity to keep the engine constantly working; or rather, to obtain an adequate rapidity of current in the chimney, to give sufficient intensity to the fire. To effect a greater rapidity or to increase the draught of the chimney, Mr. Stephenson thought that by causing the steam to escape into the chimney through a pipe with its end turned upwards, the velocity of the current would be accelerated, and such was the effect; but, in remedying one evil another has been produced, which, though objectionable in some places, was not considered as objectionable on a private Rail-road; the tube through the boiler having been increased there is now no longer any occasion for the action of the steam to assist the motion of the heated air in the chimney. The steam thrown in this manner into the chimney acts as a trumpet, and certainly makes a very disagreeable noise; nothing, however, is more easy to remedy, and the very act of remedying this defect will also be the means of economising the fuel.

In the heat of subsequent controversy as to who invented the 'blast pipe' this simple statement has been almost entirely ignored. It shows that the action of the exhaust was known and recorded so early as 1825, by men who may themselves have been unaware, or have forgotten, that it was described by Trevithick more than ten years earlier, and the peculiar value of Wood's record lies in the fact that it was made some years before a controversy commenced

[1] Wood, *Treatise on Rail Roads*, 1st ed., 1825, p. 293.

which has been continued till to-day, often in ignorance of his evidence. The fact was that, with the short boiler and large single flue of the Killing-worth engines, anything approaching a 'blast' had been found to be unneces-sary, and this, with other reasons for its abandonment, was given by Wood in evidence in April 1825 ; when asked whether horses that had never before seen one of the engines would not be startled at it he replied [1] :—

> I think they would; those engines puff very much and the cause is to get an increased draught in the chimney; now we have got a sufficiency of steam without it.

FIRST STEPHENSON
LOCOMOTIVE IN
SCOTLAND

It is recorded that the first locomotive constructed by Stephenson after the Killingworth model was to the order of the Duke of Portland, in 1817, for his tramway from Kilmarnock to Troon [2], but enquiries have failed to find any contemporary account of this engine either in the public press or among the papers of the Portland estate office. [3] An artist born in the district recorded [4] many years later that, early in 1816 a locomo-tive 'was set down on the Duke of Portland's tramroad about 400 yards below Kilmarnock House,' and he describes how he went up to the engine, caught hold of the foot-boards along which the engineman walked and stooped to make a survey of its 'underbelly gearing.' 'The carcase sat on three pairs of wheels. The fore and aft pair were turned by long connecting rods fixed to a knob on the outer flange of the wheels and by the aid of cross-beams played up and down like a pair of frame saws, turning the wheels like so many grindstones. On the centre of each axle-tree was a wheel with teeth, and an open chain revolved on the teeth in pinion form, keeping the valves (sic) in their place.' These are certainly remarkable features such as might strike the observ-ant eye of the boy who afterwards became an artist of some repute ; at the time he can only have been about fourteen years old, but if his recollection was correct the engine must have been much as shown by Losh and Stephenson's specifi-cation. This engine appears to have been too heavy for the road and to have been quickly discarded, and for some time lost sight of, but the tramroad and the horse diligencies which ran on it are frequently referred to in contemporary and later accounts. [5]

LATER
KILLINGWORTH
ENGINES

The 'Newcastle Roads' and that of Killingworth in particular, soon became a resort for mining engineers and railway projectors interested in the new locomotive power ; among these was De Gallois whose report in 1818 on 'the railways used in England, and notably at Newcastle and in Northumber-land' gave an important stimulus to the introduction of railways into France. [6]

[1] Evidence on the Liverpool and Manchester Railroad Bill, 1825. *Proc. Committee House of Commons.*
[2] Smiles *Lives of the Engineers*, 1862, Vol. III., p. 139.
[3] Letter from Mr. J. Harbin Turner to Robert Stephenson & Co., 7th June 1921.
[4] J. K. Hunter *Retrospect of an Artist's Life*, new. ed. 1912 (Kilmarnock, The Standard Press).
   (a) Tomlinson *The North Eastern Railway*, footnote to page 114.
   (b) Strickland *Report on Canals and Railroads*, 1826.
   (c) Von Dechen and Von Oeynhausen's Report, *Archiv für Bergbau und Huttenwesen*, Berlin, 1829.
[6] *Hommes et Choses du P.L.M.* (Chemin de fer Paris, Lyon, Méditerranée), 1910.

There came also in 1818 the grandfather of Robert Louis Stevenson, Robert Stevenson, civil engineer, of Edinburgh, who reported that 'some of the most striking improvements in the system of railways are the patent inventions of Mr. Stephenson of Newcastle, particularly his Locomotive Engine.' [1]

In April 1819, Simon Goodrich, whose papers bear witness to his keen interest in every kind of steam engine, after visiting Newcastle noted in his journal [2] the principal dimensions of the 'movable steam engine,' referring in particular to the 'floating pistons,' 8 inches diameter, and giving particulars of the engine's performance.

In 1821 William James visited Killingworth in his search for a locomotive to satisfy the requirements of his numerous schemes for railroads. In view of statements, made later by his descendants, on his relations with Stephenson, something more than a passing reference to this remarkable man is necessary here. Born in 1771, he qualified for the law and became land agent for extensive properties ; he was himself a proprietor and mine-owner and it is said that so early as 1799 'at the period when George Stephenson was praise-worthily learning his letters at 3d. per week Mr. James was engaged in laying out plans for rail roads.' [3] With his natural gifts, education, and relations to other landed proprietors and mine-owners, James had a peculiar opportunity for the furtherance of railway schemes, but the statement that it was he who introduced Stephenson to Edward Pease and first established his reputation cannot be supported. It appears that after seeing Blenkinsop's, Chapman's, and Brunton's engines, James went to Killingworth 'to inspect Messrs. Losh and Stephenson's improved Blackett engine' and afterwards wrote the following letter [4] :—

CHIPPING NORTON, OXFORDSHIRE,
22nd June 1821.

SIR,—It is only at this Day I am enable to address you, having ever since I saw you been employed in seeing the different Rail Roads in all parts of the Kingdom, the better to advise the Company in the adoption of a proper one on our Line, for the first Stage of which (19 miles from Stratford to Moreton in the Marsh) an Act is obtained but as the Original plan is most extensive even to the Sea at Southampton or Portsmouth it is of the greatest importance to set out well, and the Completion of this Work will be the Business of my future Life.

It can answer no other purpose than to amuse, for me to state all the different Rail Roads which I have viewed, Suffice it to say that having as a Miner at Wednesbury in Staffordshire and in Cheshire employed Rail Roads for the last 20 Years as an Engineer and Land Agent been in the Habit of seeing and using them from the Mines of Somersetshire, thro' Wales, Salop, Lancaster and Yorkshire of all Shapes & forms & in all possible Situations, I did presume to place some Confidence in my Conclusions, founded on such long Experience.

But I confess *Light* has at length *shone* from the *North*, and I pronounce as my Candid Opinion that the *Malleable Iron Rail Road* at Bleddington (*sic*) Works, is by far the best I have ever seen both in respect of its Material and form ; as to the first, I am of opinion that the process of Oxydation is in some Way prevented (perhaps by an atmosphere created by Friction, or by some other latent Cause) to a Degree I did not expect and I have little Doubt

---

[1] Report on Edinburgh Railway, 1818.

[2] Preserved at the Science Museum, South Kensington.

[3] *The Two James's and the Two Stephensons*, 1861, p. 18.

[4] Railway Collection, Newcastle Public Library. Name of addressee unknown.

but that the *Hold* (if I may be allowed the Expression) of Cast Iron Wheels upon Malleable Iron Rails will much assist the Engine in its Operation of Draught (or Draft) and as to the Form ; the Flat Top (without flanges) is infinitely preferable to the Flange Rail even without reference to the Differences of Friction from the Impossibility of being clogged or impeded by Small Stones, Cobbles, Ice & Frost. The latter Obstacles every one at all practically acquainted with Rail Roads must know is very great & attended with considerable Expense in Most Winters :— I confess to you, my good Sir, that I certainly approved very highly of the rail of Losh & Co., it is by far the best Cast Iron Rail I ever saw, but the malleable Iron is so superior to it, that I shall advise our Company to adopt it.

The *Locomotive Engine* of Mr. Stephenson is superior beyond all comparison to all the other Engines I have ever seen—Next to the immortal Watt I consider Mr. Stephenson's Merit in the Invention of this Engine.

Although my letter is to you & Mr. Pees (*sic*) & his friends of a private Nature, I feel it due to the Character & Talents of the Northumbrians to declare that in the sciences of Mining & Mechanics we can in the South in no respect be compared with them, and with such great and nobleminded Men as Mr. Blackett and Mr. Buddle and such Abilities as Mr. Stephenson's and Mr. Chapmans I cannot conceive, my Observation deserving of any other Notice, than to show how sensible I am of the Value of these Gentlemen, and of the Esteem in which I hold the plans and Characters of yourself and your Friends in Durham.

May success attend your public Spirited Exertions & Health & Happiness your Firesides is the Sincere wish of

Your friend,
W. JAMES,

Boswell Court, Lincoln's Inn, London.

My respects to E. Pees. I lament I did not See him—he is known to friends of mine.

This letter confirms the previous acquaintance of Pease and Stephenson. Pease had previously sent for Stephenson in April 1821 to come to Darlington and James found him already a man of more than local reputation, and the builder of the best locomotive then at work on a railroad. So much impressed was James that in the following September he entered into an agreement with Losh and Stephenson, by which they assigned to him one-fourth of the profits to be derived from the use of their patent engine, 'Mr. James giving his recommendation and best assistance for the using and employing of the loco-motive engine ' [1] :—

In consideration of such grant William James hereby agrees to allow the said William Losh and George Stephenson to adopt any improvements and the introduction of tubes to their boilers as contained in the letters patent of W. H. James.[2]

This agreement led to an intimacy and correspondence which continued for some years; we give as an example the following letter [3] addressed to William James :—

DEAR SIR,—I have had a visit from your neighbour Mr. Thos. Brewin & Lord Dudley's Engineer. I being at Darlington the other day, and on my leaving that place I got into the same coach, the above Gents. were in for N. Castle. We had not gone far till they found I belonged to the neighbourhood they were going to. They asked me if I knew one G. Stephenson. I answered I did. They then enquired very closely after his character. I kept myself unknown till we got near N. Castle. I soon found their knowledge on Railways was very

---

[1] *The Two James's and the Two Stephensons*, 1861, p. 84.

[2] W. H. James's subsequent patent, for a water tube boiler, bears date 1825.

[3] In possession of Messrs. Roche & Roche, by whose permission it is now published.

limited, it would take a volume to hold all our conversation on Railways, Locomotive Engines & Stephenson before I was known to them, however in the end we got very kind and I showed them our Engines & Railways which they candidly confessed were superior to anything they ever saw and far exceeded their expectations. I gave Brewin an account of what our Engines would do on various ascents and descents of which the following is a copy similar to what you wanted.

The following is calculated for a load of 12 loaded waggons each containing 3 tons exclusive of the weight of the waggons which may each weigh from 20 to 25 cwt.

When level at from 4 to 8 miles per hour.

When $\frac{1}{16}$ ascent per yd. at from $3\frac{1}{2}$ to 6 miles per hour.

,,	$\frac{2}{16}$	,,	,,	,,	3 to 5	,,	,,
,,	$\frac{3}{16}$	,,	,,	,,	3 to 4	,,	,,
,,	$\frac{4}{16}$	,,	,,	,,	$2\frac{1}{2}$ to 3	,,	,,
,,	$\frac{1}{16}$ descent per yd. at from				5 to 9 miles per hour.		
,,	$\frac{2}{16}$	,,	,,	,,	6 to 10	,,	,,
,,	$\frac{3}{16}$	,,	,,	,,	6 to 10	,,	,,
,,	$\frac{4}{16}$	,,	,,	,,	6 to 10	,,	,,

I would not recommend my Locomotive Engines to travel on a line that ascends or descends more than $\frac{3}{16}$ when there is a load both ways, but if the load was always passing on a descending line the Engines would return with the empty waggons up an ascent of $\frac{1}{2}$ an inch per yard, or in a short distance from $\frac{5}{8}$ to $\frac{6}{8}$ ascent per yard, The above is within the limits at which my Engines will work, but it is my wish to state it below its powers. I dare say the statement I gave Mr. James before may be higher than this, but they are capable of performing whatever I have stated. If your railway should be constructed agreeable to the present Act, one horse will travel with from $2\frac{1}{2}$ to 3 tons, if the new line be adopted one horse will travel with from 4 to $4\frac{1}{2}$ tons. I would advise you to lay your Rails of such a strength that may suit either horses or engines, it would not add much to the first cost, and would ultimately be a benefit were engines never to be used. The weight of Rails as 'Darlington Specification.'

I am, Sir,

Yours truly,

G. STEPHENSON.

Killingworth Coll.,
Feb. 16th 1822.

Later, in the 'first of a projected series of twelve essays intended to be published on the engine rail-road system,' [1] James, in 1823, refers to the improved locomotive steam engine of his 'greatly esteemed and scientific friend Mr. George Stephenson,' and on the cover of his pamphlet illustrates an engine of the Killingworth and Hetton type, with chain drive and steam springs. Unfortunately, owing it appears to private misfortunes, James was prevented from completing the schemes in which he had so energetically interested himself, and his connection with Stephenson did not lead directly to any extended use of the patent locomotive, either with or without W. H. James's

[1] *Report or Essay to illustrate the advantage of Direct Inland communication, by a Line of Engine Railroad.* London, J. & A. Arch, 1823.

tubular boiler. In a letter dated 28th June 1823 Thomas Bell, a partner with Losh and Wilson, writes to James [1] :—

I am quite sensible of the exertions you have made in attempting to introduce the locomotive engines, and though they have hitherto proved fruitless, I am sure Mr. Losh and Mr. Stephenson ought to consider themselves greatly indebted to you.

It has been stated that the adoption of W. H. James's tubular boiler later enabled Stephenson's 'Rocket' to win the prize at the Rainhill trials ; but a comparison of the two boilers [2] will be sufficient to show that such a claim cannot be maintained.

After 1821 numerous other engineers visited Killingworth, and on February 8th 1825 a contemporary journal records [3] :—

About a fortnight since a number of experiments with locomotive engines were performed at Killingworth, near Newcastle-upon-Tyne, by order of the Committee of the Liverpool and Manchester Rail-way. In the first instance—namely, on the 18th ult.—the trials were made with an old and imperfect engine, the results of which give a speed of not more than four miles an hour, with a moderate load. On the 22nd ult., however, a superior engine, of eight horse-power, being employed, the diameter of the wheels being four feet, five different trials of its power and speed were made. The weight moved, exclusive of the engine, was 48 tons 15 cwts. The inclination of the road was 1 in 840 ; the greatest rise in any part 11 inches in 100 yards, or 1 in 327. The engine and load being moved in *both* directions along this inclined plane, the total result may be considered as upon a horizontal plane. The average velocity was very nearly 7 miles an hour, and the greatest speed $9\frac{1}{2}$ miles an hour. As a good deal of misrepresentation has gone abroad upon the subject of these experiments, we think it well to state that the above report is upon the authority of Mr. James Walker, of Limehouse, one of seven engineers who were present, and in addition to the above, we will mention that Mr. Walker distinctly states that had the Rail-way been good and well fixed, 'the result would have been higher.' As these engines were not of the best construction for speed no doubt can be entertained that with proper engines goods and merchandise may be conveyed with a very considerable increased velocity.

In 1825 William Strickland came over from Pennsylvania to enquire about railroads and canals, and in a subsequent report when describing the Stephenson locomotives in use at Hetton Colliery states [4] :—

It may be proper to add that the Patentee of this engine recommends the employment of six wheels in order to distribute its great weight more equally on the rails, and perhaps to increase the friction of the wheels on the railway.

In December 1828 Samuel Homfray, the Welsh ironmaster, son of Trevithick's friend, having heard of the 'wonderful travelling engines at Newcastle which were reducing the cost of haulage by 50 per cent.,' sent Thomas Ellis, an engineer in his service, and Theophilus Jones, a mining agent, with a list of questions [5] ; after travelling by coach for six days they arrived at Killingworth, where they made an inspection of all engines, including the steam

[1] *The Two James's and the Two Stephensons*, 1861, p. 87.

[2] *History and Progress of the Steam Engine*, Elijah Galloway and Luke Hebert, 1831, p. 391.

[3] *The Times*, 8th February 1825.

[4] Strickland, *Report on Canals and Rail Roads*, 1826.

[5] Letter from Mr. C. W. Ellis to *The Monmouthshire Evening Post*, 23rd February 1912.

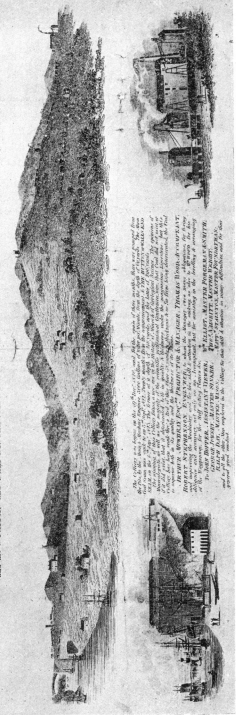

(part) from an engraving by Robson, Sunderland, date about 1823-1825.

On Monday the 18th inst. the Hetton Coal Company effected the first shipment of their coals at their newly erected staith on the banks of the river Wear, Sunderland. . . . Five (*sic*) of Mr. George Stephenson's patent travelling engines, two 60 horse power reciprocating engines and five self-acting inclined planes, all under the direction of Mr. Robert Stephenson, the Company's resident engineer, simultaneously performing their various and complicated offices . . . . exhibited a spectacle at once interesting to science, and encouraging to commerce.

Newcastle Chronicle, November 23rd 1822.

travelling engine ; the note books of Thomas Ellis record the weight of an eight horse-power engine as 6 tons 10 cwt., and the price £500, and give other interesting information.

In October 1828 an interested observer wrote from Edinburgh [1] :—

It appears by a letter now before me from Hetton Colliery, in the county of Durham, that in this end of the island we are as yet quite ignorant of the capability of Locomotive Engines when employed upon a well constructed Railway. On a portion of the Railway leading from this extensive colliery to the River Weir, on the 18th of last month, two Locomotive Engines led 83 keels of coal a distance of 2,541 yards. You are perhaps aware that a keel contains 8 waggons, and each waggon carries 53 cwt. (at least), besides the weight of the carriage. So that these two engines led 1,759 ton 12 cwt. of coal a distance of 2,541 yards, which is equal to 2,540 ton led one mile, besides taking back the empty waggons. The daily expense of two such engines is estimated at Two Pounds Nine Shillings and Two Pence, so that the cost of hauling these 1,759 ton of coal nearly 1½ miles was at the rate of 11.12ths of a farthing per ton per mile. The load of the Engines being 16 waggons, each must have travelled about 60 miles. This is not considered an extraordinary performance. It is interesting to estimate the cost of performing the same work by animal power. A horse would have taken 4 waggons to a load. and by travelling 21 miles per day would have led 28 waggons, so that 24 horses would have been necessary to do the work here performed by two engines, which at 5s. per day would amount to £6 instead of £2 9s. 2d. by the locomotive Engine. It is well known to those conversant in such matters that a short line of road such as that at Hetton is the most disadvantageous for the application of locomotive engines from the number of stoppages that must necessarily take place and that upon a line of greater length much more work could have been done. The low rate at which leading is performed upon the Stockton and Darlington Railway by these powerful machines, confirms the truth of this observation.

We may look forward with some degree of interest to the completion of these great undertakings, the Manchester and Liverpool, the Edinburgh and Dalkeith, and the Glasgow and Garnkirk railways—on all of which, most probably, these engines will be employed—for much valuable information on this interesting subject. From the daily out-put at this single colliery, some idea may be formed of the extent of the coal trade in that part of the country. Reckoning this quantity raised for only 200 days in the year, it gives an aggregate of more than 350,000 tons per annum, which is fully equal to the whole consumption of Edinburgh and Leith.

There is ample evidence from these and other sources that even after the opening of the Stockton and Darlington Railway, and until the opening of the Liverpool and Manchester Railway, the colliery lines of the north, Hetton as well as Killingworth, were the trial grounds for numberless experiments. The Hetton railway, about eight miles in length from the colliery to the coal staiths on the river Wear, had been laid out by George Stephenson but executed by his brother Robert Stephenson [2], and was said in 1825 to be 'the most perfect having locomotive engines.' [3] The line, which passed over a hill 330 feet high, was worked partly by fixed engines and partly by locomotives, and its lay-out is well shown by a contemporary print. At the opening of the railway in 1822 there were three of Stephenson's patent locomotives at work

[1] Letter from T. G. to *The Scotsman*, 1st October 1828.

[2] Evidence on the Liverpool and Manchester Railroad Bill, 1825, *Proc. Committee House of Commons*, p. 665.

[3] William Cubitt's evidence before the Board of Directors of the London and Northern Railroad, 16th February 1825.

SPRINGWELL LOCOMOTIVE
(said to have worked at Springwell Colliery till 1863, afterwards at Killingworth till 1879)

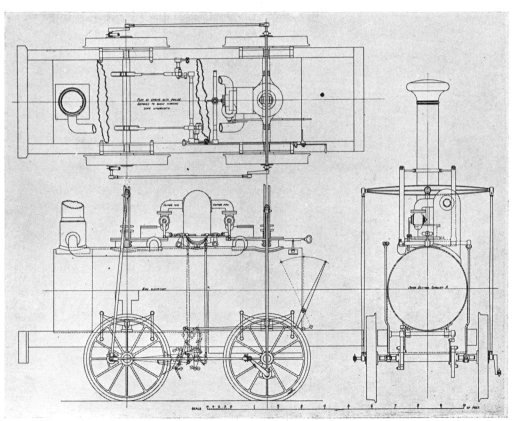

from the original (undated) drawing, endorsed

'THOMPSON'S ENGINE'
(as rebuilt by Robert Stephenson & Co. in 1839, and fitted with gab valve gear)

D

KILLINGWORTH LOCOMOTIVE

(now standing on the platform at the Central Station, Newcastle-upon-Tyne)

HETTON LOCOMOTIVE

(in service till 1908 at the Hetton Colliery where it is now preserved)

similar to those at Killingworth, and two others of the same type but with larger wheels were put to work later.[1]

In 1825 it was rumoured that the locomotives at Hetton were to be abandoned, a rumour of which full use was made by the opponents to steam locomotion, and it appears that they were, for a time at least, abandoned upon certain inclines which could be better worked by fixed engines. But it is clear that in spite of their imperfections these early locomotives of the Killingworth or Hetton type had proved successful for the purpose for which they had been designed, and, within certain limits of gradient, more economical in operation

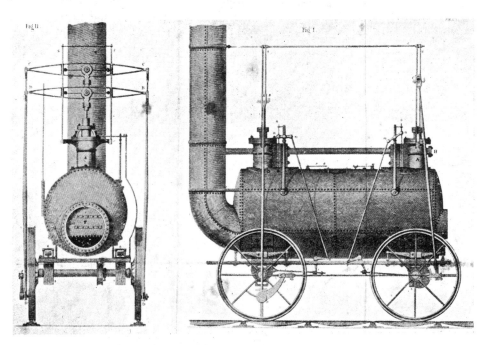

from Wood's Treatise on Rail Roads, 1831, Plate VII.

than either horses or fixed engines, though with less advantage in the latter case. George Stephenson in his advocacy of the locomotive appears to have usually carefully defined the limits within which he considered that locomotives might be economically employed.

After 1825 various improvements were introduced, such as plate bearing springs and outside coupling rods, some of these due to Nicholas Wood, but the engines as a whole appear to have remained much as they had been ten years earlier, and contemporary descriptions show that the steam springs, first applied in 1816, were still in use nine years later, 'until the progress of spring making had considerably advanced', when steel springs of sufficient

[1] Evidence on the Liverpool and Manchester Railroad Bill, 1825, p. 665. *Cf. Newcastle Chronicle* 23rd Nov. 1822.

strength superseded this highly ingenious mode of distributing the weight of the engine uniformly among the wheels.' [1]

In 1854 one of Stephenson's early locomotives of 1826 was still in use on the Springwell and Jarrow line [2]; one of the later Killingworth locomotives, much modernised, but still exhibiting the simple construction of the engine, now stands in the Central railway station at Newcastle-upon-Tyne; one of the old Hetton locomotives, more transformed, was at work until 1908 and is still preserved at the colliery, a remarkable answer to the rumours of nearly one hundred years ago.

George Stephenson in April 1825 stated his belief that he had up to that time constructed 55 engines, of which he thought that 16 had been locomotives. These were probably all made at the collieries for which they were required and were mostly of his patent type, which had come to be regarded almost as a standard when the promoters of the Stockton and Darlington Railway in 1821 decided, on his recommendation, to adopt locomotives for their line.

NICHOLAS WOOD We cannot conclude this sketch of locomotive development between 1815 and 1825 without particular reference to the man who was as much the early scribe of railroads and locomotives as Stephenson was their apostle, and from whom every writer on these subjects must inevitably quote. Wood's *Treatise on Railroads* published in 1825 was the first exhaustive work on the subject; the reasons which led to the publication of the book and his own modest account of valuable services rendered to Stephenson and the cause in which they were mutually interested are recorded in a letter to Edward Pease [3], dated :—

KILLINGWORTH,

1 Feb. 1825.

SIR,—I must apologise for not answering your letter respecting the Locomotive Engines before this, but what with my own business and in making preparation for the experiments for the other Rail Roads I have been so much occupied that I really have not had an opportunity of doing so. I had also another reason for delaying the answer—I expected from some alterations I was making to the Locomotive Engines that it would be attended with considerable improvement and their performance increased accordingly; and I waited until I had the result of those, to assist me in determining your questions. I am happy to say these alterations have answered my most sanguine expectations and have given a new turn to the action of those machines rather different from what I anticipated, and certainly the very reverse of what those opposed to them were inclined to admit.

I must however beg a little more time to arrange the materials derived from these expts. and as they are to form the ground work of my estimate of their performance I should wish to give it the most attentive consideration.—You may however depend upon me not delaying it beyond the earliest period of my coming to a final determination.

I have now to thank you for your Friendly advice contained in your last letter.—You are aware of my Friendship for Mr. Geo. Stephenson, my conduct in many instances has shown it, and I am happy my friendship has been bestowed upon so worthy a person. When he was associated with me at this Colliery we made a great many expts. on the subject of Rail Roads,

[1] Robert Stephenson's Narrative of his Father's Inventions. Smiles, *Lives of the Engineers*, Vol. III., p. 489.

[2] Longstaffe, *History of Darlington*, 1854, p. 363.

[3] *The Diaries of Edward Pease*, edited by Sir Alfred E. Pease, Bart. Headley Brothers, 1907.

and since his employment elsewhere I have made a great many more—the benefit of which he has always had from time to time as they were made.

These experiments however have not been attended without expense, and I may add also with considerable mental exertion—though thank God my circumstances are such as to enable me at present to live with the greatest comfort, yet that depends upon my constant and continual exertion both of Body and Mind, and I think it a duty therefore incumbent upon myself if these expts. are useful, and such as will afford any emolument to embrace the opportunity at present held out to render that comfort more lasting and independent.

Of course if the publishing them to the world should injure Mr. Stephenson I should, notwithstanding with-hold them, but after mature consideration I do not think they will—they are only conveying information which every man in a short time will have an opportunity of informing himself, but which at the present moment I may say only dwells with myself.

When I state to you that at this time I am several pounds the worse for all my experience in Rail Roads I trust you will not blame me for endeavouring to reimburse myself now when I think an opportunity offers—if it only be done judiciously and without injuring my Friends.

I am Sir

Your most ob: St.

N. Wood.

from Wood's Treatise on Rail Roads, 1825, Plate IV.

STEPHENSON AND WOOD'S DYNAMOMETER.

Nicholas Wood was born in 1795 and was therefore some fourteen years junior to George Stephenson; in April 1811 he was sent to Killingworth Colliery to learn the profession of viewer under Ralph Dodds, and it was as an apprentice that he commenced the happy relations with George Stephenson which led to their life-long friendship and collaboration in railway work. Wood himself became an authority in the railway world and his opinion was constantly sought for Parliamentary Committees; in addition to his book on railroads and locomotives, of which three editions appeared, he wrote on mining matters. He became president of the Institute of Mining Engineers; and was also a member of the Institute of Civil Engineers and fellow of the Royal and Geological Societies. Nicholas Wood died in 1865, but in spite of his great services to the mining industry and in connection with the development of railways and locomotives he has been ignored by our national biographers.

A

FURTHER REPORT,

ON THE INTENDED

Rail or Tram Road,

FROM

STOCKTON, BY DARLINGTON, TO THE COLLIERIES,

WITH A BRANCH TO YARUM.

"The advantages which Iron Rail-ways present are immense:
"England owes to them a part of her Wealth,—never without
"them could Lime, Coal, Minerals, and other raw Materials,
"have been conveyed to such Distances, and at the same time,
"at so trifling an Expense."
DUPIN'S REPORT TO THE FRENCH GOVERNMENT.

NOVEMBER, 1820.

——➤●◄——

Darlington:

PRINTED AT THE OFFICE OF G. ATKINSON,

HIGH-ROW.

[from the originals.]

AT A

MEETING

OF

GENTLEMEN, MERCHANTS, AND OTHERS, FOR THE PURPOSE

OF PROMOTING A

Canal or Railway

FROM STOCKTON, BY DARLINGTON,

Westwards,

HELD AT THE

HOUSE OF MR. SCOTT, THE KING's HEAD, IN DARLINGTON,

IN THE COUNTY OF DURHAM,

On Friday, the 17th day of January, 1812,

Pursuant to advertisement,—

(The Resolutions of the general Meeting, held on the 18th day of September,
1810, having been read, and the Report of the Committee then
appointed having been received and taken into
Consideration)—

RESOLVED,

THAT a Survey of the Country or District, through which
the proposed Canal or Railway is intended to pass, be forthwith
made by Mr. RENNIE. That he be instructed to make a Report
as to the practicability of those several measures, their comparative
advantages, and the best line or course and extent for each; with
an estimate of the expence which will attend the carrying it into
effect.

That a Subscription be entered into, in order to defray the
expence of such survey, and any other reasonable charges which
have already been, or shall hereafter be, incurred relative to the
projected undertakings; and that the Committee shall have power
to call for such proportion thereof as they shall find necessary, and
to direct to whom the same shall be paid.

CHAPTER IV

THE STOCKTON AND DARLINGTON RAILWAY

A great man finds himself on the river of thoughts and events, forced onward by the ideas and necessities of his contemporaries. He finds two counties groping to bring coal from the place of production to the place of consumption, and he hits on a railroad.—Emerson.

During the latter half of the eighteenth century many schemes for an extension of inland waterways were under consideration in the North of England, among them one for a canal from the coalfields of Durham to the navigable waters of the river Tees; a local historian writes in 1796[1] :—

A few years ago a navigable canal was proposed from Stockton by Darlington to Winston, with collateral branches to Piercebridge, Croft Bridge, and Yarm. . . . A survey was made of the country by Messrs. Brindley and Whitworth, engineers, and an estimate of the expense, which, it was supposed, would amount to £63,722. The utility of such a canal to the trade of Stockton, particularly with respect to the carriage of lead, butter, and cheese, and the considerable reduction that would take place in the price of coals is a great argument in its favour. The Manufacturers of Darlington would find an easy way to market, and the importation of goods at the port of Stockton, which are sent to Barnard Castle, Kendal, etc., would be increased. The heavy expense, however, attending the execution of the plan, and the uncertainty of its answering the public expectations, at the time put an end to the undertaking.

(part) from the original drawing by John Dixon, 1782.

A METHOD OF CONVEYING BOATS FROM ONE CANAL OR POOL TO ANOTHER WITHOUT THE HELP OF A LOCK

One of the earliest and most prominent promoters of the canal scheme had been George Dixon of Cockfield; born in 1731 he belonged to a talented family and has been described as himself one of the most ingenious men of his day. He owned and worked nine of the best collieries in the county of Durham and in the interests of his coal trade he made a preliminary survey for the canal. A plan engraved by him and published in 1770, to show a proposed branch to the collieries, bears evidence to his skill as an artist as well as an engineer. George Dixon actually cut a short canal upon Cockfield Fell[2], and a drawing made by his son John Dixon in 1782 shows an ingenious proposal

---

[1] Revd. John Brewster, M.A., *The Parochial History and Antiquities of Stockton-upon-Tees*, 1796.

[2] Bailey, *General View of the Agriculture of the County of Durham*, 1810, p. 275.

for avoiding locks, by transporting the canal boats from one level to another by rails laid on an inclined plane. The ultimate adoption of a railway throughout made anything of the kind unnecessary, but in the proposed canal lay the germ of the Stockton and Darlington Railway, and it may be noted that the principle of portable boats was afterwards applied successfully in America and elsewhere with the object which George Dixon had in view.

The idea of the canal died hard, and was not abandoned until after another survey, this time by John Rennie, in 1813; by this date the promoters had been 'led to believe that a rail-way or tram-road would prove of more benefit,' and such alternatives to the canal were therefore taken into consideration; valuable information was supplied by Samuel Homfray from the workings of the Sir-howy tram-road which ran for 23 miles nearly parallel with a canal and yielded eighteen per cent. per annum, while the canal yielded only eight.[1] The question was also affected by the echoes of a dispute which had arisen as to the route to be taken by the canal, which was still favoured by Stockton. Darlington, afraid that it might be left on one side, favoured the railway; financial forecasts were made by the advocates of both schemes at a meeting held on 13th November 1818 to determine which system should be adopted.

The railway had the local support of such able men as Jonathan Back-house, the banker of Darlington, John Grimshaw, the rope manufacturer of Bishop Wearmouth near Sunderland, and Thomas Meynell, a landed proprietor, of Yarm, supported by the legal advice of Francis Mewburn, the last town bailiff of Darlington, who was to become the first railway solicitor. The promoters estimated a profit of fifteen per cent. on the cost, but Edward Pease, who threw the whole weight of his influence into the scale for the railway, contented himself with promising the five per cent. which he demonstrated to be safe beyond a doubt. As in the case of the development of the locomotive, we find it difficult to give due credit to all who were concerned in the promotion of the railway, but local public opinion has always ascribed a leading part to Edward Pease.

The meeting adopted the recommendation of the committee and decided to apply to Parliament for an act to make a tram-way on the plans and system given by George Overton, 'an engineer of great experience in the construction of such roads.' They had next to consider whether to adopt his recommen-dation of a tram-road on the South Wales system, or an 'improved rail-road as in use in the north.' But on this point they did not reach any immediate decision, and the first Stockton and Darlington Railway Act, to which the Royal assent was obtained on 19th April 1821, provided for a rail-way or tram-way for the use of the public on payment of certain tolls for the conveyance of merchandise by horse traction; neither the conveyance of passengers nor the use of steam locomotives were mentioned in this first application.

It appears that various reasons, into which we need not enter, subsequently led the principal promoters of the railway to take the work out of the hands

---

[1] *Observations on the proposed Rail-way or Tram-road from Stockton to the Collieries by way of Darlington,* 1818, p. 7.

Appendix.

REVENUE EXPECTED TO ARISE.

	£.	s.	d.
From 30,794 Tons of Coal annually conveyed between the Collieries and Darlington, 14 miles, at 1½d. per ton per mile	2694	9	6
Do. 10,000 Tons of Coal annually conveyed between Coundon, Eldon, and Black Boy Collieries, and Darlington, 14 miles, at 1½d. per ton per mile	875	0	0
Do. 13,000 Tons of Coal annually conveyed between the Collieries & Yarm, 22½ miles, at 1½d. per ton per mile	1828	2	6
Do. 29,000 Tons of coal annually conveyed between the collieries & Stockton, 25 miles, at 1½d. per ton per mile	4531	5	0
Do. 82,794 Tons of Coal annually passing along the inclined planes, at 6d. per ton	2069	17	0
Do. 4,000 Tons of Lime annually conveyed between the Kilns and Yarm, 16 miles, at 1½d. per ton per mile.	400	0	0
Do. 1,000 Tons of Lime annually conveyed between the Kilns & Darlington, 5 miles, at 1½d. per ton per mile.	31	5	0
Do. The conveyance of Merchandise, Minerals, and all other sources *, say 20,000 tons, at an average of 17 miles, at 2½d. per ton per mile	3541	13	4
Total annual Revenue	£15,971	12	4
Deduct for Repairs, Salaries, Agencies, &c.	2,171	12	
Net Revenue	£13,800	0	0
15 per Cent. on the cost, viz. £92,000, (adding £10,000 to the estimate for contingencies,) is...	13,800	0	0

* To and from Stockton, Darlington, and Yarum, and all the interior parts of the County.

hand-written annotations in margins

[from an original copy of 'A Further Report on the intended Rail or Tram-Road' 1820, with notes by Edward Pease.]

43

of Overton, who had made the last survey and had perhaps been the first man to suggest a tramway in place of a canal, though he strongly opposed the use of locomotives. It is remarkable that both for the Stockton and Darlington, and later for the Liverpool and Manchester Railway, George Stephenson was called in to carry out, or modify, the work which had been commenced by another, and the facts should be noted since they were made in later years the basis for attacks upon Stephenson as having robbed other and earlier workers of their due. In both cases it appears that the persons responsible for the decisions had good reasons for their action, and in neither case did they regret the choice which was first made by Edward Pease on behalf of the Stockton and Darlington Railway. Stephenson came to Darlington to interview Pease in circumstances which have often been related, though there are two versions of the story, one that he came on his own initiative, the other, that he was sent for.[1] Pease afterwards wrote the letter to which Stephenson replied as under from :—

KILLINGWORTH COLLIERY,
April 28th 1821.

EDWD. PEASE ESQ.

SIR,—I have been favoured with your Letter of the 20 Inst., & am glad to learn that the Bill has passed for the Darlington Rail Way.

I am much obliged by the favourable sentiments you express towards me: and shall be happy if I can be of service in carrying into execution your plans.

From the nature of my engagements here and in the neighbourhood, I could not devote the whole of my time to your Rail Way, but I am willing to undertake to survey & mark out the best line of Way within the limits prescribed by the Act of Parliament and also, to assist the Committee with plans and estimates, and in letting to the different contractors such work as they might judge it advisable to do by Contract and also to superintend the execution of the work—And I am induced to recommend the whole being done by Contract under the superintendance of competent persons appointed by the Committee:

Were I to contract for the whole line of Road it would be necessary for me to do so at an advanced price upon the Sub Contractors, and it would also be necessary for the Committee to have some person to superintend my undertaking. This would be attended with an extra expence, and the Committee would derive no advantage to compensate for it.

If you wish it, I will wait upon you at Darlington at an early opportunity when I can enter into more particulars as to remuneration, &c., &c.

I remain yours

respectfully,

GEO. STEPHENSON.

Later, in July 1821, influenced by the accounts of Stephenson which they had received from various quarters as an 'intelligent, active, experienced and practical man, assiduous in his attention to what he undertook and moderate in his charges,' the directors appointed him engineer, and Edward Pease wrote[2] to advise him of their decision :—

[1] Tomlinson, *The North Eastern Railway*, pp. 71, 72. There are evidences of a confusion between two distinct visits, the first perhaps made by Stephenson on his own initiative.

[2] Jeans, *Jubilee Memorial of the Railway System*, p. 38.

THE STOCKTON AND DARLINGTON RAILWAY

DARLINGTON, *7 mo.* 28, 1821.

ESTEEMED FRIEND, GEORGE STEPHENSON.—Annexed are some resolutions passed at our last general meeting. We beg thee to take them into consideration, and so soon as thou can'st name thy charge for effecting all they contain which attaches to thee as engineer, drop me a line. The resolutions are so definite and comprehensive, it does not seem needful to add more, than to request that as soon as the crops are off the ground, no time may be lost, provided nothing can be done in the meantime. In making thy survey, it must be borne in mind that this is for a great public way, and to remain as long as any coal in the district remains. Its construction must be solid, and as little machinery as possible—in fact, we wish thee to proceed in all thy levels, estimates, and calculations, with that care and economy which would influence thee if the work was thy own; and it would be well to let comparative estimates be formed, as to the expense of a double and single railway, and whether it be needful to have it only double in some parts, and what parts; also comparative estimates as to the expense of malleable or cast iron. We shall be glad to hear from thee soon, and I am, on behalf of the committee, thy assured friend.

EDWARD PEASE.

To this letter Stephenson replied on 2nd August 1821 :—

After carefully examining your favour, I find it impossible to form an accurate idea of what such a survey would cost, as not only the old line must be gone over, but all the other deviating parts, which will be equal to a double survey, and, indeed, it must be done in a very different manner from your former one, so as to enable me to make a correct measurement of all the cuts and batteries on the whole line. It would, I think, occupy me at least five weeks. My charge shall include all necessary assistance for the accomplishment of the survey, estimates of the expense of cuts and batteries on the different projected lines, together with all remarks, reports, &c., of the same. Also the comparative cost of malleable iron and cast-iron rails, winning and preparing the blocks of stone, and all materials wanted to complete the line. I could not do this for less than £140, allowing me to be moderately paid. I assure you, in completing the undertaking, I will act with that economy which would influence me if the whole of the work was my own.

The choice between malleable (*i.e.* wrought) and cast iron rails might have been a difficult one for Stephenson, having in view his own pecuniary interest in the cast iron rail which he had patented with Losh in 1816, but it is clear that he did not allow this to affect the opinion which, as an engineer, he had already formed, and expressed in a letter written from Killingworth to Robert Stevenson, C.E.[1], under date :—

June 28th 1821.

SIR,—With this you will receive three copies of a specification of a patent malleable iron rail invented by John Birkinshaw of Bedlington, near Morpeth.

The hints were got from your Report on Railways, which you were so kind as to send me by favour of Mr. Cookson some time ago. Your reference to Tindal Fell Railway led the inventor to make some experiments on malleable iron bars, the result of which convinced him of the superiority of the malleable over the cast iron—so much so, that he took out a patent.

Those rails are so much liked in this neighbourhood, that I think in a short time they will do away with the cast iron railways.

They make a fine line for our engines, as there are so few joints compared with the other.

I have lately started a new locomotive engine, with some improvements on the others which you saw. It has far surpassed my expectations. I am confident a railway on which my engines can work is far superior to a *canal*. On a long and favourable railway I would stent[2] my engines to travel 60 miles per day with from 40 to 60 tons of goods.

[1] *Life of Robert Stevenson, C.E.,* 1874, p. 128.
[2] To 'assess,' 'rate,' North Country and Scotch.

They would work nearly fourfold cheaper than horses where coals are not very costly.

I merely make these observations, as I know you have been at more trouble than any man I know of in searching into the utility of railways, and I return you my sincere thanks for your favour by Mr. Cookson.

If you should be in this neighbourhood, I hope you will not pass Killingworth Colliery, as I should be extremely glad if you could spend a day or two with me.

I am sir,

Yours most respectfully,

G. STEPHENSON.

JOHN DIXON

1796—1865

Consistently with this opinion Stephenson recommended malleable iron rails for the Stockton and Darlington Railway, so incurring, at least for a time, the wrath of his co-patentee, William Losh, who wrote testily on the subject to Edward Pease.   Against the advice of Stephenson cast iron rails were used for a portion of the line, to satisfy the interests of other persons.

On September 27th 1821 the sub-committee of the Stockton and Darlington Railway after considering the appointment of an assistant engineer resolved :—

That John Dixon, who appears to this meeting to possess the best local knowledge, be appointed to accompany Mr. Stephenson on his survey and that the remuneration to be made him be left to the adjustment of Mr. Edward Pease and Mr. Jona Backhouse.

John Dixon, born in 1796, was a grandson of George Dixon of Cockfield ; he has recorded that he 'was brought up to land surveying in connection with the management of coal mines,' 'begun his railway career by surveying the Stockton and Darlington Railway in 1819,' 'was engaged as one of the two resident engineers to construct the railway under the directions of George Stephenson,'[1] 'began to level with Stephenson for the railway 15 of 10 mo. 1821,' and 'began cutting in 5 mo. 1822.'[2] The appointments which John Dixon subsequently received under Stephenson are evidence of the valuable services which he had rendered in the construction of the line, to which he appropriately returned in 1844 as chief engineer.[3]

As a result of his survey Stephenson suggested certain alterations[4] to the line as proposed by Overton, and in connection with their application to Parliament for an amended Bill the proprietors of the railway consequently published the following statement :—

Previously to commencing Operations, it was deemed most prudent to obtain a Re-survey of the Line ; for this purpose, Mr. Geo. Stephenson, an eminent Engineer, was employed, who discovered that the Line to which the Sanction of Parliament had been already obtained, was not the most eligible which the County afforded ; and that, by a few Variations, (which would not cause the Line to diverge widely from that authorised by the above Act), most important Advantages would be gained ; the Line would be shortened nearly Three Miles ; —a great Expense saved in its Execution ;—Impediments occasioned by frequent Curves, and great Irregularity in the Descent, avoided ;—and other formidable Difficulties removed ; which, by rendering the Carriage much easier and consequently less expensive, would very greatly increase the Benefits the Public expect to derive from this Undertaking.

The first Act had not contemplated the use of locomotives but it was inevitable that George Stephenson, with his experience at Killingworth and Hetton, should recommend a tractive power in which he had such confidence and his alterations to the line were doubtless made with the adoption of locomotives in view. In December 1821 he wrote to William James, with whom he was still on intimate terms, 'I fully expect to get the engine introduced on the Darlington Railway,' and on his recommendation a clause was included in the Act of 1823 :—

That it shall and may be lawful to and for the said Company of proprietors or any person or persons authorised or permitted by them, from and after the passing of this Act, to make and erect such and so many loco-motive or moveable engines, as the said company or proprietors shall from time to time think proper and expedient, and to use and employ the same in or upon the said railways or tramroads or any of them, by the said Act and this Act, directed or authorised to be made, for the purpose of facilitating the transport, conveyance and carriage of goods, merchandise and other articles and things upon and along the same roads, and for the conveyance of passengers upon and along the same roads.

[1] (a) Memorandum of John Dixon's evidence on his career, *MS.* undated.
(b) Draft letter to Major-General C. W. Pasley, Inspector of Railways, dated 11th January 1846.

[2] John Dixon's Notebook, in possession of his nephew, Mr. Waynman Dixon.

[3] George Stephenson on 11th January 1846 writes to John Dixon :—' You have no occasion to fret about a situation as long as I am in the land of the living' *Handbook on Rise and Development of the Railway System* Edward Baker, Birmingham, 1893. Ref. No. 368g

[4] It is interesting to note that had Overton's line been adopted the present works of Robert Stephenson & Co. could not have been situated where they are to-day.

Stephenson had won another battle for the locomotive, and in 1822 the directors of the Stockton and Darlington Railway Company informed the promoters of the Liverpool and Manchester Railway of their intention to use locomotives.   Even by this date the Stockton and Darlington Railway, though still under construction, had become a field for enquiry, the directors giving generous facilities to all visitors from home and abroad, and until after the Liverpool and Manchester line had overshadowed it the 'Quakers' Line' was 'the great theatre of practical operations on railways'[1], giving the first impetus

(part) from a contemporary lithograph, undated.

TRAIN OF WAGGONS CROSSING THE TURNPIKE ROAD NEAR DARLINGTON AT THE OPENING OF THE STOCKTON AND DARLINGTON RAILROAD.

to the general use of locomotives, and so to the development of the locomotive building industry.   On 16th September 1824 their sub-committee resolved:—

That two Locomotive engines be ordered of R. Stephenson & Co. for the sum of £500 each and that an agreement be entered into and duly signed confirming the contract.

These were the first locomotives ordered by a public railway company from a contractor ; the first of them, employed at the opening of the line on the 27th September 1825, was fortunately preserved after many years of useful service and now stands at Darlington station, a remarkable witness to the early work of Robert Stephenson & Co.

[1] Booth, *An Account of the Liverpool and Manchester Rail Road*, 1830.

CHAPTER V

EDWARD PEASE

1767-1858

Ἔργα νέων, βουλαὶ δὲ μέσων, εὐχαὶ δὲ γερόντων.
—*Hesiod.*

Work for the young, counsel for the middle aged, prayers for the old.

Edward Pease was born in 1767 at Darlington, and at the age of fourteen, was put to learn the wool business of his father in that town. Besides their wool and weaving the firm of Joseph Pease and Sons carried on a considerable banking business, and his biographer[1] tells us that by the time Edward Pease was eighteen he took a pleasure in business, and was 'travelling on horse-back from place to place, buying and selling with energy and prudence'; but 'his business life did not occupy his whole time, and as a young man he was addicted to field sports and light reading,' with both of which he reproached himself in later years. 'He did not become a wealthy man until his old age, he disliked to see anyone absorbed in business and money making, and at fifty had withdrawn from taking an active part in the family business.' It appears that before this he had interested himself in the proposals for a local canal or railroad which had led to the public meeting of 1812, and his name appears among the supporters, with that of his father   we have now to treat of his other interests and of the man himself.

Edward Pease was convinced by what he had himself seen at Killingworth, and heard from George Stephenson and others, that traction by steam loco-motives had been proved at the collieries to be economical, and he had been persuaded that the system might be adopted for the Stockton and Darlington Railway ; later he decided to lend his valuable support to the establishment of an engine works at Newcastle which Stephenson had in view 'for the purpose of realising and carrying out the improvements in detail which he was constantly making.' In this decision he gave another instance of his faith in Stephenson's worth, and we are confronted with one of those happy com-binations of capital with natural talent which have so notably contributed to the material prosperity of this country. It was thanks to this happy partner-ship that the two men became identified with the successful introduction of railways into general use ; each owed much to the other and neither has failed to admit the debt. Robert Stephenson referring many years later to his father's share in the successful issue of the 'first great experiment' wrote to Edward Pease :—

In my remembrance you stand amongst the foremost of his early partners and advisors, and I know throughout life he always regarded you as one of his very best friends and took great delight in frequently and very graphically describing his first visit to Darlington on foot to confer with you on the subject of the Stockton and Darlington Railway.

[1] Sir Alfred E. Pease, Bart., *The Diaries of Edward Pease*, 1907.

4

Edward Pease himself when asked in 1857, then 90 years of age, to take part in a public ceremony in connection with the first locomotive which had run on the Stockton and Darlington Railway, replied [1]:—

DARLINGTON, 6 *mo.* 2, 1857.

RESPECTED FRIENDS, JOHN DIXON AND THOS. MACNAY,

I have considered the request which you were deputed to make, that I should lay the foundation-stone of that building which it is proposed to erect for preserving the first locomotive engine that ever went on a public line of railway, as this did in 1825. From my very advanced age and unwillingness to enter into anything connected with public active life, I feel I must be excused accepting this mark of regard and esteem, which I cannot but appreciate, and do feel grateful in being selected for the office. Sanguine, and I may say sure, as I was of the value of railways when I first moved in their introduction with two or three able helpers, and such an engineer as the late celebrated George Stephenson, their success and importance have far, very far, exceeded the most favourable anticipations, confidently sanguine as these anticipations were. With an ample repayment of satisfaction and pleasure, I cannot, in taking a retrospective view, regret the care and attention for three or four years given to the completion of our then unpopular work, opposed by magistrates, commissioners of turnpikes, &c., to the full of their power. Steady, disinterested attention, without one shilling of fee or reward, brought our work, thankless and wageless, to its completion. And it is with inexpressible satisfaction I contemplate that so large a portion of the civilised world is now reaping inestimable benefit from this mode of transit. . . . . Again declining the kindness of your proposition, I subscribe myself, with much respect, your friend,

EDWARD PEASE.

The abundance of my years must apologise for very much in this letter.

While it is true that some of the other promoters of the railway, in particular Jonathan Backhouse, have not received the credit due to them, we may remark that Edward Pease in the letter we have quoted does less than bare justice to his own share in the work; not only by his valuable counsel, but also by the personal subscription of a large sum, he saved the railway Bill at the eleventh hour, and later on more than one occasion, particularly at a critical time in 1826, rescued the railway company from its immediate financial difficulties by various payments from his own pocket. Writing in 1857 he was able to say [2]:—

My favoured position in life did not render any remuneration for service needful, nor did I ever receive a shilling, or dinner, or anything for my exertions. When towards the close of our work, money falling short, our banker refused to grant us more, I paid all the workmen, &c., &c., employed in this way out of my own resources, until he could procure a loan. I remained in the direction one year after opening, until 1827, when seeing there was income enough to pay a handsome dividend, I retired with a resolution never to enter a railway meeting again.

He had been amply rewarded for his faith in both railways and locomotives and his friends and neighbours had received further proof of a business acumen for which the Quakers have always been renowned and which earned for the Stockton and Darlington Railway the name of 'The Quakers' Line.'

[1] Jeans, *Jubilee Memorial of the Railway System*, 1875, p. 202.

[2] *The Two James's and the Two Stephensons*, p. 47.

from the painting by Heywood Hardy, A.R.W.S., in possession of Messrs. Pease & Partners

EDWARD PEASE

1767—1858

portrait by Sir George Hayter, in possession of Sir Alfred E. Pease, Bart

JOSEPH PEASE

1799—1872

a study by the artist for his picture of the first Reform Parliament, 1832

A remarkable character, Edward Pease left, in the diaries of his old age, much evidence of the foundation on which his reputation was based ; referring in his seventy-first year to his connection with Robert Stephenson and Company he records on 20th October 1838 :—

At Newcastle attending to a manufacturing concern I have an interest in there. In the evening found that my mind had been too much occupied in consideration of its prospects and gains.

We find exemplified in him the poet's three stages in a life's development and the full recognition that man cannot live by bread alone ; success seems more and more, as he grows older, to produce the reaction which he faithfully records in the calm of evening reflection, and all through he seems to fear that much monetary gain may prove a disintegrating force in the community to which he belongs. Himself simple in habit, direct in speech and abundantly generous to those in whom he trusted, his quakerism consisted in something more than of such entries in his diary as those we have quoted, or in keeping his hat on at the funeral of his old friend George Stephenson, on 17th August 1848, as he himself records :—

. . . . In the church I sat a spectacle with my hat on, and not comforted by the funeral service.

On 9th March 1853 he notes :—

. . . giving to R. Stephenson and W. Hutchinson the profit which I cannot touch as a profit resulting from making some War Steamers' engines for the King of Sardinia.

Edward Pease died in 1858, in his ninety-second year, one of the simple, but great, figures of the nineteenth century, and one whose stature remains undiminished by time.

(from a share certificate of the Stockton and Darlington Railway.)

Memorandum for an Agreement of Copartnership between Robert Stephenson of Killingworth near Newcastle, George Stephenson of the same place, Edward Pease of Darlington, and Michael Longridge of Bedlington, for carrying on the business of Engine Builders, Mill Wrights &c at Newcastle upon Tyne and for carrying on the same trades under the Firm of Robert Stephenson &Co.

1st The Capital to be Four Thousand Pounds and to be divided into Ten Shares

2d This Capital to be advanced in the following proportions when found necessary viz

Robert Stephenson 2 Shares	£800
George Stephenson 2 do	800
Edward Pease 4 do	1600
Michael Longridge 2 do	800
10 Shares	£4000

3 If any further Capital should be wanted the same to be borrowed upon the joint security of all the Partners.

from the original Minute Book in possession of Mr. George Stephenson, son of the late Mr. George Robert Stephenson.

CHAPTER VI

THE FOUNDATION AND DEVELOPMENT

OF

ROBERT STEPHENSON & CO.

1823—1859

George Stephenson stated in 1825 that since 1813 he had built about fifty-five engines, among them about sixteen locomotives and a stationary engine of 200 horse-power ; some of these engines had been sent to France. In 1821 he entered into partnership with John and Isaac Burrell, ironfounders of Orchard Street and South Street, Newcastle, and it is recorded that this firm constructed for the Stockton and Darlington Railway a remarkable metal girder bridge designed by Stephenson himself.[1] We have no evidence that locomotives were built by him when with the Burrells, but it is possible to consider their joint establishment as having given the idea from which the works of Robert Stephenson & Co. developed later.

The actual date of foundation of the firm whose centenary we now commemorate is definitely established by the following record in the first minute book of the new company, under date June 23rd 1823 :—

MEMORANDUM for an Agreement of Co-partnership between Robert Stephenson of Killingworth near Newcastle, George Stephenson of the same place, Edward Pease of Darlington, and Michael Longridge of Bedlington, for carrying on the business of Engine Builders, Mill Wrights, etc., at Newcastle-upon-Tyne, and for carrying on the same trade under the Firm of Robert Stephenson & Co.

1. The Capital to be Four Thousand Pounds and to be divided into Ten Shares.
2. This Capital to be advanced in the following proportions when found necessary, viz.

Robert Stephenson	2 Shares	..	..	£800
George Stephenson	2 do.	..	..	800
Edward Pease	4 do.	..	..	1,600
Michael Longridge	2 do.	..	..	800
	10 Shares			£4,000

3. If any further Capital should be wanted the same to be borrowed upon the joint security of all the partners.
4. No further advance of Capital shall be made, unless the same is thought necessary, and ordered by the Partners holding eight shares, at a Meeting to be specially called for the purpose by the Managing Partner, to be held at the office of the Manufactory, and of which Meeting twenty-one days Notice shall be given in writing by the Managing Partner to each of the other Partners.

---

[1] Tomlinson, *The North Eastern Railway*, p. 93.

4ᵗʰ No further advance of Capital shall be made, unless the same is thought necessary, and ordered by the Partners holding eight shares, at a Meeting to be specially called for the purpose by the Managing Partner, to be held at the Office of the Manufactory and of which Meeting twenty one days Notice shall be given in writing by the managing Partner to each of the other Partners.

5 The said Robert Stephenson shall be the Managing Partner, &be paid a Salary of Two Hundred Pounds per annum, upon condition that his Father George Stephenson furnish the Plans &c which may be required, and take the general charge of the Manufactory as long as required by the Partners.

6ᵗʰ A compensation of Three Hundred Pounds to be paid by the Concern, at the end of three years to the said George Stephenson upon condition of his assigning to the Partners, the Patents already by Him obtained for Locomotive & other Engines, or should other

from the original Minute Book.

the said George Stephenson make any other useful discovery, for which the Company may deem it worth while to take out a Patent, the said Company shall in common with the said George Stephenson enjoy all the advantages of the said discovery, the Concern paying the expence of the Patent.

7. In case of the death of any Partner during the term of this Partnership, the amount of his Capital, together with five per Centum Interest thereon from the date of the preceeding Balance, shall be paid over to his Executors within Six Months after the decease of the said Partner.

8. In case of any Partner being desirous to retire from the Business, He shall be at liberty so to do, upon giving Six Months Notice in writing to the other Partners, who shall have the offer of his Shares at five per Cent less than they stand valued at in the Partnership Books. Should the Partners either collectively or individually refuse to purchase the Shares, the Partner wishing to

from the original Minute Book.

to retire, shall be at liberty to dispose of his shares to any other Person, provided only that no Person shall hold less than — two shares.

9   A meeting of the Partners shall be held at Newcastle upon the second Tuesday in every Month. The Managing Partner shall at this Meeting lay before the Partners the Cash Book regularly balanced to the last day of the preceding Month, & also a statement of all Debts due to & from the Partnership with every other document which any Partner present may require.

    At this Meeting the Partners shall make such Orders, as may to them seem necessary, which Orders shall be entered in a Book, signed by all the Partners present, which Orders shall be considered as binding on all absent Partners.

10   This Partnership shall be for Twenty one Years, from the 31st day of May 1823 unless previously dissolved by mutual consent.

11   Stock shall be taken annually as upon the 31st day of March — the Books shall be

from the original Minute Book.

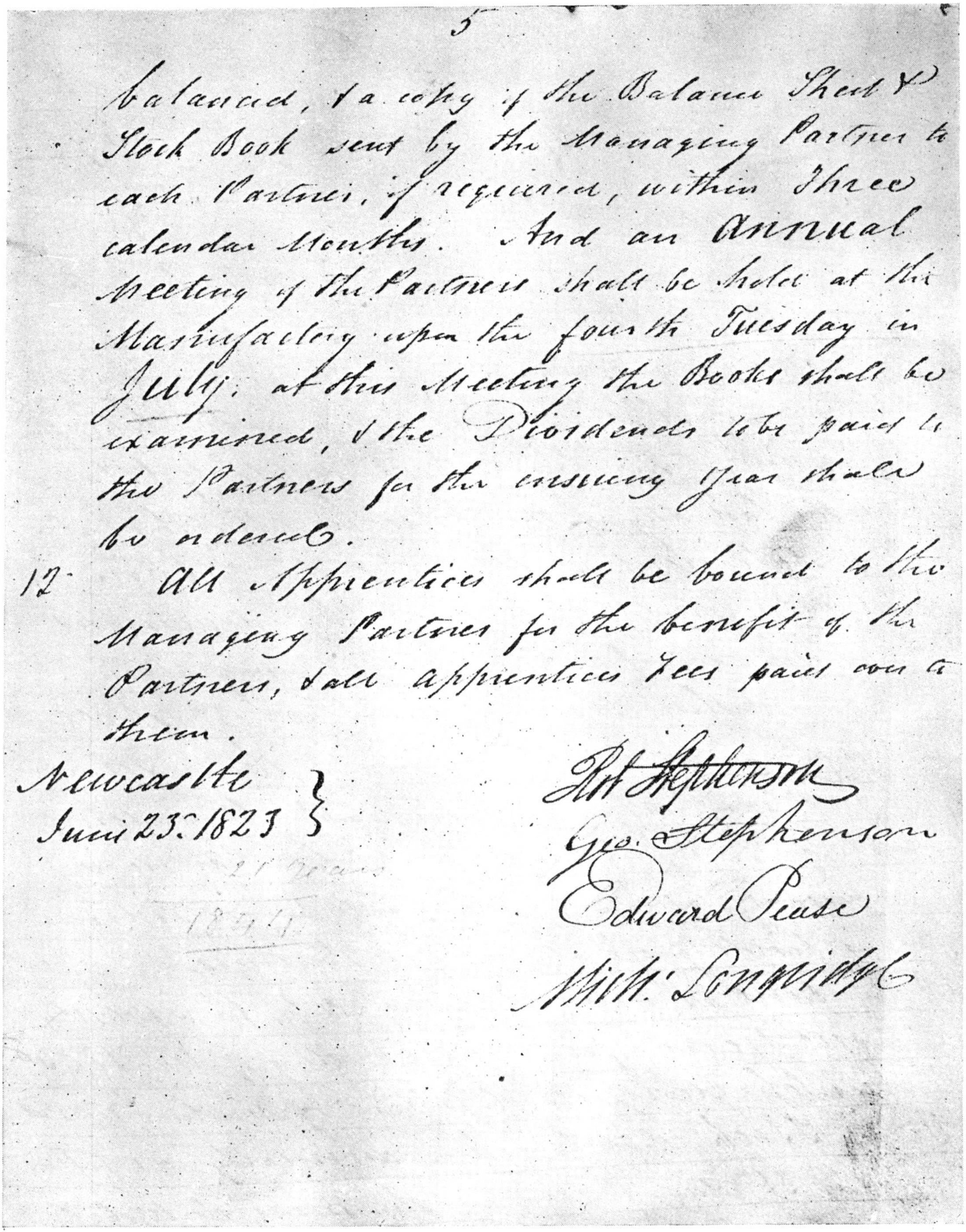

balanced, & a copy of the Balance Sheet &
Stock Book sent by the Managing Partner to
each Partner, if required, within Three
calendar Months. And an Annual
Meeting of the Partners shall be held at the
Manufactory upon the fourth Tuesday in
July; at this Meeting the Books shall be
examined, & the Dividends to be paid to
the Partners for the ensuing Year shall
be ordered.

12.   All Apprentices shall be bound to the
Managing Partner for the benefit of the
Partners, & all apprentices Fees paid over to
them.

Newcastle
June 23. 1823 }

Rbt. Stephenson
Geo. Stephenson

Edward Pease

Mich. Longridge

from the original Minute Book.

5. The said *Robert Stephenson* shall be the Managing Partner, and be paid a Salary of Two Hundred Pounds per annum upon condition that his Father George Stephenson furnish the Plans, &c., which may be required, and take the general charge of the Manufactory as long as required by the Partners.

6. A compensation of Three Hundred Pounds to be paid by the Concern, at the end of three years to the said George Stephenson upon condition of his assigning to the Partners, the Patents already by him obtained for Locomotive and other Engines, or should the said George Stephenson make any other useful discovery, for which the Company may deem it worth while to take out a Patent, the said Company shall in common with the said George Stephenson enjoy all the advantages of the said discovery, the Concern paying the expense of the Patent.

7. In case of the death of any Partner during the term of this Partnership, the amount of his Capital, together with five per centum Interest thereon from the date of the preceding Balance, shall be paid over to his Executors within Six Months after the decease of the said Partner.

8. In case of any Partner being desirous to retire from the Business, he shall be at liberty to do so, upon giving Six Months' Notice in writing to the other Partners, who shall have the offer of his Shares at five per Cent. less than they stand valued in the Partnership Books. Should the Partners either collectively or individually refuse to purchase the Shares, the Partner wishing to retire, shall be at liberty to dispose of his shares to any other Person, provided only that no person shall hold less than two shares.

9. A meeting of the Partners shall be held at Newcastle-upon-Tyne upon the second Tuesday in every Month. The Managing Partner shall at this Meeting lay before the Partners the Cash Book regularly balanced to the last day of the preceding Month, and also a statement of all debts due to and from the Partnership with every other document which any Partner present may require.

At this Meeting the Partners shall make such Orders, as may to them seem necessary, which Orders shall be entered in a Book, signed by all the Partners present, which Orders shall be considered as binding on all absent Partners.

10. This Partnership shall be for Twenty-one years, from the 31st day of May, 1823, unless previously dissolved by mutual consent.

11. Stock shall be taken annually as upon the 31st day of March—the Books shall be balanced, and a copy of the Balance Sheet and Stock Book sent by the Managing Partner to each Partner, if required, within Three calendar months. And an Annual Meeting of the Partners shall be held at the Manufactory upon the *fourth Tuesday in July*, at this Meeting the Books shall be examined and the Dividends to be paid to the Partners for the ensuing year shall be ordered.

12. All Apprentices shall be bound to the Managing Partner for the benefit of the Partners, and all apprentices' Fees paid over to them.

Newcastle,
June 23rd 1823.

ROB. STEPHENSON.
GEO. STEPHENSON.
EDWARD PEASE.
MICH. LONGRIDGE.

From an entry made by Edward Pease in his diary many years later, it appears that towards the £800 capital standing in the name of Robert Stephenson £500 was lent by Pease himself to assist the young engineer.

The new company's first minute is recorded under date :—

NEWCASTLE, June 24th 1823.

At a meeting held this day at the George Inn the articles of the agreement and Co-partnership between the undersigned were read over and agreed upon and signed by them, viz.:

Robert Stephenson,   George Stephenson,
Edward Pease,   and   Michael Longridge.

The following goods were then ordered, viz. :—
    Pair of Smith's Bellows.
    Anvils.
    Vices.
    Sundry Deals, Tiles, Stones, etc., as per Book.
    3 Lathes.
An advance of Ten Pounds per share was agreed and that the same should be remitted to Robert Stephenson on or before the 30th day of this month.
Resolved that Sir W. M. Ridley & Co. be bankers to this concern.

ROBERT STEPHENSON.   EDWARD PEASE.
GEO. STEPHENSON.   MICH. LONGRIDGE.

The most notable fact is that the Company should have taken the name of Robert Stephenson, the youngest of the four partners, who had still to prove his capacity as an engineer. But young as he was it appears that he was called upon to 'superintend its earliest operations, to supervise the building operations and engage men, take orders, advise on contracts, draw plans, make estimates, keep the accounts, and in all matters great or small govern the young establishment on his own responsibility.'[1]

The purchase of the ground is referred to in a minute dated :—

DARLINGTON, July 8th 1823.

Resolved—
    That an agreement shall be entered into with Anderson of Newcastle for the purchase of the Ground fixed upon for the Engine building Manufactory upon the most favourable terms which can be procured.
    And until a regular Bill of Sale can be procured from young Anderson a Lease shall be taken from him and his Uncle, upon such conditions as may be recommended by Mr. Jos. Bainbridge solicitor.

ROBERT STEPHENSON.
GEO. STEPHENSON.
EDWARD PEASE.
MICH. LONGRIDGE.

This original site stood to the east of South Street in the angle formed by that street and Forth Street, after which the works were at first called and for many years known, later they expanded westwards crossing South Street, which they eventually absorbed, and this became the official address, though Edward Pease continued to refer to Forth Street until his death.

The amounts of the first three fortnightly pays are stated to have been[2] :—

On 26th July, 1823	....	....	....	....	£12	2	2
do. 9th August	....	....	....	....	30	2	4
do. 23rd August	....	....	....	....	37	9	$7\frac{1}{4}$

The next minute of interest is dated 8th October 1823 :—

A letter from T. R. to G. S. read recommending his visiting London respecting an order for Engines for Columbia.

It was considered advisable that the remarks upon Perkins' Engines, drawn up by Geo. Stephenson, be forwarded to Mr. Richardson, and in case of its being considered unsatisfactory that G. S. be at liberty to go up to London at the expense of this co-partnership.

[1] Jeaffreson, *Life of Robert Stephenson*, Vol. I., p. 66.
[2] Article, 'Local Industrial Sketches,' *Northern Echo*, January 3rd 1873.

It appears that Richardson, like many others, had been attracted by the extravagant claims of Jacob Perkins; these are referred to in a contemporary letter by Joshua Field [1], the well-known engineer, who writes under date :—

LONDON, May 6th 1823.

The fame of Mr. Perkins has spread half over Europe, and I know of no invention or improvement that ever excited so much attention as this. Whether it is to be attributed to the importance of the subject, or being the production of an American of reputed genius, or to the manner in which it has been placed before the public I am unable to judge, but certain it is that the public mind has never been more agitated by a scientific question than they have been by this.

The writer records the unsatisfactory nature of the trials which he witnessed, and describes at length experiences similar to those related by Robert Stephenson in a letter [2] to Longridge dated :—

DUBLIN, Sept. 10th 1823.

We have some hopes of some orders for steam engines for South America, in the Columbian States. *This, however, depends on the success of Perkins's new engine.* My father and he have had a severe scold. Indeed the most of the birkies [3] were embittered at my father's opinion of the engine. He one day stopped the engine by his hand, and when we called the next day Perkins had previously got the steam to such a pitch (equal 15 atmospheres) that it was impossible for one man to stop it, but by a little of my assistance we succeeded in stopping it by laying hold of the fly-wheel. This engine he formerly called an 8 or 10 horse-power, but now only a 4. I am convinced, as well as my father, that Perkins knows nothing about the principle of steam engines.

Perkins' engine, which worked with a red-hot boiler, may have been the first, but it was not the last, of many 'wild schemes' put before George Stephenson; it is however only fair to say that in advocating the principle of the flash boiler Perkins was in advance of his time, though he lacked the essential grasp of practical limitations which Stephenson so eminently possessed.

At the commencement of 1824 the Forth Street factory was at work, as shown by a minute dated Newcastle, 20th January 1824 :—

Present the undersigned.

The minutes of the last meeting were read.—The Cash Account ending 31st December last was examined leaving a balance of £129 15s. 5d.—The erection of No. 2 Smith's Shop was approved of.

The Draft of the Agreement with Mr. Anderson for the purchase of the ground was laid before the meeting and ordered to be transmitted to Mr. Edward Pease for his perusal.

A further advance of Twenty-five pounds per share was agreed upon.

The following orders are in progress :—

1	Engine of 8 Horse-power for		Mr. Bragge.
2	Do. 15	do.	Stockton Steam Boat.
2	Do. 15	do.	⎫ The Stockton and Darlington Railway Co.
2	Do. 30	do.	⎭

ROB. STEPHENSON.
Pro. EDWARD PEASE, JOS. PEASE.
MICH. LONGRIDGE.

[1] Letter to Simon Goodrich ; preserved at the Science Museum, South Kensington.

[2] Jeaffreson, *Life of Robert Stephenson*, Vol. I., p. 62.

[3] Northern dialect ; 'a smart young fellow'; used contemptuously (as by Robert Burns) to imply conceit.

The engines for the Stockton and Darlington Railway were the fixed engines for the two inclines, one at Brusselton, the other at Etherley; the first locomotives for Darlington were not ordered until later.

Thomas Richardson, referred to in the minute of 8th October 1823, was a cousin of Edward Pease; as the founder of the famous discount house, of Overend, Gurney & Co., he was well known in financial circles [1]; he was not, strictly speaking, an original partner in Robert Stephenson & Co., though he eventually became one, but he was financially interested in Edward Pease's ventures and from its inception lent money to the new company. Unfortunately he was also attracted at this time by the golden visions of the Columbian Mining Association who, no doubt on his recommendation, applied for technical advice to George Stephenson, commissioning him to select workmen and officials and to purchase the materials which they required for their operations in Columbia. In the course of his connection Richardson, like others, had been impressed with the energy and capability of Robert Stephenson, and on behalf of the Mining Association suggested that he should take charge of their first expedition. Robert, keen to go, wrote to his father [2] :—

A FRIEND in Lombard Street.

from a print published 1824.

You must recollect I will only be away for a time, and in the meantime you can manage with the assistance of Mr. Longridge, who, together with John Nicholson, would take the whole of the business part off your hands, and only consider what an opening it is for me as an entry into business.

His father was only partly persuaded when Robert left Liverpool, on 18th June 1824, for Columbia, on a three years' engagement. In the previous month George Stephenson had been appointed to make a fresh survey for the Liverpool and Manchester Railway and the lack of proper management at Forth Street due to his absence is recorded by a minute dated 12 mo. 31 1824 :—

1. In consequence of the numerous engagements of Geo. Stephenson, it is concluded that he be relieved from that ostensible share of the management of the said concern during the ensuing year, which he has hitherto had, yet that the engine factory shall continue to receive any effort of his ingenuity and that of his Son for which they can spare time, and it is now agreed that the management be taken by Mich. Longridge at the rate of £200 per annum, for the year ensuing.

[1] *Dictionary of National Biography.*
[2] Jeaffreson, *Life of Robert Stephenson,* Vol. I., p. 70.

2. On considering the circumstances of the existing Patent for Locomotive Engines, and the short duration, say three years, ere that Patent expires, that it is expedient to endeavour to have the same extended if it be practicable by a Petition to Parliament as Geo. Stephenson has stated to this meeting, that he does not at present see any additions can be made to his former invention of such moment as to entitle him to sue for a new Patent; the care of this subject is committed to Edwd. Pease.

It appearing to this meeting that we labour under considerable disadvantage in not being able to found our own Cylinders and other cast metal articles,—It is resolved that an adjacent piece of ground about 1,800 yards square being Leasehold for three lives, be purchased at 4s. 6d. per yard, to erect a foundry upon, and that the care of completing this purchase be left to Michael Longridge. It is contemplated that this extension of our works may involve a capital equal, but not exceeding, the sum already invested in our Engine manufactory. A small modern built dwelling house attached to the premises above named appearing to be desirable to this concern, it is agreed that the same be purchased for £120, the same is left to care of Geo. Stephenson.

The decision by Robert Stephenson & Co. to make their own castings led to a dissolution of the earlier partnership between George Stephenson and the Burrells [1], and to the establishment of a foundry which became famous in the north of England; Burrell's, with another adjacent foundry, was eventually absorbed by the Forth Street works. [2]

It has been stated that in 1824, during George Stephenson's absence, Timothy Hackworth was appointed to superintend temporarily the new factory at Forth Street, and that Stephenson later offered him half his own share to remain [3] in this capacity. It has also been stated that James Kennedy [4], who afterwards went into partnership with Bury and Curtis as a locomotive builder, was appointed in 1824 manager of the Newcastle works where he remained for eighteen months, returning at the end of 1825 to Liverpool where he had first met George Stephenson. The two statements are obviously contradictory, but Hackworth's qualifications as a practical engineer must have been well known to George Stephenson, who indeed in 1825 recommended him for the position of locomotive superintendent on the Stockton and Darlington Railway, and it is highly probable that he may himself have previously employed Hackworth, possibly as foreman-smith. It may also be that Kennedy was for some time employed at the Forth Street works [5], but no reference to the appointment of either as manager appears in the minute book, which duly records the appointment of Michael Longridge to that position in December 1824, and we may note in this connection Robert Stephenson's recommendation of John Nicholson, though of him we know nothing else.

On 10th August 1824 Michael Longridge writes to Edward Pease :—

I now annex you a balance sheet for the accounts R. Stephenson & Coy. to the 30th June last. In the present unfinished state of the buildings, machinery, etc., no account can be accurately taken of the value of the stock and everything is therefore valued at its cost.

I have paid up my share of the Capital and will be obliged by your remitting the balance of yours, say £290 as our finances are very low.

---

[1] Advt. *Newcastle Chronicle*, 15th October 1825   [2] *Newcastle Weekly Courant*, 11th June 1881.

[3] *A Chapter in the History of Railway Locomotion*, and *Memoir of Timothy Hackworth*, p. 16.

[4] Obituary. *Proc. Inst. Mech. Engineers*, 1886.   [5] *Proc. Inst. Civil Engineers*, Vol. XVI., p. 22.

On 25th September 1824 he writes :—

I annex you a statement of Capital advanced to R. S. & Co. which I trust will be satisfactory.

The next document of importance which we quote does not refer to engine building but is evidence of the intimate connection with railway work generally which won for the two Stephensons their peculiar reputation, and eventually proved of great service to the Forth Street works ; this document sets forth :—

Proposals and agreement for opening an office of Engineering and Railway Surveying entered into and agreed this 31 day, 12 mo. 1824.

1. That the Co. shall consist of Geo. Stephenson, Robt. Stephenson, Edw. Pease and Michl. Longridge as follows :—

Geo. Stephenson	2 Shares.
Rob. Stephenson	2 do.
Edwd. Pease ($\frac{1}{2}$ T. R.'s)	4 do.
M. Longridge	2 do.
	10

2. That Geo. Stephenson and Robt. Stephenson shall take charge of pointing out, surveying, etc., all lines of Road, and all other works which the Co. may undertake and shall be provided with proper assistants at the expense of the Co.

3. Michl. Longridge shall take the charge of the correspondence and all the accounts, etc., etc.

4. All expenses for Clerks, Surveyors and other Salaries, and all other expenses shall be first discharged, after which Geo. Stephenson and Robt. Stephenson shall be paid for their joint use £1,500 per annum as a compensation for their services, and then the profits be divided according to their respective shares, provided the work done and the money received amount to the sum above named.

5. All Apprentice and other fees and remuneration shall be paid over for the joint benefit.

6. Robt. Stephenson is at liberty to conclude his present foreign engagement before he render any personal service to this company, yet the benefit to arise from any other foreign engagement is to go into the common stock. If within three months after his return to England, it is the said Robt. Stephenson's wish to terminate this agreement, it shall end upon his giving three months' notice.

7. The Office to be at Newcastle.

8. That this agreement commence on the 1st January 1825, and that the firm be Geo. Stephenson and Son.

It has been erroneously stated that the locomotive building concern was first known as 'George Stephenson and Son,' but the agreement of 30th December 1824, which we have just quoted, was for an entirely separate business.

In reference to this agreement Michael Longridge writes to Edward Pease from Edinburgh on 18th January 1825 :—

Accompanying this you will receive a sketch of Regulations, &c., for the affairs of G. S. & S.

Some few of the persons are already engaged by Geo. and he proposes to engage the others at the salaries mentioned if he should be appointed Engineer for those Rail-ways. From what I see and hear I am well satisfied that Geo. has an extraordinary field for the display of his peculiar Talents, and that if he manage well he may easily distance all his Competitors. We must however assist him much—Wood's Book must undergo a strict censorship before it is published—and I fear this will be a work of considerable delicacy, but it must be done. I have planned out an office for G. S. & Son adjoining R. S. & Coy. where the two businesses may be distinctly transacted.

EDIN., 18.1.25.

PROPOSED REGULATIONS, &c.

1.   An office shall be opened at Newcastle for the Business of Geo. Stephenson & Son, Rail-Way Engineers, where 1 or more good Draftsmen shall be employed.

2.   As soon as any Surveys of Rail-Ways are made, and in sufficient forwardness to be laid down upon Plans, they shall be sent by the Surveyor in charge of the proposed Line of Way, to the Newcastle Office, and the Draftsmen shall immediately proceed with the Plans.

3.   The Secretary shall make up the Reports from Data furnished by G. or R. S. and enter copies in the 'Report Book.'

All estimates shall also be made out by the Secretary, and copies entered in the 'Book of Estimates.'

4.   Every Surveyor shall &c. enter *daily* in his Time Book, an account of the employment of the day, and his expenditure for Travelling, &c.

These shall be regularly forwarded to the Newcastle Office, and entered by the Draftsman in the 'General Time Book.'

5.   A Minute Book shall be kept in which shall be entered such Minutes as may at any time be agreed upon—the term of each Surveyor or other Person's engagement, &c.

6.   Previously to any person being engaged as an apprentice Draftsman Surveyor, &c., &c., he shall be prepared, and the terms agreed upon by the majority in value.

PROPOSED SALARIES, &c.

No. 3, £100.   No. 4 (engaged for 3 years), £100.   No. 5 (engaged for 3½ years), Board and Lodgings.   No. 6, £40.   No. 7, £100.   No. 8, £200.   No. 9, £200.   No. 10, £250.   No. 11, £300.   No. 12, £300.   No. 13, Apprentice.   No. 14, £150.   No. 15, Apprentice—Board and Lodgings.   No. 16, Apprentice.   No. 17, £300.   No. 18, £300.   No. 19, Apprentice.   No. 20, £200.

In addition to the Salaries—the Coach Hire and travelling expenses (exclusive of Personal expenses) to be allowed them.

PROPOSED CHARGES.

Those of £300 Annual Salary, £2 2s. 0d. per day.

,, ,, £200   Do.   £1 11s. 6d.   Do.

,, ,, £100   Do.   and under £1 1s. 0d. per day.

Geo. & Robt. S. 5 Gs. per day each.

All travelling expenses (exclusive of Personal expenses) to be charged.

For Reports & Estimates   £3 3s. 0d. to £10 10s. 0d.

according to the magnitude of the Road, &c.

For Plans   £3 3s. 0d. to £ [blank.]

according to the magnitude of the Road, &c., &c.

For attendance upon Parliament *all expenses* to be charged.

1.   Geo. Stephenson   } Chief Engineers.
2.   Robt. Stephenson }

3.   Jas. Adamson,   Secretary.

London and Northern Rail Road.		*Liverpool and Birmingham Rail Road.*	
	Robert Stephenson.	12.	John Dixon.
4.	Jos. Locke	13.	Wllm. Allcard.
5.	Rob. Tayler.	14.	Wedge.
6.	Elij. Galloway.	*London and South Wales Road.*	
7.	Blackett.	15.	Hugh Steel.
8.	Palin.	16.	Tho. Gooch.
9.	Smith.	17.	Padley.
10.	Seward.	18.	Hamilton.
Liverpool and Manchester Rail Road.		19.	Birkinshaw.
11.	Thomas Storey.		

Home Office, Newcastle.

20.   Oliver.

This document has a special interest as recording the names of several men, in particular Joseph Locke, John Dixon and Thomas Gooch, who afterwards became well-known as railway engineers.

We have seen that in the absence of both George and Robert Stephenson the management of the factory had been undertaken by Longridge, and it appears that Thomas Richardson must have received from an anonymous correspondent a letter objecting either to this arrangement or to the manner in which the business was being conducted. To these objections Longridge replied in a letter to Richardson dated :—

BEDLINGTON IRON WORKS,
7th March 1825.

Dear Sir,

It is but seldom that I notice anonymous letters—and had our acquaintance been of longer standing I should have hardly deemed it requisite to have made an exception of the letter you have transmitted to me.

I will intrude but a few minutes upon your time, to state my reason for being concerned in Engine Building with G. & R. S.

George had rendered me very considerable service in giving an opinion favourable to Malleable Iron Rails, whilst *his own interest* lead him to recommend *Cast Iron*. It was not in my power to recompense the pecuniary loss he sustained, but I have ever since done what in me lay to forward his interest and Robert's.

It was against my wish they commenced engine Builders, but after they had begun, considering it beneficial to the Bedlington Iron Co. and that Geo. and Robert would benefit from my habits of business, in which they were both deficient, I offered to take a part with them. Most assuredly I never intended to have the slightest charge of the Manufactory, any further than attending the monthly meetings of the Partners, as provided for in the Minutes of our Agreement.

Circumstances, over which I had no control, have unfortunately for me thrown the responsibility upon my shoulders *for the present*; but I do hope that Robert's early return to England will soon relieve me, and in the meantime, if you or Mr. Pease can appoint a more suitable person it will much oblige,

Dear Sir,
Yours very truly,

MICH. LONGRIDGE.

This letter is of peculiar interest in view of the incident to which we have already referred in connection with George Stephenson's recommendation of malleable iron rails for the Stockton and Darlington Railway, and his letter to Robert Stevenson, C.E., of Edinburgh, on the same subject. It records the opinion of Longridge that the strength of the two Stephensons lay rather in their technical than in their business capacity; the first of George Stephenson's speculative operations in early life had been it appears, with him and Nicholas Wood in working a colliery.[1] Longridge was proprietor of the Bedlington Iron Works where were rolled, in 1820, the first malleable iron rails made under John Birkinshaw's patent[2]; later, as we shall see, he also built locomotives and severed his connection with Robert Stephenson & Co., but his correspondence with Robert Stephenson which has been preserved bears witness to the affec-

[1] Nicholas Wood, 'Address on the two late Eminent Engineers,' 2nd February 1860. *Proc. North of England Inst. Mining Engineers.*

[2] John Birkinshaw's Specification, 2nd December 1820.

5

from the painting in possession of Miss Catharine Longridge.

MICHAEL LONGRIDGE

1785—1858

tion and solicitude with which he regarded the younger man; in a long and particularly intimate letter he writes under date :—

MORPETH, 2nd Nov. 1825.

I am waiting here to accompany your father who joins me to-morrow when we go together to Edinburgh and Glasgow—and return by way of Carlisle.   This recalls to my recollection the day when, at the *same* place and nearly at the *same* time of the year, I entered the self *same* coach and found you, your Father, Mr. Hill, and our friend *James* seated 'Cheek by Jowl'— 'alas how time escapes, 'tis even so'—but why should we regret the escape of Time?   It makes us wiser and ought to make us better.

Referring to his request that Robert should undertake the duties of god-father to his youngest child he proceeds :—

from a lithograph drawn by W. A. Thompson, N.C., 1827, printed by C. Hullmandel.

BEDLINGTON IRON WORKS NEAR MORPETH

. . . my imagination pictures the time when seated around my fire-side at Bedlington Iron Works—my own head still more 'Silvered o'er with age' than it now is, I shall see you with your God-daughter sitting on your knee, and listening to the Traveller's Tales which you promise, for I shall regret if you suppress any real occurrences which befel you.   I had rather give some license to high colouring than have a bare detail of dates and journeyings.   I feel to-night as though I were sitting talking to you, and can hardly bring my pen to narrate such common matter-of-fact subjects as that we continue to be overwhelmed with business at Bedlington Iron Works.

Later we find that the boiler plates, and in many cases complete boilers, for the locomotives built at Forth Street were supplied by the Bedlington works.
Continuing the above letter Longridge writes from :—

GLASGOW, 8th Nov. 1825.

Mr. Thos. Richardson has left business and intends residing a part of the year in Cumberland so that we shall have him more amongst us than hitherto.   The Darlington Rail Way was opened in grand style upon the 27th September, but the pleasure which our Friend Pease would otherwise have enjoyed, was damped by the death of his son, Isaac, upon the very morning of the grand opening; of course, none of them were present. Herring & Co. do not seem disposed to authorize us to send out any models of the Locomotive Engines and consequently no preparations are making for it.

LONDON COFFEE HOUSE, 27th Feb. 1826.

A variety of circumstances which have occurred since the commencement of this epistle, the enumeration of which would occupy more space in these sheets than can be afforded, has retarded until this time, its conclusion. One I must mention, this was a letter from our worthy Friend Richardson, stating the wish of the Columbian Association to offer you a very handsome remuneration if you would remain in Columbia, as their Chief Agent or Director—this appeared so important a matter to you, that I communicated in writing to your Father, the objections which occurred to me as well as the reasons which would induce my recommending him to allow the offer to be sent out for your consideration. I now give you a copy of this paper and shall content myself with adding that I shall be more gratified by your declining than accepting the offer, should it now be made to you. I am inclined however to think the Directors here will consider your Father's answer to Mr. Richardson as putting a decided negative upon the question, and that they will look out for some other person.

You will learn from the Newspapers of this Country the misery which has been occasioned *chiefly* by the wild schemes which were agitated here last year—when and how it will terminate is more than human foresight can predict. Hitherto, *we*, that is at Bedlington and Newcastle have escaped with trifling injury—I should rather say *without injury*, but with *some inconvenience.* . . . .
I feel anxious for your return, and I think that you will find both your Father and your Friend *considerably older* than when you left us. Pray take care of your own [health] and let us see you able as well mentally as physically to fill up our stations.

By 1827 the reputation of the engine works had spread abroad and there is a record by two Prussian Mine Officials[1] of their visit to the works of 'Pease and Dickinson,' with a description of engines then under construction to which we shall refer at length later, also a list of current prices. It appears however that during this year both Pease and Richardson were dissatisfied with the way in which affairs were being conducted, and on 9th April 1827 Pease wrote to Robert Stephenson[2] :—

I can assure thee that your business at Newcastle, as well as thy father's engineering, have suffered very much from thy absence and unless thou soon return, the former will be given up as Mr. Longridge is not able to give it that attention it requires and what *is* done is not done with credit to the house.

To Robert, who had found in the Columbian expedition neither an El Dorado nor a bed of roses, this letter was a further incentive to return at the end of his three years' engagement; on 16th July 1827 he wrote to Longridge[3] :—

The period of my departure from this place has at last really and truly arrived though not longer than a month or two ago I was despairing of being able to get away without incurring the displeasure of the Board of Directors. . . . . Just about the same time I received a letter from Mr. Richardson in which he states that the factory was far from being in a good condition, and that unless I returned promptly to England it would not improbably be abandoned.

[1] Von Dechen and Von Oeynhausen, Report in *Archiv für Bergbau und Hüttenwesen*, Berlin, 1829.
[2] Smiles, *Lives of the Engineers*, 1862, Vol. III., p. 250.
[3] Jeaffreson, *Life of Robert Stephenson*, Vol. I., p. 101.

gelegt. Auf jeder Seite des Cylinders liegt ein solcher Balancier, der daher auch vor jeden Seitenbiegungen vollkommen gesichert ist. Nicht leicht wird es Balancier geben, die bei einem so geringen Gewichte, eine größere Widerstandsfähigkeit besitzen. Es würde bei vielen Gelegenheiten sehr nützlich seyn, von diesen wohlfeilen und leicht zu construirenden Balancier Anwendung zu machen, welche der Gefahr des Brechens weniger als gußeiserne unterworfen sind.

In der mechanischen Werkstätte der Herren Stephenson und Dickenson in Newcastle wurden uns folgende Preise der in der Fabrik angefertigten Dampfmaschinen mitgetheilt. Das Pfund Sterling zu 7 Rthl. Berl. Court. gerechnet.

Dampfwagen von 8 Pferdekräften . 3850 Rthl. -

Feststehende oder fixirte Dampfmaschinen, Hochdruck.

Wattsche

von 8 Pferdekräften ,	2200	bis	2450	Rthl.
" 12 " "	3150	"	3500	"
" 16 " "	4550	"	5040	"
" 20 " "	5600	"	6300	"
" 30 " "	8400	"	9450	"

Ein Satz verbesserter Wagenräder, Buchsen, Achsen u. s. w. 105 Rthl. frei an Bord des Schiffers in Newcastle. Diese Preise wechseln in Verhältniß der Söhne u. s. w. und gelten als Mittelsätze-Zahlung durch London, 3 Wechsel 3 Monate nach Abgang. Adresse:

Robert Stephenson & Comp.

Engineers and founders in Newcastle upon Tyne.

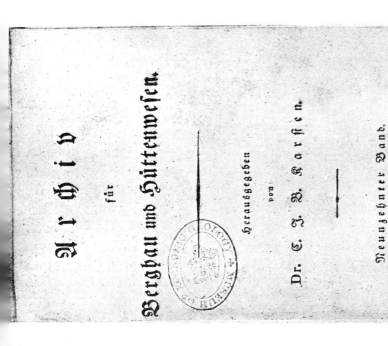

Archiv

für

Bergbau und Hüttenwesen.

Herausgegeben von

Dr. C. J. B. Karsten.

Neunzehnter Band.

Mit ... Kupfertafeln.

Berlin, 1829.

Im Verlage bei G. Reimer.

[from an original in the Library of the Science Museum, South Kensington.]

From the German *Annals of Mining and Metallurgy*, Vol. XIX., containing Von Dechen and Von Oeynhausen's account of their visit to the works of Robert Stephenson & Co., and list of prices in 1827.

Various reasons have been published for this intention ; it has been stated to have been directly due to a decision by the directors of the Stockton and Darlington Railway in 1827 to abandon the use of locomotives, and that but for the influence of Pease and Richardson, who were interested both in the railway and in the Forth Street works, the locomotives would have been abandoned.[1]   But an official examination of the railway company's original records and of a quantity of other material has failed to produce any evidence of such a decision by the directors [2], and they were in fact negotiating with Robert Stephenson & Co. for new locomotives after they were supposed to have decided to abandon steam power. In any case it is improbable that the founders of the Forth Street concern could have anticipated from the Stockton and Darlington Railway alone such a demand for locomotives as would keep their establishment going, though they were aware that for such engines as the railway might require they themselves must be the principal source of supply ; their only likely competitors, Fenton, Murray & Wood, of Leeds, who had previously built successfully for Blenkinsop, had informed the railway company in 1825 that they were not prepared to manufacture locomotive engines until they had become a regular article of sale.[3]   Moreover the Forth Street works were not limited to the manufacture of locomotives ; between 1824 and 1827 much other work was on hand, and there is definite evidence for the following orders, in some cases with the prices ; in other cases we have assumed these to be in proportion, and the following is a statement of work recorded to have been actually in hand between 1824 and the beginning of 1827, with its approximate value.

		£
1823.		
1 Engine of 8 Horse-power for Mr. Bragge	(assumed price)	300
2 ,, ,, 15 ,, ,, Stockton Steam Boat	,, ,,	1,500
2 ,, ,, 15 ,, ,, Stockton & Darlington Rly.	(recorded ,,)	1,982
2 ,, ,, 30 ,, ,, ,, ,, ,, ,, ,,		3,482
1824.		
2 Locos. for Stockton & Darlington Rly.	,, ,,	1,200
1826.		
2 Locos. ,, ,, ,, ,,	(assumed ,,)	1,200
2 ,, ,, Springwell	,, ,,	800
1827.		
Stationary and Pumping Engines for Springwell	,, ,,	500
		£10,964

[1] *A Chapter in the History of Railway Locomotion,* and *Memoir of Timothy Hackworth,* Appendix, p. 25.

[2] Tomlinson, *The North Eastern Railway,* p. 141. 'There is not the slightest foundation for the statement published in 1879, 1889 and 1892 by Mr. J. W. Hackworth and since repeated by uncritical writers.'

[3] Tomlinson, *The North Eastern Railway,* p. 118.

The above statement takes no account of other locomotives which some writers have, perhaps erroneously, recorded, nor of engine spare parts, waggons, and wheels for both engines and waggons, which were certainly ordered during the years mentioned ; for instance, a Stockton and Darlington Railway Company's minute of 16th December 1825 records that 40 sets of waggon wheels were to be ordered from Robert Stephenson & Co. ; and it seems probable that the total value of the orders received at Forth Street up to the end of 1826 must have been at least £12,000.

Such a state of affairs does not confirm the view that the concern was languishing for want of work, yet Robert Stephenson's biographer states[1] that for some years the works did not pay their expenses, and lack of funds has been given as a reason for the proposed abandonment. The early balance sheets— 1824 to 1827—confirm such a view ; they show that though the paid up capital had increased between June 1824 and December 1826 from £3,275 to £5,000, while upwards of £8,000 had been borrowed during this period (including £4,000 from Richardson), this money had been so much tied up in buildings, stock in trade, work in progress and book debts, that the business was left short, not of work or the prospect of it, but of working capital ; the value of the work in progress and of the book debts together amounted in December 1826 to over £10,000.

And in 1827 there were other reasons which may have disinclined the partners to find any more money as working capital for Forth Street ; one of these was no doubt the lack of proper technical management due to the absence of both the Stephensons, though we do not find in 1827 a repetition of the serious complaints about workmanship which had been made by the Stockton and Darlington Railway Company in 1825.[2] That there was also bad financial management is shown by a letter written by Robert Stephenson to Edward Pease nearly ten years later, in reference to the appointment of a chief clerk or financial manager, at that time under discussion ; referring to Harris Dickinson, who was evidently in a prominent position at the works in 1827, Robert remarks :—

He was active, intelligent, and what is usually termed a man of business—but the establishment would have been ruined by this time had that kind of management not been entirely altered.

Of Dickinson's appointment and the exact position held by him we have no record ; from his mode of addressing Edward Pease we judge that he was a Quaker. Simon Goodrich who visited the works on 26th March 1830 records in his journal that he saw :—

Mr. Dickinson who appeared as manager or partner, and Mr. Phipps a young man who appeared as draftsman and who took an active part in the business, he told me he came from Mr. Galloway's manufactory.

Robert Stephenson reached Liverpool from South America in November

[1] Jeaffreson, *Life of Robert Stephenson*, Vol. I., p. 76.
[2] Stockton and Darlington Railway Sub-Committee Minute, 25th Nov. 1825.

1827 and after visiting London he wrote, on 1st January 1828, a letter[1] to Longridge which shows that the matter of the locomotive had received his immediate attention :—

Since I came down from London I have been talking a great deal to my father about endeavouring to reduce the size and ugliness of our travelling engines, by applying the engine either on the side of the boiler or beneath it entirely somewhat similarly to Gurney's steam coach. . . . . There are three new steam coaches going on with, all much on the same principle as Gurney's.

To this letter we shall refer at length later when dealing with the technical work of the firm ; at the moment it is of interest as showing the advance made by the beginning of 1828 in steam locomotion on common roads.

Vertical Section of Mr. Gurney's Improved Steam Coach. 1828.
from Galloway's History of the Steam Engine, 1831, p. 549.

In 1828 the Newcastle works were visited by the French engineer Marc Séguin and by engineers from the United States of America, with the result that locomotives were exported during the year, or early in 1829, to France and America, some of them embodying the ideas expressed in the above letter. It is clear that from this time onwards Robert Stephenson's principal energies were devoted to the improvement of the locomotive by the various stages which led up to the 'Rocket' ; but with these, and the actual events of the Rainhill Trials, we must deal in our later chapters, merely noting here their effect on the locomotive building industry. The success of the Stephensons' engine on that occasion was immediately reflected in the firm's order book, and Robert was able to write to Richardson on 17th December 1829 [2] :—

[1] Jeaffreson, *Life of Robert Stephenson*, Vol. I., p. 115.
[2] Jeaffreson, *Life of Robert Stephenson*, Vol. I., p. 153.

THE LOCOMOTIVE STEAM ENGINES

Which competed for the Prize of £500 offered by the Directors of the Liverpool and Manchester Railway Comp.ᵞ — drawn to a scale ¼ inch to a foot

The ROCKET of Mr Robt Stephenson of Newcastle

Which drawing a load equivalent to three times its weight, travelled at the rate of 12½ miles an hour, & with a carriage & passengers at the rate of 24 miles Cost per mile for fuel about three-halfpence

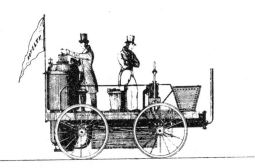

The NOVELTY of Messrs Braithwaite & Ericsson of London.

Which drawing a load equivalent to three times its weight, travelled at the rate of 20¾ miles an hour; & with a Carriage & Passengers at the rate of 32 miles' Cost per mile for fuel about one halfpenny

C. Burton del.ᵗ on Stone

The SANS PAREIL of Mr Hackworth of Darlington

Which drawing a load equivalent to three times its weight, travelled at the rate of 12½ miles an hour — Cost for fuel per mile about two-pence.

[from the Mechanics' Magazine, Vol. XII., 28th November 1829.]

The trials at Rainhill of the locomotive seem to have set people Railway mad. We are getting rapidly on with four locomotive engines for Liverpool which I am confident will exceed the Rocket in powers. One of them will leave here about New Year's Day, and the other three about the end of January.

Writing again on 28th April 1830 he says :—

I regret we are too high for the Darlington Bridge, and I am afraid we are a great deal too high for the winding engine at St. Helens, Auckland, but we really cannot compete with those engine builders in the neighbourhood of Newcastle, who not only work for nothing, but who make bad workmanship. The engine you require for St. Helens is the same power as one we made for the Liverpool Railway Coy. and will require more workmanship. For the Liverpool engine we had £1,600, but I daresay you will soon have offers for £1,000; but it is useless attempting to make engines for such prices, because I know it is impossible to make a good and substantial job without reasonable prices.

In this letter we have evidence of the higher standard which had been attained since Robert Stephenson had taken charge of the works ; the following letter from Harris Dickinson to Edward Pease, after dealing with various questions of leases also reflects the generally improved state of affairs :—

EDWARD PEASE,   NEWCASTLE-UPON-TYNE, 10 mo. 21, 1830.
ESTEEMED FRIEND,—In reply to thy favour dated 20th inst. I beg to forward the following information :—

T. Anderson is Lessee under the Hospital, and he sub-lets to R. S. & Co. The Commissioners for Public Charities express a doubt, whether the Hospital has a power of granting such Leases as T. Anderson's. In the property we have already purchased we are of course indemnified by Anderson, and it is the opinion of Counsel, that the present Leases will not be disturbed; but I think it would be folly in R. S. & Co. to purchase the field in the west of the street under circumstances as above. The whole of our property in the east of the street is purchased on a Lease under Three lives, renewable under a Penalty, in the demise of each life. The Purchase money for this part is all paid, and the Fine in the last renewal of a Life was £160. He asks 7s. 6d. p. yard for the Field in the west of the street, which contains at a rough running over 2,700 yards. The Fine is I believe arbitrary. The master of the Hospital lays upon the whole of Anderson's property a Fine, which the Lessee proportions among the Sub-Lessees as he thinks fit. Two of the Lives in our property are old men about 70 I should think, and the third is T. Anderson himself, who is 23. The Premium for the Insurance of a life of 70 is of course heavy, and I have examined two or three scales of Life Insurance, none of which go higher than 67. The premium for a life of 67 is £8 12 0 p. cent. p. ann. The premium for a life of 23 is £1 17 0.

We are still going on with the new Smith's Shop, and I suppose we must finish it now. We pay Anderson a yearly rent of £25 for the Field. If thou wish for any further information relative to the above, I shall be glad to hand it to the best of my knowledge.

Hackworth's engine has been tried, and works very well, but I am afraid there will be a deficiency in her powers of generating steam. We are doing all in our power to push the Locomotives—there are six Boilers in our own manufactory and two making at Bedlington, and I have ordered Plates for 6 more.

The Liverpool men have arrived and got to work, and seem tolerably contented; but we have not had sufficient experience to form as yet much opinion of their abilities.

We have not yet had an order from Liverpool for the large Engine mentioned in thy letter. The Coach ordered yesterday by thy Son Joseph is in hand—I have just been at the Coachmakers, and they have got most of the wood cut out. I think we will make you something neat, and in time for your Middlesbro' opening day. I have ordered a lot of plates from Low Moor and have seen two gentlemen from that concern to-day, who promise to do the best they can for us. I trust we shall very soon be able to turn out a Loco. each fortnight.

I am, Thine very respectfully,   HARRIS DICKINSON.

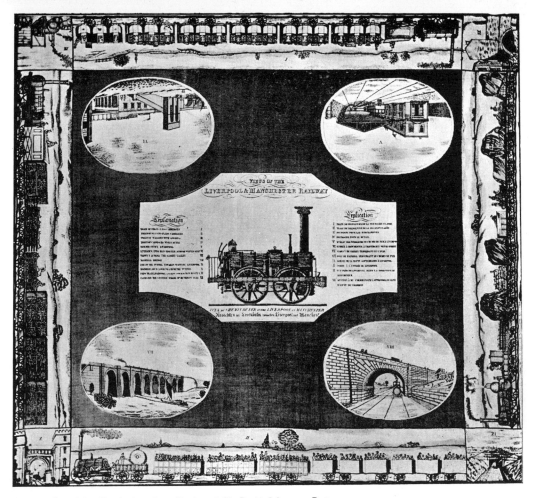

from a coloured handkerchief in the collection of Sir David Salomons, Bart.

VIEWS OF THE LIVERPOOL AND MANCHESTER RAILWAY

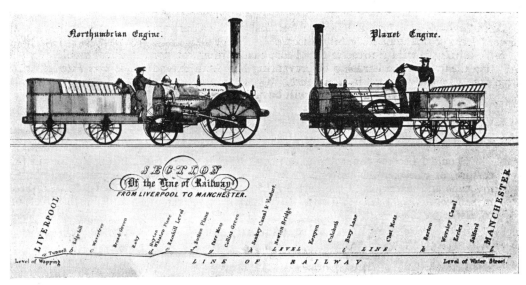

(part) from a lithograph by Baird, South John Street, Liverpool.

The locomotive mentioned, known afterwards as the 'Globe,' had been designed by Hackworth for the passenger traffic of the Stockton and Darlington Railway. The 'large engine' for Liverpool was one of two eventually ordered for working the inclined planes on the Liverpool and Manchester Railway; these two large engines were known as the 'Samson' and 'Goliath.'

Further striking evidence of the demand for locomotives is to be found in the following letter from Michael Longridge to Edward Pease dated :—

NEWCASTLE, 22 Dec. 1830.

When I last saw Robert Stephenson, he mentioned to me his having been applied to by some Parties in Liverpool to commence a Manufactory there—and that he had declined giving them an answer until he had consulted us. I agreed to visit you and him at Darlington and wrote him a letter of which I annex you a copy.

Yesterday I received from him the enclosed letter.

I am now on my way to London respecting a Contract with the Navy Office—and purpose being at Darlington by the Mail on Tuesday night the 28th inst. and shall be glad to visit Mr. Thos. Richardson and you the following day.

(Enclosed) copy of letter from M. Longridge to Robt. Stephenson.

13 Dec. 1830.

I am going to Glasgow to-morrow to meet your Father, and hope to return in time to accompany you to Darlington on Thursday the 23rd inst.

In the meantime you should consider *maturely* the effect of the proposal you intend making to Mr. Pease.

The establishment you contemplate at Liverpool appears to me fraught with injury to Forth Street, the chief employment of which will be transferred to your new establishment. How then are you ever to pay the Dividends and redeem the Capital?

The great demand for engines for a few years will be in Lancashire and Yorkshire—and if you and your Father give your time and influence to the new works—down goes Newcastle.

My own individual Interest is so very small, that it cannot be put into competition with yours, and I therefore only mention it that you may clearly understand that whatever Mr. Pease and Mr. Richardson determines upon, I shall be guided by.

Later Longridge writes on the same subject to Richardson :—

BEDLINGTON IRON WORKS,
24 Mar. 1831.

DEAR SIR—When Robt. Stephenson was last in the Country, we had the subject of the proposed Liverpool Manufactory fully discussed.

As to uniting it with Newcastle I told him that neither you nor Mr. Pease would ever consent. He then urged the hardship of preventing him from extending *his own interest*, whilst at the same time he was not injuring ours.

It is certain the demand for Engines will be much greater than we can supply at Newcastle—and if we can keep that place fully employed we shall in a few years receive back our money at any rate. The result of our conversation was Robert's giving me a letter of which the following is a copy:—

NEWCASTLE, 7 Mar. 1831.

Should I become connected with another Manufactory for building Engines in Lancashire, or elsewhere, I have no objection to bind myself to devote an equal share of my time and attention to the existing establishment at Newcastle. I will also pledge myself *not to hold a larger interest in any other Factory*, than I have in Forth Street, and to *divide the Locomotive Engine orders equally.*

Signed, ROBT. STEPHENSON.

I have no doubt that *one half* of the orders, which the Stephensons can procure will *wholly* employ us at Newcastle and therefore, if you and Mr. Pease approve of it, I am willing to accede to this proposal.

I shall be glad to hear your opinion and if you are at Ayton in the course of next month I will ride over and converse with you as to the details.

We are all in a state of high excitation as to the fate of the Reform Bill—the consequences will be dreadful if the Measure is not carried.

I hope that Mrs. Richardson is quite recovered, and am,

Dear Sir, Yours very truly,

MICH. LONGRIDGE.

Robert Stephenson's wish to carry on the business of engine builder and iron founder, at or near Liverpool, was eventually granted by his partners, who at a meeting on 27th June 1831 resolved :—

1. That the said Robert Stephenson shall be allowed to enter into and carry on Business in co-partnership with other persons upon the following conditions, viz.:—

(1) That he shall bind himself to devote an equal share of his Time and Attention to the existing establishment at Newcastle.

(2) And also pledge himself not to hold a larger interest in any other factory than he does in the Newcastle Factory and to divide the orders which may be received for locomotive Engines so that *not less than one half* of the engines shall be built at Newcastle.

(3) That the Firm at Liverpool shall be Charles Tayleur, Junr. & Co. or any other Firm not embracing the name of 'Stephenson' so as to distinguish it entirely from the Newcastle House.

(4) That during the continuance of the co-partnership, neither the said Robert Stephenson nor his father shall withdraw any part of their money which is now employed in the Newcastle Factory, either as 'Capital' or 'lent at interest' without the consent of the other partners.

The Newcastle works order book contains an entry on 12th November 1832:—

Ordered this day by letter from Mr. Phipps—for Messrs. Tayleur & Stephn, Hey Foundry near Warrington, a 20 Horse high pressure Engine. Cylinder 20 in. dia. 4 ft. stroke.

These works, which soon became, and still are, known as the Vulcan Foundry appear to have been nearing completion on 28th January 1834 ; Daniel Gooch, afterwards locomotive superintendent of the Great Western Railway, has recorded[1] that on this date he :—

. . . left home for work under Mr. Stephenson at the Vulcan Foundry near Warrington in Lancashire. . . . He and Mr. Tayleur of Liverpool had just built their works, indeed they were not quite finished when I went there.

On 9th November 1833 the Forth Street books record :—

A List of Drawings of a 60 Horse Patent Locomotive sent to Messrs. Tayleur & Co., Vulcan Foundry, by Mr. Stephenson's directions.

There are records subsequently of the following orders sent to Tayleur & Co. :—

On Feb. 1st   1834, One (of six) engines for Stanhope and Tyne Railway.
   April 5th   ,,   two engines for South Carolina.
   May 12th   ,,   one (of three) engines for the Belgian Government.

[1] *Diaries of Sir Daniel Gooch, Bart, 1892.*

from a lithograph by Baird, South John Street, Liverpool.

TRAVELLING ON THE LIVERPOOL AND MANCHESTER RAILWAY

from a modern model in the Eisenbahn Museum, Nuremberg.

'*Der Adler*'

ROBERT STEPHENSON'S PATENT LOCOMOTIVE 1833

The first locomotive in Germany, built in 1835 for the Nuremberg-Fürth Railway

The first locomotives built by the Vulcan Foundry bear the obvious marks of a Stephenson design and many, if not all, were in fact made to Stephensons' drawings ; among them were several engines of the famous 'Planet' type which had been adopted as a standard by the Liverpool and Manchester Railway Company. Later, on 7th September 1833, Robert Stephenson had patented 'certain improvements to locomotives'[1] ; the first engine built at the Newcastle works which embodied these improvements was bought by the same railway company for £1,000, and by their order afterwards called the 'Patentee'; it was practically an enlargement of the 'Planet' by the addition of a pair of wheels behind the fire-box. Engines of this type were ordered for various home and foreign railways ; it was accepted as the best of its day, and numbers were built both by Robert Stephenson & Co. and other makers, to whom they supplied drawings. Samples of these standard types were also ordered by Belgian and French firms to be copied and later, by 1835, it was recorded that locomotives of this pattern were being constructed in almost all the large workshops of France and Belgium[2] ; between 1831 and 1835 Robert Stephenson & Co. were building to this design for America and supplying most of the engines required by the Liverpool and Manchester Railway, though some of their orders were being passed on to Tayleur & Co. and others of the numerous firms in England who had by this time commenced, or, in the case of Fenton & Murray, resumed the manufacture of rail locomotives.

Robert Stephenson & Co. were not long permitted to enjoy the unique position which they had won so hardly. The enmity of professional rivals and of those who had been offended by the opinions of George Stephenson or by 'the *Newcastle burr* which through favour of the clan Stephenson is so prominent along the whole line of the railway,' culminated in an attack by an anonymous writer in the *Edinburgh Review*[3], on the Directors of the Liverpool and Manchester Railway Company and indirectly on the Newcastle firm. The anonymous critic after referring to the Rainhill Trials and the successes of the 'Rocket,' admitting that 'the prize was accordingly with justice awarded to Mr. Stephenson,' proceeds :—

The complete success of the engine furnished by Mr. Stephenson appears at once to have fascinated the Directors; and whether intentionally or not, the fact is indisputable, that the monopoly of engines has ever since been secured to the manufacturer of this particular form of machine.

Even when Mr. Stephenson was unable himself to supply engines as fast as the Company required them, and other engine-makers were employed, it was under the most rigorous conditions, to construct the engines upon the same principle and in the same form, or nearly so, as that which Mr. Stephenson had adopted. Experience, the great parent of all invention and improvement, so far as the railroad afforded it, has thus been exclusively confined to one particular form of engine. Under the influence of this, a succession of improvements, as might have been expected, have been made by the ingenious inventors of the engine above described. These improvements consist partly in the relative proportion and strength of the parts, and partly in the arrangement of the cylinders and their action upon the wheels ; but all have been

---

[1] Robert Stephenson's Specification 7th October 1833 (No. 6484).

[2] *Les Locomotives Stephenson circulant en Angleterre et en France.* Bruxelles, Champon, 1835.

[3] Article 'Inland Transport,' *Edinburgh Review*, Vol. LVI., October 1832.

suggested by the results of experiments, upon such a scale as was altogether unattainable by any part of the vast stock of national talent excluded from the road by those measures of the Directors, which limited the engines employed to a single form.

The article then criticizes the 'impolicy and injustice' of the conditions by which the whole enterprise of the country was paralyzed, and accuses the Directors of employing a large body of men, most of whom, 'from the superintendent engineer to the lowest gatekeeper', had been brought from a distant part of the country, who had become 'objects of favour and patronage' though 'strangers in the midst of the local population, distinguished by their manners, their appearance, and even by their dialect.' Reverting to the question of the engines the critic proceeds :—

The engineer of the company is necessarily the arbiter by whose judgment the directors will admit or exclude engines or waggons, not belonging to themselves, proposed to be worked upon the road. The same engineer is himself the manufacturer of engines, waggons, &c., for the Company—the said company being themselves carriers in competition with the public. They are therefore both competitors and judges, and their engineer is an extensive manufacturer in articles of which, when manufactured by others, he is constituted the arbiter. Whether fairness of conduct and justice of decision is, under such circumstances, consistent with the infirmities of human nature, is a question which admits of little doubt, but we think it will not be for a moment disputed that the decisions of such judges and such arbiter will never be received with confidence or trust by the public; and in fact they *have not* been so received. The impression against the Directors at Liverpool and Manchester is universal. The monopoly in the manufacture of engines, waggons, &c.—the invariable rejection of every suggestion for improvement coming from other quarters, the capricious objections which have excluded engines and waggons belonging to collateral companies from the road—are subjects of common animadversion by all who are acquainted with the affairs of the railway, and have excited great and universal disapprobation.

Referring to the unfair conditions under which comparative trials of engines by other makers were carried out, he remarks that :—

. . . upon such occasions the whole activity and energy of the establishment is called into requisition to put into racing order the best of Mr. Stephenson's engines :—

He later accuses the company's enginemen upon these occasions of having 'screwed down or overloaded the safety valves of Mr. Stephenson's engines' and 'secretly inflicted injuries upon those competing with them.' These criticisms he summarizes with the reflection that :—

All that is perfectly conceivable—is the natural result of human imperfections—without imputing to Mr. Stephenson any intentional participation whatever in such proceedings. Indeed, having imposed upon ourselves the painful duty of censuring the system now under examination, we feel it necessary to say that we fully acquit the engineer in question of having any share in such proceedings, nay, we will admit that he would condemn them as strongly as ourselves; but they are beyond his control. He cannot if he would change the course of nature; and while men are men, a system such as that which has been acted upon, can be attended with no other effects than those we have noticed.

The Directors, on 5th November 1832, published a reply [1] to their critic in the course of which they showed him to be Dr. Dionysius Lardner, a well-

---

[1] Liverpool and Manchester Railway, *Answer of the Directors to an Article in the Edinburgh Review for October* 1832.

known writer on scientific subjects, who before the publication of his article had been given ample opportunity to learn the falsity of the charges which he proposed to make, and to their *Answer* the Directors attached a letter previously written to the self-appointed critic by Hardman Earle, a member of their Board. Their reply to the charge of having introduced into the country a numerous body of workmen, strangers to the soil of the district, they sum up with the caustic question :—

Did it never occur to the Reviewer, that in a novel and difficult undertaking, it may possibly be as wise a mode of proceeding to employ 'workmen strangers to the soil' as labourers strangers to the work?

They showed that, out of upwards of 600 individuals in the employ of the company, only about 60 were from the counties of Durham and Northumberland. To the charge that their engineer was also arbiter by whose judgment they would admit engines, or exclude them from their road, and that he was at the same time himself a manufacturer of engines, they replied :—

It is true that the son of the engineer (Mr. Robert Stephenson) is partner in a manufactory at Newcastle-on-Tyne (Messrs. R. Stephenson & Co.), where many of the best engines on the road have been made, and on the model of which (with progressive improvements) all the most successful machines, from whatever quarter they may have come, have been built. Nor is this latter circumstance to be explained by the insinuation of the Reviewer, that no other pattern of an engine has been admitted on the road; several other patterns have been admitted and have signally failed. One of these, a competitor for the prize offered by the Directors at the Rainhill trials in October, 1829, and then bought by them for £500, chiefly out of feelings of consideration to the builder,[1] under a hope that, though manifestly inferior to the successful engine (the Rocket), it might be rendered useful, has proved of so little value, that it has just been sold for £110. But the Directors will more especially allude to three engines manufactured by Messrs. Braithwaite and Ericsson. The first of these was the 'Novelty,' which competed unsuccessfully for the above-named prize. The others were two large and beautiful engines, made to order, with a stipulation that they should carry 40 tons to Manchester, in two hours, with a consumption of half a pound of coke per ton per mile (about half the performance of the Company's improved engines at the present time) and for which the builders were to receive £1,000 each. These engines, by the terms of the contract, were to have been ready by the 1st of July, 1830. They were not, however, produced at the time, nor were they ready at the Opening, in September following. The Directors sustained great inconvenience for the want of them, having for some months previously, in expectation of their arrival, and of the superiority it was said they would exhibit, purposely abstained from ordering the necessary supply from the builders of the Rocket, Messrs. R. Stephenson & Co. But they do not, in stating this, impute any blame to Messrs. Braithwaite and Ericsson, for the failure of whose efforts they could not avoid feeling strong regret, and whose spirited exertions were deserving of much praise. The consequence of this disappointment, however, was long felt; for while the road was opened for passengers in September, 1830, it was not till January, 1831, that the Directors were prepared to carry merchandize. The pecuniary loss to the Proprietors, arising from this circumstance, was very great, and the delay gave some colour to an apprehension very generally entertained, that although the railway might be applied advantageously to the conveyance of passengers, it would be found ill adapted to the transport of merchandize. When these two engines were at length placed on the road, they were found altogether unable to perform the appointed task, and, after various alterations and trials, were finally withdrawn by the builders themselves.

The Reviewer, it will be seen, insinuates that such failures are the result of unfair play; and as a consequence, proclaims to the world that 'The mechanical ingenuity of the country is

[1] Timothy Hackworth, whose engine, the 'Sans Pareil' is shown on p. 73, *ante.*

G

excluded, by the total want of confidence which projectors must feel in the fairness of the trial to which any engines they may furnish to the Company are submitted. What do Messrs. Braithwaite and Ericsson (in opposition to this extraordinary insinuation) say, after the experiments with their large engine were nearly completed? The following is an extract from their letter to the Chairman, dated 18th January 1831:—

We consider it our duty to report to you that we have, during the trials of our locomotive engine the latter days, fully ascertained its properties and capabilities; and we feel great pleasure in expressing our gratitude for the attention we have experienced during the experiments, which have been facilitated by every assistance on the part of the Company.

(Signed) BRAITHWAITE & ERICSSON.

(part) from the Mechanics' Magazine, 25th September 1830, Vol. XIV., p. 70.

THE 'WILLIAM THE FOURTH'
built by Braithwaite and Ericsson

The next imputation is 'the invariable rejection of every suggestion of improvement coming from other quarters.' For improvement, from any quarter, the Directors have always been anxious, and large sums have been expended by them (they will not say wisely) in search of the most perfect system and the most perfect machines. At various times in the last two years they have been in communication, as Dr. Lardner himself knows, with Mr. Goldsworthy Gurney, who proposed to build for the Railway, and from whom they would gladly have purchased, a steam-engine on his principle; and it is not to be attributed to the Directors that these communications have hitherto led to no practical result. At the present time, Mr. Perkins is engaged in adapting his invention for improving the circulation of the water in the boiler, to one of the Company's engines, which they have cheerfully placed at his disposal for the purpose of the experiment. These instances suffice to show the groundlessness of the above imputation.

The Directors admit, that out of the multiplicity of suggestions which have been offered to them as improvements, they have rejected many. In so doing they have exercised, as far as they were able, a sound and impartial discretion; and they may add, that they are not aware of any scheme having elsewhere succeeded (under similar circumstances), the adoption of which they had declined.

To the charge that, upon a comparative trial of the engines, 'the whole activity and energy of the establishment was called into requisition, to put into racing order the best of Mr. Stephenson's engines' they reply :—

Had the Reviewer been at all aware of the hard service to which 'the best of Mr. Stephenson's engines' was subjected, he might, perhaps, have abated some of his indignation, that on a comparative trial of power with a new engine, the one in use should be put, as far as practicable, into complete order ?

Even more complete answers to Dr. Lardner's charges had been given by Hardman Earle writing on 16th July 1832 :—

I shall as concisely as I can commit to writing the history of our locomotive policy from its commencement.

About two years before the completion of the railway, the sort of power to be employed upon it was the subject of frequent discussion at the Board. There was much diversity of opinion, and in order to gain information upon so vital a question, a deputation, consisting of two of the Directors, was sent into the North, to witness the working of the stationary engine plan. To this mode the opinions of these gentlemen rather inclined, in which they were countenanced by some eminent engineers; but the majority of their colleagues thought otherwise, and by their well-timed confidence in the judgment of their own engineer, Mr. Stephenson, they saved the road from ruin. The happy expedient of offering a premium for the best locomotive engine was soon after proposed, and with the result every one is acquainted. Nobody has ever ventured to doubt the justness of the decision which awarded the prize to the Rocket. You, however, have questioned (in my opinion with more ingenuity than soundness) the advantages which have flowed from this competition of mechanical skill. You have stated in the article before alluded to (a part of which you did me the favour to read to me), that the Directors were so 'fascinated' with this effort of their engineer that they became blind to the merits of others, and culpably negligent of the great interest of science, by giving to their favourite a close monopoly. I do not vouch for the precise language, but this is the tone in which you write, and this is the thesis upon which you found your charge. Now, what are the facts ? A premium of £500 was offered for the best engine: one came from Glasgow, another from Darlington, a third from Newcastle, and a fourth from London. Thus the ingenuity of the two extremities of the kingdom was put in requisition. A good deal of mechanical contrivance was displayed in all, particularly in the Novelty, from London; but they were all wanting in the one thing needful, excepting the Rocket, which performed far more than the stipulated task. After such an exhibition, and under such circumstances, what, permit me to ask, would you have done had you been a Director ? Would you not have ordered engines of that plan and construction which had been found to succeed ? The road was expected to be ready for business in a few months, and what sort of an answer would it have been to the Proprietors, who had then expended more than half a million, that we were unprovided with moving power because the Rocket was thought to consume too much fuel, and was pronounced by some people to be ugly, clumsy, and unmechanical, and that we were waiting until the mechanical genius of the country had produced a more perfect machine ?

The writer, after explaining that negotiations with Gurney had broken down in consequence of his proposals for remuneration being thought inadmissible by the Railway Company, shows that, in spite of the power of veto vested in their engineer, the directors had advertised in 1831 in the public press, for locomotive engines, and he proceeds :—

The following engine-wrights have built, and are building, engines for the road, viz.:— Messrs. Hick and Rothwell, and Messrs. Crook and Deans, of Bolton; Mr. Edward Bury, and Messrs. Mather, Dixon & Co., of Liverpool; Messrs. Bowman and Galloway, and Messrs. Sharp and Roberts, of Manchester. Should it be granted, however, that some fastidious persons (a little doubtful of success perhaps) do object to build for the road—what then? Are we, for the chance of their services, to relinquish the services of, beyond dispute, the soundest railway engineer in the kingdom, or to cease to employ the most successful engine-builder, because to retain both is a violation of a mere theory? Railways, it is true, have long been in use, but it is to the genius and perseverance of Mr. Stephenson and his son that we are indebted for the present compact form of engine of the Planet class, never, however, forgetting Mr. Booth's share of the merit for the now much-reviled tube-boiler.

And here I will take occasion to remark, that it is now two years since the Planet was laid down, and upwards of twenty engines have since been launched from the Newcastle and other manufactories, and yet she comes nearer to what we consider perfection (relatively of course) than any which have succeeded her; her wheels and axles have been strengthened, but her form and general construction has never been improved upon. So much for what has so often been asserted, that Mr. Stephenson has obtained all his experience of locomotive engines at our expense; the same has been said of his engineering knowledge; but it seems to be forgotten that he constructed the Darlington road before ours was thought of, and that he had been at work upon locomotives for nearly twenty years before the Rocket was built; but speed, combined with lightness and consumption of smoke, till lately was not a desideratum—hence the little advance that has been made in this department of mechanical science.

It is impossible to imagine a reply more crushing to the critic or more creditable to the locomotives built by Robert Stephenson & Co. but some of their rivals who had inspired the attack obtained later partial satisfaction at the expense of the Newcastle firm; in the meanwhile however nothing could affect its ever increasing business.

On 25th December 1834 Robert Stephenson writes to Edward Pease from Bedlington Iron Works :—

I am now with Mr. Longridge, who, as I anticipated urges no objection whatever to your son visiting the Forth Street manufactory. The conditions stated in your former letter to me as to remuneration for the present would be perfectly satisfactory to us, if they are so to your son, and should his examinations of the financial department lead him to consider that the manufactory is likely to deserve more of his attention I apprehend he will hereafter find little difficulty in protracting his visits and giving the Establishment the full benefit of his advice.

I learnt from Hutchinson you had spoken to him in reference to the occasional superintendence of your son. To me, he has expressed an apprehension that he might not be allowed in my absence to follow up such arrangements within the walls of the manufactory as he now has the power of doing. This apprehension is quite natural, and I embrace this opportunity of mentioning it, in order that I may express to you my strongest conviction that Hutchinson is trustworthy, talented and assiduous, with the success of the concern at heart.

The energies of any man in such a situation as Hutchinson's are I believe materially influenced by the degree of independence both in thought and action, which he is permitted to exercise.

I therefore recommend that he should be permitted in all respects to hold his situation on the same conditions as he now does. I do not hesitate thus frankly to state my wishes and opinions as you kindly requested me to do so, and I am the more anxious to do it regarding Hutchinson as I feel from a long and thorough acquaintance with him that the strong interest which he now takes in the economical arrangement in the working department would be lessened by any limitation of his powers. I trust the future acquaintance between your son and him will fully justify what I have here said of him.

William Hutchinson, referred to in the above letter, had been works manager for some years, probably succeeding Dickinson; he at any rate appears to have been acting in such capacity during the construction of the 'Rocket,' in regard to which he was frequently consulted by Robert Stephenson, who greatly valued both the man and his opinion, always referring to Hutchinson as 'the oracle.'[1] Local records show him to have been a sportsman, as well as an engineer, and particularly fond of cock-fighting, a pastime not then gone out of fashion.[2] There is some evidence in a later correspondence that one of the partners did not entirely approve of Hutchinson, but whether on account of his tastes or for some other reason does not appear. We have more than one interesting reference to the interest taken, not only by the senior partner, in the habits, even the morals, of associates, staff and workmen, and in one case a comparison made of the amount of liquor consumed by foremen and draughtsmen respectively.

Joseph Pease, born in 1799, was the second son of Edward Pease and was trained to his father's business; he assisted during the promotion of the Stockton and Darlington Railway Company, was afterwards appointed its first treasurer, and appears both in family business matters and in the affairs of the railway company to have acted largely as proxy for Edward Pease; his signature so appears in the early minutes of Robert Stephenson & Co. of which firm he eventually became a partner. He became chairman of the railway company, and after the passing of the Reform Bill of 1832 was elected Member of Parliament for South Durham, the first Quaker to sit in the House of Commons; at the time when his father suggests his taking some active part in the Forth Street concern Joseph Pease, in his thirty-fifth year, was already engaged in important affairs and with large financial interests.

We have now to refer again to other activities of Robert Stephenson who had been appointed in 1833 engineer-in-chief to the London and Birmingham Railway, and had consequently left Newcastle to reside in London, though he continued to superintend the affairs of the engine manufactory. It is interesting to note that the first planning for the London and Birmingham Railway was undertaken by the firm of 'George Stephenson and Son,'[3] already referred to, but it was Robert, not his father, who actually made the survey and was eventually, at the age of thirty, appointed engineer to carry out the construction of the line. He might well have anticipated that the new line would afford the field for his locomotives to which their merits should have entitled them, but this was not at first to be the case; a resumption of the earlier attack by George Stephenson's Liverpool enemies is recorded in the following correspondence with Longridge, to whom Robert writes under date:—

LONDON, 26th January 1835.

Our enemies, viz. Rathbone & Cropper, are raising a hue and cry about our having an Engine to build at Newcastle—they say another article will be brought out by Lardner on the subject. They half intimate that I shall withdraw either from the Railway or the Engine building. *The revenge of these people is quite insatiable. This distresses me very much.* Can I withdraw temporarily from the Engine building? I wish you would think this over *for the above named parties are annoying me all they can* by advancing Vignoles and his opposite opinions. The Directors support me, *but it makes it sad uphill work.*

---

[1] Jeaffreson, *Life of Robert Stephenson*, Vol. I., p. 139.   [2] *Newcastle Weekly Courant*, 11th June 1881.
[3] Jeaffreson, *Life of Robert Stephenson*, Vol. I., p. 167.

To this Longridge replies on 4th February 1835 :—

I have maturely considered what you say concerning dispensing *pro tempore* of your shares in the Engine Building concern—this can easily be accomplished by your Father taking them on his own account with an understanding that he is to transfer them again to you upon your having finished your Agreement with the Directors of the London and Birmingham Rail Way.

I feel very solicitous that you should devote the whole of your faculties *undividedly* to this magnificent undertaking; this being once *well accomplished*, your name and future are built upon a Rock, and you may afterwards smile at the malice of your enemies. The only reason which induces me to approve of this arrangement is that it will leave your *mind quite at ease*. Were you as case-hardened in these matters as myself I would set Messrs. Cropper, Rathbone, Dr. Lardner and all such at defiance—but you have not yet attained sufficient philosophy to say 'None of these things move me,'—when you arrive at the sober age of Fifty you will bear these rubs better.

It must be noted that Cropper, one of the directors of the Liverpool and Manchester Railway, as a convinced advocate of the fixed-engine system, and afterwards as preferring the locomotives of Braithwaite and Ericsson and of Gurney, had been for some years in pronounced opposition to the Stephensons.

Robert Stephenson writes later to Longridge, under date :—

LONDON, 21st February 1835.

The subject of disposing of my Engine Building Shares *pro tempore* must stand over until I meet you in London—my Liverpool friends are annoying me more than I anticipated even when I wrote you last. They have passed a resolution in the shape of a recommendation, to our Directors, *that no Director or Engineer shall have any connexion directly or indirectly with any Contract with the Company, more particularly for Locomotive Engines.*

The Liverpool people do not disguise that this recommendation to our Directors is aimed especially at me. *The Directors will be compelled to act upon it.* This has all sprung from the Quakers and Bury our Liverpool Rival.

To this Longridge replies on 26th February 1835 :—

There are in the lives of most persons important eras which materially affect their future destiny—such an era has I think now arrived in yours.

If, as you suppose, '*The Directors will be compelled to* pass a Resolution,' that no Director or Engineer shall have any connection directly or indirectly with any Contract with the Company, you must decide whether you will resign your situation of Engineer, or dispose of your shares in the Engine Building Factories.

If you determine upon the former, you will suffer in your Fortune—and still more in your Fame—and your enemies will mightily triumph over you. If you absolutely sell your shares *bona fide* to your Father, you will not *eventually* suffer in your Fortune, and *your mind will be set at ease*, so that you can devote the whole of your Time and Talents to the great Undertaking in which you are engaged. This is the substance of what may be urged as far as your *individual interest* is concerned. And as to Messrs. Pease, Richardson and myself, if your Father will take your Shares and responsibility, I do not foresee any reasonable objections on our side. For myself I am willing to go on with your Father as I do with you, stipulating for *a little more of his presence in Newcastle*, than you can afford us. If you think well of this I should like to have an interview with your Father and yourself, and therefore propose that we should meet at Doncaster.

Robert Stephenson's worst fears were realized, and he writes under date :—

LONDON, 9th March 1835.

The Directors are compelled to pass the resolution and in fact it was passed at a meeting of the board in Birmingham. I must sell my shares or suffer the Newcastle House to withdraw from competition on this line of road, but this is matter which can only be discussed at a meeting. I cannot possibly leave this end of the line.

We have no evidence that Robert Stephenson disposed even temporarily of his shares in the Newcastle concern, and it is known that for nearly ten years the locomotives of the London and Birmingham Railway were supplied either by Bury & Co. of Liverpool, or to their designs, none being obtained from Robert Stephenson & Co. until 1846, by which time the railway company had some reason to regret the policy which they had adopted at the inspiration of George Stephenson's enemies. With the technical questions involved we shall deal later.

from the collection of Mr. C. F. Dendy Marshall.
INAUGURATION OF THE BELGIAN RAILWAY SYSTEM

In May 1835 Robert Stephenson visited Brussels with his father, at the invitation of King Leopold, to advise on a complete system of railways for Belgium ; in consideration of their subsequent services George Stephenson was created in 1837 Chevalier of the Order of Leopold, and a like honour was conferred in 1841 on his son, to mark the King's appreciation of his improvements to the locomotive ; this Belgian connection formed in 1835 was the first of many important continental engagements, which led to valuable contracts for locomotives but necessarily caused the frequent absence of Robert Stephenson from Newcastle. There appears to be an allusion to such absences in a letter written by him to Joseph Pease under date :—

NEWCASTLE-ON-TYNE,
12th April 1836.

Your letter dated the 6th from Darlington I received here last night and have to regret not having met you in the North respecting our Forth Street concern, which was my sole object in visiting Newcastle.

I had considered from previous communication with Longridge and Starbuck that M. L. had given up the intention of building Engines at Bedlington. On my arrival here however I was surprised to learn that he had resumed the intention and from what I can hear it is more than probable that he will carry this intention to effect. I have written to him and expect he will be in Newcastle to-morrow and as I shall be in London in a few days I intend taking an early opportunity of letting you know the result. If however he has made up his mind I have little hopes of changing his views.

With reference to the allusions in your letter, as to the circumstances under which the Establishment was formed—the management and the oversight it has received from the Partners, I am persuaded if you were as well acquainted with the details as I am, you would modify your opinions on these points. Because I am absent from the place you appear to conclude that the concern never obtains any of my attention, whereas I am satisfied if it had not been for exertions made away from home the Establishment would scarcely have been in existence at this moment. I cannot, therefore, avoid feeling hurt at the comparative non-success of the Establishment being entirely imputed to my absence, when, in fact, its existence has almost depended upon it. Neither do I believe that the management will be much improved by employing a manager of the description named in your letter. Dickinson was precisely the kind of man you allude to—he was active, intelligent and what is usually termed a man of business—but the establishment would have been ruined by this time had that kind of management not been entirely altered.

The concern is now I believe doing tolerably well, but the high prices which we are getting is bringing others daily into the field, and though I do not doubt that we may keep some little ascendancy over others for a few years, I am not so sanguine as to expect anything like extraordinary profits, and rather than allow Mr. Longridge to proceed in raising a similar establishment for the Bedlington Iron Co. I think it is worth considering whether Forth Street may not be offered to the Bedlington Co. I shall collect all the necessary information to enable me to lay before you the present and future prospects of the concern. If any manager is brought to Forth Street, he ought to have a share—and ought to confine his attention to the financial department, as any interference with the mechanical will I fear throw all wrong. I expect to be in London on the 18th. My father will be there at the same time when we can arrange a meeting.

We may remark Robert Stephenson's pessimism in considering the future prospects of Robert Stephenson & Co. in a field now filling with competitors; and there is other evidence that he had to struggle throughout his life against a despondency for which there seems, at the moment, to have been little justification so far as the prospects of locomotive builders were concerned. A letter written in 1835 [1] to the chairman of the Grand Junction Railway Company suggests that 'any person bold enough to lay down £70,000 for engines for the Grand Junction could demand far more than a reasonable trade profit.' This railway from Warrington to Birmingham, which was eventually to link up the Liverpool and Manchester with the London and Birmingham Railway was only one of the many important lines then under consideration or construction.

Referring to the proposed appointment of a financial manager, mentioned in a previous letter, Robert Stephenson writes further to Joseph Pease :—

WEEDON, 7th Sept. 1836.

I have been so closely engaged since the receipt of your letter at one of our difficult Tunnels in this neighbourhood that I have not been able to turn my attention to the Forth Street concern. I had a letter from Mr. Longridge the other day, in which he asks if I have found anyone to take his situation. I informed him in reply that I expected to do so, very shortly.

What we want is an experienced responsible clerk—one who knows nothing of mechanics—for if he does Hutchinson and he would soon quarrel, in which case we should be worse off than without a Manager at all.

[1] Draft letter, Edward Dixon to John Moss, *Handbook on the rise and development of the Railway System*, ref. 368c (Ed. Baker, Birmingham, 1893).

The letter contains a comment on the difficult question of apprentices :—

If it be the particular wish of your father to place the Youth (mentioned in your letter) at Forth Street, I shall of course not object, although I had given instructions that no more apprentices should be taken—they are an everlasting source of mischief—we were always in hot water with them, and I regret having made any arrangements for allowing some of them to come into the office, to become acquainted in every detail with our plans, &c. They have no sooner done so, than they leave and carry away what has cost us a great deal of money and more thought.

The problem was no new one for Robert Stephenson, who had previously, in 1833, written to Richardson on the same subject [1] :—

Taking young men though it may be a profitable part of our business is one that incurs great responsibility which we feel is now as great as it ought to be. We have at present indeed more young men than we can sufficiently employ.

A cousin of Joseph Pease, who had spent in the Newcastle works 'two years as happy as any in his life,' writes afterwards that as a result of the large number of apprentices 'the premium has a shorter time in the [drawing] office than he ought properly to have, seeing that the office is the most important place in the whole.' [2] Robert Stephenson's own objection, on the score of valuable information made public, is perhaps less valid to-day when locomotive builders' designs are circulated for the general benefit.

On the state of affairs in the locomotive building industry generally at the end of 1836 we have a memorandum to Robert Stephenson in Edward Pease's handwriting recording under date :—

DARLINGTON, 12 mo. 6, 1836.

The Proprietors in the vicinity M. L., T. R. and E. P. having met this day and taken a review of the general state and prospects of the Concern as far as was possible in the absence of thyself and Father. Setting aside some disturbances amongst the men which are likely to be settled very speedily—everything wears a business-like and cheerful aspect.

Referring to Robert Stephenson's proposal of Cook as 'a fit and proper person to fill the station of head of the Counting House,' the writer remarks :—

The Proprietors have sufficient curiosity to be desirous of knowing whether the Gentleman is a family man and in what line of business he has been hitherto engaged, where and with whom ?

On 27th October 1836 Robert Stephenson writes enclosing a testimonial to the qualifications of Edward Cook ; his letter concludes :—

It was very gratifying to me to hear that you considered the factory going on pretty well and that our prospects were tolerably good. Rivals however are now coming into the field who have not to begin by expensive experiments. There is now no groping in the dark, at least there ought not to be.

By this time Robert Stephenson & Co. were reaping a reward for their earlier experiments and their world wide reputation which seems the more remarkable when we reflect on the appliances at their disposal ; one of the

---

[1] Jeaffreson, *Life of Robert Stephenson*, Vol. I., p. 182.

[2] Thomas Whitwell to Joseph Pease, 12 mo. 17 1859.

many eminent engineers who had served an apprenticeship at the Forth Street works stated of them afterwards [1] :—

In 1837 there were no small planing or shaping machines—there was only one slotting machine the use of which was very restricted. Wheels were driven on to their axles by sledge hammers, wielded by strong arms alone. Steam hammers were of course unknown, and only hand labour was available for the ordinary work of the smith's shop and boiler yard, with the exception of the punching and shearing machinery. Riveting by machinery, and especially by hydraulic machinery which has wrought such changes, and without which some work done now would hardly have been practicable at all, was unknown.

from the Penny Magazine, 1844, Vol. XIII., p. 379.

It is scarcely credible, but it is a fact, that there was not a single crane in Robert Stephenson's shop in 1837. There were shear-legs in the yard, by which a boiler could be lifted on to a truck, and there were portable shear-legs in the shop, by the skilful manipulation of which, at no little risk of life and limb, wonders were done in the way of transmitting heavy loads from one part of the shop to another. And the only steam-engine in that which was the most important locomotive shop in the world of that day, was a vibrating pillar engine, with a single 16-inch cylinder and 3 feet stroke. The heaviest planing machine in Robert Stephenson's works in 1837, weighed probably not more than 3 tons.

The steam engine referred to is still preserved by Robert Stephenson & Co., at their Darlington works ; the reputation of their workmen of a former

---

[1] (Sir) George B. Bruce (President), Address to *Inst. Civil Engineers*, 8th November 1887.

generation is preserved in the record we have quoted, showing as it does the extent to which hand labour was employed in the construction of locomotives which were admittedly second to none.

Referring to financial matters generally Edward J. Cook, who had been appointed chief clerk, writes to Edward Pease under date :—

NEWCASTLE, 22nd Dec. 1837.

I have had the pleasure of receiving your letter of yesterday's date and altho' I may so shortly expect to be favoured by a personal interview yet I am desirous that you should have the satisfaction of knowing in the meantime that our means and prospects are much improved.

We have been very well off for some time past in money matters, and at present have a balance in cash and Bills of nearly £5,000. We are moreover looking for large remittances from Belgium, the Great Western Railway Co. and others, and may ere long look for the confirmation of a contract upon which we are to receive an advance of £4,000 the Engines to be delivered in 1839 and 1840. Now all this will not only make us quite easy, but I anticipate will enable us to pay off our borrowed Capital which will of course be very desirable, as we shall thereby save the interest. Upon these advances we pay no interest. Our orders now extend to the end of 1840. At least they will do when certain contracts are confirmed which are now pending, and there is little doubt of their being so, they will all pay us well. I am happy to say that this year we shall have finished 29 engines besides various other work, and as this is 11 more than we accomplished last year I have a sanguine expectation that our Balance Sheet will show much better things. Hutchinson is quite aware of the necessity of not keeping a surplus stock, and his attention as well as my own has been steadily directed to this point.

I am afraid there is little chance of either Mr. Stephenson or his son being in this place at present as a portion of the Birmingham line is to be opened in January.

The following minute gives an interesting record of the value of the work in hand and the profits during 1837 :—

NEWCASTLE-UPON-TYNE,
16th Feby., 1838.

The Balance Sheet and Accounts ending the 31st Dec., 1837, were examined, from which it appears that the Sales during the Year 1837 were as follows :—

29 Locomotive Engines	....	....	....	£40,305
Other Goods	....	....	....	15,395
				£55,700

And that the profits are	....	....	....	£11,333 13 2½
which with the undivided profits of 1836		....		732 16 3½
Amounts to	....	....	....	£12,066 9 6

A letter from Mr. Robt. Stephenson dated 12th Feby., 1838, was read, requesting a part of the Loan due to his father might be repaid.

It was resolved that the sum of £2,000 should be paid to Mr. George Stephenson by a Bill at 6 months date from 1st March.

Secondly, that the sum of £6,000 should be divided between the partners according to their respective shares by Bills falling due one half on 31st March and the other half on 30th June next.

A visitor to Newcastle in 1838 records that 'the marvellous manufactory of Mr. Stephenson alone occupies four hundred workmen for the supply of steam

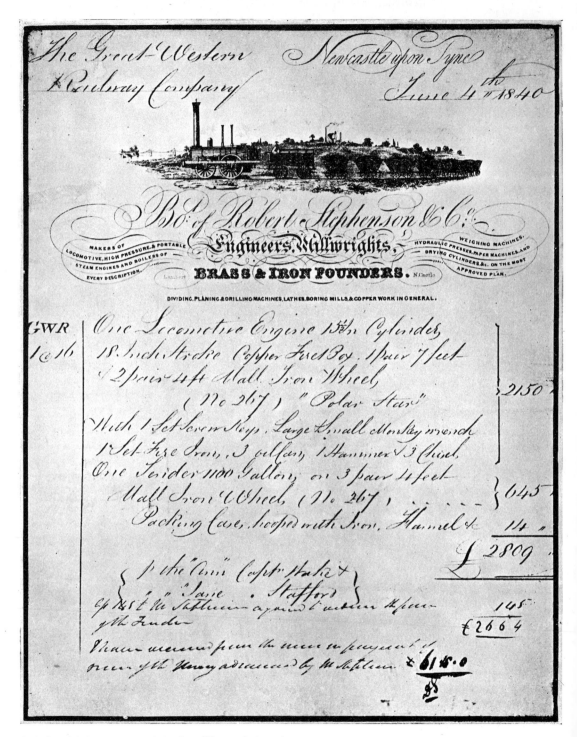

from the original in possession of the Great Western Railway Company.

engines to all parts of the world,'[1] and a minute of a year later records another good period and an appreciation of the services of William Hutchinson.

FORTH STREET ENGINE MANUFACTORY,
26 Feby. 1839.

The Balance Sheet for the year ending 31st Dec. 1838, was examined, from which it appears that the sales of the year have been as under, viz.:—

Engines,	Amounts	....	....	....	£45,270
Other Work	,,	....	....	....	15,480
					£60,750

And that the profits have been £11,474

That the sum of £1,282 17 0 has been deducted from the value of Fixed Machinery and Utensils and charged upon the undivided profits of the preceding year reducing them to the sum of £1,783 12 6.

Resolved.—That the sum of £10,000 shall be divided amongst the partners according to their Shares, a moiety of which to be paid on 31st March next, and the other moiety on 30th June next.

Resolved.—That £2,000 be added to the Capital of the Partners according to their respective Shares.

Resolved.—That in consideration of the close attention bestowed by William Hutchinson to the interests of the Manufactory and the ability displayed by him in the execution of the details of the Engines, the sum of £150 be presented to him.

The responsibility attaching to Hutchinson may be realized when we consider the other activities of the Stephensons; in 1839 George Stephenson was supervising the Manchester and Leeds, the North Midland from Derby to Leeds, the York and North Midland from Normanton to York, while Robert, whose work as chief engineer of the London and Birmingham Railway was not yet completed, was also concerned in Belgium, on lines from Ostend to Liége and Antwerp to Mons, and requests for his advice were coming from France, Switzerland and Italy.[2]   Through his work in France Robert Stephenson became intimate with Paulin Talabot, whose friendship afterwards proved of great benefit to the Newcastle firm.   Talabot, who was born in 1799, had been warmly welcomed by George Stephenson when visiting England as a young man to study its railways; he became, with Séguin, his senior, one of the leading railway engineers in France, and by his efforts did much to make up for the comparatively tardy adoption of railways in that country[3]; he was engineer for the Alais and Beaucaire, and Marseilles to Avignon lines, for which, among others in France, numerous locomotives were built by Robert Stephenson & Co.

We may record here that by 1840 Robert Stephenson & Co. had supplied locomotives to Austria for the Kaiser Ferdinand Northern Railway; to Belgium; to France for the Alais and Beaucaire, Hâvre de Grâce, and St. Étienne Railways; to Germany for the Berlin and Potsdam, Berlin and Saxony,

[1] T. F. Dibdin's *Northern Tour*, Vol. I., p. 402.

[2] Jeaffreson, *Life of Robert Stephenson*, Vol. I., p. 239.

[3] *Hommes et Choses du P.L.M.* (Chemin de fer Paris Lyon Méditerranée), 1910.

Leipzig and Dresden, and Nuremberg and Fürth Railways; to Italy for the Milan and Como Railway, and to Russia for the St. Petersburg and Pavlovsk Railway. Subsequently they built for many other German lines, for Holland, and for such important French lines as the Paris-Orleans and Marseilles-Avignon, but after 1845 French builders were able to supply the rolling stock required by their own country, and a similar movement towards independence of English supply had previously taken place in the industrial centres of other countries; by 1835 Cockerill, at Seraing in Belgium, had built his first engine on the model of Stephenson's patent type of 1833, and towards 1840 St. Léonard at Liége, Borsig at Berlin, and Haswell at Vienna, with many others, followed. [1]

from the collection of Mr. C. F. Dendy Marshall.

STEPHENSON LOCOMOTIVE AT THE OPENING OF THE FIRST RAILWAY IN RUSSIA, 30TH OCTOBER 1837

But referring to their then rapidly increasing continental connection Robert Stephenson writes to Joseph Pease under date 24th October 1840 :—

You have probably heard that Longridge and Starbuck no longer carry on business together. The latter intends commencing a commission business in his own account and has applied to me to allow him to act for R. S. & Co., more particularly on the Continent where he has already been very instrumental in establishing a connection for Longridge & Co. in their Locomotive Department.

I am of opinion that I cannot do better than arrange with Starbuck without delay in order that he may at once go abroad to apprise his correspondents personally of the change which has taken place and introduce himself as acting for us. I address you on this subject because I am informed your father is from home and I don't know his address—will you favour me with your opinion and advice.

It is most essential that we should cultivate our continental business, and I cannot conceive a better opportunity of doing so than that which has occurred thro' Starbuck.

On 13th October 1841 Cook writes to Edward Pease :—

[1] Deghilage, *Origine de la Locomotive*, 1886, p. 15.

Within the last six months we have gradually discharged about 50 hands, but looking at the work we have actually before us and in prospect I think we shall not be called upon to continue this reduction, at least to any extent, the number of engines for which we now have orders being 38, and we may with confidence look for others from parties who have been suspending them until the result of our Patent Engine be known, and since Mr. R. Stephenson, who is now here, is well satisfied with it we can have no misgivings as to what that will be. The first of these Engines was sent away early this morning to Darlington for the purpose of being tried on the Gt. North of England, and at which trial Mr. R. S. intends being present.

After discussing how reductions of wages might be most equitably effected, the letter continues :—

The talk here is that Hawthorns have little or nothing to do, but I have no direct means of knowing whether this be so, it is however certain that they have turned off a great many hands, but I have not heard that they have reduced wages.

It now only remains for me to give you an idea of our financial position and prospects, but I may first mention that we have up to this time in the present year finished and sent away 31 engines, and that, ere its close, we calculate upon the despatch of 6 or 7 more.

from a lithograph (undated) drawn by C. Cheffins.

ROBERT STEPHENSON'S 'LONG-BOILER' PATENT LOCOMOTIVE

On June 23rd 1841 Robert Stephenson had patented certain improvements to locomotive engines, which were embodied in the two referred to in the above letter. The engines of the new designs were known as Stephenson's 'Long Boilers' and they were immediately adopted for both home and foreign railways, numbers being built under license by other makers; with their technical features we shall deal elsewhere.

Towards the end of 1842 Robert Stephenson was in correspondence with

Edward Pease in regard to the dissolution of partnership with Longridge, and he writes under date 4th November 1842 :—

I was much obliged by your concurrence in the proposal I made as to the mode of closing our connection with Longridge. We can now all look back upon it with satisfaction which I certainly could not have done had we enforced the letter of an agreement. I have heard from Longridge in reply to my offer and he accepts it.

On 16th November 1842 Cook writes to Edward Pease :—

With regard to orders, we have not actually secured any new ones since I had the pleasure of seeing you, but the York and North Midland Company are going to order two engines almost directly, and we have received the hope that some of the numerous communications we have on foot with continental companies may speedily be brought to a successful issue.

from the collection of the Paris Lyons Mediterranean Railway Company.

In 1843 Robert Stephenson spent a few days at Naples, considering railway projects and more especially 'protecting the interests of the Newcastle Factory from the unscrupulous competition of persons whom he had uniformly treated with liberality.' On his return journey home he visited various parts of Germany, 'securing new and powerful connections wherever he went'[1] and it is recorded in 1843 that, out of 180 English built engines running in Germany, 81 had been built by Robert Stephenson & Co.[2] In the following year, apparently with reference to the supply of locomotives to the Avignon Marseilles Railway, Robert Stephenson enters into an agreement with the firm of L. Benet, of la Ciotat, for such supply, 'on the latest and best system for which he had obtained a patent, half of the engines to be built in the works at la Ciotat under his direction and responsibility, and on condition that the engines so built in France may be in all respects equal to those which come from his works at Newcastle.'[3]

[1] Jeaffreson, *Life of Robert Stephenson*, Vol. I., p. 259.
[2] *Mechanics' Magazine*, Vol. XXXIX., p. 288 (from *Leipzig Journal*).
[3] *Rapport à l'Assemblée Générale des Actionnaires de la Cie d'Avignon Marseilles* 29.4.44, communicated to Robert Stephenson & Co. by M. Ferdinand Achard, 6th February 1923.

On 11th December 1843 Cook writes to Edward Pease :—

Although we are now unfortunately working short handed and consequently have not sufficient to keep us going in the way we have for a long time been accustomed to, yet I am pleased to say that in addition to 3 Engines we have in hand for Yarmouth, and 2 for the North Midland we have a contract for 15 for the Marseilles Avignon line thro' our friend Mr. Talabot and which we have every reason to expect will be increased to 20, but they do not come into operation just yet. This therefore does not increase our activity at the present moment, but it is pleasant to have such an order on our books to take in hand in due time. Meanwhile we may fairly hope (altho' we have been disappointed in several instances) that some of our numerous negotiations on foot will result in orders, further to secure which, and to meet our competitors on something like the same footing as to price, Mr. Robt. Stephenson has authorized a considerable reduction, and our new prices (about 10 p. cent. less) are already gone all over the continent. This will of course affect future profits but not to the extent it would appear to do in consequence of the cost of the Patent Engines being less than those upon the old plan, and all our orders being for those of the Patent construction. If Sharp, Roberts & Co. are busy of which I was not before aware, it is not with Russian orders, none having yet been given, and I do hope and trust notwithstanding the 'Great House' insisted upon Mr. Starbuck's not going to St. Petersburg that we stand as good a chance for at least a portion of that order as any other builders should the authorities not determine, of which there is some fear, to have them all made on the spot.

I do not know when Mr. Robt. Stephenson will be in the north again, he was here for a day or so last week and left via Carlisle and Lancaster on Wednesday last for London where he now is, or at least was on Saturday. With respect to our finances the payment of the Balance of our Acct. with the Paris & Orleans Co. has put us in easy circumstances.

On 13th February 1844 Cook writes to Joseph Pease :—

I am happy to say that we are becoming more actively employed and since the 1st Jany. have orders for 5 Engines (1 for the Croydon and Dover—2 for Holland and 2 for Silesia) and shall immediately have an order for 6 more for the Yarmouth and Norwich.

We have already quoted some of the many references to the Forth Street works which are contained in the diaries of Edward Pease ; unfortunately his journals previous to 1838 are no longer in existence, and those at our disposal deal only with the last twenty years of his life, beginning when he was seventy-one years of age, but they contain much evidence of his still active interest in the affairs of Robert Stephenson & Co.

On 21st August 1845 he records the first change in the partnership :—

Went to Newcastle with cousin T. Richardson to settle our co-partnership with George and Robert Stephenson, and it was agreed that W. Hutchinson should come in as a fifth paying £7,000 to £8,000.

William Hutchinson's partnership was the fitting reward for many years valuable service, in the consciousness of which he had written to Robert Stephenson under date :—

NEWCASTLE, May 2nd, 1845.

I sit down to address you upon a subject which I had fully made up my mind to speak personally to you about when you were down in Newcastle and which diffidence alone prevented me doing at that time. I hope that nothing which I may say here will be taken amiss as I am very far from wishing to write anything that should prove in the least offensive to you, in whom I have ever believed I had a friend.

I may state then that I have now served you twenty-four years, the best part of my lifetime and I begin to feel that I ought to have some little interest in a place for which I have laboured so long and so earnestly, particularly when I see others, who have left the factory in

H'

South Street, have advanced themselves so much before me that have stuck so closely to it. Many of those who have left, have in a few years either become partners in large concerns, or by the change made more thousands than I have hundreds, and this by no superior ability, neither by greater economy on their parts, or more extravagance on mine, but simply by their advantage being so much greater.

I trust then Sir that you will not think, after I have so long been a servant, that I am either seeking too much or presuming too far, in asking for a small share in the works, which I have so long conducted with what success and ability you best know. If you consider from my character and services I am worthy of becoming a partner, I hope you will grant what I ask— I need scarcely say that during the Twenty-four years I have been with you, I have refused many good offers, and remained with you, under a firm belief that you would never see my services worse requited than those of others.

I trust you will give my request your fullest consideration, for I find it a duty I owe to myself thus to address you. Age is creeping upon me and I must now endeavour before I

from a lithograph (undated) drawn by C. Cheffins, photo in the collection of the Locomotive Publishing Co.

ROBERT STEPHENSON'S PATENT REAR-DRIVER LONG-BOILER LOCOMOTIVE

built for the London and North Western Railway, 1846

become older, to try and make some provision for myself and Family. A change has occurred lately which has made me think more deeply, than I might otherwise have done and reflection tells me that other friends may go, it therefore behoves me to try and advance myself in every legitimate way whilst friends remain who can assist me and whilst such assistance may be of use.

Should this letter be at all deficient on the score of politeness, or not sufficiently plain in any of its details, you must attribute to its true cause 'a not over good letter writer.'

In reply to this letter Edward Pease had been advised, that Robert Stephenson had talked the matter over with his father, and that they considered Hutchinson was entitled to a permanent interest in a concern which he had 'so ably supported for so many years.' It appears from Hutchinson's statement that he must have entered George Stephenson's employment in 1821, previously to the foundation of the Forth Street works.

The year 1845 brought to Robert Stephenson & Co. a curious revenge for the attacks by their rivals which had closed the London and Birmingham Railway as a field for their locomotives.   By this time the directors had cause to regret the policy of Edward Bury, their locomotive engineer, of employing only four-wheeled locomotives to deal with a heavy traffic, and they ordered several lots of six-wheeled engines 'on the principle of Mr. R. Stephenson,' some to be built at the Newcastle works, some by Tayleur & Co.   Later we find the secretary of the London and Birmingham Railway Company, R. Creed, writing to Robert Stephenson & Co., on 30th October 1845 :—

I am desired to say that our Company are prepared to deal with you for a supply of Engines to an extent that would probably make it worth your while to devote your establishment to the execution of our orders exclusively, and with a view to a more prompt delivery of them than might under other circumstances be thought convenient. If an arrangement of this nature should be likely to accord with your views, as it possibly may, it is desirable that we should know within as brief a term as you can answer this communication, the extent to which you can pledge yourselves for the early and continued delivery of Engines of the character required by our Company (1) for the conveyance of heavy loads of goods, (2) fast Passenger Trains, &c.

(part) from the Railway Magazine No. II., June 1835.

AN ATMOSPHERIC RAILWAY

The firm's records show that this offer was not accepted in its entirety.   In the following year the amalgamation of the Liverpool and Manchester, Grand Junction, and London and Birmingham Railways took place and locomotives were supplied later by Robert Stephenson & Co. for the Southern division of the new line, afterwards famous as the London and North Western Railway.

In 1845 a Bill for a single line of railway on the atmospheric system, from Newcastle-on-Tyne to Berwick-on-Tweed, was under consideration in Parliament, and Robert Stephenson, who with his father disapproved the proposal, had, not for the first time, to fight Brunel, who on behalf of the supporters of this Bill had brought war into a district which the Stephensons might with some justification regard as peculiarly their own province.   They supported the rival scheme for a double line to be worked by locomotives, and this was eventually adopted.   But the outstanding event in the railway world of 1845 was the appointment of a Royal Commission to decide in the general interests of the country whether the gauge of future railways in Great Britain should be determined by legislation. Robert Stephenson as the protagonist of the 4 ft. 8½ or 'Narrow Gauge' found himself again leader of the opposition to Brunel the champion of the 'Broad' or '7-foot Gauge,' which had been adopted by him for the Great Western Railway. The controversy had greatly excited public opinion for some years but its effect on the locomotive building industry was negligible. With the technical aspects of the struggle, and their influence on the design of the locomotive, we shall deal in a later chapter.

During 1845 George Stephenson visited Spain, to survey for a railway in the north of that country, but this journey does not appear to have led directly to any useful connections for the Newcastle firm.

Resuming now our consideration of domestic affairs, we find an interesting record of working conditions at this period in a printed bill, dated 1st February 1846 :—

REGULATIONS

FOR

THE DRAWING OFFICE

OF

ROBERT STEPHENSON & CO.

Hours of Attendance.—From Seven o'clock in the Morning until Six in the Evening, except on Saturdays, when the Office Hours terminate at Four; subject however, at all times, to extra Attendance whenever Business requires it.

Meal Times.—BREAKFAST, from Half-past Eight till Nine o'clock;—DINNER, from One till Two; Head Draughtsman, from One till Half-past Two.

Management.—The Head Draughtsman to have the sole Management and Control, and to be considered Master in the Absence of Mr. Hutchinson.

Order.—Each Draughtsman to assort and carefully put away every Evening, all such Drawings, Papers, and other Documents and Instruments, he may have been engaged with, or using during the Day.

Removing of Documents.—No Drawings, Papers, or any other Documents whatever, belonging to the Establishment (or Copies thereof), to be removed or taken from the Office, or out of the Works, without the Sanction of Mr. Hutchinson.

Instruments.—Every Draughtsman, before entering the Office, or as soon after as convenient, must provide himself with all necessary Drawing Instruments.

Leave of Absence.—No Absence is allowed without Leave from Mr. Hutchinson; or, in case of his Absence, from the Head Draughtsman.

Time.—Each Person to enter an Account of his Time in a Book, and deliver the same once a Fortnight (on the Thursday Morning) into the Counting House.

Note.—We hereby appoint MR. WILLIAM WEALLENS to the Situation of Head Draughtsman, who has our Authority to enforce the strict Observance of these Regulations.

On 12th March 1846 W. Budden, who had been appointed secretary in place of Edward Cook deceased, writes to Edward Pease in reference to the value of the buildings, fixed machinery, etc., and refers to extending the existing fire policies to cover the West Factory, this being the large extension westwards. The balance sheet for the following year (31st December 1847) first records separately the profits made at the 'South Street Factory and at Forth Bank West.'

The boom in railways, known as the 'Railway Mania,' was now at its height; these were good times for the locomotive building industry, and it is recorded that in May 1846 locomotive builders throughout the country had more orders in hand than they could complete for the early deliveries required, and would not enter into fresh engagements for a less term than two years. The average price of a locomotive is recorded as 'about £1,800 but expected shortly to be £2,000.' Robert Stephenson & Co. alone had 224 engines on order, and as a consequence Edward Pease is able to record in June 1846, that his 'collieries have lost £1,400 in five months, but the Forth Street concern is doing well.' On 19th June he goes to Newcastle to settle a new deed of partnership with Robert Stephenson, and on 28th October he puts his son Joseph into the deed of partnership. The balance sheet at the end of this year records the capital holdings in the new partnership as below :—

					£
R. Stephenson	....	....	....	....	6,600
Geo. Stephenson	....	....	....	....	6,600
Jos. Pease	....	....	....	....	6,600
Thos. Richardson	....	....	....	....	6,600
Wm. Hutchinson	....	....	....	....	6,600

A memorandum by Joseph Pease records that at this time there were 150 locomotives on order, of which 52 of those built during the year had been of 'Forth Street make,' '8 from the West Factory'; the wages had amounted to £1,650 per fortnight. Among the engines particularly noted are two three-cylinder (long-boiler) locomotives for the York, Newcastle and Berwick Railway. These were of a new design, patented by George Stephenson with William Howe, who had been formerly employed as a patternmaker at Forth Street but was now engineer at Stephenson's Clay Cross Collieries.[1] The cost of these patent engines is recorded as £1,872 each; their technical features we shall describe in a subsequent chapter.

We may note here that, though the raising of the customs duty in France was now seriously affecting the importation of English built locomotives into that country, Robert Stephenson was still receiving the benefit of royalties paid on engines built by French makers to his long-boiler design patented in 1841; in one case the amount of this royalty is recorded as 1,250 francs on each, in an order for thirty-four locomotives.[2]

Starbuck, who had been appointed, in 1840, continental agent to Robert Stephenson & Co., now received a commission of $2\frac{1}{2}$ per cent. on foreign orders, and $1\frac{1}{4}$ per cent. on home orders.

[1] Obituary *Proc. Inst. Mechanical Engineers*, 1880.
[2] Communicated to Robert Stephenson & Co. by M. Ferdinand Achard, 6th February 1923.

LOCOMOTIVE, BUILT BY GOUIN, FOR THE PARIS ORLEANS RAILWAY, WITH THE SPECIAL COACH OF THE PRINCE PRESIDENT LOUIS NAPOLEON, 1852

from a model of a Stephenson Long-Boiler Locomotive in the Conservatoire des Arts et Métiers, Paris.

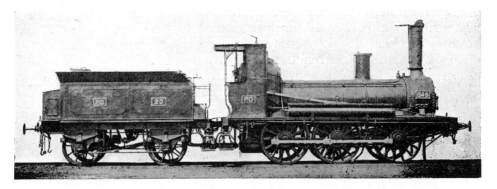

from a photo by the Paris-Orleans Railway Company.

THE ·MAMMOTH'

This locomotive built by Robert Stephenson & Co. in 1844 became the model for hundreds built afterwards in France and was itself in service (rebuilt) in 1905; the original tender is not shown

On 12th April 1847 Edward Pease records :—

At Newcastle with my son Joseph and Cousin T. Richardson. Looked over the very inter
esting large Forth Street Works, etc.—all things appear in good order and we agreed to divide
£1,000 each—how unexpectedly has this been made a source of considerable income to me.

The association which had lasted for a quarter of a century, and proved
of such unexpected benefit to those concerned, was now to be broken.
George Stephenson died on 12th August 1848, and on the 18th of that month
Edward Pease, the oldest of the original partners, thus refers in his diary to
this first breach made by death in their ranks :—

Left home in company with John Dixon to attend the interment of George Stephenson at
Chesterfield, and arrived in the evening. When I reflect on my first acquaintance with him and
the resulting consequences my mind seems almost lost in doubt as to the beneficial results—
that humanity has been benefited in the diminished use of horses and by the lessened cruelty
to them, that much ease, safety, speed, and lessened expense in travelling is obtained, but as
to the results and effects of all that Railways have led my dear family into, being in any sense
beneficial is uncertain.

On 28th December 1848 he records :—

Pecuniarily I have cause to admire how an effort to serve a worthy youth, Robert, the son
of George Stephenson, by a loan of £500, at first without expectation of much remuneration,
has turned to my great advantage. During the course of the year I have received £7,000 from
the concern at Forth Street.

This is one of the many references by Edward Pease, in writing and in
speech, to his regard for Robert, and to the extent by which his faith in the
younger Stephenson had been rewarded. Robert himself was now to benefit
by his father's share in the Forth Street concern ; a minute of 9th September
1849 records :—

In consequence of the lamented demise of George Stephenson, C.E., the interests of that
gentleman now merges into that of Robert Stephenson, Esq., M.P., &c.

It is fitting to mention here that, in 1847, Robert Stephenson had been
elected without opposition Member of Parliament for Whitby, which con-
stituency he represented until his death ; in the House of Commons he was,
as elsewhere a popular figure, and his unique experience in railways and the
parliamentary procedure connected with railway bills gave a peculiar value
to his opinion on such matters. No one was better aware than he of the
evils which had resulted from short-sighted, or too tardy, legislation, but his
parliamentary connection came perhaps too late to give the country the full
benefit of his experience and knowledge, and since it can hardly be said to
have affected directly the subject of our present notes we need not here refer
to it further.

Although Robert Stephenson had now the largest holding in the locomotive
works, his other engagements permitted only occasional visits to Newcastle,
but the design of the locomotive had been so firmly established on sound
principles that he was able to devote his energies in increasing degree to the
large civil engineering interests which centred in Great George Street, now the
home of the consulting engineering business which had commenced at New-

castle in 1824 under the title of George Stephenson and Son. Evidence of those activities which have made him famous as a civil engineer are to be found in a letter written to Edward Pease under date 15th May 1850 :—

I am prevented having the pleasure of a visit to Darlington on the 22nd owing to that and the following day being fixed for floating the next Tube at the Menai Straits, and as this movement depends on the tide, it is of course impossible for me to alter the arrangements.

I sincerely regret this circumstance, for every early association connected with my profession would have tended to render my visit a gratifying one; it would have given me moreover an opportunity of saying publicly how much the wonderful progress of Railways was dependent upon the successful issue of the first great experiment, and how much that issue was influenced by your great discernment and your kindness and confidence in my late revered father.

In my remembrance you stand amongst the foremost of his early patrons and advisers and I know throughout life he always regarded you as one of his very best friends, and took great delight in frequently and very graphically describing his first visit to Darlington on foot to confer with you on the subject of the Stockton and Darlington Railway.

A month later he writes of his feelings respecting retirement :—

I find it a very difficult matter to bring to a close so complicated a connection in business matters as that which has been established by 25 years of active and arduous professional duty.

SALOON LOCOMOTIVE BUILT BY ROBERT STEPHENSON & CO. FOR THE VICEROY OF EGYPT.

On his return from Egypt in the spring of 1851 he writes to Edward Pease of a 'journey full of interest', and mentions the wish of Abbas Pasha, then Viceroy, that he should undertake the construction of a railway from Alexandria to Cairo. This railway he adds—'I regard as an important instalment of the entire communication between the Mediterranean and Red Seas.' From a previous study of the question, and a survey of the country in 1847 with the engineers Talabot and de Negrelli, Robert Stephenson had come to the conclusion that the Suez Canal was impossible[1]; this was one of the few instances in which his professional judgment has proved to be at fault, but his conclusion explains the special interest with which he regarded the proposed railway from Alexandria to Cairo. His visit to Egypt led to a warm friendship with the succeeding Viceroy, Mohammed Saïd, and to valuable orders for locomotives and bridges.

[1] Jeaffreson, *Life of Robert Stephenson*, Vol. II., p. 149.

In 1852 Robert Stephenson was asked to advise[1] on the design of a bridge to carry the Grand Trunk Railway of Canada across the River St. Lawrence and was eventually appointed engineer-in-chief for the great structure designed on the tubular system which he had previously adopted for his bridge over the Menai Straits. Visiting their country in connection with the new bridge, Robert Stephenson took the opportunity to advise the Canadians, when projecting their railway system to avoid the mistakes which had been made by those countries which had permitted the promotion of rival lines 'for reasons entirely apart from their real merits, or scientific questions involved in the details.' Within his own knowledge sixty million pounds had been wasted in England alone on duplicate lines, 'which would never have been built had a directing genius presided over the chartering of them'—'such competition' he said 'had answered no useful purpose —like poverty, a mother of invention, it had invented the remedy—amalgamation.'

from a painting in possession of Sir John P. Fry, Bart.

THOMAS RICHARDSON, 1771–1853

The Canadians were able to avoid such errors, but in determining the gauge for their Grand Trunk Railway, they were not warned by the course of events in England. The first locomotives sent by Robert Stephenson & Co. to Canada, in 1856, were built for a gauge of 5 feet 6 inches which had been adopted by a special committee in Canada after consideration of evidence given by engineers and railwaymen from the United States. This evidence, we are told, tended rather to confuse, than eludicate, the problem, since at the time there were still in the United States gauges varying from 4 feet $8\frac{1}{2}$ inches to 6 feet. In both countries the importance of uniformity, and similar commercial and political conditions, led later to the general adoption of the 4 foot $8\frac{1}{2}$ inch gauge, to which the Grand Trunk Railway was eventually converted.[2]

On 9th March 1853 Edward Pease records :—

The accounts of the Forth Street Works were received and made it appear that I may be benefited by the last year's work £2,000, after giving to R. Stephenson and W. Hutchinson the profit which I cannot touch as a profit resulting from making some war steamers' engines for the King of Sardinia.

Thomas Richardson died on 27th April of this year, in his 82nd year. His cousin Edward Pease notes the event in his diary, describing Richardson as

[1] Jeaffreson, *Life of Robert Stephenson*, Vol. II., p. 181.
[2] Edward Woods (President) Address, *Proc. Inst. Civil Engineers*, 9th November 1886.

'a man of great integrity . . . . . a kind, amiable, generous disposition, largely manifested in founding the Agricultural School at Ayton, and encouraging education among Friends and others.' On 16th May following he records going to Newcastle :—

. . . . to arrange about Thomas Richardson's share in R. Stephenson's. We were most pleasantly met by R. S. who appeared to have a very sincere satisfaction in having his (T. R.'s) share transferred into Joseph's name, so after my decease my three dear sons will stand possessed of two-fifths of that concern.

On 20th October 1853 he records :—

S. Smiles was with me to obtain particulars for a memoir of the life of George Stephenson. It appears to me that Railways will be a favour to the world, and I do not regret, but far otherwise, that my time, care and attention was occupied for many months.

Three days later he notes :—

My friend, Robert Stephenson, the engineer, to spend two or three days with me—a man of most highly gifted and talented power of mind, of benevolent, liberal, kindly, just, generous dispositions, in company most interesting.

On 29th November he refers to :—

The £500 we (Robert Stephenson & Co.) have given for the establishment of schools at Newcastle on the broadest and most tolerant religious principles, etc.

On 5th May 1855 Robert Stephenson writes :—

My Dear Mr. Pease,—I am glad to receive your note of this morning expressing your satisfaction generally as to what was doing in Forth St.

I was much disappointed myself at the result of the year's work, but in consideration I am satisfied that it is fairly accounted for by the low prices of several of our contracts the rise in wages and materials subsequent to the time when the contracts were made. These are fluctuations in trade which we must be prepared for occasionally.

I trust now we are in a position to stop any increase to our capital—the point you refer to shall have my attention when next I visit Newcastle—I shall probably give you a call, but I have two or three engagements to stay with friends which may prevent my extending my call into a stay—I enjoyed my last sojourn with you exceedingly and felt much obliged to all the members of your family for their kind attentions.

Yours faithfully,

Rob. Stephenson.

The letter bears a note by Edward Pease, in writing now shaky with age, from which it appears that the point to be considered at the works was access to Forth Street for the transit of the heavy work on the west side. The letter is also interesting from the less formal mode of address now adopted by the quickly ageing man of fifty-five, to the old man of eighty-eight, who had been such a friend to his father and himself ; this friendship between the original partners, amounting, if we may judge by the letters, to an almost brotherly affection, is one of the remarkable features of their correspondence which has been preserved.

During this year a further change in the partnership took place, consequent on the death of William Hutchinson about two years previously, and on 10th August 1855 Edward Pease records ' an agreeable meeting with Robert

Stephenson admitting W. Weallens into partnership in the Forth Street concern.' On 20th November 1855 Weallens writes to Edward Pease :—

Although we are very full of work at present, Locomotive orders do not come in as I should like to see. We are doing well with marine engines.

Though any detailed reference to their work other than in the manufacture of locomotives is beyond our present scope and limits of space, it seems fitting to note here that the manufacture of marine engines and boilers formed a large part of the activities of Robert Stephenson & Co. ; during the

first forty years of their existence 115 marine engines, 206 marine boilers, and 263 stationary engines and boilers, of 35,000 total horse-power, were built at the Forth Street and South Street works.[1]

As witnesses to the quality of the work turned out by the firm, hundreds of locomotives were at work in the closing years of the nineteenth century, both at home and abroad, which had been built forty years earlier, during the life-time of Robert Stephenson. Many of these are still in service, rebuilt, and of course with new boilers, but in some cases with their original frames, wheel centres, and certain parts of the motion details. Among the engines still at work are five built for the Midland Railway in 1852, and no less than fifty of the same type built for the same railway in the succeeding decade. They have a peculiar interest as embodying the principle of

[1] J. F. Tone, *A History of the Trade and Manufactures of the Tyne, Wear and Tees* (British Assn., 1863).

from Bourne's Treatise on the Steam Engine, 1872.

ONE OF FIFTY LOCOMOTIVES BUILT BY ROBERT STEPHENSON & CO. FOR THE
LOMBARDO-VENETIAN RAILWAY, 1857-8

photo from the collection of Mr R. Bleasdale.

BUILT BY ROBERT STEPHENSON & CO. FOR THE MIDLAND RAILWAY, 1852

This engine, re-boilered, was in service till 1899

the outside frame introduced by Robert Stephenson & Co. in 1830, and for many years their standard practice ; it is probable that this form of construction has contributed to the longevity of these particular engines.

After 1855 there was no further change in the partnership until after the death of Edward Pease, which took place in 1858, in his 92nd year.   He had outlived all but one of his first associates in locomotive building, but was not long survived by Robert Stephenson who, prematurely aged by a life of continuous and strenuous toil, and broken in health, died on the 12th of October 1859, in his 56th year—'he was buried on 21st October in Westminster Abbey, that celebrated resting-place of the illustrious dead of so many generations, a great number of gentlemen from Newcastle attended the funeral —the North Eastern Railway Co. gave them return tickets.   Robert Stephenson was most popular among his workmen, and at their request the Vicar of Newcastle performed the service, on the day of the funeral, in St. Nicholas Church at which they attended.'[1]

In his later years Robert Stephenson, referring to the circumstances in which the Forth Street works had been established, stated that one of his father's great objects had been 'to concentrate a number of workmen for the purpose of carrying out improvements in detail which he was constantly making, and to educate a class of workmen in skilled labour who should be able to execute the many ideas which presented themselves to his active and practical mind.'[2]   The son lived to see the full realization of his father's plans but in the statement we have quoted, as in many others, he was modestly silent on his own part in their accomplishment.   There is ample evidence that the improvements made in the locomotive after his return from South America at the end of 1827, which can be seen by comparing the 'Lancashire Witch' of 1828 with the Stephenson locomotive of 1859, were due largely to Robert Stephenson himself, in collaboration, as he was the first to admit, with a staff of most capable men.

Among those who appear to have contributed in no small degree to the success of the Forth Street works were G. H. Phipps, who had been chief draughtsman while the 'Rocket' was under construction[3], R. L. Whyte, who followed[4], William Weallens appointed chief draughtsman in 1846, and the late Edward Snowball[5], who held that office from about 1852 till 1858, and in after years, in the same capacity with another well-known firm of locomotive builders, maintained the traditions in which he had been reared and established for himself a reputation second to none for sound judgment in design.   Of William Hutchinson we have already written ; on his appointment as managing partner he was followed later in the works by George A. Crow, whom the

---

[1] Francis Mewburn, *The Larchfield Diary*, Darlington, 1876.

[2] Robert Stephenson's Narrative of his Father's Inventions.   Smiles, *Lives of the Engineers*, 1862, Vol. III., p. 494.

[3] Obituary, *Proc. Inst. Civil Engineers*, Vol. XCVI.

[4] *American Machinest*, 11th February 1904.

[5] Obituary, *The Engineer*, 30th June 1911.

Long-Boiler Engine 'Edward Pease' built in 1856 for the
Stockton and Darlington Railway

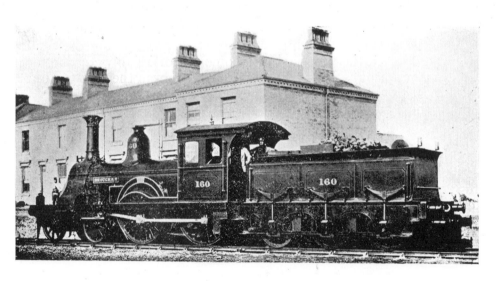

Bogie Engine 'Brougham' built in 1860 for the
Stockton and Darlington Railway

writer of a private letter to one of the partners describes as 'the cleverest practical man' he knew.[1]   In the same letter we are told that the shops ' could not be bettered in foremen, so far as getting the work well done goes.'

There were also such men as William Williams, the draughtsman, and William Howe, the patternmaker.   Many of the eminent railway engineers of the nineteenth century had been apprenticed to Robert Stephenson & Co., and there must have been many others, whose names are unknown to us, who likewise contributed to the development of the Stephenson locomotive.   But no one man among them combined in so remarkable a degree the long experience, and practical qualities, of Robert Stephenson himself.   A letter written in 1839 to the son of his old schoolmaster[2] shows the foundations on which was based his reputation as a sound practical man.   Referring to his own 'taste for mathematical pursuits', and 'facility for applying this kind of knowledge to practical purposes and modifying it to circumstances', Robert Stephenson wrote :—

This latter qualification is of the utmost importance, for I have had numerous examples of the danger of applying abstract mathematical truths to practice, without reference to circumstances.   To an Engineer mathematical truths are like sharp instruments, they require to be handled with care and circumspection—in short they are only truths so long as certain conditions obtain.

With the death of the last of the original partners we may fitly mark the end of an epoch in the history of Robert Stephenson & Co., and resume our description of the firm's work in the development and improvement of the locomotive, which in a previous chapter we left much as George Stephenson had made it in 1822.

(from a lithograph by J. D. Harding, printed by C. Hullmandel.)
George Stephenson's Locomotives at Hetton
1822

[1] Thomas Whitwell to Joseph Pease, 12 mo. 17 1859.
[2] Letter to Rev. John Bruce, M.A. *Northern Daily Express*, October 13 1859

from a photograph taken in 1875, the property of Mr. W. Richardson, Darlington.

No. 1 LOCOMOTIVE OF THE STOCKTON AND DARLINGTON RAILWAY BUILT BY ROBERT STEPHENSON & CO. IN 1825

A comparison with the drawing on page 114 shows that the engine, though more than once rebuilt, preserves its original form and general appearance; the wheels are however of the pattern introduced by Hackworth, not as supplied with the engine

CHAPTER VII

THE FIRST LOCOMOTIVES OF
THE STOCKTON AND DARLINGTON RAILWAY

1825—1829

We have now to resume our technical notes on the evolution of the Stephenson locomotive which we left in a previous chapter as in use at Killingworth and Hetton in 1825. Some writers state that the first two engines built by Robert Stephenson & Company were for the Hetton Colliery; if so they were no doubt of George Stephenson's patent design with chain coupling; but the firm have now no contemporary record of these engines though they have a reference in an old notebook to 'Springwell locomotives,' and Robert Stephenson in 1830[1] refers to two locomotives on the Springwell railway, which had been at work for some years.

The only contemporary evidence which we have of an order for locomotives between 1823 and 1825 is for the first locomotives of the Stockton and Darlington Railway Company, whose sub-committee on 16th September 1824 resolved :—

That 2 locomotive engines be ordered of Robert Stephenson & Co. for the sum of £500 each, and that an agreement be entered into and duly signed confirming the contract.

The earliest original drawing of a locomotive now in the firm's possession is endorsed 'Locomotive Engine, Darlington'; it is undated but the paper bears water mark 1822 and, excepting Trevithick's drawing at the Science Museum, South Kensington, it is probably the oldest drawing of a rail locomotive in existence. This drawing shows the arrangement of cylinders and driving gear as on the engine now preserved at Darlington station, and it also records alternative methods for driving and coupling evidently under consideration when the engines were being designed. There are indications, partly erased, of what appears to be a suggestion to couple the axles by an intermediate gear wheel; alternatively by means of beams to transmit the drive from the front cylinder to the rear wheels, and *vice versa*. The drawing also shows the outside coupling rods which were eventually adopted.

The drive from the cylinders, and the half beam parallel motion on the first Stockton and Darlington locomotive appears to be a retrogression from the more simple construction of the Killingworth and Hetton engines. We have no evidence to show why the more complicated arrangement was adopted, but the drawing is evidence that considerable thought was given to the design of both driving and coupling gear and that some radical departures from existing arrangements were considered. It has been stated that James Kennedy, to whom we have already

[1] Robert Stephenson and Joseph Locke, *Observations on the Comparative Merits of Locomotive and Fixed Engines*, 1830.

referred, planned the first three locomotives for the Stockton and Darlington Railway and is to be credited with the success of these engines which led later to the general adoption of locomotives.[1] It has been suggested on the other hand that the design was influenced by Timothy Hackworth ; as in other cases with which we have had to deal, these claims are irreconcilable.

We cannot find that this remarkable drawing has been previously noticed though No. I engine of the Stockton and Darlington Railway and the engines which followed it have been a constant theme for historians of the locomotive. The makers' records for the succeeding engines built between 1825 and 1828 are incomplete, but a search for evidence from outside sources brought to light the report[2] by two Prussian mining engineers whose visit to Newcastle in 1827 we have mentioned.   These observers appear to have made an exhaustive

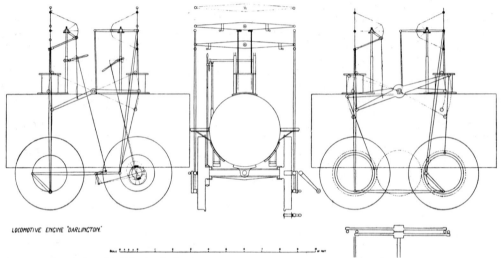

LOCOMOTIVE ENGINE 'DARLINGTON.'

from a tracing of the original (undated) drawing.

study of the railways in England, and have left an account of the Stockton and Darlington Railway, and a contemporary description of its first locomotives and fixed engines, more complete than anything yet published in England ; they give details of such interest to the historian that we shall give a full translation of a report which, supplemented by such evidence as has already been published from the records of the railway company and from other sources, will throw some light on an interesting chapter in the early history of the locomotive and help to correct erroneous statements which have long been current.

The portion of the Prussian report in which we are interested can be conveniently divided into sections, with each of which we shall deal separately.

[1] (a) Obituary, *Proc. Inst. Mech. Engineers*, 1886 ; (b) Bourne, preface to *The Steam Engine*, 1861.

[2] Railways in England.   Observations made during a journey in the years 1826 and 1827.   *Archiv für Bergbau und Hüttenwesen*, Vol. XIX., Berlin, 1829.   Translation by Mr. H. W. Dickinson and Mr. E. A. Forward.

THE STOCKTON AND DARLINGTON RAILWAY, 1825-1829

[Translation.]

TRANSPORT ON THE STOCKTON AND DARLINGTON RAILWAY.

On this railway transport is effected partly with horses and partly with locomotives. Five locomotives are in operation and a sixth serves as reserve. On the inclined planes the waggons are drawn up by stationary steam engines. The Company is at present in possession of six locomotives, four of them have two cylinders 9 inches diam. In all cases the stroke is 24 inches. The usual pressure of the steam is 52 lb. per square inch and such an engine will attain to 10 horse-power. The power of the engine corresponding to the diameter and the given pressure would amount to 15 horse-power. In winter, or when the rails are wet such a locomotive draws 16 waggons, in summer, however, when the rails are dry, 20 waggons, each holding one chaldron of coal.[1] This gives a load:—(1) 16-20 Empty waggons   320-400 cwt.

                     (2) 16-20 Chaldrons of Coal   848-1,060 cwt.

            Total   ....   1,168-1,460 cwt.

This would be the work of 4-5 horses; yet the machine can draw 24 waggons easily. Further it is to be noticed that the speed is greater.

In such places where the machine on account of the fall in the railway has nothing to draw, its speed attains 10 miles per hour; on the average its speed is 5 miles per hour or 7·3 feet per second, *i.e.* at least double as much as that of a draft-horse and the effect of the locomotive is therefore equal to 8-10 horse-power. A journey to Stockton and back, a total distance of 40 miles is accomplished in 9-11 hours, according to the speed at which the loading and unloading, shunting, etc., takes place. In case of necessity the locomotive can complete two such journeys in one day and cover a distance of 80 miles. On the upward journey with empty wagons 5 miles per hour is considered a good speed.

Six water tanks, of which there are two at the ends of the railway (that is to say of the gently falling part, for the locomotives are not able to go on the inclined planes) provide the same with water. On a journey to Stockton and back (40 miles) 1¼ to 1½ tons of coal are burnt. This coal is carried in a special wagon immediately following the engine.

The weight of a locomotive of 10 horse-power amounts to about 132 cwt. the weight of the water contained in it is 20 cwt.[2] and the weight of the tender together with the coal 40 cwt. Beyond its load of 1,168-1,460 cwt. the locomotive has therefore to draw a dead load of $132 + 20 + 40 = 192$ cwt. or in round numbers 200 cwt.

The price of such a locomotive including the tender is about £600.

Each locomotive has an attendant who receives from the Company one farthing per ton per mile, that is to say one-half as much as the horse-driver receives. For this pay he must himself provide the coal necessary for firing as well as the lubricating oil and also a helper, since two men are necessary to attend one locomotive.

Assuming that such an engine brings daily to Stockton 1,000 cwt. of coal 20 miles he will receive therefore a daily pay of 21s. On the average the monthly receipts of a locomotive attendant amount to £28 out of which he must pay for the helper, the coal, the oil, etc.

Besides these two persons there are required for attending 16-20 waggons usually two persons who are paid by the Company day wages.

From this statement it follows that the immediate expenses of transport with locomotives is only half as great, but if one brings into account the interest on the capital expenditure as well as the very considerable cost of repairs in the locomotives themselves, which at present do not yet admit of being brought to a fixed principle, it will be seen that a large part of the saving is absorbed. It is maintained also, and rightly so, that with transport by locomotives the waggons as well as the rails are more damaged than with horse traction. On these grounds it may be difficult to ascertain exactly how much advantage, or whether any advantage at all, results from traction by locomotives. Opinions were at the time still divided on this point and exact figures were not yet set out.

[1] The Newcastle chaldron, declared to be 53 cwts. by Statute 6 & 7 William III., c. 10. (See p. 9, *ante* note (2).)

[2] This is an understatement. The water must have been about 30 cwt., the engine, in working order, at least 8 tons.

THE NUMBER OF ENGINES AT WORK We shall now consider how far this general description can be reconciled with other known records and with statements as to the number of engines at work in the early part of 1827. It has been generally supposed that by this time the railway company was in possession of six engines, as shown by a list which has been widely published.[1]

Railway Co's. No.	Name.			Maker.		Date of Delivery.
1	Locomotion	....	....	R. Stephenson & Co.	....	1825
2	Hope	....	....	,,	....	1825
3	Black Diamond	....		,,	....	1826
4	Diligence	....		,,	....	1826
5	Chittaprat	....		R. Wilson	....	—
6	Experiment	....		R. Stephenson & Co.	....	1826 or 1827

It must first be noticed that the total of six engines given in this list agrees with that given by the Prussian engineers; in most published lists these engines are named as above, but it is practically certain that names were not given to the early engines until some time after they had been put into service, and this point must be noticed, since the ante-dating of the names in later descriptions has added to the difficulty in arriving at the truth about engine No. 6, usually known as the 'Experiment.' As to the dates when the engines were ordered we have evidence from the railway company's sub-committee minutes as below. On 16th July 1824 they record :—

Resolved that R. Stephenson & Co. be applied to for the terms on which they will make two Locomotive Engines, and that our Engineer furnish specifications for the same.

The company's engineer was George Stephenson; the engines which were Nos. 1 and 2, were ordered by the minute of 16th September 1824, which we have previously quoted; the first engine was delivered in time for use at the opening of the line in September 1825, the second was delivered in November of the same year. Meanwhile the sub-committee minutes record on 30th September 1825 :—

Resolved that Robert Stephenson & Co. be requested to make an offer to this Company to build other two Locomotive Engines and to state the time they will undertake to have the same completed and delivered respectively at Darlington.

These engines were Nos. 3 and 4; the first was delivered in April 1826, the second in May of the same year.

We have an intervening reference to another locomotive, in a sub-committee minute of 25th November 1825 :—

Timothy Hackworth reports that he saw a Locomotive Engine on sale belonging to Mr. Wilson, of Newcastle. The price he asks is £380, to come on trial for 1 month, a suitable person coming along with it to witness the same.

Resolved that this Company take the same on trial for 1 month, and it is accordingly ordered.

Assuming the completeness of these sub-committee records Wilson's engine was the fifth bought by the company; all authorities agree that it

[1] Tomlinson, *The North Eastern Railway*, 1914, p. 142, and earlier writers.

proved unsuccessful and was eventually rebuilt, or rather that parts of it were used in the construction of a new engine, the 'Royal George,' which commenced work in November 1827, and eventually bore the company's No. 5. Detailed statements have been made and elaborate drawings published to show Wilson's engine as originally built, but none of these are contemporary and all must be discounted as largely imaginary.

Now between 25th November 1825, and 9th November 1827, there is no further reference in the sub-committee minutes to the trial or purchase of any new engine, and it is therefore difficult to understand the Prussian engineers statement that early in 1827 there were five in operation and a sixth in reserve. It seems possible that in referring to a sixth there may have been a confusion with an engine which was being constructed to the designs of Hackworth at the time of their visit ; to this engine we shall refer later.

CONDITIONS OF WORKING The reporters record the differences of opinion which they found as to the relative advantages of traction by horses and locomotives respectively, and we can perhaps find in this question which was exercising the minds of the directors, one of the foundations for the story to which we have already referred and which still has a wide currency—that the first locomotives of the Stockton and Darlington Railway had failed the company and were to be abandoned. It is clear that though the greater economy of steam compared with horse traction had been proved for colliery purposes at Wylam, Killingworth and Hetton under the conditions prevailing at these places, the directors of the Stockton and Darlington Railway at the beginning of 1827 were not satisfied on this point ; later however, in a *Report of the Committee to the Proprietors*, they definitely state, on 10th July 1827 :—

It may be satisfactory to the general meeting to be informed, as a result of the strict scrutiny into the subject, that there appears to be a saving of nearly 30 per cent. in favour of haulage performed by locomotive engines, when compared with its being done by horses.

It must be noted that this economy had been proved under conditions of joint working most disadvantageous to the locomotive ; there appears to be some reference to these conditions in a letter written by Edward Pease to William James on 3rd February 1826 in which he stated that [1] :—

. . . . the Stockton and Darlington Railway had been open four months—they ran a daily coach carrying twenty to thirty passengers drawn by one horse . . . . they had placed locomotive engines on the line for the haulage of coals only, before it was either creditable to them or of advantage to the Company.

The line had in fact been originally intended for horse traffic only and for some years it was a public highway on which horse trains might be privately operated by persons who paid the company's tolls. It is difficult to imagine more awkward conditions under which to operate the company's locomotives, indeed these conditions seriously handicapped the working of the traffic and

[1] *The Two James's and the Two Stephensons*, p. 47.

retarded the development of the locomotive on the Stockton and Darlington Railway until the use of horses was eventually prohibited by the company.

LOCOMOTIVES AT WORK We have now to consider the Prussian engineers' description of the locomotives actually at work at the time of their visit. All these engines had been built by Robert Stephenson & Co.

[Translation.]

REMARKS ON THE CONSTRUCTION OF LOCOMOTIVES WHICH ARE IN USE ON THE DARLINGTON RAILWAY.

CYLINDERS The steam cylinders that supply the moving power stand perpendicular partly in the steam boiler and their upper ends project 12 inches exclusive of the flange.

BOILER The boiler is cylindrical of plate $\frac{1}{2}$ inch thick, $11\frac{1}{2}$ feet long and $4\frac{1}{2}$ feet diam. provided with a furnace 25 inches diam., which lies 2 inches distant from the bottom; this contains in front the grate and at the opposite end finishes in the chimney which projects about 8 feet above the boiler. Another boiler serving for a similar locomotive is cylindrical 10 feet 10 inches long, closed at one end by a hemisphere and at the other end by a cast iron plate. Its diam. is 4 feet 4 inches; the furnace 26 inches diam. does not however lie in the centre but more towards one side and is joined by a semi-circular formed end to a return tube $18\frac{1}{2}$ inches diam. which enters into the chimney at the end where the firing takes place.

FRAME The boiler rests by means of four short pipes or supports (which have at the upper part flanges formed to the curvature of the boiler and below horizontal flanges) on a cast iron frame that is 8 feet $2\frac{1}{2}$ inches long, 3 feet 7 inches wide and $8\frac{1}{2}$ inches by $1\frac{1}{12}$ inch section.

AXLES Immediately under the supports lie the axles either both in cast iron tubes or one in one such tube and the other in plain-bearings. The axles are round $3\frac{1}{2}$-$3\frac{3}{4}$ inches diam. with a total length of 5 feet 2 inches.

WHEELS The wheels have been constructed, after many trials, in a lasting manner, as it is specially difficult to prepare large wheels for waggons on railways. These consist of two parts, an inner and an outer part, of cast iron and fastened together with wooden wedges. The naves are round, internally bored accurately according to the diameter of the axles, and they are fastened by keys let half into one and half into the other. The d ameter of the inner part of the wheel is 30 inches that of the outer with the tread 47 inches. The depth of the nave is 5 inches; the width of the inner part of the wheel is 4 inches. This has 12 spokes $\frac{7}{12}$ to $\frac{3}{4}$ inch thick, which increase in width towards the middle. The spokes are bound together by a ring of 17 to $18\frac{3}{4}$ inches diam. In the outer circumference semi-circular notches of $1\frac{5}{6}$ to 2 inches diam. are arranged in the direction of each spoke so that exactly similar notches in the inner circumference of the outer wheel exactly coincide and wooden wedges are driven in, in order in this manner to bind together both parts. The tread is in new wheels $4\frac{1}{8}$ inch wide and conical diminishing towards the front $\frac{1}{6}$ of an inch. The thickness of metal is in front $1\frac{1}{4}$ inch and behind $1\frac{5}{8}$ inch. The flange projects three-quarters of an inch and the whole breadth of the wheel inclusive of the flange amounts to $5\frac{5}{6}$ inches; in some old wheels this is only $4\frac{1}{2}$ inches.

CRANKS AND COUPLING In the inner part a hole is arranged in which to set the crank pin to which the connecting rod of the cylinder is attached; the length of the crank arm is $11\frac{3}{4}$ inches; in another locomotive it is 10 inches. Through the connecting rods one pair of wheels is connected with one cylinder and the other pair with the other cylinder. But since one cylinder must always stand at half stroke in relation to the other the wheels on one side of the locomotive are connected by horizontal coupling rods, and accordingly the crank pins are arranged so that on two of the wheels standing opposite to one another diagonally, curved arms for the horizontal coupling rods are employed. The distance apart of the wheel centres is 5 feet 1 inch (in other cases 5 feet 3 inches).

CONNECTING RODS

The connecting rods have a length of 8 feet and are, in common with the whole arrangement of the straight line motion of the piston rods, of wrought iron. These (*i.e.* piston rods) constitute with the latter a cross which is at the end point of a half beam whose fulcrum is movable, and can follow the straight line motion through the working of counter rods. These half beams are double $33\frac{1}{4}$ inches long; the counter rods are 15 inches long and the lever for the movement of the fulcrum of the half beam is $28\frac{1}{2}$ inches high. The fixed points for these different rods are arranged above on the boiler and stand out from the cylinder towards the middle.

VALVE GEAR

The valve gear of the cylinder works through perpendicular valves; the steam surrounds the valve. The pipe which leads the exhaust steam to the chimney into the atmosphere opens under the slide valve. The movement of the valve is 2 inches. In order to achieve this there are in the middle of the horizontal coupling rods of the locomotive wheels perpendicular coupling rods which are in connection above with cranks standing at right angles on a shaft which moves equally with the locomotive wheels and with the strokes of the cylinder. This shaft is the common valve shaft for both cylinders. On it are two excentrics, which are not fast upon it but are movable round it and driven by hooks which engage in cut-out quadrants in them. In this way in order to make the engine go backwards and forwards the excentrics, or rather the hooks by which they are moved, stand on the shaft at a right angle. From each excentric leads the driving rod, which can be put in and out of gear with the lever arms which move the valves. This method of reversing the piston stroke is the simplest and renders unnecessary many valve rods, which were formerly required in the application of the excentric. With this arrangement the change in the direction of going can be undertaken with one cylinder, the other cylinder helping to come in, in order to bring the crank pins over the dead points.

On both sides of the boiler there is a platform 9 inches wide for the locomotive attendant; this lies just above the wheels. On one side there is a still higher plank by which all the parts of the machine can be got at and the valve gear looked to.

PUMP

The force pump which feeds the boiler with water is arranged on the side of the boiler and is moved by a rod which is attached to one of the half beams. From this pump a leather hose leads to the water tank which is arranged on the waggon coupled next to the locomotive and therefrom the boiler is fed.

GENERAL

The cylinders are high pressure engines without condensation, the exhaust steam being discharged without further ado into the atmosphere.

It appears therefore that the construction of these locomotives is in general very simple. There are two steam cylinders in order to achieve rotary motion without a flywheel through simple coupling of the locomotive wheels with the piston rods. The steam cylinders are of the simplest construction, double acting without condensation. In practice it is particularly objectionable that many of the moving parts get out of repair, to which result the continual rattling during the motion of the engine contributes. This is principally produced by the fact that it is scarcely possible to retain four points of the rails on which the wheels of the locomotive rest continuously in one plane, so that the parts of the locomotive must give somewhat in order that they may be able to find their proper bearing.

We find in this account a good general description of the first four locomotives, and the principal dimensions given agree closely, though not exactly, with those of No. I engine, or as shown by the makers' original drawing. The account also shows that by 1827 one at least of these first four Stephenson engines had been fitted with a simple return flue[1]; it also confirms the statement, made many years later[2], that some of these engines had a valve gear different

---

[1] Later double return flues were fitted:—De Pambour, *A Practical Treatise on Locomotive Engines*, 1836, p. 343. Observations. 'No. 1 Engine,' 'Locomotion,' 'Boiler with a flue and two returning tubes. (This engine to-day has a single flue, as originally.)

[2] J. W. Hackworth, letter to *The Engineer*, 1857, Vol. IV., p. 115.

from that still to be seen on the old engine preserved at Darlington, on which the valves are worked by a single excentric on one of the main axles. The curious arrangement of the axle for one pair of wheels, mentioned by the Prussian engineers, is shown on the makers' original drawing; it was evidently intended to provide a three-point support for the engine, in an attempt to ensure contact at all times between the four wheels and the rails. Some writers state or imply that these first engines of the Stockton and Darlington Railway had steam 'springs'[1], but there is no suggestion of this in the Prussian report, and the existing engine has the axle journals carried by brackets of bent bar fixed to the underside of the boiler; there are no evidences on No. I. of either 'springs,' frame, or swivelling axle.

Coming now to the later locomotives, the Prussian engineers unfortunately give no description of either the fifth engine, which they say was at work, or of the sixth, in reserve; most writers describe the railway company's sixth engine as having been built in 1826, with outside cylinders carried on the boiler at the fire end, inclined downwards and driving directly on to the leading pair of six coupled wheels. But all the evidence available to us shows that this cylinder arrangement was not adopted until 1828, when it was first applied by Robert Stephenson & Co. to the 'Lancashire Witch,' an engine with which we shall deal fully later. Here we have to note the complete silence of the Prussian report on a design which, if in existence at the time of their visit, would have been remarkably in advance of anything they have recorded as seen at Darlington. So far therefore they have not enlightened us on the 'experiment', whatever it was, which led to such a name being given later engine No. 6, but we shall now deal with a portion of their report which offers valuable evidence towards the identification of this engine.

[*Translation.*]

LOCOMOTIVES OF STEPHENSON AND DICKINSON (*sic*) AT NEWCASTLE.

In the works of Stephenson and Dickinson (*sic*) at Newcastle there has been built recently (at the beginning of 1827) a locomotive which so far has had no trial on the large scale although it has already been proved in the workshop. In its construction and highly careful execution, it appears to surpass the present practice. Also regard is being paid to a better use of the fuel. Besides changes in the construction of the fire grate and the boiler, there is this essential difference that the cylinders lie horizontally entirely in the boiler.

BOILER The boiler is of iron plate with a strong cast iron front plate; it is cylindrical 13 feet long and 4 feet diam., in it lies, a few inches above the bottom, a fire tube of 2 feet 3 inches diam., wherein at the front end lies the fire grate and which at the back communicates with a chimney of 20 inches diam. and 16 feet high which by means of a slide can be raised 8 feet higher. On the under curvature of the chimney there is a flap which is fastened by cotters and can easily be removed in order to clean the chimney and the fire tube.

WATER TUBES
AND DRUM The grate consists of eight hollow wrought iron tubes $1\frac{1}{2}$ inches inside diam. $\frac{1}{4}$ inch thick and 4 feet long. These open at the front end into a box of cast iron in which on the front surface there are eight openings which are closed with screws and serve for cleaning the grate bars. At the back end these grate bars open into a round tube of 20 inches diam. which lies in the fire tube; it is $3\frac{1}{2}$ (*sic*) feet long and reaches as far as underneath the chimney. This latter is in communi-

---

[1] (*a*) Coste and Perdonnet, *Annales des Mines*, second series, Vol. VI., 1829, p. 199. (*b*) De Pambour, *A Practical Treatise on Locomotive Engines*, 1836, p. 38.

cation with the upper part of the boiler through a rectangular opening which goes through the upper part of the combustion chamber. The boiler itself is in communication with the front iron box through two curved pieces of tube. The grate bars are filled with water and constitute part of the boiler; also the fire tube constitutes an annulus which inside and outside is filled with water.

CYLINDERS The cylinders lie over the fire tube in the boiler and are 9 inches diam. by about 2½-3 feet stroke. They are bolted by their flanges to the cast iron front plate of the boiler. They are united with one another by a cast iron piece through which steam is led to the slide valves and whose opening, close under the crown of the boiler, is provided with a valve moveable from outside in order to regulate the entry of the steam.

FEED HEATER The waste steam flows from the cylinders through an iron tube lying in the boiler towards the chimney where both these tubes are bent upwards. Before the curved part there leads out a descending tube which opens into a small water tank lying under the chimney. This is used as a feed heater, from which the force pump, situated on the side of the boiler, lifts the feed water. In this way part of the exhaust steam is further utilized.

DRIVING AND VALVE GEAR The piston rod is fastened to the middle of a short arm whose ends are in connection with the half beams above and below. On the axis of the upper beam there is at the outer end a somewhat shorter lever arm which through a connecting rod is united to the wheel of the locomotive. On the axle of the locomotive moved in this manner are the excentrics which, through several coupling rods, set in motion the valves lying likewise inside the boiler. The bearings of the upper half beam are arranged on the front iron plate and on the cast iron frame which carries the whole boiler.

WHEELS AND COUPLING The wheels, and their connection by horizontal coupling rods, are arranged as in the locomotives previously described.

This locomotive shares the improvements in those designed for the Darlington Railway, with some not inconsiderable additions.

The principal faults of the locomotives at present are still that they are not constructed sufficiently durable and therefore require many repairs. This locomotive works with 45-52 pounds per square inch on the cylinder area, and in doing so is said to perform the duty of 15 horse-power.

AN 'EXPERIMENT' Firstly we note the obviously experimental nature of the engine described; it had water-tube firebars, and an internal water drum, both novel attempts to increase the heating surface. But most remarkable are the horizontal cylinders. It is possible to reconstruct the engine on the information given, though there is a discrepancy between the length given for the boiler—13 feet—and the part lengths given for the grate bars and the water drum; the sum of these two lengths amounts only to 7 feet 6 inches implying a boiler length of about 8 feet, but since the object of the design is clearly an increase in heating surface we may assume the shorter length given to be incorrect, since it would afford a total heating surface actually less than was obtainable with the return flue as fitted to one of the first four engines.

The account given above agrees with a description of the Stockton and Darlington Railway Company's engine 'Experiment' published many years later that [1] :—

It ran on four wheels four feet in diameter; the cylinders were placed horizontally half in the boiler and fastened to the flue; action between the piston rod and crank pin outside the wheels was made by means of levers.

[1] Links in the History of the Locomotive, *The Engineer*, 1879, Vol. XLIX., p. 322

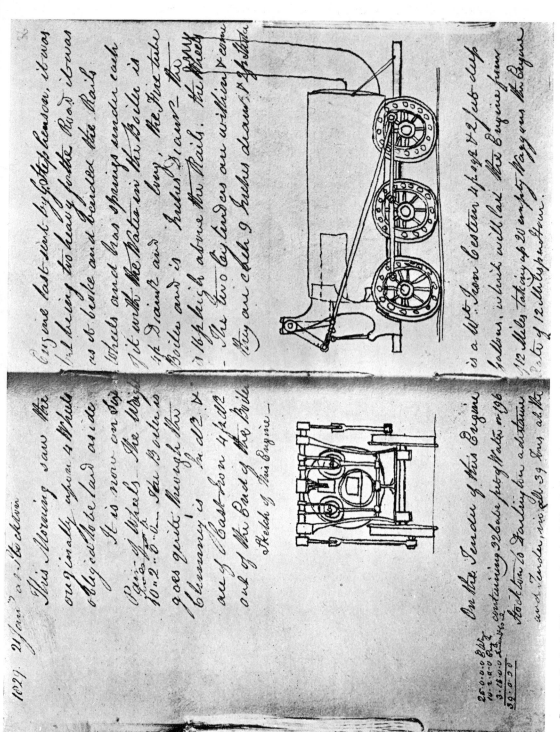

from Rastrick's Notebook, 1829, preserved in the Goldsmith Company's Economic Library, University of London.

THE 'EXPERIMENT'

completed by Robert Stephenson & Co. early in 1827, supplied to the Stockton and Darlington Railway in 1828 on four wheels, afterwards fitted with a new frame, springs, and an additional pair of wheels.

Now the Prussian engineers saw this locomotive in Robert Stephenson & Co's. works at Newcastle early in 1827, but the firm possesses no record of its delivery to the Stockton and Darlington Railway. There is however evidence in one of Hackworth's notebooks [1] that an engine on four wheels, which he called the 'Quadrant,' or 'Lever' engine, came on to the line at the end of January 1828. Hackworth further records that this engine, being found to be too heavy for the road, was ordered to be laid off, and that in May 1828 he was making arrangements with the makers to have it placed upon six wheels and springs.

Now a railway company's sub-committee minute of 28th March 1828 records that it was:—

Ordered that the last engine from Newcastle be laid off until it be placed on six wheels.

And on 4th July 1828 the sub-committee:—

Resolved that the last locomotive engine purchased by the Company shall be wholly laid aside until the alteration prescribed of placing it on six wheels be carried into effect, its weight having been proved to be too great for the strength of the Company's rails.

On the following day they were informed that R. Stephenson & Co. were pushing their six-wheel frame as much as possible, and the altered engine appears to have been at work before 31st October 1828, when the sub-committee records:—

From an accurate observation of the locomotive with six wheels and springs the Committee have every reason to be satisfied the same is a great improvement. It is resolved Timothy Hackworth be directed to attend to having a similar improvement made in all our engines as early as possible.

This minute suggests that the rebuilt experimental engine, though not the first of the company's engines to be carried on six wheels, may have been the first to be fitted with springs, and the fact that Hackworth went to Killingworth at the railway company's expense 'to see the locomotive engine with springs and malleable iron rims' [2] seems to confirm that the first useful application of plate springs had been by Nicholas Wood, some time after 1825, as was undoubtedly the first adoption of wrought iron tyres.[3]

A synopsis of the evidence which we had obtained in the course of our present enquiry, suggested the identity of the 'Lever' engine with the horizontal cylinder engine built by Robert Stephenson & Co. in 1827. Fortunately this question has now been placed beyond doubt by the recent discovery of a notebook [4] containing a sketch made on 1st January 1829 by J. U. Rastrick, who with James Walker, another engineer, visited the Stockton and Darlington

---

[1] In the possession of his grandson, Mr. Robert Young, by whose permission quotation is now made.

[2] Tomlinson, *The North Eastern Railway*, p. 144.

[3] Wood, *Treatise on Railroads*, 1831, p. 145—'About four years ago I had a rim or tire of wrought iron put upon one set of the Killingworth engine wheels . . . the trial being so very satisfactory the Bedlington Iron Company were induced to erect a pair of rolls for the purpose of rolling the tires by machinery . . . the first set of tires from which are still at work on one of the Killingworth engines; since that time similar tires have been extensively used not only for locomotive engine wheels but also for the wheels of common carriages on public Railways.'

[4] In the Rastrick Collection, preserved at The Goldsmith Company's Economic Library, London University.

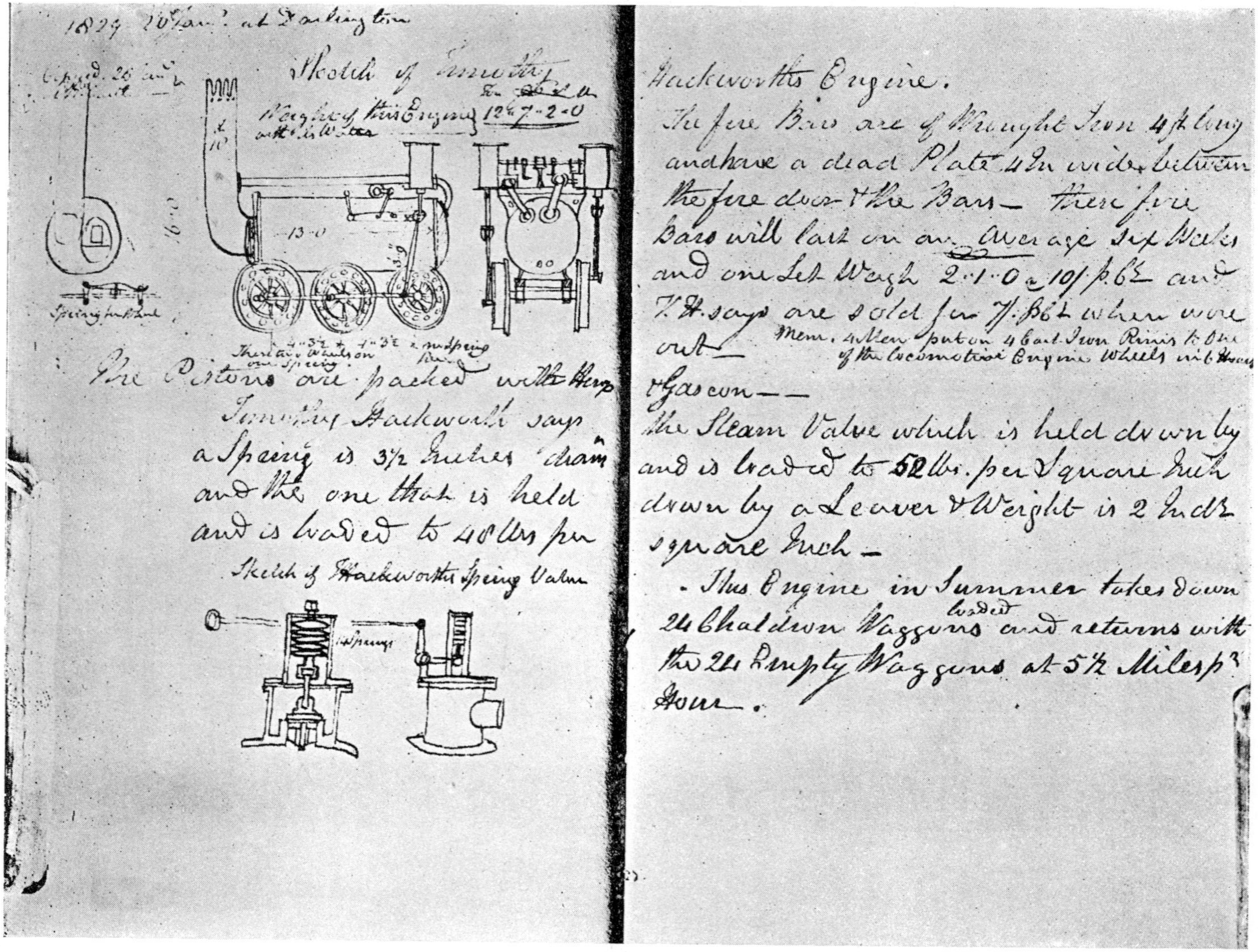

from Rastrick's Notebook, 1829, preserved in the Goldsmith Company's Economic Library, University of London.

THE 'ROYAL GEORGE'

Railway for the purpose of making a report to the Liverpool and Manchester Railway Company on the comparative merits of fixed and locomotive engines.[1]

Rastrick's note-book contains the following record :—

This morning saw the engine last sent by G. Stephenson, it was originally upon four wheels, but being too heavy for the road it was obliged to be laid aside as it broke and bended the rails. It is now on six wheels and has springs under each pair of wheels. The weight of it with the water in the boiler is 10 t. 2 c. 0 q. The boiler is 4 feet diam. and .... long. The fire-tube goes quite through the boiler and is .... inches diam. The chimney is .... in. dr., and is 16 feet high above the rails. The wheels are of cast iron 4 feet dr. . . . . The two cylinders are each 9 inches diam. and 2 feet stroke.

On the tender of this engine is a wt. iron cistern 4 feet square and 2 feet deep containing 32 cubic feet water or 196 gallons, which will last the engine from Stockton to Darlington a distance of 12 miles, taking up 20 empty waggons, the engine and tender, in all 39 tons at the rate of 12 miles per hour.

It is to be regretted that Rastrick omitted to fill in the very dimensions for the boiler on which the Prussian engineers too have left us in doubt. In other respects, except for the alteration from four to six wheels, his sketch and their description are in close agreement.

The 'Experiment,' now for the first time brought fully to light, is one of the most remarkable engines built by Robert Stephenson & Co., it is the first recorded rail locomotive with two horizontal cylinders, and the first which we know to have had the drives from the two cylinders combined on one axle.

LOCOMOTIVES PROJECTED

Those portions of the Prussian engineers' account which we have quoted have described engines which they actually saw at work or completed early in 1827. We have now to consider their report on some designs for locomotives, of which one at any rate was constructed at the railway company's works at Shildon, by Timothy Hackworth who, on the recommendation of George Stephenson, had been appointed in 1825 to the position of locomotive superintendent.[2] At the time of the Prussian engineers' visit Stephenson and Hackworth appear as the only two men seriously working for the development and improvement of the locomotive.

[Translation.]

LOCOMOTIVES WHICH HAVE BEEN DESIGNED FOR THE DARLINGTON RAILWAY.

At the beginning of 1827 they were busy with the construction of some other locomotives. The designs prepared were communicated to us by Mr. Hackworth, mechanician in the service of the Railway Company.

The changes in prospect are that both cylinders are not to be tandem but side by side; that they are not to stand in the boiler but on a cast iron frame over or in front of the boiler; that the piston rods are not to work upwards but downwards. Both cylinders are to engage with one pair of wheels on one axle and the second pair of wheels is to be connected with the first by horizontal coupling rods. Thereby the construction will be in many ways simpler and the whole more secure.

(I) In one project the locomotive has four wheels. The wheel base is $5\frac{1}{2}$ feet, the boiler is 9 feet long and is $4\frac{1}{2}$ feet diam., each cylinder is $10\frac{1}{2}$ inches diam., by 22 inches stroke; the

---

[1] Liverpool and Manchester Railway Directors' Minute, 17th November 1828.

[2] Stockton and Darlington Railway Sub-Committee Minute, 13th May 1825.

length of the connecting rod is 3 feet 2 inches; the length of the half beam at the end of which the piston and connecting rod are connected is 3 feet; the radius arm for the fulcrum of this half beam is 17 inches. The valve gear shaft for both cylinders hangs over the boiler and is moved in similar fashion by the half beam as in the first locomotive described. The cylinder centres stand vertically over the crank pins in the wheels and are $5\frac{1}{2}$ feet distant from one another.

(2) The second project departs from the previous one only in that the locomotive has six wheels in order to offer more supporting points to the boiler and to increase the rolling friction of the engine as its useful effect subsists therein. In order that these wheels shall always be able to bear on the rails, only the pair of wheels on which the connecting rods work are constrained by the bearings on the locomotive. The other bearings are carried by levers so that the wheels can adjust themselves to the small unevenesses of the road. The wheel centres are 4 feet 3 inches distant from one another. The boiler is 12 feet 10 inches long, 4 feet 5 inches diam., each cylinder is 10 inches diam. and 22 inches stroke. The locomotive wheels, inclusive of the flanges are 50 inches diam.

(3) In the third project the cylinders stand in front of the boiler, the connecting rods go out upwards. The cylinder centres stand $5\frac{1}{2}$ feet apart; the cylinder is 9 inches diam. and the stroke 3 feet; but the connecting rods are situated closer to the fulcrum of the beam and have therefore only 2 feet stroke. The whole length of the beam amounts to 8 feet, the length of the connecting rods $6\frac{1}{2}$ feet. The engine has six wheels which are arranged as in the second project; the centres of the wheels are 4 feet 4 inches apart. The boiler is 13 feet long and is 4 feet 3 inches diam. The cylinders stand on the same plate on which the boiler rests and on which are the bearings for the axles of the wheels. These are connected with one another by horizontal coupling rods. One sees in this project what has not been proved in practice hitherto in the usual construction of locomotives, namely, the position of the cylinders.

THE 'ROYAL GEORGE.' Of the three projects described above, the second is clearly for the engine afterwards called the 'Royal George,' which was put to work in November 1827; there is no evidence that either of the other engines described was completed. The 'Royal George' has been often illustrated and described, but, as in the case of the 'Experiment,' a recently discovered sketch by Rastrick, made in 1829, is the earliest pictorial record which we know of this engine; that the commonly accepted drawing is of much later date is shown by the form and height of the chimney.

This engine must be specially mentioned here as an important link in the evolution of the locomotive between Stephenson's 'Experiment,' completed early in 1827, and the 'Lancashire Witch' of little more than a year later. But it is now established that the 'Royal George' was not, as has been hitherto supposed, the first locomotive to combine the drive from the two cylinders on one axle; it was however the first of which we have any contemporary record to show this combination with a direct drive from the cylinders to the crank pins. The elimination of the levers adopted by Stephenson for the 'Experiment' was another important step towards simplification, though the vertical arrangement of cylinders in the 'Royal George' was a continuance of a practice from which Stephenson was evidently trying already to break.

The 'Royal George' embodied some other innovations, and the Prussian engineers' description is generally in agreement with what is recorded elsewhere of this engine, but their account makes no mention of springs. Indeed they refer to the bearings of the coupled wheels as being carried by levers, and it is possible that these may have been at first in use and later replaced by springs, after

Hackworth's visit to Killingworth and before the engine was seen by Rastrick. There is no doubt that, whatever the details of the design, the 'Royal George' when first put to work was the most powerful locomotive anywhere in service [1], and on account of greater weight and heating surface it was capable of a heavier duty than the first four Stephenson engines on the Stockton and Darlington Railway. We can however find no evidence for two statements which have had a wide currency and credence [2]:—

(1) That it was 'the first to exceed in efficiency the working of horses.'
(2) That it 'decided the question of locomotive practicability' and 'finally and forever settled the expediency of the locomotive and railway system.'

So far as the working of the Stockton and Darlington Railway was concerned the first statement is disproved by the committee's report of 10th July 1827, and we may note that the experiments on which they had ascertained a 30 per cent. economy of steam as compared with horse traction had been carried out by the four Stephenson engines five months before the 'Royal George' was put to work.

In regard to the second statement it appears that the success of the 'Royal George' did not dispose of rumours that the locomotives were to be abandoned, for we find Robert Stephenson writing to Hackworth from Liverpool under date 7th July 1828 [3]:—

The directors having heard here, by some channel or other, not favourable to the locomotive engines, that there has always been a great number of horses on the line, and that the horses were beating the engines off—in answer to this I understood you to say, that at one time you had completely run the horses off, but in consequence of the late accident and the heavy engine being laid aside, you had been obliged to employ horses again. Was not this the sole cause of the horses being employed? and was there not an instance, a little while ago, of the horses being entirely removed from the line of road? Please write by return of post, or, at all events, at your earliest convenience, answers to these queries. I cannot wonder at the travelling engine having so much to contend, when I come in contact with enemies to them every hour; and they prove to be enemies without reason, they oppose the engines merely because certain things have been said against them.

And for some time afterwards, indeed until after the Rainhill trials in October 1829, both the engineers who were deputed by the Liverpool and Manchester Railway Company to report on the performance of the Stockton and Darlington engines, and others of the engineering profession, with the public generally, remained unconvinced of the suitability of locomotives for public railways. We find Robert Stephenson writing to Hackworth so late as 17th March 1829 [4]:—

The reports of the engineers who visited the North to ascertain the relative merits of the two systems of steam machinery now employed on railways, have come to conclusions in favour of stationary engines. . . . they state it positively as their opinion that a locomotive

---

[1] James Walker, *Report on the Comparative Merits of Locomotive and Fixed Engines*, 1829 :—'Hackworth's engine is undoubtedly the most powerful that has yet been made, the boiler is longer, with a returned or double flue ; there are six wheels and the weight is increased nearly in the proportion of the power.' (The 'Royal George' weighed 12 tons 7½ cwt., the Stephenson engines about 8 tons 5 cwt. The nominal capacity of the 'Royal George' was therefore about 50 per cent. greater.)

[2] *A Chapter in the History of Railway Locomotion*, p. 35.　　　[3] *Ibid.*, p. 5.　　　[4] *Ibid.*, p. 6.

engine of 10 horse-power, or say of the usual size, will not convey more than 10 tons, exclusive of the waggons, at the rate of 10 miles per hour in the winter time, and in summer the same engine will take 13½ tons. . . . . will you be kind enough to state at what speed your own engine returns from Stockton with a given number of empty waggons, and the rates of ascent? . . . also at what speed the six-wheeled engine made by R. S. & Co. will return with any given number of waggons?

To these and other questions Hackworth replied in a lengthy letter from which we can only quote briefly [1] :—

The statement you allude to, that a complete locomotive will take but 10 tons at 10 miles per hour, is quite at variance with facts; as an opinion merely, this I would forgive. Four of waggons, laden for depots, frequently take from 12 to 13 tons of coals, exclusive of the waggons, Our engines never take less than 16 laden waggons in winter, and in summer from 20 to 24 and 32 laden, and can maintain a speed of five miles per hour, except in case of stoppages by means of horse waggons at the passing places. Engines thus loaded have frequently travelled at nine miles per hour, sometimes more. It is unsafe to aim at speed upon a single line of railway, the danger is at the passing places. I am verily convinced that a swift engine, upon a well-conditioned railway, will combine profit and simplicity, and will afford such facility as has not hitherto been known.

I am well satisfied that an engine of the weight you mention, will convey, on a level, in winter, 30 tons of goods, 10 miles per hour, exclusive of carriages, and 40 tons in summer, exclusive of carriages. The six-wheeled engine fitted up at the company's works, generally takes 24 waggons, 53 cwt. to three tons of coals each, speed five miles per hour, empty waggons 24 cwts. each. The six wheels by R. Stephenson & Co.—20 waggons, five miles per hour, weight as above.

As to my general opinion as to the locomotive system, I believe it is comparatively in a state of infancy. Swift engines upon a double way, I am convinced, may be used to the utmost advantage. Improvements upon anything yet produced, of greater importance in all respects, are clearly practicable; and I am sure this will prove itself by actual remuneration to such parties as prudently, yet diligently, pursue the execution of this kind of power, with their eyes open to those alterations and advantages which actual demonstration of local circumstances point out.

After expressing his opinion as to the unsuitability of stationary engines for public railways, and commenting on the rumoured decision of the Liverpool and Manchester Company to use fixed engines, Hackworth concludes :—

Do not discompose yourself, my dear Sir; if you express your manly, firm, decided opinion, you have done your part as their adviser. And if it happened to be read some day in the newspapers—'Whereas the Liverpool and Manchester Railway has been strangled by ropes,'—we shall not accuse you of guilt in being accessory either before or after the fact.

Very noticeable in Hackworth's letter is his firm faith in the future of the locomotive, and we find no suggestion in his reply that the early engines were not doing their share of the work; indeed the performances quoted agree with those given by the Prussian engineers and by Walker respectively.[2] It is indeed remarkable that the 'Royal George,' with its much greater nominal capacity, should not have performed a greater proportionate duty; but in common with the other engines it had to work under the great disadvantages

[1] *A Chapter in the History of Railway Locomotion*, p. 7.

[2] James Walker, *Report on the Comparative Merits of Locomotive and Fixed Engines*, 1829.

described both by Hackworth, in the letter we have just quoted, and by Robert Stephenson writing in 1830[1]:—

Scarcely a single journey is performed by these engines without being interrupted by the horses or other trains of carriages passing in a contrary direction there being only a single line of road with passing places. At each end of the distance traversed by the engines great delay is occasioned from the irregular supply of carriages which from the nature of the trade and other local circumstances it is impossible to avoid.

Referring now to the economies claimed for it, we may note that the driver of the 'Royal George' was paid at the same rate as the drivers of the older engines, one farthing per ton per mile, and an analysis of the leaders' books for the year 1828 again confirms that, whatever its maximum capacity, the 'Royal George' in normal service hauled a load about 30 per cent. only in excess of the loads hauled by the older and much smaller engines.[2]

Name of Engineman.	No. of days employed.	Gross Earnings.			Deduction for Fire Bars.			Net Earnings.			Average amount per day.		
		£	s.	d.	£	s.	d.	£	s.	d.	£	s.	d.
James Stephenson	260	263	0	10	8	2	10	254	18	0	0	19	7
Robert Morrow	271	285	12	6	9	3	4	276	9	2	1	0	8
William Gowland	269	354	4	7	9	5	0	344	19	7	1	5	8
Michael Law	244	278	1	10	8	6	0	269	15	10	1	2	1
John Cree	125	125	12	11	4	1	6	121	11	5	0	19	5
Edward Corner	79	77	12	0	2	9	8	75	2	4	0	19	0
		1,384	4	8	41	8	4	1,342	16	4			

Of these six engines, five had been built by Robert Stephenson & Co., one of them being the 'Experiment.' Gowland's engine is known to have been the 'Royal George,' and a comparison of his earnings with those of the other drivers gives one obvious reason for the popularity of his engine, and for the local tradition which still maintains that it was the 'first successful locomotive.'

For an independent account of the capabilities of the earlier four-wheeled engines built by Robert Stephenson & Co. we have a contemporary record by Rastrick of his 'observations at Darlington' on January 17th, 1829. He states that the engine on four wheels driven by James Stephenson (brother of George Stephenson) 'has gone 600 miles per week with 20 waggons.' He meets 'Mr. Pease senior and junior, Otley and Tulley,' who tell him that:—

The Company contracted with the men who manage the locomotive engines at ¼d. per ton per mile, who find coal, oil and tallow, hemp and assistance as well as oil and grease for coal waggons in his train; the Company do all repairs and find engines and waggons. During the winter the average load has been 20 waggons each 53 cwt. of coal and 25 cwt. waggon. . . . . . . Mr. Otley thinks ⅛th of a penny per ton per mile will cover all the expenses of wear and tear of engines and wheels and all other parts of the engine. The price of taking coal by horse-power is ½d. per ton per mile.

Not only is there no discrimination between the cost per ton mile performance of the six-wheeled, as compared with the four-wheeled engines, but one of these

---

[1] *Observations on the Comparative Merits of Locomotive and Fixed Engines*, 1829.

[2] Tomlinson, *The North Eastern Railway*, p. 151.

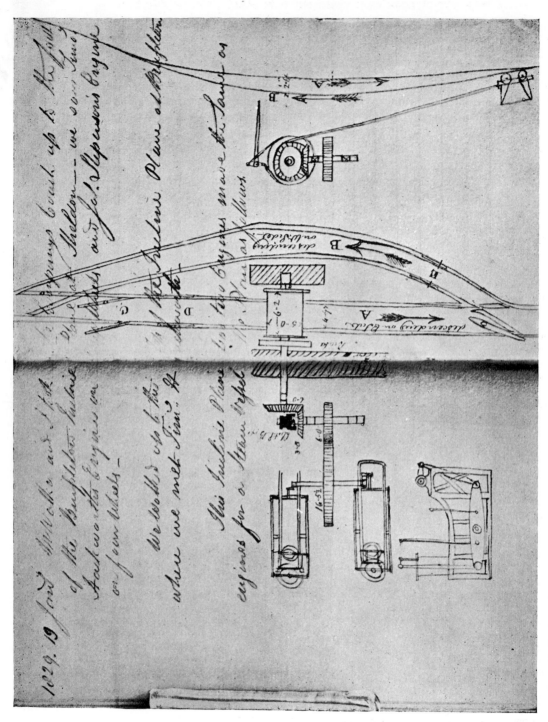

from *Rastrick's Notebook*, 1829, *preserved in the Goldsmith Company's Economic Library, University of London.*

THE STATIONARY ENGINES FOR THE BRUSSELTON INCLINE

is shown to be good for six hundred miles in one week—a remarkable record at that time.

STATIONARY
ENGINES
We now come to the concluding portion of the Prussian engineers' report on the Stockton and Darlington Railway, dealing with the stationary engines for working the inclines at Brusselton and Etherley; these engines had been ordered in October 1823, at a cost of £3,482 15s. od. and £1,982 15s. od., respectively, and the drawings for the Brusselton engines had been finished by Robert Stephenson just before leaving for Columbia in June 1824.[1] Since these engines were among the first built by Robert Stephenson & Co., and had many features of interest, we quote in full the report on their design and working ; its value is enhanced by a sketch made by Rastrick in 1829.[2]

[Translation.]

TRACTION ON THE INCLINED PLANES.

At Greenfield on the high ground between two inclined planes are erected two steam engines of Watt type working together, of 21 inches diam. (cylinder), which together are adequate to the development of 30 horse-power.   Two similar engines, each of 30 inches diam. cylinder and together of 60 horse-power are erected in a similar manner at Brusselton.

The Brusselton as well as the Greenfield engines draw up each at one time 8 loaded waggons holding a chaldron of coal; as soon as these have reached the high ground they are lowered together by means of a brake arrangement.   The descending waggons could have been used as a counter balance for those which are to be drawn up; this, however, does not take place since the steam engines have adequate power and the waiting of one load for another only occasions a halt.   The steam engines would be able without difficulty to draw up 12 loaded waggons at one time.

The whole load to be raised or lowered amounts to :—

8 empty waggons....	160 cwt.
8 chaldrons of coal of 53 cwt.	424 ,,
Total	584 ,,

This load is made fast to a rope 7¼ inches circumference (2⅜ inches diam.) which is wound on a cylindrical drum.

The Brusselton engine is 5 feet stroke and makes about 20 revolutions per minute, which gives $20 \times 1.822 = 36.44$ revolutions of the rope drum.   The rope drum can be reckoned to have a mean diameter of 5½ feet and hence winds on 207·6 yards of rope per minute.   The longest inclined plane of 1,851 yards is therefore surmounted in 8 minutes 57 seconds.   The engine can however go considerably faster and this length can be travelled even in 6 minutes.

The steam engine was originally intended for a steamboat; the beams lie below and the coupling rods are united with the piston rod by a crosshead.   Each cylinder is 90½ inches high and stands on an iron tank.   The air pump piston rod is hung from an ordinary crosshead like that of the piston; the coupling rods of the latter are however prolonged as far beyond as the first (10½ feet long), and are here tied together with a pair of arms 2 feet 10½ inches long.   To the ends of the coupling rods for the air pumps are attached radius rods of 2 feet 5⅛ inches long, whereby the movement of the piston rod is made approximately rectilinear.   Each engine has two beams and each of them consists of two cast iron plates which are 3¼ inches apart from one another.   They are from centre to centre 11 feet 9 inches long; in the middle 1 foot 11½ inches

---

[1] Robert Stephenson to Smiles, *Lives of the Engineers*, 1862, Vol. III., p. 242.

[2] In the Rastrick Collection, preserved at the Goldsmith Company's Economic Library, University of London.

high; at the point of attachment of the rods at the end $3\frac{1}{2}$ inches the rim is $1\frac{1}{4}$ inches thick, the metal is $\frac{3}{4}$ inch [thick].

The connecting rod is from centre to centre 8 feet long; the cranks of both engines are attached at right angles on a shaft 11 feet 2 inches long. In the middle of this shaft there is a large toothed wheel with 224 wooden teeth $9\frac{3}{4}$ inches wide and $16\frac{1}{4}$ feet diam. This engages with a smaller wheel entirely of iron of 88 teeth and 6 feet 5 inches diam. On the same axis there is a bevel wheel of 63 teeth 4 feet diam. to which is fixed a disengaging coupling, the latter engages in a second bevel wheel of 88 teeth and $5\frac{1}{2}$ feet diam. whose axis lies at right angles to the rails. On the latter is the rope drum 4 feet diam. and 6 feet long; the centre of it lies 11 feet above the rails. On one side there is on the rope drum a rim 8 feet diam. and on the other side a brake wheel of the same diameter covered on the outside with wood. The brake consists of a strong wrought iron band completely encircling the wheel; the band can be tightened hard by compound levers. The two boilers are cylindrical $15\frac{2}{3}$ feet long, $7\frac{1}{2}$ feet diam. with flues which run round the sides.

The Greenfield engine does not go so quickly; it has only 3 feet stroke and makes over 50 revolutions per minute which may be adequate to about 20 revolutions of the drum. This engine is in general quite of the same construction and arrangement in its parts, as the engine at Brusselton; it has likewise two cylinders, &c.

The beams of this engine are worthy of notice; they are 8 feet 8 inches long and consist each of two rolled iron plates $\frac{9}{16}$ inch thick which stand $2\frac{3}{8}$ inches apart and are united with screws. In the middle and particularly where axes go through it, pieces of cast iron are placed between. On each side of the cylinder lies one such beam, which therefore is completely ensured from side bending. It will not be easy to get beams, which possess greater power of resistance for so small a weight. It would be very useful on many occasions to employ cheap and easily constructed beams which are less subject than cast iron to the danger of breakage.

PRICES OF ENGINES

The Prussian engineers' report concludes with the following interesting note on the prices charged by Robert Stephenson & Co. in 1827.—

[Translation.]

In the mechanical workshops of Messrs. Stephenson and Dickinson in Newcastle the following prices for steam engines constructed in the factory were communicated to us.

Locomotives of 8 h.p. £550
Fixed stationary engines of high pressure Watt type—

8 h.p.	£300 to £350
18 h.p.	£450 to £500
16 h.p.	£650 to £720
20 h.p.	£800 to £900
30 h.p.	£1,200 to £1,350

A spare set of improved waggon wheels, axle boxes, axles, &c., £15 free on board ship at Newcastle. These prices change in proportion according to the wages, &c., and hold good as average terms payment through London, 3 bills 3 months after dispatch. Address:

Robert Stephenson & Comp.
Engineers and Founders in Newcastle upon Tyne.

A MISSING LINK

With the help of the report made by the Prussian engineers in 1827 and the later record by Rastrick, we have now identified a locomotive which had been supplied to the Stockton and Darlington Railway in January 1828, and afterwards became their No. 6. We have not mentioned in its chronological order a locomotive sent by Robert Stephenson & Co. to Darlington in November 1827, and we must now return in an attempt to identify this engine and complete another link in the history of the locomotive. Although no definite record of an enquiry appears in the sub-committee minutes of the railway company, it seems that they were considering in the autumn of 1827 a further addition to their locomotive stock, and on 9th November 1827 resolved :—

That T. Hackworth write to R. Stephenson & Co. declining a trial of their new engine unless they are satisfied that its weight without water is below 7 tons.

A later minute records, on 16th November 1827, that :—

Stephenson's have guaranteed their locomotive engine not to exceed 6 tons 15 cwt. It is therefore on its way to Darlington for trial.

It appears that this engine had water tubes of some sort, for, before it had been sent to Darlington, Harris Dickinson on behalf of the makers had written to Edward Pease on 24th October 1827 [1] :—

In answer to thy favour of the 20th inst., respecting our new locomotive engine, we are of opinion that there is little or no more risk attending this engine than the former ones. The only danger, I apprehend, is from the bars burning away, and so blowing out the hot water and scalding those who may be employed at the engine; but how can these hollow tubes burn away so long as they are filled with water? And if, from any neglect, the communication between the boiler and fire tubes should be stopped, so that the tubes burned into holes, there could not then be any water to blow up.

The sophistry of this argument is perhaps more creditable to 'what is usually termed a man of business' than to an engineer, and a subsequent correspondence suggests that the railway company did not find it convincing. Alterations to the fire grate, and possibly to the fire place, were suggested, which Hackworth feared might throw too great a proportion of the weight on to the two hind wheels ; Dickinson however suggested that an experiment should be tried and proposed, should the results be unsatisfactory, to bring the engine back to Newcastle and fit it up with six wheels which he considered would be an entire remedy.[2]

Now at first sight the fact that this November 'Trial' engine had water tubes, and that it was proposed to put it on six wheels, together suggest identification with the engine afterwards called the 'Experiment,' but the recorded weight of the 'Trial' engine, 6 tons 15 cwt. light, shows it to have been of approximately the same weight as the first four Stephenson engines, whereas the 'Experiment,' according to Hackworth's notes, weighed 7 tons 8 cwt. light when delivered to the railway company. It is clear therefore that, though the sub-committee minutes do not record the actual dates when the 'Experiment' was ordered and delivered to the railway company, this engine cannot be identified with the 'Trial' engine of November. We have still to find out what became of this latter engine, and learn what we can of its design. No drawing of it can now be found; and we have only the makers' statement of its weight and the knowledge that it had some form of water tube.

---

[1] Tomlinson, *The North Eastern Railway*, p. 146, et seq.   [2] *Ibid.*, p. 147.

Now in the year 1828 Robert Stephenson & Co. sent to France two locomotives, fitted with water tubes which eventually proved unsuccessful[1], and we are led by this similarity to consider the possible identity of one of these engines with the engine sent for trial to Darlington; but since direct evidence is lacking we shall have to rely on a coincidence of dates and on such information as can be obtained from foreign sources.

We have no direct evidence as to the date when this 'Trial' engine was returned to Newcastle, but it was still on the railway, awaiting repairs, in May 1828, so that during at least part of that year there must have been seven locomotives on the Stockton and Darlington Railway. On the other hand we know that a locomotive built by Robert Stephenson & Co., called 'Rocket,' after their successful engine on the Liverpool and Manchester Railway, was supplied to the Darlington Railway in the autumn of 1829, and eventually bore the company's No. 7. From this we may conclude that one of the previous seven engines, which we may reasonably suppose to have been the 'Trial' engine of November 1827, was no longer in the railway company's possession in 1829.

Our further speculations on the ultimate destination of this engine we must reserve for our next chapter.

BRUSSELTON INCLINED PLANE

[1] Robert Stephenson's Narrative of his Father's Inventions, Smiles *Lives of the Engineers*, 1862, Vol. III., p. 495.

CHAPTER VIII

THE FIRST LOCOMOTIVES IN FRANCE

1828—1829

MARC SÉGUIN — Before considering the evidence as to these engines we must record the circumstances under which they were introduced into France, and a few facts about the distinguished engineer who was responsible for their introduction.

Marc Séguin, born in 1786, was the eldest of five brothers, and is usually known on this account as Séguin aîné ; he was a nephew of the brothers Montgolfier, inventors of the fire or hot air balloon. It seems that his early education was neglected, and we are told that the development of his brilliant qualities was due to the tuition of an uncle who had recognized his nephew's studious disposition.[1] Séguin the elder appears to have distinguished himself as a civil engineer by the construction, in 1820, of an iron suspension bridge, a model for many later constructions of the same type. In 1825 he was associated with others in a first attempt at steam navigation on the Rhône, and later became a pioneer in railway construction.

The first railway in France was, however, due to the engineer Beaunier and several mine owners, who, influenced by the writings of de Gallois after his visit to Killingworth in 1818, had obtained a concession from the French Government to establish a railway with inclined planes in the mining district of St. Étienne. This railway, like the Stockton and Darlington line, was intended for minerals and merchandise, neither the promoters nor the Government anticipating the carriage of passengers. The railway from St. Étienne to Andrézieux was opened on 1st October 1828. Like the Stockton and Darlington Railway it was a single line, with sidings for the passing of the trains, which were hauled by horses. This railway followed the contour of the country, avoiding natural and other obstacles by numerous curves of small radius.[2]

In the meanwhile the brothers Séguin, with others, had petitioned for the right to construct a railway from St. Étienne to Lyon—'the most certain and only practicable means for realising the great benefit, so long desired, of a junction between the Loire and the Rhône.' The concession was granted in June 1826 to the Séguin brothers, E. Biot et Cie, and later, in connection with their enterprise, Marc Séguin with other scientific men visited England, viewing the most important manufactories, and the railways then under construction, and meeting George Stephenson. The duration of their visit, 9th December 1827 to 3rd February 1828, is curiously defined by a report of the administration a year later, in which the company's auditors criticize the personal expenses of the deputation, which had worked out at 31 francs 75 centimes per day for each

---

[1] Perdonnet, *Chemins de Fer*, 1865, Vol. III., p. 64.

[2] *Hommes et Choses du P.L.M.* (Chemin de fer Paris, Lyon, Méditerranée), 1910, p. 15 *et seq.*

(part) from the Bulletin de la Société Industrielle de Mulhouse, Vol. V., 1832.

(part) from a lithograph (undated) by Engelmann, père et fils, in the collection of Sir David Salomons, Bart.

Chemin de Fer de Lyon a St. Étienne

person ; but they leave 'those who have visited England to say whether the expense is too high.' They further criticize the purchase of two travelling cloaks, which the brothers Séguin had considered to be indispensable for their work of observation in all weathers.[1]

After his return from England, Marc Séguin had to decide important questions of material and traction, as *e.g.*—Could they make use of locomotives throughout or must they have recourse to haulage by fixed engines on the inclines? He decided from what he had seen on the Stockton and Darlington Railway to experiment with locomotives, and determined accordingly to lay out his railway with as easy inclines and curves as possible. Great natural difficulties were overcome in a manner which earned the praise of Stephenson; and 'the illustrious English engineer, who had come to assist his young French confréres with his advice,' himself received an honorarium of 12,500 francs from the Lyon St. Étienne Railway Company.[2]

Coming now to the locomotives we have Séguin's own statement [3]:—

The Government granted to the industry leave to introduce into France free of duty two engines from the works of Messrs. Robert Stephenson of Newcastle-on-Tyne, such as were then employed on the Stockton and Darlington Railway. One of these was sent to M. Hallette, a distinguished machine constructor at Arras, for him to study, and the other was taken to Lyon to serve as a model for those which I was to construct for the service of the St. Étienne-Lyon Railway.

Of these two Stephenson engines no drawings can be found, but published drawings are available showing the engines built in 1829, and after, by Séguin himself, and there is a model of his engine at the Conservatoire des Arts et Métiers Paris, though of much later date and less complete than the drawings. The arrangement of the cylinders and driving gear in Séguin's engine is remarkable, and we have to consider whether the Stephenson engines sent to France had such an arrangement, or whether it was first applied by Séguin himself. On this point we have a statement in his own book [4]:—

In the Stephenson engines the two cylinders are placed vertically on each side of the boiler. The movement communicated to the pistons by the steam is transmitted to the wheels by means of long connecting rods which connect the beam at the end of the piston rod with pins fixed to the middle of one of the spokes of each wheel.

We have also an earlier statement, made by Coste and Perdonnet in recording their visit to Newcastle in 1828. Of the locomotive sent to Séguin, they say [5]:—

The steam cylinders are vertical and carried on either side between the wheels which have different axles; they communicate the motion to these by a system of levers and rods.

This evidence shows conclusively that the Stephenson engines sent to France had the cylinder arrangement afterwards adopted by Séguin, and bearing in

---

[1] *Hommes et Choses du P.L.M.* (Chemin de fer Paris, Lyon, Méditerranée), 1910, p. 17.

[2] Report to the shareholders of the Lyon St. Etienne Railway Co., 21st December 1829. P. C. Laurent de Villedeuil, *Bibliographie des Chemins de Fer*, 1906, p. 106 (communicated to Robert Stephenson & Co., in 1923, by M. Ferdinand Achard).

[3] Séguin, *De l'Influence des Chemins de Fer et de l'art de les tracer et de les construire*, 1839, p. 425.

[4] *Ibid.* p. 425.   [5] *Annales des Mines*, 2nd series, 1829, Vol. VI., p. 205.

mind his remark that they were 'such as were then employed on the Stockton and Darlington Railway,' and that he was in England from December 1827 to February 1828, during which time the 'Trial' engine of November 1827 was at work on the line, we can hardly avoid the inference that this engine may have been one of the two sent subsequently to Séguin.   But there are discrepancies between the weights of the English built engines as recorded by Coste and Perdonnet, and the weight given by Robert Stephenson & Co. for their 'Trial' engine of 1827; it is however possible to reconcile these, and further search may discover the conclusive evidence which is still lacking.

Meanwhile however, we find both in the engine sent to Séguin, and in those built by him, two interesting links in the development of the locomotive, which on account of their cylinder arrangement alone deserve more notice than they have generally received.   Séguin's own engine has a further and peculiar interest on account of its boiler.   With the English engines he had to face

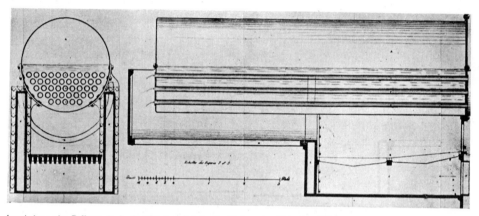

(part) from the Bulletin de la Société Industrielle de Mulhausen, Vol. V., 1832.

the problem which Hackworth had met for the time being by the adoption of Trevithick's return flue, and which Robert Stephenson & Co. had been trying to solve by an internal water drum and water tube fire bars, both attempts to obtain greater steaming capacity than was possible with a single flue.

Séguin states that the insufficiency of the speed of the engines as used in England made it necessary for him to augment the means for producing steam, and he therefore pursued a plan of small fire-tubes, which he tells us he had commenced in 1827.   He had in fact applied for a patent on 12th December of that year, before his journey to England, and he subsequently patented a multi-fire-tube boiler, the main principle of which he eventually applied to his own locomotive, as shown by the model and contemporary drawings.   His first experiment was with a stationary boiler, in which he obtained artificial draught from a fan; he then 'regarded the question as completely solved,' but he found that 'many grave difficulties presented themselves,' which however 'they had the happiness some time after to overcome, by the discovery of a means, simple and ingenious, which consisted in injecting the exhaust steam into the chimney.'

Séguin's multi-fire-tube boiler preceded in conception that of Stephenson's 'Rocket' by nearly eighteen months, but his locomotive fitted with his own boiler was not tried until two months after the 'Rocket.' We have no evidence, but it has sometimes been suggested, that the idea of the one was borrowed from the other. Perdonnet[1] asks the natural question, whether Henry Booth of the Liverpool and Manchester Railway, and the Stephensons, who first applied in England the idea of small fire-tubes to the locomotive, were aware of Séguin's boiler. This question he answers by remarking that 'the idea may have occurred simultaneously to two men of genius,' and we have in this remark a pleasing lack of those reflections on personal character which have been so conspicuous in regard to some other claims for priority of invention. We have indeed to thank Auguste Perdonnet for a graceful appreciation of two eminent men in a medal, which he offered in 1867, to encourage investigation into the resistances of trains and the steam production of locomotives.

from the collection of Mr. C. F. Dendy Marshall.

'*PRIX OFFERT PAR PERDONNET*'

[1] Perdonnet, *Chemins de Fer*, 1865, Vol. III., p. 65.

[2] *Mémoires et comptes rendus de la Société des Ingénieurs Civils de France*, 1867, p. 59. Communicated to Robert Stephenson & Co., 1923, by M. le Professeur E. Sauvage, Ingénieur en Chef des Mines.

CHAPTER IX

THE 'LANCASHIRE WITCH'

1828

In our last chapter we anticipated events in the development of the Stephenson locomotive, in order to do justice to the distinguished French engineer who had been considering the use of multiple fire-tubes to obtain increased heating surface so early as 1827. The idea was, even then, no new one—Goodrich records it by a sketch made in 1803—but these earlier considerations of the problem are beyond our present scope. We must now resume our account of the Stephensons' work in the same direction, showing how the end eventually attained by them, independently of Séguin and others, was being reached on converging lines.

Taking the through single flue as the basic idea, we have seen that the next step would be the doubling of this flue, by returning it to a chimney placed beside the fireplace. But though this method had been already adopted, in the first instance by Trevithick, and later by Hedley, it was at first avoided by George Stephenson, who, from the beginning of his work on the locomotive, appears to have aimed at what we may call a 'straight line' construction, and we have seen a novel attempt on such lines, in his 'Experiment,' to obtain increased heating surface by the adoption of an internal water drum within the single flue, and by the use of water-tube firebars.

The next step appears to have been taken by the Stephensons during the construction of a locomotive ordered for the Liverpool and Manchester Railway; this engine possessed many remarkable features, and so clearly shows the logical sequence of development in both boiler construction and engine arrangement, that it deserves more notice than it has hitherto received. It appears that this 'Liverpool Travelling Engine,' as it was first called, was ordered by the railway company on 7th January 1828, after consideration of a report from George Stephenson 'on a new construction, the result of experiments by himself and the Treasurer [1],' which had been authorized by the company so early as 30th April 1827 [2], when :—

The Treasurer reported that he had discovered a method of producing Steam without Smoke, which he considered might be applied to Locomotive and other Engines; Mr. Stephenson attended and having given his opinion that the Invention, if it succeeded on a large scale, would be highly important to the Company, he was directed to make any experiments requisite to decide the real merits of the scheme, it being understood that an expenditure of £100 would be sufficient for the purpose.

[1] Henry Booth, Secretary to the Liverpool and Manchester Railway Company.

[2] Liverpool and Manchester Railway Directors' Minutes, preserved at the Euston offices of the London, Midland and Scottish (formerly London and North Western) Railway Company; published by permission.

Subsequently, at a directors' meeting on 7th January 1828, 'a drawing of the boiler was exhibited and after some discussion and explanation it was resolved' :—

That the engineer construct a locomotive engine on the principle and plan proposed. The engine to be calculated to draw 20 tons of goods and fifty passengers. Mr. Stephenson having stated that the weight of such engine would be about six tons and the cost £550.

A later minute, on 21st April 1828, records that it was proposed to transfer the engine to the Bolton and Leigh Company whose railway would be ready about the following June, and it was accordingly resolved :—

That Mr. Stephenson be directed to transfer the order for the engine to the Bolton and Leigh Railway Company, and follow their instruction as to the time and mode of delivering the same on the Bolton Line.

The original drawing of this engine has fortunately been preserved among the makers' records, and we have some published extracts from a correspondence relating to it. Robert Stephenson's biographer tells us that he consulted a number of letters between the two Stephensons dealing with the vital question of boiler design; but all trace of the originals has now been lost and the first record now available to us is an extract from a letter written from Liverpool by George, to Robert, Stephenson on 8th January 1828[1]; the post-script reads :—

The small tubes will not require to be so strong as the other parts of the boiler, and you must take care that you have no thick plates and thin ones, as is often the case with those which come from Bedlington. *You must calculate that this engine will be for all the engineers in the kingdom—nay, indeed, the world—to look at.*

Later, on 31st January, he writes again :—

With respect to the engine for Liverpool, I think the boiler ought not to be longer than eight feet. The engine ought to be made light as it is intended to run fast. Mr. Booth and myself think two chimneys would be better than one, say eight inches in diameter and not to exceed fifteen feet.

That there were considerable practical difficulties in the construction of this boiler is shown by a later letter to Robert, dated 15th April 1828 :—

I am quite aware that the bent tubes are a complicated job to make, but after once in and well done it cannot be any complication in the working of the engine. This bent tube is a child of your own, which you stated to me in a former letter.

Writing again to Robert from Liverpool, on 20th April 1828, he says :—

I duly received yours dated the 16th inst. I do not think there can be much difficulty in cleaning the refuse matter of the fire from the locomotive-engine boiler. I would make the nozzle pipe that goes in from the blast to be a kind of grating rather than of a conical shape, and to project about two feet into the fire. The grating to be on the upper side. The nozzle piece to be made with a flange, fitting very nicely to the plate at the front of the fire to prevent the escape of air, and kept on by a bolt and cotter, or two screw-bolts. This nozzle piece could easily be taken out at any time and the fire cleaned at the hole. This I think may be done while the engine is working upon an easy part of the road. It appears to me it will be found

---

[1] Jeaffreson, *Life of Robert Stephenson*, Vol. I., p. 119.

better to feed one time with coke and the next with coal. I think the one would revive the other. I do not think there can be so much difficulty in firing on this plan as on the old one. If you wish me to see the boiler tried before it is put into its seat I will endeavour to come.

If this new engine is found to answer, it will be the best way to alter all the Darlington engines to the same plan. By doing so the last engine will not be found too heavy for the road.

On 25th July 1828 George Stephenson writes to Hackworth[1]:—

We have used the new locomotive engine at Bolton which works beautifully. There is not the least noise about it. We have also tried the blast to it for burning coke and I believe it will answer. There are two bellows worked by eccentrics underneath the tender.

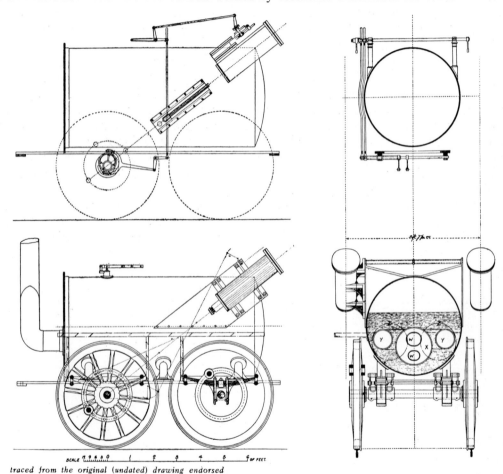

traced from the original (undated) drawing endorsed

ROUGH SKETCH OF LIVERPOOL TRAVELLING ENGINE

This letter explains the reference on 20th April to the 'blast'; the word is evidently used to describe a forced draught; we have no evidence of its use at this time to describe the action of exhaust steam. This bellows 'blast'

[1] *A Chapter in the History of Railway Locomotion*, p. 5.

at the fireplace appears to have been introduced by George Stephenson as an experiment, to meet difficulties which he anticipated in burning coke.[1]

We are told that 'the engine with the bent tubes, like other attempts made in that year to improve the locomotive, was a failure [2],' but we have no definite statement as to the form of the bent tube referred to in the letter of 15th April which we have quoted. Fortunately we have the evidence of the original drawing, still in the possession of Robert Stephenson & Co.; this drawing is endorsed 'Rough Sketch of Liverpool Travelling Engine' and shows what appears to be a main flue (which we have marked X) having two branches (YY) forming a double return flue, the ends of which are connected by an external breeches at the front end of the engine, uniting upwards in a single chimney.

It seems probable that these were the 'bent tubes' which Robert Stephenson had fathered, and which he had found to be so complicated a job, and on this supposition the discussion with Booth as to the desirability of having two chimneys is at once explained by the drawing. But the drawing shows two other circles (ZZ) and these are no doubt intended to represent the parallel through flues which were eventually adopted for the 'Lancashire Witch,' as the engine was afterwards called. There are other remarkable details apparently connected with the 'bent tube' arrangement; inside the main flue (X) two oval tubes are shown (W), which may have been some form of water tube, possibly bent in U form downwards.

But the most remarkable feature of the engine is the arrangement of the cylinders, apparently the first step taken by Robert Stephenson in following up certain suggestions described by him to Longridge in his letter of 1st January 1828, which we have already mentioned, but must now quote at greater length [3]:—

Since I came down from London, I have been talking a great deal to my father about endeavouring to reduce the size and ugliness of our travelling-engines, by applying the engine either on the side of the boiler or beneath it entirely, somewhat similarly to Gurney's steam coach. He has agreed to an alteration which I think will considerably reduce the quantity of machinery as well as the liability to mismanagement. Mr. Jos. Pease writes my father that in their present complicated state they cannot be managed by 'fools,' therefore they must undergo some alteration or amendment. It is very true that the locomotive engine, or any other kind of engine, may be shaken to pieces; but such accidents are in a great measure under the control of enginemen, which are, by the by, not the most manageable class of beings. They perhaps want improvement as much as the engines.

It is clear that Robert Stephenson & Co. were already striving to escape from the tradition of the vertical cylinder; they had made one attempt in their 'Experiment' with horizontal cylinders inside the boiler; but a direct drive from piston rod to crank pin could not be obtained by this method. They now adopted a position for the cylinders intermediate between the vertical and the

---

[1] The use of coal on the Liverpool and Manchester Railway was practically prohibited by a smoke clause in the Act.

[2] Jeaffreson, *Life of Robert Stephenson*, Vol. I., p. 121. It must be noted that in his own deductions Jeaffreson appears on p. 118 to confuse the 'Lancashire Witch' with the 'Twin Sisters,' an entirely different engine. Though the 'bent tube' was a failure, the engine on which it was tried was subsequently a remarkable success.

[3] Jeaffreson, *Life of Robert Stephenson*, Vol. I., p. 115.

horizontal, and giving a direct drive ; they abandoned for the time the ideal of the horizontal cylinder, but the intermediate levers of the 'Experiment' had been eliminated, and the whole engine lightened and simplified. By the use of the twin flues they had obtained, with a shorter and lighter boiler, a larger heating surface than in the early single flue engines, and having in mind the difficulties

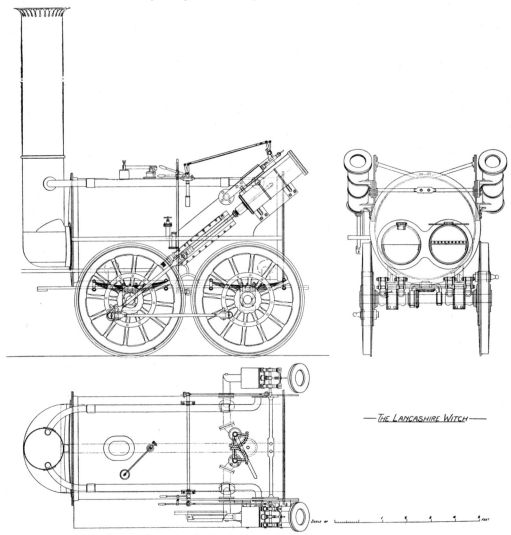

traced from an original (undated) drawing, height of chimney doubtful.

THE 'LANCASHIRE WITCH'

which were being experienced on the Darlington Railway owing to the increasing weights of the engines, we can understand George Stephenson's suggestion that if the 'new engine' were found to answer it would be the best way to alter all the Darlington engines to the same plan.

Besides the original sketch, Robert Stephenson & Co. have another early drawing, and list of dimensions, but there are evidences which suggest that both were prepared two or three years after the 'Lancashire Witch' was built; the description of this engine is however the earliest among the firm's records :—

BOILER

Diameter	.... 4 feet 0 inches	
Length....	.... 9 ,, 0 ,,	
Size of fire tubes (two)	.... 1 ,, 6 ,,	
Dimensions of fire-place	.... 4 feet by 3 feet	
Heating surface of boiler	.... 66 square feet	
Weight of water in boiler	18½ cwt.	
Proportion of space for water in boiler to contents of cylinder	30 times	
Proportion of space for steam in boiler to contents of cylinder	42 times	

CHIMNEY

Size of chimney	.... 1 foot 8 inches

PUMP

Size of hot water pump	1½ inches
Length	2 feet 0 inches
Proportion of quantity injected to cylinder	$\frac{1}{16}$

CYLINDER

Diameter	9 inches
Length of stroke	2 feet 0 inches
Angle of cylinders to the horizontal	39°
Size of steam passage	4¼ by ¾ inches
Proportion of steam passage to cylinder	$\frac{1}{20}$

WHEELS

Diameter of wheels (wood)	4 feet 0 inches
Extreme length of engine	.... 12 feet
Extreme height	.... 8 feet 4 inches

For a detailed contemporary description we have to borrow from the French engineers Coste and Perdonnet, who appear to have appreciated very highly the remarkable features of this engine, of which they published an elaborate account after they had seen it at work on the Bolton Railway in 1828. After describing it as the 'most perfect which had yet been constructed,' and observing that it had not, to their knowledge, been quoted in any book, their account proceeds [1] :—

[Translation.]

It is from the workshops of Mr. Robert Stephenson of Newcastle and it seems that it will serve as a model for all those which will run upon the Liverpool and Manchester Railway.

The following particulars distinguish this locomotive from others which have been described :—

(1) It is carried on springs while the other engines are not so carried, or only as we have just explained. [*i.e.* by the steam springs of Losh and Stephenson].

The method of spring suspension has been recognized by Mr. Stephenson himself, inventor of the steam support, to be superior to the latter.

(2) The steam cylinders are inclined at 45° to the horizontal instead of being vertical.

Vertical cylinders presented an inconvenience which, without being entirely removed, is less with inclined or horizontal cylinders.

(3) The wheels are of wood, with a rim of wrought iron, in place of being in cast iron chilled.

Cast iron wheels break or wear out more quickly than those in wood with a wrought iron tyre. Mr. Wood who has now for eighteen months tried wheels with a wrought iron tyre is in complete agreement with Mr. Stephenson as to their superiority. We ourselves saw at Killing-worth cast iron wheels which, after having been in use only four months, were already strongly scored, and whose profile had become so worn that the friction was thereby considerably increased.

[1] *Annales des Mines*, 2nd series, 1829, Vol. VI., p. 199.

K

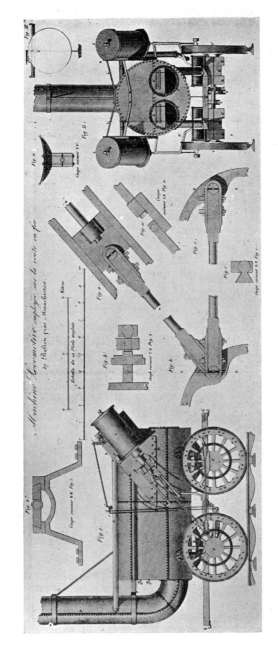

Machine Locomotive employée sur la route de fer de Bolton près Manchester

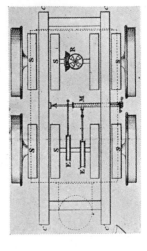

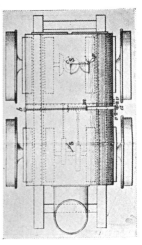

(part) from 'Annales des Mines,' 2nd Series, Vol. VI., 1829.

ROBERT STEPHENSON & CO.'S 'LANCASHIRE WITCH' AS SKETCHED BY COSTE AND PERDONNET

Wheels in wrought iron, on the contrary, at the end of seven months were not visibly affected. In England there is nothing against such wheels except the difference in price.

The wrought iron tires are made in a rolling mill and fixed to the wood by nails with invisible heads, and the ends of the tire are welded where they meet.

(4) The wheels are connected by horizontal rods, in place of endless chains passing over tooth wheels on the axles.

We reproduce some of the illustrations published with the above account; certain discrepancies between them and the makers' early drawings are apparent, but the French observers explain in their report that they were only able to sketch the engine when at work, adding that, though 'some of the details may be inaccurate, perfect correctness of the important dimensions can be relied upon.' Their drawings generally explain themselves, but they give no indication of the bellows blast with which two engines were fitted; the description however states :—

The nozzle of the bellows passes into one of the fire-places. When it is wished to reduce the current of air the nozzle is withdrawn and the opening of the ashpan closed with a little plate. In new engines being constructed it is intended to abandon the bellows because it continuously lifts the back end. The tubes for the fire-places will then be arranged differently.

Space will not permit us to quote fully the description of the engine parts, but we must particularly note the arrangement adopted for obtaining expansive working of steam :—

On one of the axles is fixed a toothed bevel wheel (R) which turns another bevel wheel, placed horizontally and attached to a vertical shaft, which (passing through the boiler) operates a rotating plug valve; by means of this valve it is possible to obtain the expansive action of the steam during half the stroke of the piston. We were unable to see the inside of the boiler or to obtain in this respect sufficient explanation, but it appears that the two pipes which carry the steam to the steam chests unite in a vertical pipe in which the turning plug valve operates.

There are two toothed quadrants (S¹) which the engineman by a handle can turn at will through a quarter of a revolution about their centres; in their first position they permit the rotating valve to produce its effect by causing the steam to work by expansion, in the second position they prevent this and the steam acts only by the effect of its elasticity on its entry into the cylinder.

Ordinarily the cut off is operated at the beginning of the run in order to economize the steam when only a small quantity has been formed, and it is used without expansion when in full activity.

We gather from this description that the plug valves operated by the bevel wheel on the axle must have rotated in sleeves having ports whose position relative to the steam passages to the cylinder could be altered by means of the quadrants.

Apart from this ingenious apparatus we find in the 'Liverpool Travelling Engine' one of the most important steps taken by the Stephensons in simplifying and improving the locomotive since George Stephenson had adopted the direct drive for his Killingworth engine, and combined the drive from both cylinders in one axle in the 'Experiment' for the Stockton and Darlington Railway. The improvements which were embodied in the 'Lancashire Witch' appear to have been due largely to Robert Stephenson, and an examination of the design shows that in cylinder arrangement, and some other respects, it may justly be considered the proto-type of the 'Rocket,' and therefore a most important link in the development of the locomotive. This was the first locomotive recorded as having any attempt at an expansion gear, and in both design and performance it was far in advance of any contemporary. But as the boiler was not fitted with a lock-up safety valve its performance was discounted by Walker when reporting to the directors of the Liverpool and Manchester Railway, although he records[1] that on 15th January 1829 he was 'accompanied by Mr. Stephenson to the Bolton Railway' :—

> The principal object of our survey there was a locomotive engine made by him upon what he considers the best principle of any he has yet constructed, and the report we have since received proves the great power which the engine is capable of exerting.

Rastrick, who accompanied Walker, has recorded in his own note-book[2] an experiment in which the 'Lancashire Witch' drew thirteen loaded waggons, at eight miles per hour, up an ascent of 12 feet per mile for a mile and a quarter, and he calculates that the engine exerted 21·71 effective horse-power with an effective steam pressure of 25·2 lbs., adding that the valve on boiler being fastened down the pressure must have risen to a very dangerous height. He records the weight of the engine, tender and carriages :—

					T.	c.	q.
Engine	....	....	....	....	....	7	0	0
Tender and Carriage		....	....	....	3	15	0
13 Empty Carriages		....	....	....	18	4	0
13 Loads	....	....	....	....	....	29	5	0

The subsequent reports of Walker and Rastrick to the Liverpool and Manchester Railway Company left the superiority of locomotives to fixed engines in doubt; Robert Stephenson replying later objected that sufficient account had not been taken of recent improvements in the locomotive[3] :—

> The 'Lancashire Witch' was the most efficient Mr. Walker had examined and deductions from its performances would have approximated nearer the truth than data drawn from the Darlington engines that have been several years in use and working under great disadvantages.

How the 'Lancashire Witch' received her name is best told in the words of a contemporary journal[4] describing the opening of the Bolton and Leigh Railway :—

8th August 1828.

> On Friday last (August 1st) this great and useful undertaking being nearly completed, the road was opened in form, by the passage over it of a chained row of coal carriages, some of which were tastefully fitted up for the reception of a select company of the friends of the proprietors, drawn by a locomotive steam-engine. The line of carriages provided contained about 230 persons, and covered a portion of the road measuring about 70 feet; the whole weight,

---

[1] *Report on the Comparative Merits of Locomotives and Fixed Engines*, 1829.

[2] In the Rastrick Collection, preserved at the Goldsmith Company's Economic Library, University of London.

[3] Robert Stephenson and Joseph Locke, *Observations on the Comparative Merits of Locomotives and Fixed Engines : A Reply to the Report of Mr. James Walker*, 1830.

[4] *Liverpool Mercury*, August 8th, 1828.

including the engine, was about forty tons, which was carried forward at the rate of four and a half miles per hour. When it arrived at the summit of the inclined plane, the engine was detached, for the purpose of bringing up six other carriages, containing each three tons of coals. The engine was then impelled separately upon the road, in view of the company, to show its power, and moved, for a few minutes, at the rate of eleven or twelve miles per hour. Preparations were next made for the christening, when Mrs. Hulton (wife of the chairman of the company) stepped on to the engine with a garland of flowers, which being attached to the chimney, that lady addressed the meeting as follows:—

> Gentlemen,—I sincerely congratulate you on the arrival of this day, which I trust will form a new era in the prosperity of the trade and manufactures of this great county, especially of the town of Bolton. No one can observe without admiration this beautiful engine, I therefore beg leave to name it after an object universally attractive—'The Lancashire Witch'.

This address was received with loud and long continued cheering. The carriages, with the waggons of coal, descended the inclined plane to the depot, in the town of Bolton, and we may safely say that a more animating sight than was presented on this occasion has been rarely witnessed.

The engine employed on this occasion was originally constructed for the Liverpool and Manchester railroad, by Mr. Robert Stephenson, the son of the engineer of that magnificent undertaking. It is of eight horse-power, and is calculated to convey a load of twenty tons, at the rate of seven miles an hour. To economize the fuel, an apparatus had been attached to the engine for working the steam expansively, which fully answers the expectation of the makers: the advantage gained by this modification of high-pressed steam, has been sufficiently proved in fixed engines, by various engineers, but this is the first locomotive to which it has been applied.

With the influence of the 'Lancashire Witch' on the design of the locomotive we shall deal in our next chapter.

CHAPTER X

THE FIRST LOCOMOTIVES FOR AMERICA
AND SOME REMARKABLE DESIGNS

1828—1829

THE
'AMERICA'

The first locomotive sent by Robert Stephenson & Co. to America was for the Delaware and Hudson Canal Company; Horatio Allen, who as a young man had been sent to England as the canal company's agent, recorded many years later[1] the circumstances which led to the order :—

During the years 1826 and 1827 the use of the locomotive on the Stockton and Darlington Road, England, had become known to many, and especially to civil engineers in this country, and among others to myself, then a Resident Engineer on the line of the Delaware and Hudson Canal, the great engineering enterprise of the time, the first of the great works, canal and railroad, that were to bring the anthracite coal of the valley of the Susquehana into the valleys of the Delaware and of the Hudson and to the ocean.

Such consideration as was within my power led me to a decided conviction as to the future of the locomotive as the tractive motor power on railroads for general freight and passenger transportation, as it had begun to be for mine transportation. . . . . . Early in the year 1827 I had given all the attention that it was in my power to give, and having come to conclusions as to the locomotive, that all subsequent experience has confirmed, and believing that the future of the civil engineer lay in a great and most attractive degree in the direction of the coming railroad era, I decided to go to the only place where a locomotive was in daily operation and could be studied in all its practical details.

Closing my service on the Delaware and Hudson Canal, some two months were appropriated to certain objects and interests after which I was again in New York, preparatory to going to England. On my return to New York from these visits, I found that it had been decided by the Delaware and Hudson Canal Company to intrust me, first, the having made in England for that Company the railroad iron required for their railroad. . . and having built in England, for the Company, three locomotives, on plans to be decided by me when in England.

In 1828 the committee of the canal company's board report :—

That they deem it advisable to authorize Mr. Allen to procure one locomotive engine complete, as a pattern, and that the Chief Engineer is making enquiries to ascertain whether it may not be expedient to authorize the construction of all the locomotive engines in England.

Definite instructions to their representative are given in a letter addressed to him by John B. Jervis, chief engineer, who referring to the locomotives writes under date 16th January 1828[2] :—

It is desirable, in order to dispense with the tender carriages, to have a water tank fixed to the engine carriage that will contain about 100 gals.

[1] Pamphlet by Horatio Allen, *The Railroad Era*, reprinted from the *Railroad Gazette* 4th, 11th April 1884.
[2] Forney, *Memoir of Horatio Allen*, reprinted from *Railroad and Engineering Journal*.

After dealing with the design and capacity of the tank and pump for feeding the boiler, the writer proceeds :—

The weight of the engine, carriage, and water, if placed on six wheels, to be from 6 to 7 tons, but 6½ tons preferred. If it should be found that a six-wheel carriage has any important difficulty in working well on curved roads, that in your judgment would counterbalance the advantage of a heavier engine and give the preference to the four-wheel carriage, then the weight must not exceed 5½ tons; but the six-wheel carriage will be preferred if it can be made to work. If a six-wheel carriage the axle need not exceed 2¾ or 3 inches at the bearing. The diameter of the wheels 3 to 4 feet, as you find most approved from experiments in England for similar purposes and rate of travelling, say 3½ to 5 miles per hour. . . . . . . The diameter of the wheels of the engine carriage will affect the velocity, or distance traveled at a given number of strokes of the engine, but I would take 3 feet as the minimum diameter and make them as much larger as the arrangement of the working parts will admit, without giving too great a velocity. The length of the stroke must depend something on the facilities of securing firmness to the cylinder and this may lead you to prefer a larger or smaller diameter for the cylinder; the pressure of the steam has also a bearing on the question; on account of the weight I think the cylinder should not exceed 8 inches.

Basing his calculations on the experiments of Wood, he then gives at some length his views as to the most suitable size of cylinder, pressure of steam, and diameter of wheel, and referring to the boiler remarks :—

I am of opinion that the furnace had better be of the oval form laid flat, otherwise the furnace may be the same as for bituminous coal. It is supposed anthracite coal does not require so high a chimney as other fuel, but I am not possessed of any particular facts on this subject; I presume you can have the chimney so constructed that an additional piece may be attached if it is found on trial to require it. On this presumption I would not have it more than 10 feet high. As the height of the chimney will affect the calculation of bridges, it is advisable to understand this question as early as possible.

After stating the rail gauge as 4 feet 3 inches, and giving particulars of the curves, Jervis proceeds :—

It is determined by the Board that you will procure from England one locomotive engine with carriage complete for work. The three others will be wanted to depend on the cost at which they can be delivered at New York. It is supposed that they can be obtained of American manufacturers for $1,800, and I presume it will not be economy to procure them from England at a greater cost unless you perceive a superiority in the workmanship of English engines that in your opinion will justify the additional cost.

As a preliminary step I should advise, previous to the purchase of the locomotive steam engine, that you visit the Killingworth Railroad near Coventry (sic), the Hetton Railroad, and Darlington and Stockton Road; the two latter near Sunderland. At Killingworth the locomotive engine is said to have been in regular use (working by the adhesion of the wheels) since the year 1814; but the Hetton Road is more in the character of the proposed work.

As a result of his enquiries in England, Horatio Allen ordered four locomotives, one from Robert Stephenson & Co. and three from Foster and Rastrick of Stourbridge.[1] The Stephenson engine was the first to be delivered, arriving in New York about the middle of January, 1829, but it does not appear to have been ever put into service, and there are no records of its performance

---

[1] Walker in his *Report on the Comparative Merits of Locomotive and Fixed Engines*, 1829, states: 'On the 10th January I arrived at Stourbridge . . . going there to see a locomotive engine intended for America.' Rastrick in his *Report*, 2nd ed., refers to three locomotives for America.

or ultimate fate.   Allen, in his old age, referred to this locomotive as the 'proto-type' of the 'Rocket [1],' and made out that if it had been used in America the performance of the 'Rocket' in England would have been anticipated there.   In making this statement he was certainly under a misapprehension, for, though no drawings of the first Stephenson engine for America can be found, a brief description in the makers' records states that it had inclined outside cylinders and twin flues.   It was undoubtedly similar to the 'Lancashire Witch' which it immediately followed, but probably embodied certain alterations to the spring gear, described by Coste and Perdonnet as improvements which were being carried out on an engine seen by them under construction at Newcastle in 1828, and like the 'Lancashire Witch' intended for the Liverpool and Manchester Railway.   It would seem that this engine with the 'improvements' went instead to America where one of the original cylinders has been preserved.[2]

Now we have seen that the 'Lancashire Witch' was in fact the proto-type of the 'Rocket,' and at the time of its construction, and during the period of Allen's visit to England, was intended as a model for the locomotives of the Liverpool and Manchester Railway; this no doubt explains his erroneous assumption that the 'Rocket' and the engine sent to America were identical.

CAPTAIN WHISTLER'S ENGINE The second locomotive sent by Robert Stephenson & Co. to America is recorded in the makers' books as built in 1829 for Captain Whistler, presumably one of a deputation of American engineers which had visited England in 1828, for the special purpose of examining existing railroads and those in the course of construction.[3]   Of Whistler's engine no drawings can be found, but the makers' records show that it must have generally resembled the first of the engines we have next to describe.   It should be noted that these first two Stephenson locomotives sent to America had bar frames; this type of frame was later abandoned by Robert Stephenson & Co. but as developed by others became the standard for American practice.

We have now to consider four original drawings still in the possession of Robert Stephenson & Co., undated, but evidently contemporary, and all showing markedly the influence of the 'Lancashire Witch'; these four originals bear reference letters, A B, C and D, and we shall refer to them in this order.

DARLINGTON ENGINE A This drawing, which is endorsed 'Locomotive Engine for Darlington, Expansively,' no doubt shows an engine which was delivered to the Stockton and Darlington Railway Company in the autumn of 1829; it agrees with most hitherto published accounts of this railway company's engine No. 7, that it was carried on six wheels, and had inclined cylinders with a direct drive on to the crank pins of the leading wheels.   There can be little doubt now that it was the

---

[1] Allen, *The Railroad Era*, published in *Railroad Gazette*, 4th, 11th April 1884.

[2] In the Smithsonian Institution, the National Museum, Washington U.S.A.   See p. 159 following.

[3] *Proc. Inst. Civil Engineers*, Vol. XVIII., p. 52.

first engine of this type supplied by Robert Stephenson & Co. to the Stockton and Darlington Railway, though some writers appear to have confused it with the 'Experiment' of 1827, which has been conclusively shown to have been of an entirely different design.

The most interesting feature of 'Darlington Engine A' is the arrangement for expansive working by cut-off in the steam pipe, by means of a mushroom valve, operated from a cam on the trailing axle; a simplified development of a principle first applied in the 'Lancashire Witch', which the 'Darlington Engine' generally resembles in cylinder arrangement and driving gear. The latter has however an additional pair of wheels, and the boiler is fitted with a return

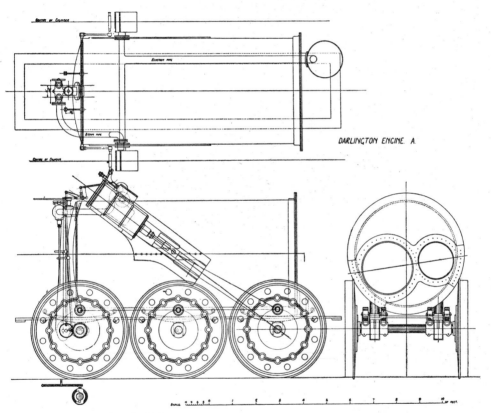

DARLINGTON ENGINE. A.

traced from the original (undated) drawing.

flue. But even with its additional pair of wheels it is probable that the 'Darlington Engine A' weighed little more than a four-wheeled, single flue, engine of the type first built by Robert Stephenson & Co., and it may be taken as embodying George Stephenson's recommendation[1] that the engines of the Stockton and Darlington Railway should be altered to the same plan as the 'Liverpool Travelling Engine.'

[1] Jeaffreson, *Life of Robert Stephenson*, Vol. I., p. 121.

'HUMPHREY'S'
ENGINE
WALES
B

The second drawing in the series which we are now considering shows an engine built for Samuel Homfray of the Tredegar Iron Works, ordered probably after the visit of his deputies Thomas Ellis and Theophilus Jones to Newcastle in December 1828.[1] It is recorded that this engine started running at the Tredegar works in October 1829, and that

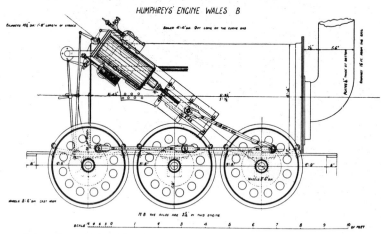

traced from the original (undated) drawing.

on a subsequent occasion it ran over the Sirhowy and Monmouthshire Tramroad into Newport, a distance of 28 miles, the journey being the occasion of much

from the original drawing in possession of Mr. C. W. Ellis.

THOMAS ELLIS' TREDEGAR LOCOMOTIVE, 1848

[1] C. W. Ellis, Letter to *Monmouthshire Evening Post*, 23rd February 1912. See p. 32, Chapter III. *ante*

local rejoicing though the proceedings were interrupted by a collision between the chimney and a tree in Tredegar Park.[1]   Locomotives subsequently built at Tredegar show the influence of this first Stephenson engine sent to Wales, where, just as on the Stockton and Darlington Railway, the slow speeds, and general conditions of service, permitted the survival of the steeply inclined cylinder arrangement after it had been generally abandoned elsewhere.   A drawing[2] of one of these South Wales engines, as rebuilt in 1848, shows both the inclined cylinders and a valve gear having some of the peculiar features shown on the original drawing of Homfray's engine.

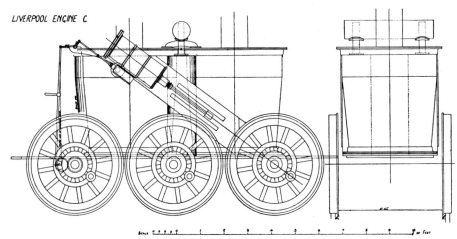

LIVERPOOL ENGINE C

(part) traced from the original (undated) drawing.

THE 'TWIN SISTERS'

LIVERPOOL COKE ENGINE 'TWIN SISTERS' C

The third drawing also shows the influence of the 'Lancashire Witch' on the engine work, and it has a special interest on account of its twin boilers ; of these unfortunately we have found neither detail drawings nor contemporary description, but there appears to be some reference to them in a letter written by Robert Stephenson to Longridge from Liverpool on 1st December 1828[3] :—

Since I wrote you last we have had my new boiler tried at Laird's boiler manufactory in Cheshire.   You are probably aware that this boiler is made to burn coke.   The experiment was completely successful, indeed, exceeded my expectations.   Six of the directors went the other day to witness a second experiment.   They were all perfectly satisfied.   The enemies to the locomotive said the experiment had answered to the fullest extent.   The boilers were shipped to-day in the steamboat via Carlisle, from which place they will be forwarded to Newcastle.

[1] *The Early Days of the Monmouthshire Railways.   Great Western Railway Magazine*, Vol. XXIV., No. 2. February 1912.

[2] Photo, sent in his 81st year, to Robert Stephenson & Co., 8th July 1921, by Mr. C. W. Ellis, grandson of Thomas Ellis above referred to.

[3] Jeaffreson, *Life of Robert Stephenson*, Vol. I., p. 121.

From the fact that these 'boilers' were intended to burn coke it seems possible that they may have been for the 'Liverpool Coke Engine,' and that this was so called in consequence and not, as has been stated, because it was employed after the opening of the line in hauling coke trains. The original drawing bears this name, by which the engine is also described when employed on the construction of the line more than a year before the opening, for we find George Stephenson writing to Phipps, then chief draughtsman at Newcastle, under date 13th August 1829 [1] :—

As I understand Robert is gone to Canterbury I may mention to you that I have put on to the coke engine a longer exarsting pipe, riching nearly to the top of the chimeney but find it dose not do so well as putting it into the chimeney lower down. I think it will be best near the level of the top of the boiler, by doing so it will look neater. The coke engine is doing extremely well—but the 'Lankshire Witch' is rely doing wonders. A statement of her performance you will see in the paper in a few days.

It should be noted that, in describing his experiments to promote combustion, George Stephenson refers to the 'exarsting' pipe, not to the 'blast' pipe.

An interesting statement relating to this, or a similar, experiment was made many years later, generally confirming the facts, though not the date, implied by George Stephenson's letter; the writer [2] states that the 'Twin Sisters' was at work on the Olive Mount cutting on the Liverpool and Manchester Railway in 1828. Though direct evidence is lacking we may be sure that this cannot have been the case, and we can find some contributory evidence from the minutes of the railway company, which record on 16th March 1829 :—

It being thought desirable to work part of the line between the Marle Cutting at the West of Olive Mount and the Broad Green Embankment with a locomotive engine, Mr. Stephenson was directed to provide an engine for the purpose which he stated he could have ready in six or eight weeks.

Later, a minute of 6th July 1829 records :—

Read a letter from Robert Stephenson & Co. stating that the locomotive engine was shipped from Newcastle via Carlisle and might be expected to arrive in Liverpool on the 10th inst.

And on 13th July 1829 it was reported :—

That the locomotive engine had arrived . . . and was expected to be ready for operations at Olive Mount in a week.

A contemporary journal [3] referring to the excavation work in progress on the railway states, on 25th July 1829, that a locomotive of 10 horse power had been expected to arrive on the previous day 'to supersede 30 horses' :—

This engine which is one constructed by Mr. Stephenson, the engineer of the railway, arrived about the time we mentioned and has since been regularly at work. We have had several opportunities of seeing it and consider it decidedly the best locomotive engine we have ever seen. It has two cylinders, each 9 inches in diameter, with a stroke of 2 feet and works at a pressure of 50 lbs. on the square inch. We have more than once seen it driving before it twelve waggons, each weighing a ton and each carrying 4 tons of clay; and when propelling this weight,

[1] Jeaffreson, *Life of Robert Stephenson*, Vol. I., p. 148.
[2] John Rowland, letter to *The Engineer*, 1857, Vol. IV., p. 227.
[3] *Manchester Guardian*, 25th July 1829.

amounting altogether to 54 tons, it travelled with great ease at the rate of six or seven miles an hour. When in full employment it burns, we are told, from 12 to 15 cwt. of coals per day and will travel 10 or 12 miles at its ordinary rate before it requires a fresh supply of water. The coal (*sic*) and water are conveyed in a separate carriage which is attached to the engine by chains. In order to prevent the loss of time and power, which would result from injecting cold water into the boiler, means have been provided for supplyng it in a boiling state. . . . From what we have seen of the operations of the engine, we are of the opinion that, unless it be liable to get out of repair, it will work decidedly cheaper than horses.

A railway company's minute of 17th August 1829 records :—

Read a letter from Mr. Dixon with a statement of performance of the locomotive engine at Eccles and the expense of working it exclusive of repairs.

Mr. Dixon made the cost of working for 12 hours say for coal, attendance and oil, 13s. 8d., and to do the work of about 10 horses, or when working night and day the work of 20 horses for 27s. 4d.

This was the first six-wheeled engine supplied by Robert Stephenson & Co. to the Liverpool and Manchester Railway, and perhaps the first six-wheeled engine to work on that line; as 'The Sisters' she is referred to in a directors' minute of 2nd August 1830, when it was ordered that in preparation for the opening of the line 'all locomotive engines with the exception of 'The Sisters' should be taken off the way.' After the completion of the railway 'The Sisters' appears to have been employed for a short time in ballasting.

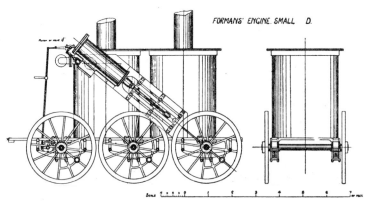

FORMANS' ENGINE. SMALL D.

traced from the original (undated) drawing.

FORMAN'S ENGINE (SMALL) D — The fourth drawing in the series shows presumably the engine referred to by Robert Stephenson writing to Longridge on 1st December 1828 [1] :—

I have had two letters from Forman about the locomotive engine and he has given us the order at last, but nothing can be done to it until I reach the manufactory.

The drawing which we illustrate shows a proposal to use twin boilers, as for the 'Liverpool Coke Engine,' but another drawing, dated July 1828, shows an

[1] Jeaffreson, *Life of Robert Stephenson*, Vol. I., p. 121

alternative proposal for a horizontal cylindrical boiler, and a note among the makers' early records which describes the engine as having one flue, 'straight

elliptical,' suggests that this single boiler may have been adopted.   Forman, to whom this engine was no doubt supplied, is recorded in 1817 as having been a partner with Thomson in the Pen-y-darren Iron Works, which had formerly belonged to Homfray, since gone to Tredegar.[1] Forman's engine was at first designed for a tramroad of 3 feet gauge, but some later drawings which have been preserved among the makers' records show proposals for alterations to this locomotive to suit a wider gauge, of 4 feet 6 inches.

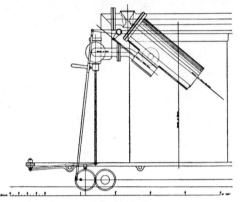

traced from the original (undated) drawing.

DARLINGTON
ENGINE
'QUICKSPEED'

There remains for notice one other original Stephenson drawing for the year which intervened between the completion of the 'Lancashire Witch' and the building of the 'Rocket.'   This drawing shows an application of the 'sun and planet' motion for driving purposes, and what appears to be an arrangement for expansive working, as in the other drawings we have

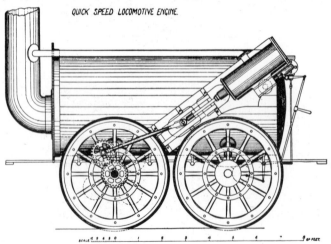

QUICK SPEED LOCOMOTIVE ENGINE.

traced from the original (undated) drawing.

just described; the method for obtaining synchronization between the operation of the slide valves and that of the piston is not recorded, and we have no evidence that an engine was ever built to this design.

With the various original drawings described in this and previous chapters we have now exhausted the original records still in the possession of Robert

---

[1] Simon Goodrich's *Journal*, preserved at the Science Museum, South Kensington.

Stephenson & Co. to show their work in the improvement of the locomotive between the foundation of the firm in 1823, and the spring or summer of 1829. But these few drawings give ample evidence of the designers' ingenuity in the striving for improvement which was to lead to the 'Rocket,' the next engine which we have to consider.

Before dealing with this engine we must interrupt our technical notes for a description of the Liverpool and Manchester Railway, whose requirements were to prove the greatest stimulus yet offered to the further development of the locomotive, and within less than a year to render obsolete even the improved types we have just described.

CYLINDER OF THE FIRST STEPHENSON LOCOMOTIVE IN AMERICA, 1829

preserved in the Smithsonian Institution, Washington, U.S.A.

This cylinder is almost identical with that of the 'LANCASHIRE WITCH' as shown by the makers' drawings, and closely resembles the cylinders of the succeeding engines described in this chapter.

CHAPTER XI

THE LIVERPOOL AND MANCHESTER RAILWAY

The advantages which Iron Rail-ways present are immense; England owes to them a part of her wealth . . . . . . never without them could Lime, Coal, Minerals, and other raw Materials, have been conveyed to such Distances, and at the same time, at so trifling an expense.

Baron Dupin's Report to the French Government.

There is on record [1] a remarkable list of tramways and railways which were in existence even before 1821, commencing with the Surrey Iron Railway from Wandsworth to Croydon, and there were others by this date, scattered over England, Wales and Scotland, which without including the colliery railways of the North had an aggregate length of over 200 miles; the longest, from Plymouth to Dartmoor, was about 30 miles. While the Stockton and Darlington Railway was under construction, and even earlier, a few far-seeing men had appreciated the great advantages to be derived from an extended application of the railway system, particularly between such towns as Liverpool and Manchester, both of which had increased in population with phenomenal rapidity during the latter half of the eighteenth century, and by 1820 had a daily traffic between them of about 1,000 tons of merchandise, at the mercy of the canal proprietors, and the carriers, who held what appeared to be an unassailable monopoly.

We have already referred to Thomas Gray's writings, so early as 1820 [2], to show the vast superiority in every respect 'over all the present pitiful methods of conveyance by turn-pike roads, canals, and coasting traders'; he suggests that :—

The plan might be commenced between the towns of Manchester and Liverpool where a trial can soon be made as the distance is not very great and the commercial part of England would thereby be better able to appreciate its many excellent properties and prove its efficiency.

Further on he observes :—

The London and Edinburgh mail steam carriages might take all the mails and parcels on the line of road between these two cities which would exceedingly reduce the expense occasioned by mail coaches on the present footing.

How far William James was influenced by the extensive writings of Gray does not appear, but he became equally enthusiastic on the subject of a railway to be operated by steam power and to carry passengers as well as goods. Though Gray was perhaps the first to broach the subject to the merchants of Liverpool and Manchester, James appears to have completed in November 1822, and submitted to Lord Stanley, certain plans and sections for a railway; he also approached Joseph Sandars, a Liverpool merchant, who became warmly inter-

---

[1] Francis, *A History of the English Railway*, 1851, p. 57 *et seq.*

Observations on a General Iron Railway, 1820, and subsequent editions.

ested and himself guaranteed some of the preliminary expenses. James at the same time, impressed by what he had seen at Killingworth, submitted plans for an 'improved steam engine' as shown on the cover of his pamphlet[1] already mentioned. The design is obviously based on Stephenson's Killingworth engine, then the best at work; in this he was in advance of Gray, who continued to urge the superiority of Blenkinsop's rack and pinion railway. Unfortunately for James he became involved in financial troubles, precipitated it seems by a member of his own family; his health subsequently broke down, with the result that Sandars found it necessary to write to him on 25th May 1824[2] :—

Your letter, dated the 7th inst., is before me. I cannot send you a copy of Hartly's report; it is very long. I think it right to inform you that the committee have engaged your friend Mr. G. Stephenson. We expect him here in a few days.

The subscription list for £300,000 is filled, and the Manchester gentlemen have conceded to us the entire management. I very much regret that, by delay and promises, you have forfeited the confidence of the subscribers. I cannot help it. I fear now that you will only have the fame of being connected with the commencement of this undertaking. If you will send me down your plans and estimates, I will do everything for you I can; and I believe I possess as much influence as any person. I am quite certain that the appointment of Stephenson will, under all circumstances, be agreeable to you. I believe you have recommended him yourself. If you consent to put your plans, etc., under my control and management, your name shall be prominent in the proceedings; and this, in such a mighty affair, will be of importance to you. You may rely upon my zeal for you in every point connected with your reputation.

This letter shows that George Stephenson's connection with the Liverpool and Manchester Railway, which was to affect so vitally his own career and the development of the locomotive, was due in the first instance to the recommendation of James. But that fact does not seem to justify the attacks made in later years on Stephenson's good faith in accepting an appointment for which James had first recommended him, or for reaping certain advantages which James had most tragically lost, through no fault of Stephenson. Robert Stephenson, who had assisted James during his survey[3], makes a feeling allusion to the latter's accumulating misfortunes, in a letter dated 29th August 1823[4] :—

It gives rise to feelings of true regret when I reflect on your situation; but yet a consolation springs up when I consider your persevering spirit will for ever bear you up in the arms of triumph, instances of which I have witnessed of too forcible a character to be easily effaced from my memory. It is these thoughts, and these alone, that could banish from my soul feelings of despair for one (sic); the respect I have for him can be easier conceived than described. Can I ever forget the advice you have afforded me in your last letters? and what a heavenly inducement you pointed before me at the close, when you said that attention and obedience to my dear father would afford me music at midnight. Ah, and so it has already. My father and I set off for London on Monday next, the 1st, on our way to Cork. Our return will probably be about the time you wish me to be at Liverpool. If all be right, we may possibly call and see what is going on. That line is the finest project in England.

[1] *Report or Essay to illustrate the advantages of Direct Inland communication by a Line of Engine Railroad, etc.*, 1823. (See p. 25, Chap. III., *ante*).

[2] *The Two James's and the Two Stephensons*, 1861, p. 59.

[3] *Ibid.*, p. 54.

[4] *Ibid.*, p. 55.

L

A new survey was carried out by George Stephenson under such difficulties as he describes in writing to Joseph Pease on 19th October 1824 [1]:—

We have sad work with Lord Derby, Lord Sefton, and Bradshaw, the great canal proprietor whose grounds we go through with the projected railway. Their ground is blockaded on every side to prevent us getting on with the survey. Bradshaw, fires guns through his grounds in the course of the night, to prevent the surveyor coming on in the dark. We are to have a grand field-day next week. The Liverpool Railway people are determined to force a survey through if possible. Lord Sefton says he will have a hundred men against us. The company think those great men have no right to stop a survey; it is the farmers only who have a right to complain, and by charging damages for trespass, it is all they can do.

The promoters of the first Bill, which was brought before a Select Committee of the House of Commons in March 1825, had to face the opposition of the canal proprietors, and of those interested in the turn-pikes, together with that of the landed proprietors, whose physical resistance made a proper survey very difficult. The combination of these powerful interests would in itself have been sufficient to wreck the Bill, and its opponents found an additional argument in serious errors which were discovered in the levels as stated by the promoters, and they made a full and successful use of this argument. Robert Stephenson refers to this in a letter to Longridge written from South America on 15th December 1825 :—

The failure of the Liverpool and Manchester Act, I fear, will retard much this kind of speculation; but it is clear that they will eventually succeed, and I still anticipate with confidence the arrival of a time when we shall see some of the celebrated canals filled up. It is to be regretted that my father placed the conducting of the levelling under the care of young men without experience. Simple as the process of levelling may appear, it is one of those things that requires care and dexterity in its performance.

On 27th February 1826 Longridge himself writes to Robert :—

Railways still continue to be the fashion though I am sorry to add that your father has not that share of employment which his talents merit. It is expected that the Liverpool and Manchester Bill will pass this session. Perhaps an amended Act will afterwards be procured.
The Newcastle and Carlisle Railway Bill will not be brought into Parliament until another year. Your Father has been employed by the party who oppose this Railway and on examining the line has found greater errors in the levels than were committed by his assistants in the Liverpool road. Robert, my faith in engineers is wonderfully shaken. I hope that when you return to us your accuracy will redeem their character.

On 29th May 1826 he writes from Liverpool :—

Having been informed that you were so soon to return to England I deferred sending off my letter lest you should have left. I now proceed to acquaint you that an Act has been passed for the Liverpool and Manchester Railway and that the first general meeting of the proprietors is this day to be held here. Mr. Rennie has been their engineer.

Longridge adds on 14th June following :—

There was nothing fixed about an Engineer at the Liverpool Meeting—your Father is now in correspondence with some of the Directors and it is probable that it may issue in his being appointed Chief Engineer.

[1] Jeans, *Jubilee Memorial of the Railway System*, p. 55.

After the rejection of their first Bill the promoters had a new survey made, this time by George and John Rennie; well known engineers whose name had a prestige which that of Stephenson had not yet attained, whose evidence would be accepted with less question by other members of their own profession, and who would be less likely to become butts for the wit of parliamentary lawyers. Having obtained their improved revised plans and estimates, and bought off their principal opponents, the promoters were successful in their second attempt, obtaining their Bill on 1st May 1826. After the opening of the line a contemporary journal wrote [1] :—

The Directors having thus through the instrumentality of Messrs. Rennie concluded their labours it was natural to suppose that the execution of the undertaking would have been entrusted to them. The Directors thought otherwise. The whole was most unaccountably taken out of their hands and transferred to those of Mr. Stephenson.

The reasons for the directors' choice are given at length by their secretary [2] :—

It was obvious, that in an undertaking of such magnitude, a *resident* engineer of experience and ability was indispensable; and the Directors naturally turned their attention to Mr. Stephenson, of Newcastle, a gentleman thoroughly acquainted with practical mechanics, and possessing more experience in the construction and working of Railways than perhaps any other individual. The Directors, at the same time, wrote to Messrs. Geo. and John Rennie, requesting them to undertake the professional superintendence of the undertaking. On the 17th of June, Mr. Geo. Rennie had an interview with the Directors, on which occasion the subject was discussed; and, in conclusion, Mr. Rennie proposed to the Directors to superintend the execution of the work, making six visits per annum, and remaining on the ground seven or ten days at each visit, but stipulating, at the same time, that the *resident* Engineer should be of his own appointing. On the 19th of June, the Directors took Mr. Rennie's proposition into consideration. They would have been glad of the professional assistance of Mr. Rennie, but it was their duty to take advantage of the best practical knowledge within their reach. The trust reposed in them, and the responsibility attaching to its due fulfilment, were too weighty to allow of their being much influenced by ordinary punctilios. Their course was direct to the great object they had in view. Mr. Rennie's proposition was respectfully declined, and Mr. George Stephenson was elected Principal Engineer to the Company.

These reasons must be accepted as conclusive, but the facts must be remembered to the credit of the two Rennies, and of Charles B. Vignoles, who planned much of the work afterwards executed by Stephenson, and at first assisted him. The accomplishment of the stupendous task was however left to Stephenson and his assistants, among them John Dixon, who was appointed resident engineer of the Chat Moss section [3]; those who are interested will find in the evidence for the first Bill some idea of both the physical difficulties, and the prejudices, with which Stephenson had to contend. The technical details of the construction of the line are beyond the scope of these notes, we have here simply to consider the demands made by the Liverpool and Manchester Railway on the locomotive and their effect on its development; so far as the railway

---

[1] *Gentleman's Magazine*, October, 1830, Vol. C. part 2, p. 351.

[2] Booth, *An Account of the Liverpool and Manchester Railway*, 1830, p. 37.

[3] John Dixon's *MSS.* preserved by his nephew, Mr. Waynman Dixon; they include an account of Chat Moss supplied by Dixon to Smiles for his *Life of George Stephenson*.

from an aquatint by T. T. Bury, published by R. Ackermann, February 1831.

THE TUNNEL

from an aquatint by T. T. Bury, published by R. Ackermann, February 1831.

VIEW OF THE RAILWAY ACROSS CHAT MOSS

itself is concerned we must be content with recording here the opinion of the directors 'after a journey of inspection and trial of one of their new locomotive engines.' At a board meeting on 14th June 1830 it was resolved :—

That the Directors cannot allow this opportunity to pass without expressing their strong sense of the great skill and unwearied energy displayed by their engineer, Mr. George Stephenson, which have so far brought this great national work to a successful termination, and which promise to be followed by results so beneficial to the country at large, and to the proprietors of this concern.

During the journey there and back, the weather was too wet to allow a minute inspection of the cuttings and embankings, or of the works generally. But the Directors were particularly pleased with the state of the roadway over Parr Moss and Chat Moss and the performance of the engine was highly satisfactory.

The construction of the railway alone, whether through the ground or floated on a bog, was in itself a career, but for George Stephenson it meant something more ; it meant the making of a road for the steam locomotive. Robert too shared his enthusiasm [1] :—

I will fight for them until the last, they are worthy of a conflict.

It was however one thing to make a railway, another to persuade all his directors to use locomotives on it, and George Stephenson found himself again the champion of the locomotive ; not now against the horse but against the fixed engine and rope haulage. Fortunately there were on the board of the railway company several men who shared his faith, and themselves showed a more than usual ability to grasp the essentials of the problem before them ; there was also the company's secretary and treasurer, Henry Booth, a capable and versatile man [2], who seems to have realized quickly that improvement in the steaming power of the locomotive boiler was one key to the solution of the problem, and was himself heartily engaged with Stephenson in experimental work to this end. There were others with a different view, among them James Cropper, but their minutes show that the board as a whole were prepared to consider any reasonable proposal for locomotive engines, and they record that on 29th September 1828 :—

A discussion took place on the various and contradictory accounts which prevailed with respect to the power and relative economy of Locomotive Engines on the Darlington Railway, as compared with Horses. The subject being of the first importance it was considered desirable that one or two of the Directors, accompanied by the Treasurer should proceed to Darlington to ascertain as correctly as practicable the result of the experience on that Line, taking into the account, first cost, wear and tear, both of the Engines and the Road, and as far as possible all the circumstances involved in the question.

Cropper and Booth, who had been appointed to the deputation, afterwards visited Darlington—'the great theatre of practical operations where all the established modes of conveying carriages on railways were exemplified, Horses, Locomotives and Fixed Engines.' To the report of this deputation their engineer replied, on 5th November 1828, in a document which has fortunately been

---

[1] Jeaffreson, *Life of Robert Stephenson*, Vol. I., p. 124.

[2] The screw coupling for railway rolling stock was invented by Henry Booth. Lecount, *Treatise on Railways*, 1839, p. 191.

preserved [1]; it has for railwaymen even to-day something more than an academic interest, and we therefore quote in full the :—

REPORT BY GEORGE STEPHENSON TO THE DIRECTORS OF THE LIVERPOOL AND MANCHESTER RAILWAY.

5th November, 1828.

GENTLEMEN,

Agreeably with your request I have examined the report, drawn up by the Deputation, which visited the North.

Respecting the detailed account taken from the Darlington Railway I have little to remark further than that Locomotive Engines, will be found to do much more work upon the Liverpool & Manchester Line of Road than they can possibly do on the Darlington Line, and that the wear and tear of Engines made on the improved plan will not be one half of that at present.

I may observe that the wear and tear of the Stationary Engines on the Darlington Railway is not noticed by the Deputation.

With reference to the wear and tear of the Rails by Locomotive Engines, I readily admit that on the Darlington Rly. where the road is very slight some effect may be perceived, but on this Line I do not see how any just comparison can be drawn; here we have, however, Rails and blocks, and what is of much more consequence, a better foundation for them to rest upon, besides having fewer and less acute curves; all which will have a great tendency to preserve the good condition of the road.

On the Bandon and Wideopen Railway, where Stationary Engines are employed, had the Deputation remained at the changing places any length of time I have no doubt they would have found, that the stoppages or delays exceed what they now appear to anticipate.

The good state of the road is easily accounted for by the light loads, which are carried on it.

The wear and tear of ropes is certainly at variance, not only with my experience, but also with the information which the Deputation themselves received on the Hetton Railway.

In this instance they attribute the increased consumption to the acuteness of the curves. I concede that this cause does operate, but I cannot admit the difference calculated upon in the report. I still remain of opinion that on this Road the expence of Ropes will much exceed the estimated sum.

I shall now proceed to examine some of the items in the estimate made by the Deputation.

In their estimate on the necessary capital for fixed Engines, they reckon a 14-horse Engine will lead over one mile 1,600 Tons of goods per day. From the following calculation this power is evidently inadequate. The friction of the rope, that is the resistence which the rope makes to the fixed Engines, over and above that of the carriages and load being very important, it is necessary to determine it with some precision before we proceed to calculate the requisite power for moving the load. In ascertaining this particular I have been guided by my experience on planes where the descending load is found bearly sufficient to overcome the resistence of the rope, from which I find that a mile of 4 in. rope, weighing 32 cwts., will require a power equal to $2\frac{3}{4}$ horses moving at the rate of $2\frac{1}{2}$ miles per hour. Again, the effect of a horse-power upon a Railroad is now well known from numerous experiments to be equal to 10 Tons of goods moved at the rate of $2\frac{1}{2}$ miles per hour. It is therefore evident that 20 tons (*the load calculated upon in the report*) without ropes will require 2 horses at the rate of $2\frac{1}{2}$ miles per hour and to this add $2\frac{1}{4}$ horses, the requisite power for the ropes, will give $4\frac{3}{4}$ horses the power required for moving both rope and load at that speed.

But as the speed is reckoned at 10 miles per hour, and the power required increasing in the direct ratio of the velocity it is obvious that a power of 19 horses will be required at each station to drag the above load.

Let us now endeavour to ascertain if each load containing 20 Tons of goods moving at the rate of 10 miles per hour is adapted for the conveyance of 1,600 Tons per day in one direction as stated by the Deputation.

[1] At the Euston Offices of the London, Midland and Scottish (formerly London and North Western) Railway Company.

It is clear that the load will pass from station to station in six minutes; on the arrival of the load the rope must be detached from the waggon and attached to the tail ropes, when a signal must be given, before the other Engines can commence, let us allow for this, one minute at each end (surely no one can suppose that it can be done in less) and also that the rope returns at the rate of 15 miles per hour, which gives for each trip 12 minutes or 5 loads per hour, or for 12 hours 60 loads of 20 Tons each=1,200 Tons per day.

In this calculation the operations are supposed to go on with the utmost celerity without any provision being made for the slightest accident; yet notwithstanding this it is evident that not more than 1,200 Tons can possibly be conveyed in twelve hours. On this data the following Estimate is made. The cost of ropes I take as stated in the Report, viz.—1d. per Ton for the whole distance.

Capital for Fixed Engines.

54 engines, 19 horses each at £1,200	£64,800
Sheaves	£7,128
Extra power, say	£1,740
Cost of ropes	£6,500
Contingencies	£832
	£81,000

Interest on capital at 7½% is £6,075, which divided into 2,400 tons per day gives 1·94d. per ton for the whole distance.

Working the Fixed Engines. I will take as detailed in the report, viz., 11,500 annually which divided into 2,400 Tons per day gives 3·67d. per ton for the whole distance.

Attendance upon trains and oil for carriages I will also take at 1·25d. per ton for the whole distance.

Summary of Expenses per Ton by Fixed Engines.

Ropes	1·00d.
Capital	1·94d.
Working engine, etc.	3·67d.
Attendance, oil, etc.	1·25d.
	7·86d.

Locomotive Engines.—The Deputation in making their calculations on the expense of conveying goods by this kind of Engine have taken the price per ton paid upon the Stockton and Darlington Railroad as their guide, viz., ¼d. per Ton per mile.

This data is far from being applicable to the Liverpool & Manchester Road, for in the former the descents and ascents in the line are beyond what is desirable, and moreover the load is solely in one direction. The engines therefore have to travel over one half the distance without any useful effect whatever which is a disadvantage I do not contemplate on this road, indeed, if we go so far as to suppose the load even on this road altogether in one direction the Engines would produce a greater effect than on the Darlington Road not having in any instance to contend with ascents that would materially reduce their performance.

The following is an estimate of expense of leading goods by Locomotive Engines on the Liverpool & Manchester line :—

48 Engines @ £600=£28,800=Capital.

Interest of this sum at 7½%	£2,160
Repairs at £50 per annum including wheels, Fire bars, etc.	2,400
One Engineer and boy at each Engine	3,840
Each Engine 250 tons of coals at 7/-	4,200
Oil Hemp, &c., &c.	480
	£13,080

This sum divided into 2,400 Tons per annum gives 4·18d. per ton for the whole distance, to which must be added ¼d. per ton for oiling the waggons, making the total cost by Locomotive Engines 4·43d. per ton for the whole distance. Being rather more than ½ the expense by Stationary Engines there will consequently accrue to the Company an annual saving in the items of leading of £10,000.

It will be observed that in the above calculation £50 has been allowed for the annual cost of repairing Locomotive Engines, which exceeds that thought sufficient by the Deputation after having minutely investigated the charges at Darlington. The same caution has been adhered to throughout the whole of the items, and particularly with respect to the consumption of coals, where it will be seen that more is allowed for one Locomotive Engine than for one 19-horse permanent Engine.

Fixed Engines.—In reply to the remarks made against fixed Engines I shall take them as they are placed in the report:—

- 1st. The greater capital required is an objection too well understood to require any comment from me.
- 2nd. The crossing of public roads with Ropes would assuredly be very objectionable unless bridges were built which would require a still further increase of capital as well as make very abrupt ascents in crossing these roads where the Railway now crosses on a level. But a still greater difficulty than this exists, in preventing the occupier of such lands as may lie between the Engine Stations, from having that free access to and use of the Railway, to which by the present Act of Parliament he is entitled.
- 3rd. I should conceive that 54 Stationary Engines of 19 horse-power each would emit as much smoke as 48 Locomotives, therefore this objection applies as much to one mode as to the other.
- 4th. This remark is by far the most important of the whole and admits of being widely enlarged upon. It will, I think, be readily admitted that where an engine is working for twelve hours a day, one accident in twelve months may be expected, and I will suppose that it only requires three hours to repair the damage. It must not be forgotten that this delay is experienced throughout the whole line for this space of time, and that there are 54 Engines, which will make a total yearly stoppage of 162 hours, equal 13½ days, or a reduction of the quantity of goods conveyed of 16,200 tons per annum.

  Accidents with the ropes I consider still more probable than with the Engines to which the last objection applies with equal force. I will suppose further that a waggon should get off the way when the train is moving at 10 miles per hour (and this may be expected to occur sometimes) the rope must either break or the waggons continue to move forward, which would be serious on high embankments. The consequence is you may conceive in case of such an accident on Broad Green.
- 5th. You are no doubt well aware of the prejudice existing in the public mind, to require any observations from me.

Locomotive Engines.—The Directors are aware that an apparatus for experiments is now in progress for ascertaining the practicability of burning coke or materially reducing the smoke from half baked coal the result of these experiments will probably be laid before you in a fortnight.

The second objection alleged against Locomotive Engines will certainly not be found to operate for in the whole of our deep excavations, there will be found to exist a continual current of air which will prevent the lodgment of sulphurous vapors, but without the aid of such a current, the velocity of the Engines and carriages will of themselves cause agitation in the air, quite sufficient to obviate any inconveniences on this score. The smoke emitted from a locomotive Engine cannot equal the smoke from the chimnie in a line of Street where the inconvenience is not felt.

In answer to the third objection let us suppose for the sake of argument that the rails sustain some injury from the Locomotive Engines. The extent of this injurious effect has been drawn from the Darlington Railway where the Rails are certainly too light, and the Engines moving on four wheels, which of course transfers the weight of the Engine to the rails by four points only; but if six wheels are employed the weight upon the rails becomes reduced in the ratio of 3 : : 2. This alteration which amounts to the same per thing as reducing the weight of the Engine together with the additional strength of the rails used on the Liverpool and Manchester line in a great degree removes the objection.

But I will go further and suppose that the rails are injured and in thirty years they are so reduced in strength that new ones are required from end to end of the line. The whole weight of a single line of road 30 miles in length is 1,650 Tons. This quantity let us suppose that by wear and tear is reduced one-fifth, there will remain—

1,320 tons at £8 per ton	....	....	....	....	....	....	£10,560
1,650 tons at £12 ,, —the original cost		....	....	....	....		19,800
Wear and tear of rails in 30 years	....	....	....	....	....		£9,240

during which time 1,600 tons per day have passed along the road, making a charge for the above expense of $\frac{147}{1000}$ of a penny for the whole distance, or $\frac{1}{200}$ of a penny per ton per mile.

In this explanatory calculation I am aware that nothing appears for relaying the rails, but there is ample allowance made for it in the reduction, in the weight and also in the price of the worn out rails.

The difficulty of crossing Chat Moss is not so serious as is generally imagined. The Engines being placed upon 6 wheels is one step towards removing this objection but I am decidedly of opinion that the yeilding of the moss will be entirely overcome when the covering which we are now spreading over the surface for receiving the rails and sleepers, becomes compacted.

Let us suppose however that the moss does yeild it is easy to allow the Locomotive Engines to travel at some distance before the train of waggons and to carry this idea still further the train of waggons might also be divided into such portions as may be found most desirable by experiments. It is sufficient for the present to prove that the difficulty brought forward does not militate against the Locomotive Engine.

The fifth objection that 20 or 30 Locomotives would be in the way at one end of the line is certainly true if so many are allowed to come together, but this ought never to be the case. Different stations ought to be prepared on the line in situations where this objection would not apply. Such an arrangement would certainly be found indispensible to secure regularity.

I do not see that it is necessary for more than 10 to be together at any one station a number very easily managed. No bustle or inconveniences whatever arises from 6 being together at Darlington nor would there be if the number were doubled.

From 10 to 12 I consider quite a manageable number, there is no necessity for having more at one station.

General Observations. I now beg leave to lay before you a few other observations, which appear to have escaped the notice of the Deputation.

To the mode of conveying intelligence from one station to another there is also a great objection. In clear weather a flag or Telegraph is found to answer the best purpose providing there are no obstructions; but in dull thick weather this mode cannot be available. A Bell is the next method, which is very uncertain from the variations of the wind and in calm weather the number of Bells at the different stations would be apt to misguide.

The next is by attaching the rope to the Engine which is pulled a few yards so as to communicate motion to the adjoining station, and although this is the most certain way in all weathers, there is necessarily a great loss of time and puts the dispatch calculated upon quite out of the question.

It must be expected that most of the embankments will shrink for a few years after operations are commenced and from time to time will require ballasting to keep the level. The ballast must be brought to the place by a waggon which must either be attached to the rope or a separate road laid down for the purpose. The former plan will involve the stoppage of the work the latter an additional expense. It is evident that whatever be the power of the fixed Engines proposed to be erected, the quantity of goods which they will convey must be limited, which is not the case with Locomotives for these may be increased in proportion as the trade increases, and setting aside the two ends of the line, there would not be more bustle in leading 10,000 Tons per day by the latter mode, than there would be in leading 2,400 by the former.

It is quite certain from the number of branches which will join this main line, that the trade in different parts will fluctuate exceedingly. This circumstance renders it imperative to employ more powerful Engines and stronger Ropes than will be required for the general traffic.

For instance a large quantity of coal will be sent from the Whiston Collieries to Liverpool. The Engines and ropes between Liverpool and that place must be made stronger than has been calculated upon in the report of the Deputation. The capital therefore which they have assumed must be modified and much difficulty will be experienced in adjusting the powers of the various Engines on the line excepting indeed, that they are all made very powerful to meet any contingent increase. If this provision be not made we may suppose that goods from Manchester or that end of the line, are equal to the full performance of the Engines in this case the goods from the intervening places as Whiston, Rain Hill, &c., must be detained until the more distant trade subsides.

These difficulties which will inevitably be experienced, are from the very nature of Locomotive power simply and most effectually obviated. Should the trade at any part undergo a temporary increase or decrease the necessary power may be immediately applied or withdrawn and disposed of as circumstances may require.

It is also clear that if permanent Engines be adopted, every branch Railway must form a junction at an Engine and a train from the branch must be joined to the train in the main line by the aid of horses or men.

At each end of the Line Locomotive Engines would have a desired advantage, in dragging and moving the carriages backwards and forwards amongst the various branches, which will certainly be required; and not only at the ends of the line but at every situation where goods are to be delivered upon the line.

When these observations have been duly considered by the Directors they will perceive that in point of convenience and dispatch the two systems do not bear a comparison.

I am Gentlemen,

Your obedt. servt.

(*Signed*) GEO. STEPHENSON.

Nov. 5th, 1828.

P.S.—It is perhaps necessary to add that in the above estimate of the expenses by fixed Engines, I have taken the items generally from those stated by the Deputation. In doing this it must not be concluded that I consider them scrupulously correct.

For instance the Engines are taken at the precise power the traffic requires, I have never thought it advisable in any instance to calculate in this manner.

Again, there will be required on Chat Moss at least 3 Engines if not 5, that will need to be supported entirely on piles. I would estimate £1,000 each above the average price £1,200 which is certainly very moderate including appurtenances.

There are other points which would admit of further observations.

(*Initialled*) G. S.

The directors' minutes subsequently record, on 6th November 1828:—

A discussion of great length took place, after which it was Ordered, That Mr. Stephenson's Report be lithographed for the use of the Directors: and the Treasurer was instructed to write to Mr. Ben Thompson to enquire whether he would object to a Deputation (including one or two professional or scientific men) visiting his Railway with a view to ascertain what quantity of work could be performed in 12 hours, on two successive days. Also the power of the engines and such other particulars as may be found requisite to afford complete information on the subject.

Benjamin Thompson of the Brunton and Shields Railway who is referred to in this minute was a convinced advocate of fixed engines, and had carried on a heated newspaper controversy[1] with Nicholas Wood, the equally convinced advocate of locomotives.

On 17th November 1828 the minutes record :—

Read several letters from Mr. Braithwaite and Mr. Cropper on the subject of Locomotive and Fixed Engines, and decidedly recommending the use of this latter power on the Liverpool and Manchester line : A discussion at some length took place, after which with a view to obtain the most complete and satisfactory information on the comparative merits of the two descriptions of mechanical power, It was Resolved, That Mr. Walker of Lime House, Civil Engineer, and Mr. Rastrick of Stourbridge, be written to, requesting them to undertake a journey to Darlington, Newcastle, and the neighbourhood to ascertain by actual inspection and investigation the comparative merits of Fixed Engines and Locomotives, as a moving power on Railways, and especially with reference to the Liverpool and Manchester Line ; and to visit Liverpool on their way to the North, in order to receive from the Directors more specific instructions as to the several points on which their professional opinion would be required.

Subsequently, on 12th January 1829 :—

Mr. Walker and Mr. Rastrick attended according to appointment, when the written instructions agreed on, were read, and handed to them, with section of the Line of Railway, after which a discussion took place on the general objects of their mission to the Railways in the North. As to the speed with which Passengers were proposed to be conveyed they were informed that 8 miles per hour was the lowest rate that could be allowed, and that a quicker speed was desirable. They were further informed that as regards the Locomotive Engine, they need not consider themselves restricted by the smoke clause in the Act of Parliament, but make their estimate and calculations as if no such clause existed.

Eventually, on 9th March 1829 :—

The Treasurer laid on the Table separate Reports from Mr. Walker and Mr. Rastrick on the subject of Locomotive and Fixed Engines. Mr. Walker's Report was read, after which it was Resolved, That 500 copies of the two Reports be printed in the form of an octavo pamphlet.

This is the report[2] from which we have already quoted in reference to the locomotives of the Stockton and Darlington Railway and the 'Lancashire Witch'; it concludes with Walker's summing up on the question which he had to investigate :—

Your next inquiry is, 'Whether goods and passengers can be conveyed upon the two lines already provided, and if so by what system the desired object can be best attained?'

Upon the consideration of the question in every point of view, taking the two lines of road as now forming, and having reference to *economy*, *despatch*, *safety* and *convenience*, our opinion is, that if it be resolved to make the Liverpool and Manchester Railway complete at once, so as to accommodate the traffic stated in your instructions, or a quantity approaching to it, the *stationary reciprocating* system is the *best*; but that if any circumstances should induce you to proceed by degrees and to proportion the power of conveyance to the demand, then we recommend *loco-motive* Engines upon the line generally, and *two fixed* Engines upon *Rainhill* and *Sutton* planes, to draw up the loco-motive Engines, as well as the goods and carriages.

Should the latter plan be adopted, you would of course only order such a number of Engines as you might see occasion for, both on account of saving expense, and to enable you to take

---

[1] *Newcastle Magazine*, 16th March, 1822.

[2] *Report on the Comparative Merits of Locomotive and Fixed Engines*, 1829.

advantage of the improvements which might be made; with a view to encourage which, and to draw the attention of Engine-makers to the subject, something in the way of a premium, or an assurance of preference, might be held to the person whose Engine should, upon experience, be found to answer the best. The Rainhill Engines would at the same time enable you to judge of the comparative advantages of the two systems, and if upon any occasion the trade should get beyond the supply of *loco-motives*, the *horse* might form a temporary substitute.

On 13th April 1829 the directors read George Stephenson's observations on the reports of both Walker and Rastrick, and after a lengthy conversation 'on the advantages and disadvantages of the two kinds of mechanical moving power' the discussion was adjourned. But so far had their minds remained open on the subject that, on 20th April 1829 :—

It was Resolved as a preliminary point that in the opinion of the Board it would not be expedient, at the present moment, to adopt any system of moving power which would preclude the Company from Benefiting by any Mechanical Improvements in the conveyance of Carriages on Railways that may hereafter take place, and that therefore to determine on a system of Fixed Engines for the whole line would not be advisable.

A further discussion then took place on the advantages and disadvantages of Stationary and Locomotive Engines, after which it was Resolved that it is desirable to postpone the further discussion of the subject till the Locomotive Engine which has been ordered, and is expected to arrive in about a month, has been tried.[1]

Resolved that a Premium of £500 be advertised for a Locomotive Engine which shall be a decided improvement on those now in use, as respects the consumption of smoke, increased speed, adequate power, and moderate weight, the particulars of which shall be specified in detail by the Preparation Committee.

On 4th May 1829 :—

A discussion took place on the subject of the Premium of £500 for the most Improved Locomotive Engine, and especially whether it was essential that it should be a Steam Engine, or whether any improvement in the Carriages or Waggons by which a greater weight could be drawn by the same power would be entitled to the Prize. The Board was of opinion that it was not essential that the Locomotive should be a Steam Engine: what was required was an *improved Moving Power*. Any improvements in the waggons therefore would not be entitled to the Premium but might be matter for separate negotiation.

After this there are many interesting references in the minutes to proposals by engineers and engine-makers offering to compete for the premium, and others not mentioned were afterwards described with a delightful humour by Booth [2] :—

Multifarious were the schemes proposed to the Directors, for facilitating Locomotion. Communications were received from all classes of persons, each recommending an improved power or an improved carriage; from professors of philosophy, down to the humblest mechanic all were zealous in their proffers of assistance; England, America, and Continental Europe were alike tributary. Every element and almost every substance were brought into requisition, and made subservient to the great work. The friction of the carriages was to be reduced so low that a silk thread would draw them, and the power to be applied was to be so vast as to rend a cable asunder. Hydrogen gas and high-pressure steam—columns of water and columns of mercury—a hundred atmospheres and a perfect vacuum—machines working in a circle without fire or steam, generating power at one end of the process and giving it out at the other—carriages that conveyed, everyone its own Railway—wheels within wheels, to multiply speed without diminishing power—with every complication of balancing and countervailing forces,

[1] This was the 'Liverpool Coke Engine' or 'Twin Sisters,' described on p. 155, Chapter X. *ante*.
[2] *An Account of the Liverpool and Manchester Railway*, 1830, p. 69.

to the *ne plus ultra* of perpetual motion. Every scheme which the restless ingenuity or prolific imagination of man could devise was liberally offered to the Company; the difficulty was to choose and to decide.

The directors' minutes record that on 18th May 1829 was :—

Read a letter from Timothy Hackworth of the Darlington Railway enquiring whether if he were to make a Locomotive Engine which should be *very nearly* as complete and good in all respects as the one which should gain the premium, the Directors in that case would *purchase* his engine. The Treasurer was instructed to reply that the Directors would be disposed to deal liberally with the Proprietor of an Engine under those circumstances, but strictly they were not under obligation to purchase more than one Engine.

On 29th June 1829 was :—

Read a letter from Mr. William Brown to Mr. Moss on the subject of the Prize Locomotive Engine, enquiring whether it was essential that it should be a Steam Engine or whether a Gas Engine might be entitled to the Prize. Mr. Moss was requested to reply to Mr. Brown that the best Engine, all things taken into consideration, would be entitled to the Premium, whether it was a Steam or a Gas Engine.

On 7th September 1829 was :—

Read a Letter from Mr. Crawshaw of Merthyr Tydvil, requesting to know the Stipulations and conditions on which the Premium was offered for the most improved Locomotive Engine.

Mr. Tayleur stated that he had paid a visit to Mr. Foster's and Lord Dudley's Railway in Staffordshire (accompanied by the Treasurer and Engineer) and had inspected the Locomotive Engine made by Mr. Rastrick, and which drew the Coal Waggons for a length of about 2 miles between the Inclined Planes on that Railway. The Road descended about 16 feet in the mile, and the Engine moved smoothly from 9 to 12 miles per hour with about 20 tons of coal in 6 waggons. The Engine made very little of the puffing noise so common in Locomotive Engines. There was a Glass Tube to show the height of water in the Boiler which Mr. Tayleur thought a very desirable appendage. Coke, half burnt, was the fuel used, and there was very little smoke. The Engine was not fully loaded, but it exhibited the practicability of moving at a speed of from 10 to 12 miles per hour with ease and smoothness.

Meanwhile, on 31st August 1829, it had been ordered :—

That the place of tryal for the Specimen Engines on the 1st October next, be the level space between the two inclined Planes at Rainhill; and that the Engineer prepare a double Railway for the two miles of level, and a single line from Rainhill down the plane to the Roby Embankment.

Resolved, That Mr. Rastrick and Mr. Nicholas Wood be written to, to request their attendance professionally on the first or second week in October, to inspect the construction and working of the Locomotive Engines which may be produced for tryal, and to report to the Directors the result of their investigation. Mr. Hodgson was requested to write to Mr. John Kennedy of Manchester to beg the favour of his joining the above professional gentlemen, in their examination of the different Engines, in order that the Directors may benefit by his judgment on the respective merits of the Machines produced.

Two letters were then read from Mr. O. W. Hahr and Mr. Timothy Burstall, giving notice of two Locomotive Engines to be offered for trial on the 1st October.

On 14th September 1829 :—

Mr. Stephenson was requested to report to the Directors what measures, in the way of precaution, it would be requisite to adopt, to prevent accident from the insufficiency of the valves or from any other cause. Mr. Stephenson was also instructed to affix a second safety valve to the Locomotive Engine at Eccles, which should be at liberty to work, and be out of the control of the Engineman, at all times.

After discussion it was Ordered, That the Specimen Engines on their arrival at Liverpool may be brought to the Company's yard at Millfield, there to be put together by the Company's men, under the Direction of the Proprietors of the Engines, or their Superintendents.

On 28th September 1829 :—

The Treasurer stated that two Locomotives (Specimen Engines) had arrived at the Yard. The one belonging to Mr. Burstall and the other to himself and Messrs. Stephenson. Also that Mr. Brandreth had called to give notice that he should have ready on the day appointed a Locomotive Horse Engine, called a Cycloped, which he would submit to inspection with the other engines.

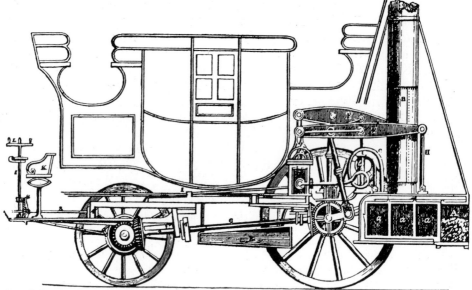

from Galloway's History and Progress of the Steam Engine, 1831, p. 522.

PATENT STEAM COACH BY MESSRS. BURSTALL AND HILL, OF LONDON AND EDINBURGH 1824.

('The mechanical combinations' in the Perseverance 'are nearly similar')

The Treasurer stated on behalf of Mr. Burstall, that part of his Steam Engine was not on springs, and that he had not provided a mercurial Steam Gauge, as he had a valve with a graduated scale of weights which he thought answered the purpose better. The Directors declined entering into any discussion respecting a compliance or non-compliance with the Stipulations and Conditions prescribed.

On 5th October 1829 :—

The Treasurer reported, There were now four Specimen Engines to contend for the Premium, viz. :—

    One built by Robt. Stephenson & Co., Newcastle.
    One ,,   ,, Mr. Burstall of Leith.
    One ,,   ,, Mr. Hackworth of Darlington.
    One ,,   ,, Mr. Braithwaite of London.

Here we will leave the other starters to their own devices, and consider the steps which had been taken by the Stephensons in preparation for the trial on which, not only their own reputation, but that of the steam locomotive, was to depend.

CHAPTER XII

THE 'ROCKET'

THE
MULTI-TUBULAR
BOILER We have described the various stages by which the idea of a multitubular locomotive boiler was being arrived at in England, the last recorded being the twin flue arrangement of the 'Lancashire Witch,' each flue containing its own fireplace. The logical development, in the locomotive, by multiplication into a bundle of small tubes is ascribed to Henry Booth, with whom George Stephenson had been for some time in close collaboration. Certain it is that Booth was directly interested in the 'Rocket' which is referred to [1] 'as belonging to himself and Messrs. Stephenson,' and though it is now impossible to define his particular contribution to the ideas embodied in its boiler, and what was equally important, its firebox [2], we have Robert Stephenson's statement that, whatever may have been done elsewhere and previously, the successful establishment of the multitubular boiler was 'more immediately owing to the suggestion of Mr. Henry Booth and to his father's practical knowledge in carrying it out'. [3] Here again we must note the son's modest silence as to his own share in the work; but Phipps, who had himself taken part, wrote many years later [4]:—

It must not be supposed that when Mr. Robert Stephenson decided upon the construction of the Rocket there were no difficulties to be overcome in the application of Mr. Booth's invention, for many a time good inventors fail of success through the absence of sufficient care and mechanical skill. Having made the original drawings under Mr. Robert Stephenson, I can bear witness to the care and judgment bestowed by him upon every detail. In the arrangement of the tubes, with the method of securing their extremities, the detached firebox, and many other matters of detail, all requiring much consideration, Mr. Stephenson was well aided in all the mechanical details by the late Mr. William Hutchinson.

In addition to this testimony we fortunately have, in his letters to Henry Booth, a record of the part played by Robert Stephenson himself during the construction of the 'Rocket'; they describe graphically the various critical stages and great practical difficulties which were successfully overcome, and we shall leave them to tell their own story. [5]

[1] Liverpool and Manchester Railway Directors' Minutes 28th September 1829.

[2] Nicholas Wood in his *Address on the two late Eminent Engineers*, 1860, states:—'Mr. Booth laid claim to the merit of having suggested to Mr. Stepenson that as Hackworth's engines on the Stockton and Darlington Railway which had a double or return tube raised more steam than Stephenson's engine with a single tube, the application of more tubes might be useful. Stephenson however never admitted that this communication was of any assistance to him in the adoption of the multitubular principle of tubes and outside firebox.

[3] Robert Stephenson's 'Narrative of his Father's Inventions,' Smiles, *Lives of the Engineers*, 1862, Vol. III., p. 469.

[4] 'Links in the History of the Locomotive,' No. IX., *The Engineer*, 1883 Vol. L., p. 217.

[5] The original letters were destroyed by fire when on exhibition at Brussels, but photographs have been preserved at the Euston Offices of the London, Midland and Scottish (formerly London and North Western) Railway Company, by whose permission they are reprinted here.

Mechanics' Magazine,

MUSEUM, REGISTER, JOURNAL, AND GAZETTE.

No. 324.]   SATURDAY, OCTOBER 24, 1829.   [Price 3*d*.

"THE ROCKET," LOCOMOTIVE STEAM ENGINE OF MR. ROBERT STEPHENSON.

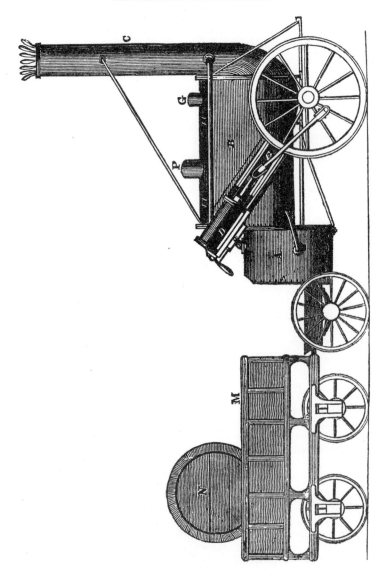

[The earliest known contemporary illustration of the 'Rocket']

NEWCASTLE UPON TYNE,
Aug. 3rd 1829.

MY DEAR SIR,

Since my arrival arrangements have been made which I expect will enable us to have the premium Eng. working in the Factory say this day 3 weeks—this will give us time to make experiments or any alterations that may suggest themselves. The tubes are nearly all made, the whole number will be completed by to-morrow night, they are an excellent job—the only point I consider at all doubtful is the clinking[1] of the ends of the tubes.

The Body of the boiler is finished and is a good piece of workmanship. The cylinder and other parts of the Engine are in a forward state. After weighing such parts as are in progress the following is an Estimate of the weight:—

	c.	q.	lbs.
Boiler, without the tubes	9	3	7
25 Copper tubes	4	2	22
Frame carriages and Bolts	4	3	3
1 pair of 4 ft. 8½ in. wheels and axle	13	1	0
1 pair of waggon wheels and axle	5	0	0
4 Springs and Bolts	2	0	20
Copper fire place including bars, etc.	6	0	0
Chimney and soot	2	0	0
4 Supports for Boiler on Frame	1	2	4
2 Engines complete each 8 cwt.	16	0	0
Water in Main Boiler	11	3	0
Water in Copper fire box	3	0	0
Cwt.	80	0	0

This weight I believe will cover everything. The wheels I am arranging so as to throw 2½ Tuns upon the large wheels in order to get friction upon the rail. *Will there be any fatal objection raised to this?* You had better get the tender made in Liverpool, the coach makers that made the last tender will make one neater than our men. The barrel might be covered with something like the body of a coach. It may be made lighter than the last.

We are daily expecting the arrival of the fire box.[2] I hope you will despatch it as quickly as possible, as we shall require it in 4 or 5 days.

I have heard from Dixon that the Iron hoops are failing upon the Locomotive at that end of the line. Supposing that you would require spare wheels I have ordered 4 metal ones to be got ready immediately, if you do not mean to have any spare ones, they can be used elsewhere. I thought it might be useful to have them ready. I am apprehensive that wooden wheels will be abandoned; a pair of them failed at Darlington some time ago—on the common waggons they appear to stand well—The failure of the hoops on travelling Engine I am inclined to attribute to the horizontal connecting rods confining the wheels when partially and unequally worn to revolve in the same time whilst the circumferences are unequal. This indeed, appears the only distinction between the two applications. In the small Engine the objection will not exist, and I am further persuaded a considerable loss of power is to be ascribed to this defect.

Yours most respectfully,

ROB. STEPHENSON.

I will write you in a few days detailing Hackworth's plan of boiler, it is ingenius but it will not destroy the smoke with coal, which I understand is intended to form a portion of his fuel; coke will be the remainder—he does not appear to understand that a coke fire will only burn briskly where the escape of the carbonic acid gas is immediate.

[1] North Country and Scotch, corresponds to 'clinch' or 'clench,' *i.e.*—to rivet.

[2] Enquiries have failed to discover the name of the makers of the firebox.

If the two large wheels having $2\frac{1}{2}$ Tuns upon them is an objection, please inform me, some reduction may perhaps be made, but it must be very little or the friction upon the rail will be inadequate to the load assigned.

NEWCASTLE UPON TYNE,
August 21st 1829.

MY DEAR SIR,

Having been a good deal from home since I wrote you last, I have not had an opportunity of writing you particulars of our progress so promptly as I promised. The tubes are all clunk into the Boiler which is placed on the frame :--wheels, springs, and axle carriages are all finished. The clinking of the tubes is tight with boiling water. I am arranging the hydraulic pump to prove the Boiler up to 160 lbs. before proceeding any further. The cylinders and working gear is very nearly finished. I expect the mode for changing the gear will please you it is now as simple as I can make it and I believe effectual. The fire box is put into its place, but it is not quite square built which gives rise to a little apparent neglect in the workmanship, I have endeavoured to hide it as much as possible. To-morrow week I expect we shall be ready for trial in the evening.

I should like much to see you at N Castle on the following Monday to make further trial, so that we might consult respecting any alterations that may suggest themselves during trial.

I will write you between now and then to say positively when we shall make the trial, in the meantime let me know if you could get away from L.'pool. My father may perhaps also come altho he had better not be pressed for fear of something happening in his absence. Hackworth's boiler you will comprehend from the following rough sketch [see photo]. He has a double tube as usual, but he makes the boiler only 5 ft. long. Beyond the length he supplies the defficiency in length by a small cylinder around the fire tube which he makes surround it $\frac{1}{2}$ inch from it; this clearly saves weight, but I think not to the extent he anticipated for his boiler when finished including tubes weighs 2 tuns, 3 or 4 cwt. he saves in water decidedly in this point we are about equal. I fully hope our Engine will be 13 or 14 cwt. lighter than his.

The part of a tube which projects beyond the Boiler and which contains the fire is not continued below the fire bars so that the part that projects is only a semi cylinder, this with the sketch will enable you to comprehend fully his intentions. His cylinders are 7 inches—the gear arranged in the same manner as the large Engine at Darlington.[1] Please inform my father and Mr. Locke the progress we have made.

Could you without inconvenience procure us any money on account of the Locomotive last sent[2]—if you could do so I should feel particularly obliged--The price is £550.

Hoping to hear from you to say if I may expect the pleasure of seeing you in N Castle,
I am yours faithfully,

ROB. STEPHENSON.

NEWCASTLE TYNE, Aug. 26th 1829.

MY DEAR SIR,

I am quite of opinion that the projecting part of Hackworth's tube will be very liable to burn away from the water being blown into the large part of the boiler—We must however leave his alone and attend to our own, it will require all our attention.

On Wednesday I had the boiler filled with water and put up to the pressure of 70 lb. per sq. inch when I found that the yielding of the boiler end injured the clinking of the tubes. I therefore thought it prudent to stop the experiment until we got some stays put into the boiler longitudinally. The boiler end at 70 lb per sq. inch came out full 3/16 of an inch. This you may easily conceive put a serious strain on the clinking at the tube ends. To-day I had the pressure up to a little above 70 the tubes were nearly every one tight, but the deflexion of the end still was more than it was prudent to pass over. I am therefore putting in 5 more stays

[1] The ' Royal George.'
[2] The ' Liverpool Coke Engine ' or ' Twin Sisters.'

(part) from a photo of the original in possession of the London Midland and Scottish (formerly London and North Western) Railway Company.

ROBERT STEPHENSON'S LETTER TO HENRY BOOTH 21ST AUGUST 1829

which I believe will be effectual.   A circumstance which has occurred within a few days induces me to regard severe pressures upon boilers as injudicious—We put up two hydraulic presses in a paper mill, which are to bear 6½ Tuns per square inch—the pipes which lead to the presses from the pumps were proved up to the pressure previous to leaving the factory and continued to act well for a week, when they burst with 5 tuns per square inch—A new set of pipes were made which withstood the proof pressure but afterwards burst with a much less pressure—Query therefore is it judicious to prove the boilers to 150 lbs. per sq. inch I should say not.—A pressure of lbs. 100 per sq. inch would not I think be objectionable. If the Engines were not so limited in weight then I would say prove them to 150 lbs. or more.

The Chimney is made 14 inches diameter, being a little less than the area of the horizontal tubes.   I think it should be less, the air being cooler and consequently occupies less space in the Chimney than in the tubes.   I am still sanguine as regards the weight, 4 Tuns I believe will cover all.   Of course I am calculating that if the Engine is reduced in weight below 4½ the load dragged will be reduced in the same proportion.

I am much pleased to hear of the performance of the Lancashire Witch, the more I hear and experience I have in the Locomotive principle the more thoroughly I am convinsed of its convenient adaptation to public Railways.

The putting in of the stays will delay the trial of the Engine until Tuesday.   If anything unexpected start up I will let you know.

Yours faithfully,
ROB. STEPHENSON.

The wheels are made 4 ft. 8½ ins.—the small pair 2 ft. 6 ins.

NEWCASTLE, August 31st 1829.

MY DEAR SIR,

After the stays were put in, we tried the boiler up to 120 lbs. per sq. inch, when I found it necessary to put in two more stays in order to make the ends withstand 150—this would be totally unnecessary if the fixed pressure for trial were 120. We can however make it stand the required pressure altho I scarcely think it prudent from what I stated in my last.

The putting in of these stays has put off the trial of the Engine off until Wednesday.— The Mercurial guage, is nearly finished, it will look well—The pipes being of wrought Iron has taken more time than I expected.   The Wheels of the Engine are painted in the same manner as coach wheels and look extremely well.

The same character of painting I intend keeping up, throughout the Engine it will look light which is one object we ought to aim at.

Mr. Burstall Junior from Edinburgh is in N Castle.   I have little doubt for the purpose of getting information.

I was extremely mistified to find that he walked into the manufactory this morning and examined the Engine with all the coolness imaginable before we discovered who he was.   He has however scarcely time to take advantage of any hints he might catch during his transient visit.   It would have been as well if he had not seen anything.

I will write you on Wednesday Evening or Thursday Morning.

Yours faithfully,
ROB. STEPHENSON.

NEWCASTLE TYNE, Sept. 5th 1829.

DEAR SIR,

I daresay you are getting anxious but I have delayed writing you until I tried the Engine on Killingworth Railway.   It appeared prudent to make an actual trial and make any alterations that might present themselves during an experiment of that kind.   The fire burns admirably and abundance of steam is raised when the fire is carefully attended to.   This is an essential point because a coke fire when let down is bad to get up again; this rather prevented our experiment being so successful as it would have been throughout—We also found that from the construction of the working gear that the Engine did not work so well in one direction as in the other, this will be remedied. The mercurial guage was not on, not from any defect but from my wish to get the Engine tried. We started from Killingworth Pit, with five waggons each weighing four Tuns.

Add to this the tender and 40 Men we proceeded up an ascent 11 or 12 feet per Mile at 8 Miles per hour after we had fairly gained our speed.

We went three Miles on this Railway the rate of ascents and descents my father knows— on a level part laid with Malleable Iron Rail, we attained a speed of 12 Miles per hour and without thinking that I deceived myself (I tried to avoid this), I believe the steam did not sink on this part. On the whole the Engine is capable of doing as much if not more than set forth in the stipulations.—After a great deal of trouble and anxiety we have got the tubes perfectly tight. As requested by you in Mr. Locke's letter, I have not tried the boiler above 120 lbs. The Mercurial Guage and some other nick nacks are yet to be put on. On Friday next the Engine will leave by way of Carlisle and will arrive in L'pool on Wednesday week.

I am Dear Sir,
Yours faithfully,
Rob. Stephenson.

	T.	C.	Qr.
The weight of the Engine complete	3	10	1
Water say		15	0
Tuns	4	5	1

A manuscript [1] preserved by a former official of Robert Stephenson & Co. is still extant giving 'A few particulars respecting the 'Rocket' Locomotive Engine.' This document, compiled apparently many years after the trial, states that 'after such alterations had been made as the experiments at Killingworth had shown to be necessary 'the 'Rocket' was taken to pieces and sent by cars and wagon to Carlisle; the boiler, which was the last thing sent from the factory, left at four o'clock on Saturday afternoon, the 12th September 1829, arriving at Carlisle on the Monday afternoon following, at two o'clock.' Arrived at Carlisle 'it was then transferred to a lighter lying in the canal basin, and conveyed to Bowness, and there put on board the Cumberland steamer, which took it to Liverpool, where it arrived on Friday the 18th.[2] It was then transferred from the steamer to carts and wagons, and taken to the railway workshop at Crown Street, and there put together and tried. The tender, which was entirely made at Liverpool, was here attached to the engine and the necessary connection made. The tender consisted simply of a large puncheon or water barrel fixed to the wooden frame carried on four small cast iron wheels having outside bearings.'

This description further states that these outside bearings were the 'first ever used,' but a statement has been published elsewhere [3] to the effect that

---

[1] *A few particulars respecting the 'Rocket' Locomotive engine.' MS.* from a document at one time in the possession of William Weallens, communicated to Robert Stephenson & Co. by a former chief draughtsman, the late Mr. J. D. Wardale, on 16th July 1913.

[2] Jeaffreson, *Life of Robert Stephenson*, Vol. I., p. 141, states that the Rocket was taken to the Tyne and shipped for Liverpool; but having in view the record in a Liverpool and Manchester Directors' Minute of 13th July 1829, that the previous engine, the 'Twin Sisters,' had 'arrived from Newcastle via Carlisle,' the *MS.* account seems the more probable.

[3] John Gray, letter to *Railway Times*, 1842, Vol. V., p. 55.

George Stephenson had already adopted this system in 1827 'to suit the construction of a wider tender and also some wider coaches which were then made'; whatever the exact date it appears probable that the outside bearings which were subsequently adopted for both locomotives and carriage stock generally were first introduced on the Liverpool and Manchester Railway in the tender of the 'Rocket.'

The earliest descriptive record now in the possession of Robert Stephenson & Co. is from a 'Description Book' commenced in 1831; it gives the following particulars :—

BOILER.

Diameter	3 feet 4 inches.
Length	6 ,, 0 ,,

TUBES (copper).

Number of fire tubes.	25
Size of fire tubes (outside diam.)	3 inches.
Distance from centre to centre	4½ inches.

FIREBOX.

Depth outside from bottom of boiler to bottom of firebox	1 foot 3 inches.
Dimensions of fireplace	2 feet 7 inches. by 2 feet.

CHIMNEY.

Size of chimney	1 foot 2 inches.

PUMP.

Size of hot water pump	1½ inches.
Length of stroke	1 foot 5 inches.

CYLINDERS.

Diameter of steam cylinder	8 inches.
Length of stroke	1 foot 5 inches.
Angle of cylinders to the horizontal	35°
Distance of cylinders from centre to centre	5 feet 9 inches.

VALVES.

Single slide.

WHEELS.

Diameter of driving wheels	4 feet 8 inches.
Diameter of small wheels	2 ,, 6 ,,
Distance of wheels from centre to centre	7 ,, 2 ,,

AXLES.

Diameter of large axle in middle	3¼ inches. [doubtful]
Diameter of small axle in middle	3¼ inches.
Weight of engine without water	3 tons 9 cwt.
Weight of water	13 cwt.

These dimensions agree generally with those given in Robert Stephenson's letter and by other contemporary accounts which we shall quote when describing the Rainhill Trials. The manuscript 'particulars' previously mentioned bear no date of origin but are known to have been in existence in 1859; they give additional information, but where the dimensions in this undoubtedly later document differ from the earlier record of 1831 or from those given by Robert Stephenson himself we have omitted them from the following extracts :—

EXHAUST PIPES.—The exhaust pipes were made of copper leading from the cylinders to the chimney.

BLAST PIPES.—There were two cast iron blast pipes fixed inside the chimney, the diameter of which at the narrowest part was 1½ inches. No alterations were made in these pipes from the time the engine left the works until it won the prize.

CHIMNEY.—The chimney was fixed to the end of the boiler by tap bolts, the bent part of the chimney being swelled out so as to cover the ends of the tubes, it was 15 feet high and supported by two wrought iron stays.

PRESSURE GAUGE.—A Mercurial Gauge was fixed on one side of the chimney and was nearly of the same height, the bottom of the gauge resting on the frame, a small copper pipe ¾ of an inch diameter connected the bottom of the gauge with the bottom of the boiler.

WATER GAUGE.—A water gauge was fixed on one side of the boiler at the back of the cylinder; two gauge cocks were also fixed to the side of the boiler near the chimney end.

PUMP.—There was one brass feed pump fixed between the motion bars and the boiler and worked from the crosshead; this pump had mitre valves the lift of which was regulated by small spiral springs; a leather hose connected the suction pipe of the pump with the tender.

MOTION BARS.—The motion bars were of wrought iron as were the connecting rods.

SLIDE VALVES.—The slides were single and made of brass and were worked by two loose eccentrics with the intervention of rods, levers, and hollow weighbars. In reversing the engine the eccentric rods were lifted out of gear and the slides reversed by hand. The eccentrics were driven by drivers screwed fast into the axle.

WHEELS.—The rim and spokes of the front or driving wheels were made of wood and the boss or nave of cast iron; the tyres were wrought iron $4\frac{1}{4}$ or $4\frac{1}{2}$ inches in width, the height of the flange being about $\frac{7}{8}$ of an inch. The hind wheels were made of cast iron entirely.

FRAME.—The frame of the engine consisted of wrought iron bar, 4 inches by 1 inch bent to support the firebox and to take the hind wheels.

SPRINGS.—The whole weight of the engine was supported by four steel springs which were made of plates about $\frac{1}{4}$ inch thick in the centre and tapered towards the ends; the two front springs were above the two hind ones below the axle.

SAFETY VALVES.—There were two safety valves about $2\frac{1}{2}$ inches diameter one of which was a lock up valve, covered by a tin dome fastened down to the boiler by two small padlocks; the remaining valve was a lever valve fixed to the boiler near the firebox end.

STEAM PIPES.—The steam from the boiler was admitted to the cylinders by means of a copper pipe about 2 inches diameter branching away from the regulator cock which was fixed to the end of the boiler above the firebox, an internal steam pipe led from the steam dome on the top of the boiler to the regulator.

CYLINDERS.—The cylinders were fixed to the side of the boiler at an angle of about $36\frac{1}{2}°$ (sic) from the rail.

We note the obvious derivation of the cylinder arrangement from that of the 'Lancashire Witch'; the reduction in stroke, the increase in the diameter of the driving wheels, the use of one pair only and the abandonment of coupling rods, being consistent with the higher speed anticipated.

FIREBOX.—The firebox was made of copper with water spaces at the sides, top and back about $2\frac{1}{2}$ inches in width, the front of the box was lined with firebricks as shown on drawing No. 2. Two copper pipes about 2 inches diameter supplied the firebox with water from the boiler, these pipes were fixed one on each side of the firebox; there were also two copper pipes which connected the top of the firebox with the end of the boiler, allowing the steam gathered in the firebox to pass into this boiler.

TUBES   The fixing of the tubes in the tube-plates appears to have been the most difficult problem which Robert Stephenson had to solve; of the method finally adopted by him we have unfortunately found no contemporary description. George Stephenson's biographer [1] referring to 'the principal circumstances connected with the construction of the 'Rocket' as described to him by Robert Stephenson,' states that the tubes 'were manufactured by a Newcastle coppersmith and soldered (sic) to brass screws, which were screwed into the boiler ends, standing out in great knobs'; he adds that the joints so made failed under hydraulic test pressure and that Robert, after writing hastily to his father of another failure, subsequently decided 'to bore clean holes in the boiler ends, fit in the smooth copper tubes as tightly as possible, solder up and then raise the steam.'

[1] Smiles, *Lives of the Engineers*, 1862, Vol. III., p. 264, and previous editions.

Robert Stephenson's biographer [1] repeats this account of the experiment with screws and the subsequent fitting of the tube ends directly into 'clean holes' bored to the diameter of the tubes; but he adds that 'steel ferrules or hollow conical wedges were driven into their ends, by this means the copper of each tube was forced powerfully against the circumference of the hole and caused to fit perfectly water tight.' We must bear in mind that this description was written after the death of Robert Stephenson, presumably on documentary evidence still available in 1864, or on verbal description by surviving witnesses. It is curious that in the previous account, based on the evidence of the man most directly concerned, all mention of such an important feature as the ferrules should have been omitted; we have now no contemporary evidence of their application to the tubes of the 'Rocket'; there is however a definite record of the use of such ferrules by Robert Stephenson & Co. about seven months later, when it is recorded of engines under construction in March, 1830, that 'an iron ferrule is inserted into the end of each pipe and riveted with it into the boiler end.' [2]

The use of such ferrules may have enabled Robert Stephenson to overcome difficulties with which he was first faced in the construction of the 'Rocket's' boiler; but whether or no this be the case the account of the experiment with tubes having screwed ends must be accepted with great reserve; we have found that in paraphrasing information given to them on technical details the biographers of both George and Robert Stephenson have sometimes erred. In the present case we have the evidence of Robert Stephenson's letter written at the time, to show that after his first attempt at fixing the tubes the boiler end plate bulged. This could not have happened if the tubes had been screwed into the plate as described. It seems more likely that his first failure was after the tubes had been fixed by 'clinking,' i.e., rivetting only and that subsequent expanding by tapered coned ferrules proved a cure.

No original working drawings of either engine or boiler are now in existence; there are two drawings in the possession of Robert Stephenson & Co. which appear to be those referred to in the manuscript 'particulars,' one of them showing the boiler complete; but when we come to consider the design of the firebox itself we find serious discrepancies in the evidence available. Since they involve questions of construction rather than of principle we shall deal separately and at greater length with this vital feature of the multitubular boiler; we have here given sufficient information to make it possible to appreciate the general construction of both boiler and engine; for an impression of its appearance we must rely on the illustration from the *Mechanics' Magazine*.

We shall describe in our next chapter the ordeal through which both engine and boiler had to pass.

---

[1] Jeaffreson, *Life of Robert Stephenson*, 1864, Vol. I., p. 140.

[2] *Journals* of Simon Goodrich, preserved at the Science Museum, South Kensington.

CHAPTER XIII

THE RAINHILL TRIALS

It is certainly some consolation to those who are to be whirled at the rate of eighteen or twenty miles an hour to be told that they are in no danger of being sea-sick while on shore ; that they are not to be scalded to death nor drowned by the bursting of the boiler ; and that they need not mind being shot off by the scattered fragments, or dashed in pieces by the flying off, or the breaking of a wheel. But with all these assurances we should as soon expect the people of Woolwich to suffer themselves to be fired off upon one of Congreve's 'ricochet' rockets as trust themselves to the mercy of such a machine going at such a rate.

Quarterly Review, March 1825, 'Canals and Railroads.'

To appreciate the full significance of these trials to those who witnessed them, we must imagine an Englishman still dependent for locomotion on his own legs or those of his horse ; we must try to understand the mentality of men who, for lack of a better, were accustomed to measure the capacities of their steam engines by the standard of 'horse-power' and had not yet seen their best horse beaten for speed on a railway. If we can reject from our minds the locomotive engine of to-day and, by reading Jane Austen or Washington Irving, fill the picture with country inns, stage coaches and farmers' wains, we shall understand something of the point of view of most of the spectators at the Rainhill Trials. Some had, it is true, seen Gurney's or other steam coaches on the turnpike roads, and among the engineers present were many who had visited the colliery railways of the north and witnessed the performances of the locomotive engines there in use ; but generally we may be assured that in one respect alone was the point of view the same as it is to-day— in the native love of a contest which appealed to the public mind as somewhat in the nature of a race. In relating the tale of that contest we shall depend upon the accounts of eye witnesses, following our principle that only such evidence can be accepted as conclusive.

The most authoritative contemporary published accounts are that by Booth, the secretary and treasurer, in his *Account of the Liverpool and Manchester Railway*, and that by Wood in the second edition of his *Treatise on Railroads* ; there is also a scientific but entirely unofficial account in the *Mechanics' Magazine*, which was published while the trials were in progress.[1] Now Booth, as we have seen, was directly interested in the result of the trials, and Wood was one of the judges, but the editor of the *Mechanics' Magazine*, J. C. Robertson, had no such direct interest ; he appears at the time, and indeed afterwards, to have been prejudiced against George Stephenson ; the account which he published was based partly on information given by C. B. Vignoles, a qualified engineer, and partly on his own observations ; for these reasons we shall quote largely from the *Mechanics' Magazine*.

We have also the more popular reports of contemporary local journals and last, but not least, accounts given in private letters, two of which are now published for the first time ; being written with all the freedom of expression

---

[1] Vol. XII., p. 115, *et seq.*

from a watercolour by George Walker, 1814.

from an aquatint by T. T. Bury, published by R. Ackermann, 1st February 1831.

RAINHILL BRIDGE.

possible to such correspondence they possess a peculiar interest and value. Believing that the thought and emotions of a period are best expressed in its own language we shall give the evidence of the various witnesses with as little paraphrase as is possible.

For a first general picture of the scene we quote from a contemporary journal [1] :—

Wednesday, Oct. 7 1829.

The Directors of the Liverpool and Manchester Rail-Road having offered, in the month of April last, a prize of £500 for the best Locomotive Engine, the trial of the carriages which had been constructed to contend for the prize commenced yesterday. The running ground was on the Manchester side of the Rainhill Bridge, at a place called Kenrick's Cross, about ten miles from Liverpool. At this place the Rail-Road runs on a dead level, and formed, of course, a fine spot for trying the comparative speed of the carriages. The directors had made suitable preparations for this important as well as interesting experiment of the powers of Locomotive Carriages. For the accommodation of the ladies who might visit the course (to use the language of the turf), a booth was erected on the south side of the Rail-Road, equi-distant from the extremities of the trial-ground. Here a band of music was stationed, and amused the company during the day by playing pleasing and favourite airs. The directors, each of whom wore a white ribbon in his button-hole, arrived on the course shortly after ten o'clock in the forenoon, having come from Huyton in cars drawn by Mr. Stephenson's Locomotive Steam Carriage, which moved up the inclined plane from thence with considerable velocity. Meanwhile, ladies and gentlemen, in great numbers, arrived from Liverpool and Warrington, St. Helen's and Manchester, as well as from the surrounding country, in vehicles of every description. Indeed all the roads presented, on this occasion, scenes similar to those which roads leading to race-courses usually present during the days of sport. The pedestrians were extremely numerous, and crowded all the roads which conducted to the race-ground. The spectators lined both sides of the road, for the distance of a mile and a half; and, although the men employed on the line, amounting to nearly 200, acted as special constables, with orders to keep the crowd off the course, all their efforts to carry their orders into effect were rendered nugatory, by the people persisting in walking on the ground. It is difficult to form an estimate of the number of individuals who had congregated to behold the experiment; but there could not, at a moderate calculation, be less than 10,000. Some gentlemen even went so far as to compute them at 15,000.

Never, perhaps, on any previous occasion, were so many scientific gentlemen and practical engineers collected together on one spot as there were on the Rail-Road yesterday. The interesting and important nature of the experiments to be tried had drawn them from all parts of the kingdom, to be present at this contest of Locomotive Carriages, as well as to witness an exhibition whose results may alter the whole system of our existing internal communications, many and important as they are, substituting an agency whose ultimate effects can scarcely be anticipated; for although the extraordinary change in our river and coast navigation, by steam-boats, may afford some rule of comparison, still the effect of wind and waves, and a resisting medium, combine in vessels to present obstructions to the full exercise of the gigantic power which will act on a Rail-way unaffected by the seasons, and unlimited but by the demand for its application.

There were only one or two public-houses in the vicinity of the trial-ground. These were, of course, crowded with company as the day advanced, particularly the Rail-Road Tavern, which was literally crammed with company. The landlady had very prudently and providently reserved one room for the accommodation of the better class visitors. The good lady will, we imagine, have substantial reasons for remembering the trial of Locomotive Carriages. But there is nothing like making hay while the sun shines.

[1] *Liverpool Courier*, 7th October 1829.

The conditions of the Trial had been published [1] six months previously under date :—

Rail-way Office, Liverpool, 25th April 1829.

STIPULATIONS AND CONDITIONS.

On which the Directors of the Liverpool and Manchester Rail-way offer a Premium of £500 for the most improved Locomotive Engine.

1st. The said engine must 'effectually consume its own smoke,' according to the provisions of the Rail-way Act, 7 Geo. IV.

2nd. The engine, if it weighs six tons, must be capable of drawing after it, day by day, on a well constructed Rail-way on a level plane, a train of carriages of the gross weight of twenty tons, including the tender and water-tank, at the rate of ten miles per hour, with a pressure of steam on the boiler, not exceeding 50 lbs. per square inch.

3rd. There must be two safety valves, one of which must be completely out of the control of the engine-man, and neither of which must be fastened down while the engine is working.

4th. The engine and boiler must be supported on springs, and rest on six wheels, and the height, from the ground to the top of the chimney, must not exceed fifteen feet.

5th. The weight of the machine, *with its complement of water* in the boiler, must, at most, not exceed six tons, and a machine of less weight will be preferred, it if draw after it a proportionate weight; and if the weight of the engine, &c., do not exceed five tons, then the gross weight to be drawn need not exceed fifteen tons, and in that proportion for machines of still smaller weight; provided that the engine, &c., shall still be on six wheels, unless the weight (as above) be reduced to four tons and a half, or under, in which case, the boiler, &c., may be placed on four wheels. And the Company shall be at liberty to put the boiler fire-tube, cylinders, &c., to a test of a pressure of water not exceeding 150 lbs. per square inch, without being answerable for any damage the machine may receive in consequence.

6th. There must be a mercurial gauge affixed to the machine, with index-rod, shewing the steam pressure above 45 lbs. per square inch.

7th. The engine to be delivered complete for trial at the Liverpool end of the Rail-way, not later than the 1st October, next.

8th. The price of the engine, which may be accepted, not to exceed £550 delivered on the Rail-way; and any engine not approved to be taken back by the owner.

N.B.—The Rail-way Company will provide the engine tender with a supply of water and fuel, for the experiment. The distance within the rails is four feet eight inches and a half.

We shall now quote the account in the *Mechanics' Magazine* of the first trials, which took place on 6th October 1829.

The number of competitors was at first reported to be ten, and we have reason to know there was at least as many engines as this in preparation. In this new sort of race, however, as in others, there were some withdrawn, and some prevented by accidents from making their appearance; and the number was reduced on the morning of trial, to five, who were thus described on the official list of the running coaches :—

No. 1, Messrs. Braithwaite and Ericsson, of London; 'The Novelty'; copper and blue; weight, 2 tons 15 cwt.

No. 2, Mr. Hackworth, of Darlington; 'The Sans Pareil'; green, yellow, and black; weight, 4 tons 8 cwt. 2 qrs.

No. 3, Mr. Robert Stephenson, Newcastle-upon-Tyne; 'The Rocket'; yellow and black; white chimney; weight, 4 tons 3 cwt.

No. 4, Mr. Brandreth, of Liverpool; 'The Cycloped'; weight, 3 tons; worked by a horse.

No. 5, Mr. Burstall, Edinburgh; 'The Perseverance'; red wheels; weight, 2 tons 17 cwt.

---

[1] Wood, *Treatise on Rail Roads*, 2nd edition, 1831, p. 361.

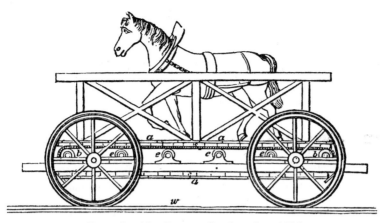

(Brandreth's Patent Cyclopede. 1829.)

from Galloway's History and Progress of the Steam Engine, 1831, p. 619.

The engine which made the first trial, was the 'Rocket' of Mr. Robert Stephenson (the son, we believe, of Mr. George Stephenson, the engineer of the railway). It is a large and strongly-built engine, and went with a velocity, which, as long as the spectators had nothing to contrast it with, they thought surprising enough. It drew a weight of twelve tons, nine cwt. at the rate of ten miles four chains in an hour, (just exceeding the stipulated maximum,) and, when the weight was detached from it, went at a speed of about eighteen miles an hour. The faults most perceptible in this engine, were a great inequality in its velocity, and a very partial fulfilment of the condition that it should 'effectually consume its own smoke.'

The next engine that exhibited its powers was 'The Novelty' of Messrs. Braithwaite and Ericsson. The great lightness of this engine, (it is about one half lighter than Mr. Stephenson's,) its compactness, and its beautiful workmanship, excited universal admiration; a sentiment speedily changed into perfect wonder, by its truly marvellous performances. It was resolved to try first its speed merely; that is at what rate it would go, carrying only its complement of coke and water, with Messrs. Braithwaite and Ericsson to manage it. Almost at once, it darted off at the amazing velocity of twenty-eight miles an hour, and it actually did one mile in the incredibly short space of one minute and 53 seconds! Neither did we observe any appreciable falling off in the rate of speed; it was uniform, steady, and continuous. Had the railway been completed, the engine would, at this rate, have gone nearly the whole way from Liverpool to Manchester within the hour; and Mr. Braithwaite has, indeed, publicly offered to stake a thousand pounds, that as soon as the road is opened, he will perform the entire distance in that time.

It was now proposed to make a trial of the 'Novelty,' with three times its weight attached to it; but through some inattention as to the supply of water and coke, a great delay took place in preparing it for its second trip, and by the time all was ready, the day was drawing so near to a close, that the directors thought it proper to defer the prosecution of the competition till the following day.

Continuing our quotation from the same source we have an account of the performances on the two following days :—

SECOND DAY, 7TH OCTOBER.

'The Novelty' engine of Messrs. Braithwaite and Ericsson was this day tried with a load of three times its weight attached to it, or 11 tons 5 cwt.; and it drew this with ease at the rate of 20¾ miles per hour, thus proving itself to be equally good for speed as for power. We took particular notice to-day of its power of consuming its own smoke, and did not any time observe the emission of the smallest particle from the chimney.

The weather now became wet, and the rail-ways clogged with mud, which made it necessary to suspend the prosecution of the experiments before the day had half elapsed. The attendance of the spectators this morning was by no means so numerous as on the preceding day; but there were few of those absent—the engineers, men of science, &c.—whose presence was most desirable.

THIRD DAY, 8TH OCTOBER.

Before the commencement of the experiments to-day, it was announced that the judges on reconsidering the card of 'Stipulations and Conditions' originally issued had considered them so defective as to make it necessary to substitute the following:—

The weight of the locomotive engine, with its full complement of water in the boiler, shall be ascertained at the weighing machine, by eight o'clock in the morning, and the load assigned to it shall be three times the weight thereof. The water in the boiler shall be cold, and there shall be no fuel in the fire-place. As much fuel shall be weighed, and as much water shall be measured and delivered into the tender-carriage, as the owner of the engine may consider sufficient for the supply of the engine for a journey of thirty-five miles. The fire in the boiler shall then be lighted, and the quantity of fuel consumed for getting up the steam shall be determined, and the time noted.

The Tender-carriage, with the fuel and water, shall be considered to be, and taken as a part of the load assigned to the engine.

Those engines that carry their own fuel and water, shall be allowed a proportionate deduction from their load, according to the weight of the engine.

The engine, with the carriages attached to it, shall be run by hand up to the starting-post; and as soon as the steam is got up to fifty pounds per square inch, the engine shall set out upon its journey.

The distance the engine shall perform each trip, shall be one mile and three-quarters each way, including one-eighth of a mile at each end for getting up the speed, and for stopping the train; by this means the engine with its load will travel one and a half mile each way at full speed.

The engine shall make ten trips, which will be equal to a journey of thirty-five miles; thirty miles whereof shall be performed at full speed, and the average rate of travelling shall not be less than ten miles per hour.

As soon as the engine has performed this task, (which will be equal to the travelling from Liverpool to Manchester,) there shall be a fresh supply of fuel and water delivered to her; and as soon as she can be got ready to set out again, she shall go up to the starting-post, and make ten trips more, which will be equal to the journey from Manchester back again to Liverpool.

The time of performing every trip shall be accurately noted, as well as the time occupied in getting ready to set out on the second journey.

Should the engine not be enabled to take along with it sufficient fuel and water for the journey of ten trips, the time occupied in taking in a fresh supply of fuel and water, shall be considered and taken as a part of the time in performing the journey.

> J. U. RASTRICK, Esq., Stourbridge, C.E.
> NICHOLAS WOOD, Esq., Killingworth, C.E.   } *Judges.*
> JOHN KENNEDY, Esq., Manchester

Liverpool, Oct. 6th 1829.

The *Mechanics' Magazine* then remarks:—

We shall not go into a question which has been raised, as to the fairness of the judges making any alteration in the conditions originally promulgated. We have a perfect persuasion that they have no other desire than to ascertain, in the best manner possible, the relative powers of the competing engines, and shall not quarrel with them for any mere irregularity in the mode of their proceedings. The 'new' appears to us to be also, on the whole, a 'much amended' edition.

The writer appears here to be under a misapprehension; the original *Conditions* published on 25th April 1829 did not in any way define the method by which the trials were to be conducted. After further observation on the 'new conditions' as they would affect an engine carrying its own fuel and water in comparison with an engine requiring a tender for this purpose the account proceeds :—

Nothing was said in the new conditions as to each engine's 'effectually consuming its own smoke'; but this omission could only have arisen from oversight; for the Act of Parliament, under the authority of which the railway has been formed, orders imperatively that no engines shall be suffered to ply upon it which does not possess this qualification.[1] Having set these preliminary matters to right, we now proceed with our narrative of the experiments.

The engine which exhibited on this the third day was 'The Rocket' of Mr. Stephenson. The trial was conducted in the manner laid down in the 'Ordeal' we have just quoted; and it was understood on all hands that this trial should be considered decisive of its merits. The engine, with its complement of water in the boiler, weighed 4 tons 5 cwt. and the load attached to it was 12 tons 15 cwt., or including a few persons who rode, about 13 tons. The journey was $1\frac{1}{2}$ miles each way, with an additional length of 220 yards at each end to stop the engine in, making in one journey $3\frac{1}{4}$ miles. The first experiment was for 35 miles, which is exactly 10 journeys, and, including all the stoppages at the ends, was performed in 3 hours and 10 minutes, being upwards of 11 miles an hour. After this a fresh supply of water was taken in, which occupied 16 minutes, when the engine again started, and ran 35 miles in 2 hours and 52 minutes, which is upwards of 12 miles an hour, including all stoppages. The speed of the engine, with its load, when in full motion, was, at different times, 13, $13\frac{1}{2}$, 14 and 16 miles an hour; and, had the whole distance been in one continued direction, there is little doubt but the result would have been 15 miles an hour. The consumption of coke was on an average about half a ton in the 70 miles.

Fourth Day, 9th October.

To-day a public notice appeared from Messrs. Braithwaite and Ericsson, stating, that in consequence of the alterations made in the conditions of the competition, the trial of their engine in the manner prescribed by the new 'Ordeal,' had with the approbation of the judges, been deferred till the following day. The 9th became thus a *dies non* in the competition.

Fifth Day, 10th October.

At the appointed hour this morning 'The Novelty' was weighed, and three times its weight assigned to it by the judges. The steam was got up in 54 minutes from the time of lighting the fire. The engine then went one trip by way of rehearsal, when a small pipe accidentally gave way, and it was found necessary to send to Prescot, a distance of two miles, to have it repaired. In the interval, Mr. Stephenson's locomotive engine was run twice down the course and back, making in all 7 miles, but with the whole load taken off from behind, including even the tender-carriage with the water tank and fuel. Thus 'stripped for the race,' 'The Rocket' performed the seven miles in the space of 14 minutes 14 seconds being at the rate of 30 miles an hour. This was a rate of speed nearly equal to the utmost which 'The Novelty' had achieved; but as it carried with it neither fuel nor water, it is not a speed which it could have long sustained. 'The Novelty,' having now had its broken pipe repaired, made several trips, but solely for the gratification of the spectators, who were to-day extremely numerous, and not with any view to a decisive exhibition of its powers.

[1] For the purposes of their report, Walker and Rastrick were informed by the Directors of the Liverpool and Manchester Railway on 12th January 1829 that, as regards the locomotive they need not consider themselves restricted by the Smoke Clause in the Act of Parliament, but make their estimates and calculations as if no such clause existed. But the smoke of the 'Rocket' was due to an accidental mixture of coal; the recognised fuel was coke.

The *Mechanics' Magazine* then gives a statement by Vignoles of the 'Novelty's' performances, from which it appears that 'the engine went off from the starting-post at the rate of 12 miles an hour and its velocity rapidly increased during the trip,' a speed of $21\frac{1}{6}$ miles per hour being attained in one instance.

SIXTH DAY, 13TH OCTOBER.

Mr. Hackworth's engine, 'The Sans Parcil,' was pronounced to be this day ready to exhibit its powers. We were informed that, on weighing it, the judges found it to exceed by two or three hundred-weight the maximum; it was, nevertheless, allowed to start to do 70 miles, in the same manner as 'The Rocket,' with three times its great weight attached to it. It was soon manifest that a very powerful competitor had entered the field. For two hours 'The Sans Pareil' kept going with great regularity, and during that time completed upwards of 25 miles. It went occasionally, when at its utmost speed, a mile in 4' 10" and 4' 17", being at the rate of nearly 15 miles an hour. While thus bidding fair—if not to win the prize, at least to come in second best—a similar accident happened to it as befell 'The Novelty'; one of the feed pipes burst, and it was rendered for the time incapable of proceeding.

We understand the judges subsequently resolved that 'The Sans Pareil' should have another trial on Friday, the 16th.

from a drawing in the Science Museum, South Kensington.

THE 'SANS PAREIL'

SEVENTH DAY, 14TH OCTOBER.

It being generally understood that this was to be the day of a more decisive trial of Messrs. Braithwaite and Ericsson's engine—that is, according to the new conditions named by the judges—there was almost as numerous an assemblage of spectators as on the first day of the competition.

A fresh pipe had, it appeared, been substituted for the one which failed on the preceding trial; one or two other parts of the machinery that were in a faulty state, had also been renovated; but the engine, with the exception of some of the flanges of the boiler being as Mr. Ericsson expressed it, rather 'green,' was pronounced in a working state.

After giving particulars of the weights assigned for the load of the 'Novelty' the account proceeds :—

The steam was on this occasion got up to a pressure of 50 lbs. in somewhat less than 40 minutes, and at an expenditure of about 15 lbs. of coke.

The engine now started to do the 70 miles for a continuance; but just as it had completed its second trip of three miles, when it was working at the rate of 15 miles an hour, the new cement of some of the flanges of the boiler, yielded to the high temperature to which it was exposed, and the spectators had again the mortification to hear it announced that it was, under these circumstances, impossible the trial could go on.

Mr. Burstall's engine, 'The Perseverance,' which had met with an injurious accident on its way to Liverpool, but been since repaired, was now allowed to make some experimental trials.

We left it returning from a third or fourth trip; but if we may judge from the degree of speed which it then exhibited—not more, certainly, than five miles an hour—it has no chance.

We were informed that, early on Wednesday morning, before we reached the course, an experiment had been made with Mr. Stephenson's engine on a part of the railway which runs with an inclination of 1 in 96, and that it drew up this plane a carriage containing 25 passengers with great ease.

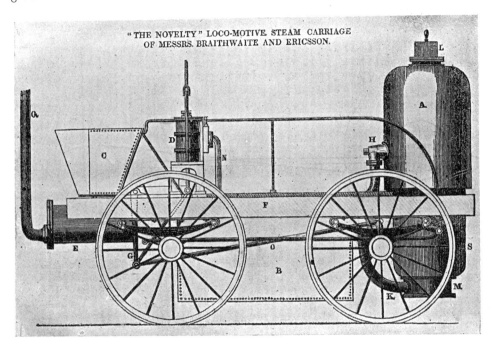

"THE NOVELTY" LOCO-MOTIVE STEAM CARRIAGE OF MESSRS. BRAITHWAITE AND ERICSSON.

from the Mechanics' Magazine, Vol. XII., p. 129.

(For the relative sizes of the competing engines, drawn to scale, see p. 73, Chapter VI. *ante*).

In a description which it gives of the competing engines, the *Mechanics' Magazine* remarks :—

The external view of 'The Novelty,' given in our present number, will at once satisfy our readers, that it has not been unmeritedly extolled by all who have seen it, for its singular lightness, elegance and compactness. All locomotive engines have been hitherto so constructed as to require a separate tender to carry the water and fuel necessary for these operations (we cannot as yet except Mr. Gurney's); but 'The Novelty' includes within itself every necessary accommodation for these purposes, and is, nevertheless, much lighter than any engine on the old plan. 'The Rocket' of Mr. Stephenson, which is one requiring a separate tender, weighs 4 tons 3 cwt. while 'The Novelty' weighs only 2 tons 15 cwt.; making a difference in favour of the latter of 1 ton 8 cwt.[1]

The means by which the inventors of the 'Novelty' had been able to 'combine so much lightness with great power' are then described, and referring to the 'Rocket,' the writer, after describing its boiler proceeds :—

[1] This comparison is incorrect since the weight of the 'Rocket' is given *with* water in the boiler, that of the 'Novelty' *without*. See footnote to p. 199 following.

N¹

The performances of this engine indicate a very abundant and well sustained production of steam, but the extent of surface which it has been found necessary to expose to the heat in order to obtain that effect, the great size of all the parts, and the quantity of fuel required—are faults which even a still more copious generation of steam would scarcely compensate.

The 'Sans Pareil' is described as exhibiting :—

. . . . . in its general appearance, particularly in its large dimensions, a near resemblance to Mr. Stephenson's engine; but it is much more compactly arranged, and on account of this compactness travels with much greater steadiness. . . . The furnace and boiler are of simple construction, and of unquestionable efficiency; but their great size, and the large supply of fuel and water they require, render them but ill-adapted to the purposes of a locomotive engine.

Such criticisms as these from a professed authority on technical matters seem to show how few at the time understood the boiler to be the measure of the power. This was a fact on which Hackworth and the two Stephensons had no illusions; they had learnt the truth in the hard school of experience.

The account of the performance on the seventh day concludes :—

'The Novelty' still remains at Liverpool and Messrs. Braithwaite and Ericsson have publicly announced that as soon as it is repaired, and the cement of the joints sufficiently hardened, they will (with the leave of the Directors) complete the exhibition of its powers; and show that but for the accidents which it unfortunately met with, it was more than equal to the accomplishment of the task that was last assigned to it.

The prize is not expected to be positively awarded for some little time yet to come. It appears that the gentlemen who were appointed to act as *judges*, have had only the name and not the usual powers of *judges* conferred upon them. All that they have been required and permitted to do is to make an exact report to the Directors of the performances of the competing engines; the Directors reserving to themselves the power of deciding which is best entitled to the premium . . . but it so happens, that this competition has taken a course which makes it difficult for the Directors to go far wrong in their decision. What *all* the tests were by which the comparative merits of the competing engines were to be tried, it would be hard to say, neither the original 'Conditions and Stipulations,' nor the 'Ordeal,' which was subsequently substituted in their place, being, separately considered, sufficiently full and explicit on the subject; but this much is certain, that the performance of seventy miles, for a continuance, was one criterion of excellence to which all the competitors expressed a willing submission. 'The Rocket' started on this understanding; and performed the distance at a rate of speed, which, *for a continuance*, stands as yet unrivalled in the annals of railway-racing. 'The Sans Pareil' next made the attempt; but in consequence of part of its machinery giving way, only performed about half the distance. 'The Novelty' followed; but had scarcely started, when it was brought by a similar accident to a dead stand. Now, though we are of opinion that 'The Novelty' is the sort of engine that will be found best adapted to the purposes of the railway, and are inclined to think that 'The Sans Pareil' is at least as good an engine as 'The Rocket'; yet as neither the one nor the other has equalled 'The Rocket' in performance, which had the winning of the prize of £500 expressly for its object, we do not see how the Directors can in justice do otherwise than award that prize to Mr. Stephenson. Besides, whatever may be the merits of 'The Rocket,' as contrasted with either of its rivals, it is so much superior to all the old locomotive engines in use, as to entitle Mr. Stephenson to the most marked and liberal consideration, for the skill and ingenuity displayed in its construction.

After such 'damning with faint praise' the writer gives a lengthy analysis of the various performances, in the course of which a strong preference for the 'Novelty' is again noticeable, and he concludes with an extract from the letter of a correspondent to his periodical :—

Liverpool, 26th Oct. 1829.

The prize has been at length awarded, and as you rightly conjectured in your last, to Mr. Stephenson. The directors had no alternative, since 'The Rocket' was the only engine which fulfilled the conditions of the competition. There are people here, however, who think that the interests of the public would have been quite as well served had the directors adjudged the premium on a more general view of the matter, and conferred it on that engine which is, upon the whole, 'the most improved.' I have seen at the Railway Office the Report of the Judges; but cannot say that I have been at all gratified by the perusal. It is confined to a simple report of the performances of the different engines, drawn up with but little discrimination, and in some instances (as I imagine) rather ignorantly. It might have been expected of two gentlemen, who were called in to aid a body of directors with their scientific knowledge on the occasion, that they would have made it their business to point out the improvements which the competition has been the means of producing in locomotive machinery, by whom they have been effected, and to what results they lead. But there is nothing of the kind. The directors are left to cull conclusions for themselves out of the facts presented to them; and for aught that appears in the face of the report, it might be inferred that all the novelty is on the side of the 'Rocket' and that the 'Rocket' is the only real 'Sans Pareil.' I need not, however, enlarge on the merits of this document; it will, of course, be soon given to the public, and speak for itself. The directors have offered to purchase both the unsuccessful engines—unsuccessful, at least, as regards the prize; but the offer does not seem to have been viewed in the same light by their respective owners. Hackworth, who had embarked all his means in the building of 'The Sans Pareil,' has gladly accepted the offer; Messrs. Braithwaite and Ericsson have declined it, under an impression that it might seem their engine was bought less for its merits than on account of its misfortunes. They say they want nothing in the way of favour; and that if they can prove, as they trust to do that their engine is better adapted to railway purposes than any other which has yet appeared, it will not be an order for one, or a dozen, or yet fifty engines, that will satisfy the wants of our railway. 'The Novelty' is still here, undergoing a general repair, and is expected to exhibit again on the railway in the course of next week, when it will be brought to a final test, whether it can maintain, for a length of time, the extraordinary speed which its partial performances during the competition displayed.

The results of the trial were also announced by a contemporary journal[1]:—

We may consider the trial of the Locomotive Engines as now virtually at an end. It is much to be regretted, that 'The Novelty' was not built in time to have the same opportunity of exercising that Mr. Stephenson's engine had, or that there is not in London, or its vicinity, any railway where experiments with it could have been tried. It will evidently require several weeks to perfect the working of the machine and the proper fitting of the joints, and under this impression, Messrs. Braithwaite and Ericsson have acted wisely in withdrawing, as they have done, from the contest.

The course is thus left clear for Mr. Stephenson; and we congratulate him, with much sincerity, on the probability of his being about to receive the reward of £500. This is due to him for the perfection to which he has brought the old-fashioned locomotive engine; but the grand prize of public opinion is the one which has been gained by Messrs. Braithwaite and Ericsson, for their decided improvement in the arrangement, the safety, simplicity, and the smoothness and steadiness of a locomotive engine; and however imperfect the present works of the machine may be, it is beyond a doubt—and we believe we speak the opinion of nine-tenths of the engineers and scientific men now in Liverpool—that it is the principle and arrangement of this London engine which will be followed in the construction of all future locomotives. The powerful introduction of a blast bellows, the position of the water tank below the body of the carriage, by which means the centre of gravity is brought below the line of central motion, the beautiful mechanism of the connecting movement of the wheels, the absolute absence of all smell, smoke, noise, vibration, or unpleasant feeling of any kind, the elegance of the machinery, in short the *tout ensemble* proclaim the perfection of the principle.

[1] Quoted by *Mechanics Magazine*, Vol. XII., p. 146, 24th October 1829.

In withdrawing so honourably from the competition, Messrs. Braithwaite and Ericsson have done themselves the highest credit; and they may rest assured that the scientific world will do justice to their efforts, and look with anxiety to a speedy completion of their elegant and compact engine prepared to bear the fiercest 'ordeal' which the judges may please to direct.

In a later notice the *Mechanics' Magazine* observes [1] :—

We are glad to learn that the locomotive experiments on the Liverpool and Manchester Railway have not ceased with the winning of the prize recently offered by the Directors, but that every day some new trial is made, and some new result obtained, which serve to render more conspicuous than ever the vast capabilities of steam-carriages when employed on railways.

On Saturday last, Mr. Stephenson's engine, which has received several material improvements since the late competition, exceeded all its previous performances in an extraordinary degree. It drew after it, on a dead level, 40 tons, at an average rate of 14 miles an hour, being more than three times the weight which it drew at the rate of 12½ miles per hour when competing for the prize. It afterwards drew 18 tons up a plane, having an inclination of 1 in 96, at the rate of 8 miles an hour.

'The Novelty' had not, at the date of our last advices from Liverpool, made its re-appearance upon the railway, but it was expected to exhibit again before the close of this week.

We shall now quote briefly from Wood's published record of the proceedings. The '*Stipulations and Conditions*' of the trials as originally laid down, and as afterwards amended, we have already given, and can therefore proceed to his account, as one of the judges, of the method by which the trial was conducted.[2] Wood states that :—

The ground was marked out according to the diagram below :—

```
        No. 1.                    Level                         No. 2.
West |———(|)—————————————————————————————————————————(|)———| East
      ⅛ mile.                   1½ mile.                        ⅛ mile.
```

and the mode of conducting the Experiment agreeable to the conditions, was as follows. One of the judges was stationed at the post, No. 1, and the other at the post No. 2. The engine, when ready, started off from the extremity of the stage, and when it arrived at the station No. 1, the time was taken; it then proceeded on until it arrived at the station, No. 2, when the time was again taken. The velocity was then checked, and when it arrived at the end of the stage, was stopped, and set in motion in the opposite direction; and when it again passed the station, No. 2, the time was marked, and the engine proceeding at full speed, until it arrived at the station, No. 1, when the time was again recorded. By this method, the time occupied in traversing the 1½ mile stage at full speed, and also the time occupied at each end, was ascertained. The first two or three days were occupied in preparing the engines for the contest, and in shewing their powers to the numerous company assembled on the occasion; after which, it was determined, to avoid confusion, that each engine should be tried separately, and on different days.

The 'Rocket' being first ready, was put upon trial, and having got a proper supply of water, was weighed, and found to be 4 Tons 5 cwt.; the load affixed agreeable to the resolutions of the Directors, was therefore three times that weight, or 12 tons 15 cwt., viz.:—

	Tons.	cwts.	qrs.	lbs.
Engine	4	5	0	0
Tender, with water and coke	3	4	0	2
Two carriages loaded with stones	9	10	3	26
Whole mass in motion	17	0	0	0

[1] Vol. XII., p. 180, 7th November 1829.

[2] Wood, *Treatise on Rail Roads*, 2nd edition, 1831, p. 366.

The engine was then taken to the extremity of the stage, the fire-box filled with coke, and the fire lighted; the water in the boiler being quite cold, the time occupied in raising the steam until it lifted the safety valve, loaded to a pressure of 50 lbs. per square inch, was 57 minutes. Immediately the steam was at the above pressure, which was at 10 h. 36′ 5″, the engine started from the west extremity of the stage, and arrived at the same place, after performing ten trips. or 35 miles, precisely at 1 h. 48′ 38″.

After an analysis of the performances Wood records :—

The greatest velocity attained, being in the last eastward trip, which was performed in 3′ 44″, being at the rate of $29\frac{1}{9}$ miles per hour.

The quantity of fuel put into the fire-box for getting up the steam, was	222 lbs.
Deduct remaining, when the steam was at 50 lbs. per square inch	80 ,,
Consumption of fuel in getting up the steam	142 lbs.

The quantity of coke consumed by the engine, in performing the two experiments, was 1,085 lbs., which, for 70 miles, is :—

Including the engine and tender	0·91 lbs.	per ton per mile.
Exclusive of ditto	1·63 lbs.	

The quantity of water used, was 579 gallons, or 92·6 cubic feet; consequently the consumption of fuel was $11\frac{7}{10}$ lbs. of coke, for each cubic foot of water evaporated.

On examining these experiments, it will be seen, that the eastward trips were invariably performed in less time than those of the opposite direction. In going east, the engine dragged the carriages after it, while in travelling west, the carriages were pushed before the engine; as the road was said to be perfectly level, we can only attribute the difference of effect, to the disadvantageous action of pushing the carriages, instead of dragging them; and as in the practical application of this mode of conveyance, these engines will always drag the carriages after them, if the plane be perfectly horizontal, we ought, perhaps, to take the performance of the eastward trip, as the work done, which will be as follows:—

h. m. s.

1st journey,	1 2 21, or $14\frac{1}{2}$	miles, per hour, or average 15 miles, per hour.
2nd journey,	0 57 12, or $15\frac{3}{4}$	

It would, however, be assigning a performance greater than the experiment would warrant to take the above as the performance of the engine; for although the above was the effect at full speed, and though, undoubtedly, a great loss of effect was also occasioned by the stops at each end of the stage; yet it should not be lost sight of, that during the time the engine was stopped at each end of the stage, there was no waste of steam, and the evaporation in the boiler was going on all the time, not with that rapidity which would take place had the engine been working, but still such as the exhausting power of the chimney could effect. Perhaps, therefore, under all the circumstances, the real performance of the engine, compared with what it would have been, had the distance been travelled right forward, should be the 70 miles travelled in the observed time occupied between the inner stations, and half the time at each end. This would make the performance 17 tons, including the engine, or $9\frac{1}{2}$ tons, exclusive of the engine, conveyed 70 miles in about five hours, or at the rate of 14 miles per hour. And this would give the evaporation of water, 114 gallons per hour, and the consumption of coke, 217 lbs. per hour.

Wood then deals with the next engine brought forward for trial, Hackworth's 'Sans Pareil' :—

It was the original intention of the judges, to have ascertained the time, and quantity of fuel necessary to raise the water in the boiler to the temperature equivalent to the elasticity of 50 lbs. per square inch; but when this engine came to the starting-post, it was found, that Mr. Hackworth had been running it back and forward to ascertain if some leaks in the boiler (which had delayed its trial for some days), had been effectually stopped, and the water being consequently warm, no measure could be taken either of the fuel, or the time required to raise the steam to the necessary elasticity.   The engine was, therefore, put on its trial, and this part of the enquiry omitted.

When the requisite quantity of water was put into the boiler, and the engine placed upon the weighing machine, it was found to weigh 4 tons, 15½ cwt. On perusing the conditions issued by the Directors, it will be seen, that if any engine should be more than 4½ tons weight, it was to be placed upon six wheels; the weight of the 'Sans Pareil,' therefore, excluded it from competing for the prize; but on further consideration, the judges determined to put the engine through the same trial, as if it conformed with the proposed conditions, to ascertain if the performance was such, as would enable them to recommend this point to the favourable consideration of the Directors.

The weight of the engine, and the load assigned agreeable to the conditions, were as follows, viz. :—

	Tons	cwt.	qrs.	lbs.
Engine	4	15	2	0
Tender with water and fuel	3	6	3	0
Three carriages loaded with stones	10	19	3	0
Total mass in motion	19	2	0	0

Having had a sufficient quantity of fuel supplied, and the steam raised to the regulated elasticity, the engine was brought up to the starting-post, and proceeded on its task in a similar way to the 'Rocket.' In traversing the eighth trip to the west, the pump that supplies the boiler with water, got wrong, which, checking the supply, the water in the boiler got below the top of the tube, and melted the leaden plug inserted for the purpose of preventing accidents in such a case, and put an end to the experiment.

Wood's analysis of the performance of the 'Sans Pareil' shows :—

The greatest velocity attained, being in the 5th trip, going east, the 1¼ miles being traversed in 3' 59", which is at the rate of 22⅔ miles per hour.

The whole distance traversed by the engine was 27½ miles, and the consumption of coke was 1,269 lbs.,

which is { including the engine and tender   ....2·41 lbs. } per ton per mile.
         { exclusive of ditto.   ....4·2 lbs. }

The quantity of water used was 274 imperial gallons, or 43·84 cubic feet, and consequently the consumption of coke was 28·8 lbs. for each cubic foot of water evaporated.

Making the same allowance as in the case of the 'Rocket,' for the loss of effect at the ends of the stage, the performance would be 19½ tons, or 11 tons exclusive of the engine and tender, conveyed at the rate of about 15 miles per hour, and the evaporation of water nearly 150 gallons per hour, and of coke 692 lbs. per hour, or 28·8 lbs. for each cubic foot of water evaporated.

Of the 'Novelty,' the next engine to be put on its official trial, Wood states :—

The owners not having had any opportunity of trying that engine upon a Railway, previous to its arrival at Liverpool, it was found, when placed upon the road there, that some alteration of the wheels was necessary. This, together with the lateness of its arrival, and the occurrence of some trifling casualties in starting, produced considerable delay; and it was not until the 10th that the engine could be put upon its trial. It had been previously determined by the judges that it should be tried on the Monday, in order to give the owners more time to perfect the different alterations, but, at the urgent request of Mr. Braithwaite, it was brought out on the Saturday.

This engine, as will be afterwards shewn, differs from the previous ones, in the water and fuel being carried on the same wheels as the engine, and not on a separate carriage; and as the weight to be dragged was to be three times the weight of the engine only, and not of the engine and watertank, it was determined by the judges, that the load assigned to this engine, in order to place it on the same footing as the others, should be the same proportion of useful load, compared with the weight of the engine, that the useful load taken by Stephenson's engine, bore to its weight; leaving both engines to carry the fuel in their own way. The weight of Stephenson's engine was 85 cwt. and the load taken (exclusive of tender and water) was 191 cwt. Messrs. Braithwaite and Ericsson's engine (exclusive of water tank) weighed 61 cwt. Therefore, as 85 : 191 :: 61 : 137 cwt., the load assigned to the 'Novelty.' [1]

The weight of the whole train in this experiment, was, therefore, as follows:—

			Tons.	cwt.	qr.	lbs.
Engine with water in the boiler	....	....	3	1	0	0
Tank, water and fuel	....	....	....	0	16	0	14
Two carriages loaded with stones	....	....	6	17	0	0
Gross weight in motion	....	....	10	14	0	14

The engine was then brought up to the place of starting, and the fuel having been previously weighed, the fire was lighted, and the time in getting the steam up to an elasticity of 50 lbs. per square inch, was 54' 40". The quantity of fuel delivered to raise the steam was 66 lbs., but as we had no means of ascertaining what was left in the fire, no account could be had of what was actually consumed. The engine then started to traverse the stage in a similar way to the others. When the engine arrived at the post No. 1, in returning, it was found that the pipe conveying the water from the forcing pump to the boiler had been burst open, occasioned, Mr. Ericsson said, by the cock which opens or shuts the communication from the pump with the boiler having been accidentally shut while the pump was working. This being repaired, it was too late to go on with the experiment this day, but the engine, according to a statement by Mr. Vignoles, published in the *Mechanics' Magazine*, with a calculated weight of 10 tons 6¼ cwt. traversed the eastward trip of 1½ miles in 4 minutes 39 seconds, being at the rate of 17½ miles per hour, and the westward trip in 5 minutes 54 seconds, being at the rate of 15 miles an hour. The loaded carriages being detached, the engine made a trip with passengers, going at the rate of between 20 and 30 miles an hour. Two or three days being allowed to get the engine into complete working order (as many as Messrs. Braithwaite and Ericsson requested) it was again, on the 14th, put upon its trial.

On the arrival of the judges at Rainhill at the appointed time, they found that several parts of the engine having been taken to pieces, were not put together, and a considerable time elapsed before this was done; to prevent unnecessary delay, therefore, no account was taken of the quantity of fuel necessary to raise the steam to the proper degree of elasticity. The engine being ready made a trip to see if everything was right, and then came up to the starting-post. It was then set off upon its task in the same way as the others. In returning westward the second trip some of the joints of the steam generator gave way and put an end to the experiment: after which, Mr. Ericsson declared to the judges his wish to withdraw from a further competition for the prize. No conclusion whatever could be formed from these experiments, of the power of this engine; none of the experiments were continued sufficiently long to shew the quantity of steam which could be raised in a given time, or the fuel required to generate it.

The 'Perseverance,' of Mr. Burstall, having met with an accident in its conveyance to Liverpool, and having been found, on trial, not to be adapted for the purposes of the Company, this gentleman, in a very handsome manner, withdrew from competing for the prize.

[1] Mr. E. A. Forward, of the Science Museum, South Kensington, points out that the 'Novelty' was unfairly *underloaded*. It weighed with water in boiler (but without tank, tank water and fuel) 3 tons 1 cwt., and if treated like the other engines should have had a total load of 9 tons 3 cwt. Deducting the weight of tank, water and fuel the load to be hauled should have been over 8 tons 6 cwt. 3 qrs.—instead of only 6 tons 17 cwt.

The prize was then awarded to the 'Rocket,' of Mr. Stephenson, as having performed all the conditions and stipulations required of the competitors.

Wood then gives an account of the constructive details of the competing engines which we shall quote at length since it affords contemporary evidence on the fire-box of the 'Rocket' :—

The 'Rocket' engine, of Mr. R. Stephenson, shewn in the engraving, differs from the loco-motive engines previously described in this work, in the mode of raising steam. The boiler A, is cylindrical, with flat ends, 6 feet long, and 3 feet 4 inches diameter. To one end of the boiler is attached a square box, or furnace B, 3 feet long, by 2 feet broad, and about 3 feet deep; at the bottom of this box, the fire-bars F, are placed; and it is entirely surrounded by a casing, except at the bottom, and on the side next the boiler, leaving a space of about 3 inches between

from Wood's Treatise on Rail Roads, 1831. p. 383.

this casing and the furnace, which space is kept constantly filled with water;—a pipe C, on the under side, communicating with the boiler, supplying it with water; and another pipe D, at the top, allowing the steam to pass off into the boiler. The upper half of the boiler is used as a reservoir for steam, the lower half being kept filled with water. Through this part of the boiler, copper tubes reach from one end of the boiler to the other, being open to the fire-box at one end, and to the chimney at the other. In the boiler of the 'Rocket,' there were 25 tubes, 3 inches in diameter. The cylinders were placed, one on each side of the boiler, as shewn in the drawing, and worked one pair of wheels only, were 8 inches diameter, with a stroke of $16\frac{1}{2}$ inches[1]; diameter of large wheels, 4 feet $8\frac{1}{2}$ inches. A slight inspection of the drawing will shew that the principle of generating steam by this engine, is the *exhausting power of the chimney*,

[1] The makers' records give the stroke as 17 inches.

which is aided by the impulse of the steam from the cylinders, being thrown into the chimney by two pipes E, one from each of the cylinders. The area of surface of water, exposed to the *radiant heat* of the fire, was 20 square feet, being that surrounding the fire-box or furnace; and the surface exposed to the heated air or flame from the furnace, or what we shall call *communicative heat*, 117·8 square feet; the area of the grate-bars being 6 square feet. The end view will shew the disposition of the tubes in the end of the boiler, with the fire-box surrounding the end.

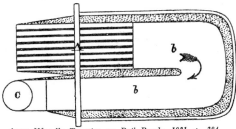

from Wood's Treatise on Rail Roads, 1831, p. 384.

BOILER OF 'SANS PAREIL' IN PLAN

The 'Sans Pareil,' of Mr. Hackworth, is of the same principle as the 'Rocket'; the combustion of the fuel being effected by the *exhausting power of the chimney*, and the ejection of the steam from the cylinders into the chimney. The boiler is cylindrical, 4 feet 2 inches diameter, with one flat, and one hemispherical end, and 6 feet long. The cylinders were placed one on each side of the boiler, and immediately above one of the pairs of wheels; the other two wheels being connected with them by side rods. Cylinders, 7 inches; length of stroke, 18 inches; diameter of wheels, 4½ feet.

The steam is generated by means of a double tube passing nearly from one end of the boiler to the other and then returning; the fire-grate and chimney being thus both at the same end of the boiler A. The tube projects, from the end of the boiler, about 3 feet; and at the fire end a semi-circular casing surrounds the top of the tube, as shewn in the drawing, and the whole 3 feet; but at the chimney end the casing, extends only 2 feet. This was for the double purpose of obtaining an area of heating surface, and sufficient air to pass through the fire-grate, which tubes, entirely within the backs, (*sic*) do not possess. At the fire end the tube was 2 feet diameter, tapering away to 15 inches, the diameter at the chimney; the length of grate-bars being 5 feet. The area of surface of water exposed to the direct action of the fire or *radiant heat*, is therefore 15·7 square feet; and to the *communicative power* of the heated air and flame, 74·6 square feet, the area of fire-grate being 10 square feet.

Messrs. Braithwaite and Ericsson's engine, the 'Novelty,' is of a different principle, the air being driven or *forced* through the fire by means of a bellows. The accompanying drawings will shew the general construction of this engine, and more particularly the generator, or mode of raising the steam, which constitutes its prominent peculiarity. A is the generator, the lower part of which is filled with water, and the upper part is a chamber for the steam; connected with this is the horizontal generator B, which being placed below the top of the water in the upright generator A, is constantly filled with water. A tube C, passes through the upright generator from top to bottom; near the bottom it is increased in diameter, for the purpose of receiving the fire-grate F; the fuel being supplied from the top, kept air-tight by sliding shutters. The bottom of this tube containing the fire-grate, is closed, and the supply of air is

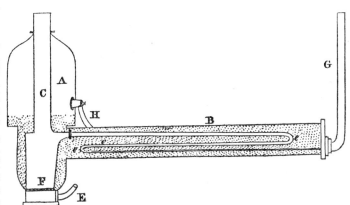

from Wood's Treatise on Rail Roads, 1831, p. 387.

BOILER OF 'NOVELTY.'

effected by the bellows D, worked by the engine, and communicated through the pipe E. The air, after passing through the fire, is made to traverse through a winding tube, within the horizontal generator, and to pass into the atmosphere through the pipe G. K is the cylinder, working one of the pairs of wheels, by means of a bell crank, the others being connected, when necessary, by a chain similar to the old engines.

The area of grate-bars, in this engine, is only about 1·8 square feet. The *radiant surface*, about 9·5 square feet; and the area exposed to the heated air, by means of the tube traversing the generator B, about 33 square feet.

Mr. Burstall's engine, not being adapted for the present celerity of Rail-road conveyance; the boiler, consisting of an upright generator, the heated air and flame escaping up the chimney immediately from the fire-place, without any flues to abstract the redundant heat,—not being of that form which combined lightness with economy of fuel; it will not, perhaps, be necessary to attempt a more particular description of it. But we must add, that though its general construction rendered it inapplicable for the use of the company, yet several of the individual parts displayed great ingenuity.

The following Table will exhibit, as nearly as we could obtain, the peculiarities of the different exhibiting engines.

Names of Engines.	Area of Fire-grate in feet.	Area of radiant surface in feet. (Firebox surface).	Area of communicative surface in feet. (Tube surface).	Cubic feet of water evaporated per hour.	Lbs. of coke required to evaporate a cubic foot of water.
Rocket	6	20	117·8	18·24	11·7
Sans Pareil	10	15·7	74·6	24	28·8
Novelty	1·8	9·5	33	—	—
Old Engines	7	11·5	29·75	15·92	18·34

After comparing the boilers of the 'Rocket' and the 'Sans Pareil' and giving reasons to account for the great difference in the consumption of fuel by the two engines respectively, Wood remarks :—

Some explanation is, perhaps, necessary, why the 'Sans Pareil' should, in this respect, be more extravagant than the old engines, while the extent of surface compared with the area of fire-grate, is much greater, and therefore should exhibit a more economical result; and this explanation is the more necessary, as, though not appearing at first sight, it involves a principle of the greatest importance in the economy of those engines; and which, if not acted upon, would render the use of the tubes, however otherwise valuable, considerably less effective. It will readily occur to any one, paying a little attention to the matter, that the system of tubes may be carried so far, as to reduce the temperature of the flame and heated air, nearly equal to that of the water in the boiler; in which case, when it reaches the chimney, it will be incapable, from its reduced temperature, of producing a sufficient draught of air through the fire-grate. This would prevent all the advantages being taken of the refracting powers, which would otherwise result from the use of these tubes. It is stated, in another part of this work, that on the introduction of those engines [*i.e.* the early Killingworth engines with a single flue] it was necessary to resort to the application of the waste steam thrown upwards into the chimney, to create a sufficient current of air through the fire; which was afterwards laid aside, or only partially used, when only slow rates of speed were required.[1]

Mr. Hackworth had, it appears, in his engine, resorted to the use of this in a more forcible manner than before used, throwing it up as a jet, which, when the engine moved at a rapid rate, and the steam thereby almost constantly issuing from the pipe, had a most powerful effect. This, though effecting the object for which it was intended, being carried too far,

[1] Wood, *Treatise on Rail Roads*, 1st edition, 1825, p. 293 (see facsimile, p. 26, Chapter III. *ante*).

partly in consequence of the rapid speed at which the engine was made to travel, was productive of another evil, which, though operating fatally so far as regarded that particular experiment, was capable of easy remedy. The consequence was, that when the engine began to travel at the rate of 12 or 15 miles an hour, the draught was so great that it actually threw the cinders out of the chimney with considerable force, producing a destruction of fuel enormously great, so much so, that the consumption was at least 692 lbs. per hour.

He proceeds to describe the exhausting arrangement in the 'Rocket':—

In the 'Rocket' engine, this mode of increasing the draught of the chimney, was but partially used; the steam was made to pass into the chimney, by two pipes, one from each cylinder, and the size of the aperture was not, therefore, sufficiently small to cause the steam to pass into the chimney with adequate force; still, in that engine, we find it only required 11·7 lbs. to evaporate a cubic foot of water,—36 per cent. less than with the old engines. We shall afterwards find, that this has been considerably more reduced in the engines lately made.

The 'Novelty' engine is on a different principle from those previously considered, the necessary supply of air to the fire, being produced by a bellows. In this case, a chimney becomes unnecessary, and from the way in which the 'Novelty' is constructed, the air was forced through the fire in a very condensed or compressed state. The area of fire-grate being little more than one-third of that of the 'Rocket,' and the surface exposed to the radiant action of the fire less than one half, the temperature to which the fire was raised must, of course, be considerably greater, to evaporate an equal quantity of water in the same time. The abstraction of heat would be probably more perfect in the 'Novelty,' for the tube through which the flame and heated air passed in its exit to the atmosphere, was 36 feet in length, in one tube; whereas in the 'Rocket', there was the same length, though subdivided into six tubes. It is, however, extremely questionable, whether one tube, 36 feet long, or 6 tubes, each 6 feet long, of the same sectional area, are more preferable; the latter would, of course, give a much greater exposure of surface. The area of exit of the heated air, into the atmosphere, of the 'Rocket,' was 25 times that of the 'Novelty'; from which we may imagine the degree of compression necessary to force the same quantity of air through the fire; though we do not say, that to raise an equal quantity of steam, an equal quantity of air, in that highly compressed state, is necessary.

Wood expresses the opinion that :—

It was much to be regretted that the experiment with the 'Novelty' could not be continued sufficiently long to ascertain the power of raising steam by this method; the enquiry was of the utmost importance. Theoretically considered we are of opinion that this mode of generating steam, is more economical in point of fuel, than in engines, the combustion of the fire of which is kept up by the rarefaction in the chimney; but there are practical objections to set against this, of which the destruction of fire-bars and the power required to work the bellows are not the least.

He then explains that the cause of the 'Novelty's' failure was not 'defect in the principle but only in the construction of that engine.' Wood appears indeed to have been as favourably impressed by it as were other engineers, among them William Laird, the founder of the well-known firm of shipbuilding engineers, who was himself an eye witness of the trials and has recorded his impressions in the letter[1] we give below. Although throwing no light on

[1] William Laird to C. W. Williams, Dublin; letter communicated to Robert Stephenson & Co. on 29th July 1921, by a great-grandson of William Laird, Mr. J. W. P. Laird, who states that :—'William Laird apparently came to Birkenhead from Greenock about 1811, and after engaging in various businesses, among which was this manufactory of boilers, he became convinced there was a future for iron shipbuilding, and in 1822 or 1823 bought certain land in Birkenhead as a shipyard, on a site which is now part of the public docks.'

subsequent controversy his account is interesting as giving the opinion of a marine engineer who was not directly interested in the locomotive, and as showing the extravagant hopes—or fears—which were roused by the 'Novelty.' It is somewhat curious that Laird's letter should express no interest in the 'Rocket' although, as we have seen, he had experimented with and built locomotive boilers for the Stephensons'; it is even possible that the first fire-box of the 'Rocket' may have been made at his manufactory; but on this point we have no evidence, though it is known to have been made in Liverpool.

Laird writes under date :—

Liverpool, 28th October 1829.

You have no doubt seen all the newspaper reports of the trials of the Locomotive on the railroad, the result far exceeded the most sanguine expectations even of the engineers themselves, the London Engine attracted particular attention going with great ease at the rate of 32 miles per hour with upwards of 40 people on the carriage attached to it, the mode of generating steam is quite new and I think may be applied successful to steam navigation, the engine is 12 horse power, the boiler is a copper cylinder of 12″ diameter and 20 ft. long, at one end is a cupola or blast furnace which forces the heat through a tube of $3\frac{1}{2}$″ diameter and which makes three turns inside the cylinder as I shall endeavour to give you some idea of by the above (*sketch*), the end of the cylinder is closed by a cam with flanges, the necks of the tubes are also fastened by screws and can be taken off to clean the tubes, but the combustion is so perfect that not a vestige of anything is left in the tubes, I saw them opened after working and they are quite bright, in short it promises fairer than anything I have yet heard of, and if it does answer it will form a new era in Steam Navigation and *knock Boiler making* in the head. A cylinder for engines of 120 horse will be about 4 ft. diameter and will occupy the space between the engines, consequently the space now occupied by the boiler will be saved and the consumption of fuel reduced to less than $\frac{2}{3}$ the present quantity and, the balance can be placed on deck or in any other situation where it can be worked by the engine, the present carriage was only intended to go 12 miles an hour, the engine to work 70 or 80 strokes, but it went 210 strokes and abundance of steam so that by increasing the diameter of the wheels and the power you may go 100 or even 200 miles an hour if it were desirable, but at 32 miles it passed like an arrow from a Bow and yet so easy that Dr. Traile wrote a note with his pencil during the ride.

I should have given you some account of this affair sooner but expected your return home, it is my intention to go to London to see one fitted up for a 70 Horse Engine next week, and I shall then form a more correct idea of its merits. It can be worked to any pressure, the carriage Engine is 40 pounds per inch, if it is to become general I should like to commence it here, and if another Tow Boat is wanted it would be a good opportunity, the Iron Barge attracts great attention, she will complete in a few days.

P.S.—In a large boiler additional tubes are put in but not increased in size.

We may note in passing the interesting reference to iron ship construction, and regarding the principle of the new boiler we find that, when giving evidence in proceedings taken against Braithwaite and Ericsson by another maker for infringement of patent, Laird stated in July 1830[1] that :—

. . . . the great advantages stated to be derived from the use of the defendants' boiler had occasioned a great stagnation in the business of boiler making, which had since been removed by the defendants' invention having been proved to be of great advantage and superior to any boiler hitherto known.

[1] *Mechanics' Magazine*, Vol. XIII., p. 311.

Laird was referring to marine construction, and it is recorded later that boilers on Braithwaite and Ericsson's principle were constructed at his manufactory for the Steam Packet 'Hibernia,' effecting a saving of space equivalent 'on the most moderate computation' to 180 tons of goods.[1]

As our last witness we shall quote John Dixon, who at the time of the Rainhill Trials was still in the service of the Liverpool and Manchester Railway Company; later he had charge of their locomotives and, as we shall see, himself contributed to their improvement. In his later years he published for private circulation the results of his observations on train resistance and boiler performances, describing himself as having been 'from its earliest forms intimately associated with the progressive improvement of the locomotive engine.' Dixon's dislike of advertisement, and a quizzical humour which prefers truth to sham, are still matters of local tradition; evidences of both are to be found in a letter[2] written by him immediately after the Rainhill Trials to his brother James, employed at the time in the Railway Office, Darlington.

JOHN DIXON'S SKETCH OF THE 'NOVELTY'S' BOILER

Patricroft, Oct. 16 1829.

Dear James,

We have finished the grand experiments on the Engines and G. S. or R. S. has come off triumphant and of course will take hold of the £500 so liberally offered by the Company: none of the others being able to come near them. The Rocket is by far the best Engine I have ever seen for Blood and Bone united. Story will give you particulars besides the Newspaper accounts.

Timothy has been very sadly out of temper ever since he came for he has been grobbing on day and night and nothing our men did for him was right, we could not please him with the Tender nor anything; he openly accused all G. S's. people of conspiring to hinder him of which I do

[1] *Mechanics' Magazine.* Vol. XIV., p. 210. See also Vol. XIII., p. 308. Application in the Court of Chancery by Lord Cochrane and Mr. Alexander Galloway.

[2] In the possession of John Dixon's nephew, Mr. Waynman Dixon, by whose permission it is now published for the first time.

Patricroft Oct 16. 1829.

Dear James

We have finished the grand experiments on the Engines and G S or R S has
come off triumphant and of course will
take hold of the £500. so liberally offered by
the Company. none of the others being able to
come near them. The Rocket is by far the best
Engine I have ever seen for Blood and Bone united
Henry will give you particulars besides the Newspaper accounts

Timothy has been very sadly out of temper ever
since he came for he has been grubbing on
Day & night and nothing our men did for him
was right, we could not please him with the
Tender nor any thing, he openly accused all G S
people of conspiring to hinder him of which
I do believe them innocent, however he got
many trials but never got half of his
70 Miles done without stopping. He burns
nearly double the quantity of coke that
the Rocket does and rumbles & rolls about
like a Empty Beer Butt on a rough
Pavement and moreover Weighs above
4½ Tons consequently should have

first page from the original in possession of Mr. Waynman Dixon.

JOHN DIXON'S LETTER TO HIS BROTHER JAMES
describing the Rainhill Trials, 1829

he altered and amended some part every day till he was last of all to start & a sorrowful start it was; full 6 Miles an hour cranking away like an old Wickerwork pair of Panniers on a Cantering cuddy Ass. Vox populi was in favour of London from appearances but we shewed them the way to do it. for Mess Rastrig & Walker in their Report as to Fixed & Locomot Engines stated that the whole power of the Loco Engines would be absorbed in taking their own bodies up Rainhill Incline 1 in 96 consequently they could take no load, Now the first thing old George did was to bring a Coach with about 20 people up at a Gallop & every day since has been bringing up & down to let them see what they could do up such as ascent & has taken 40 folks up at 20 Miles an hour. He is now going on with an extension of the Way to Derbyshire & I am to begin on Monday to Survey the from Manchester to meet the others. Robert is about a new Line in Leicester Shire — I dined with Storey at Mr J's & were all as kind as Cousins

Love to all friends & believe me Dr Jenny
Thy affectionate Brother Coste
John Dixon

JOHN DIXON'S LETTER TO HIS BROTHER JAMES
describing the Rainhill Trials, 1829

believe them innocent, however he got many trials but never got half of his 70 miles done without stopping. He burns nearly double the quantity of coke that the Rocket does and mumbles and roars and rolls about like a Empty Beer Butt on a rough Pavement and moreover weighs above 4½ Tons consequently should have had six wheels and as for being on Springs I must confess I cannot find them out either going or standing neither can I perceive any effect they have. She is very ugly and the Boiler runs out very much, he had to feed her with more Meal and Malt Sprouts than would fatten a pig. . . . .

The London Engine of Braithwaite & Erickson called the 'Novelty' was a light one, no chimney upright but a Boiler thus (*sketch*) blown by a Blast at A by Bellows and pipes carried like a Still worm along the Tube B C to the discharge C point on Chimney E. She only weighed 3 . 7 . 3 and did not stand 10 ft. high. Two 6 in. cylinders working a Bell Crank lever to turn the Axle which was cranked so as to be turned by the Bell and Bob lever out of sight, but a very weak form of axle, a Water Tank under the Carriage close to the ground and Boiler Bellows Flues, etc., were all covered with Copper like a new Tea Urn all which tended to give her a very Parlour like appearance and when she started she seemed to dart away like a Greyhound for a bit but every trial he had some mishap, first an explosion of inflammable gas which Burst his Bellows then his feed pipe blew up and finally some internal joint of his hidden flue thro his boiler so that it was no go.

Burstall from Edinbro, upset his in bringing from L'Pool to Rainhill and spent a week in pretending to Remedy the injuries whereas he altered and amended some part every day till he was last of all to start and a sorrowful start it was; full 6 miles an hour cranking away like an old Wickerwork pair of Panniers on a cantering Cuddy Ass. Vox Populi was in favour of London from appearances but we showed them the way to do it for Messrs. Rastrig & Walker in their report as to Fixed and permt. Engines stated that the whole power of the Loco. Engines would be absorbed in taking their own bodies up Rainhill Incline 1 in 96 consequently they could take no load, now the first thing old George did was to bring a Coach with about 20 people up at a galop and every day since has run up and down to let them see what they could do up such an ascent and has taken 40 folks up at 20 miles an hour.

He is now going on with an extension of the Way to Derbyshire and I am to begin on Monday to survey, etc. from Manchester to meet the others. Robert is about a new line in Leicestershire. I dined with Story at Mr. S.'s and we were all as kind as cousins.

Love to all friends and believe me, Dr. James,

Thy affectionate Bro. in haste,

JOHN DIXON.

In the various accounts from which we have quoted we find a general agreement that the 'Novelty' excited the greatest admiration, and that, not only '*Vox Populi*,' but many engineers, would have welcomed a decision in its favour; it was by one popular account 'universally allowed to exhibit the beau-ideal of a locomotive engine,' and having inside cylinders it ran no doubt more smoothly than either of the other competing engines.

The 'Sans Pareil' impressed observers principally with its appearance of power, with the noise it made, and by the violent emission from its chimney and great consumption of fuel.

The 'Rocket' was by no means the favourite; it was 'pronounced by some to be ugly, clumsy and unmechanical,' and it won the prize, not on account of its popularity, but because it was the only engine which completed the stipulated task. It was at the time, and by some writers is still, claimed on behalf of the 'Sans Pareil' that it was as good an engine as the 'Rocket'; but such a view is not supported either by the evidence of independent observers or by the official records of the railway company. It is true that it had boiler

troubles, some of which may have been due as much to design as to workmanship, and that various accidents, including a cracked cylinder[1], finally put an
end to its performance at the trials ; it is conceivable that the excessive consumption of fuel may have been partly caused by the passage of steam direct
to the chimney through the crack, but is equally probable that it was due
principally to the very powerful 'blast,' commented on by Wood, and perhaps
the cause of the roaring described by Dixon. There appear to have been
other reasons which would have justified its disqualification ; the competing
engines were required to have springs, but the cylinder arrangement of the
'Sans Pareil' was such that any vertical disturbances due to the pressure of
steam on the piston acting alternately on each side would have their maximum
effect in producing a rolling motion. There is no evidence that springs were
fitted, John Dixon could not see them and they are not shown on the existing
copy of the original drawing.[2] The use of effective springs was in fact even
more inconsistent with the cylinder arrangement of the 'Sans Pareil' than with
that of the old Killingworth type of engine, and if they were not fitted the
engine obviously failed in this respect to satisfy one of the conditions
of the competition.

The success of the 'Sans Pareil' would probably have encouraged a return
to the vertical cylinder with direct drive, which had been definitely abandoned
by Robert Stephenson in 1828 ; for this reason alone it is perhaps fortunate
that she failed. It has been argued that the subsequent purchase of this
engine by the Liverpool and Manchester Railway Company is evidence that
they were satisfied with her, but we have already noted the directors' statement that she was bought out of consideration for her builder and in the
hope that she might perform some useful service. In this they were disappointed
and she was sold within three years for £110 ; had she been as good an engine
as the 'Rocket' they would have kept her at a time when, owing to the failure
of Braithwaite and Ericsson's promises, they could not meet urgent requirements for locomotive power. Rapidly increasing demands soon rendered
the 'Rocket' too out of date for the traffic of the Liverpool and Manchester
Railway, and there is evidence that she was employed principally on the
ballasting and other work in connection with the road for which George
Stephenson had recommended her immediately after the trials[3] ; but she
remained in the service of the company until 24th October 1836 when the
treasurer reported to the directors that he had sold her to Mr. James Thompson
of Carlisle for £300.

Allegations were made, both during and after the trials, that the 'Sans
Pareil' did not receive fair treatment ; some of these are alluded to in John
Dixon's letter and dismissed by him with the full knowledge of a man who was
himself behind the scenes ; others are disposed of by the consideration shown

[1] Designed by Hackworth but supplied by Robert Stephenson & Co., who are said to have made six
castings 'before two perfect ones were got.' *A Chapter in the History of Railway Locomotion*, p. 9.

[2] At the Science Museum, South Kensington. See page 192 *ante*.

[3] Liverpool and Manchester Railway Directors' Minute, 19th October 1829.

throughout to Hackworth by the directors of the Liverpool and Manchester Railway. It is noticeable that no similar allegations were made in the case of the 'Novelty,' though many engineers were of opinion that she was the best of the competing engines; so much so, that the influence of her design is to be seen in engines built later by Sharp Roberts & Co., Forrester and others. The method of drive adopted was less objectionable than that of the 'Sans Pareil' since it permitted the use of springs, and her makers themselves were so confident in its advantages that the 'two large and beautiful engines,'—'William the Fourth' and 'Queen Adelaide,'—which they later submitted for trial were designed generally on the same principle, though in these they substituted exhaustion by a fan for forced draught by a bellows; to these engines we shall refer again later, we have already seen that they too were unsuccessful.

No doubt the 'Novelty', but for accidents, might have accomplished its task and had train loads been once and for all limited to three times the weight of the engine, and speeds to 15 or 20 miles an hour, such a design might have survived for some time; but for the rough work of the railroad the 'Novelty' savoured too much of the road carriage or fire-engine, on the lines of which it had indeed been designed; in comparison with its competitors it was in fact little better than a toy, and fortunately for the rapid development of the railroad locomotive on sound lines it too was unsuccessful. 'Her makers experimented with her for many months after the trial endeavouring to remedy her several defects but with so little success that they at last withdrew her from the road.'

The 'Rocket' alone had the 'Blood and Bone' which the Stephensons' hard experience on the colliery lines of the north had taught them to be necessary; far from being the most unmechanical, it alone was designed on lines which have been proved capable of a vast extension to meet ever increasing demands on the power of the locomotive. It is this fact which makes the 'Rocket' as remarkable to-day as it was successful in 1829.

(part) from a drawing by Wm. Smoult, 3rd February 1830, printed from stone by George Smith, Liverpool.

THE 'ROCKET' WITH TRAIN ON THE SANKEY VIADUCT.

CHAPTER XIV

THE FIREBOX OF THE 'ROCKET'

We have already mentioned the serious discrepancies in the evidence which we meet when we attempt to define the details of this vital feature of the multitubular boiler. The original working drawings of the 'Rocket' must have long ago disappeared, they were possibly little more than sketches, barely keeping pace with a construction, which, in the case of the boiler and firebox, was entirely experimental. Robert Stephenson's letters to Henry Booth show that various alterations were made as the work proceeded, with the consequence that we have not now even such drawings as are still preserved for the engines which immediately preceded and followed the 'Rocket.' Probably the only working drawing showing the engine as a whole was that which is said to have been made by Robert Stephenson and Phipps on the floor of the drawing office [1]; any evidence by Phipps on the design of the 'Rocket' is therefore of value. It seems that at some time after the events with which he had been intimately concerned, but at a date unknown to us, Phipps himself was again employed by Robert Stephenson & Co. to make a drawing of the engine 'compiled from such drawings as could be found in the office, aided by his own knowledge' [2]; this drawing cannot be definitely identified with any of those now in the possession of the firm.

The earliest contemporary drawing at present known to us as purporting to show the 'Rocket' is that by C. B. Vignoles, published in the *Mechanics' Magazine* of 24th October 1829 with the account of the trials from which we have already quoted.[3] The next in point of time is the drawing in the second edition of Wood's *Treatise on Rail Roads*, published in 1831;[4] this drawing shows the firebox in transverse section, and though a difference in the finish of the top corner at the back is to be noticed, both illustrations show, though crudely, a practically rectangular form. The only other undoubtedly contemporary evidence known to us on the details of the design is what may be gathered from Robert Stephenson's letters to Booth, from the descriptions published with the two early drawings above mentioned, and last, but not least, what may be obtained from such of the original parts of the engine as are still preserved at the Science Museum, South Kensington. Of these it seems probable that the main frame, the boiler barrel, firebox back, cylinders, driving wheels, and much of the valve motion are original; the cylinders are however in the position to which they were altered after the trials, probably some time between 1831 and 1833; the engine frame has the modifications and additions necessary to suit this alteration.

---

[1] Memoir, *Proc. Inst. Civil Engineers*, Vol. XCVI., p. 330.
[2] 'Links in the History of the Locomotive,' *The Engineer*, 1880, Vol. L., pp. 217 *et seq.*
[3] See p. 176, Chapter XII. *ante*   [4] See p. 200, Chapter XIII *ante*

The present smokebox was added presumably between September 1830 and February 1831, if we may judge by representations of the 'Rocket' published at those dates. The first smokebox of this type was apparently fitted to the engine 'Phœnix,' which had been delivered to the Liverpool and Manchester Railway in June 1830. A contemporary aquatint [1] shows an engine which, if correctly represented by the artist, can only have been the 'Rocket,' since the cylinders are in a steeply inclined position. The picture suggests a smokebox as now on the engine (having a large door to give access to the tubes), with a small door to an ashbox below; this contemporary picture shows a man engaged in removing the ashes. The firebox cannot be seen.

A comparison with these early illustrations shows at once that the 'Rocket' as we see it to-day, in the Science Museum, South Kensington, is very different in general appearance from the engine as it was at Rainhill. But it would be possible by a re-arrangement of certain parts, by the renewal of others, and

(part) from an aquatint by T. T. Bury, published by R. Ackermann, 1st February 1831.

the removal of the smokebox and buffer beam, to restore the engine to something like her original lines; the most important re-arrangement required would be of the cylinders, and the most important restoration would be to the firebox, of which only the back portion now remains. A careful study by the Museum Authorities some years ago suggested that reconstruction should be on the lines shown by the drawing which they have since prepared [2] and which we now publish. It will be observed that by this reconstruction we should obtain very much the effect shown by the drawing in the *Mechanics' Magazine*, i.e., of a practically rectangular firebox, which in side elevation appears flat on the top, with a vertical back plate, and with the back top corner apparently bevelled off.

Since this theory for reconstruction was advanced two drawings have been brought to light which offer valuable evidence in its support; both show the

---

[1] *Entrance of the Railway at Edgehill, Liverpool*, drawn by T. T. Bury, published by R. Ackermann, February 1st 1831. The artist has mistakenly brought his chimney too far down in front.

[2] By Mr. E. A. Forward. See also letter by Mr. H. W. Dickinson, *The Engineer*, 23rd Jan. 1914, Vol. CXVII., p. 107.

THE 'ROCKET' AT THE SCIENCE MUSEUM, 1923

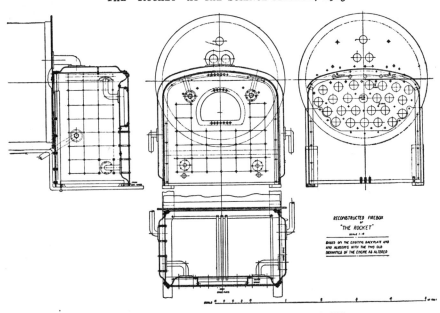

RECONSTRUCTED FIREBOX
OF
"THE ROCKET"

traced from a drawing made at the Science Museum by Mr. E. A. Forward, 1923.

PROPOSED RECONSTRUCTION OF THE FIREBOX
to suit the existing back plate and to agree with Drawings A & B

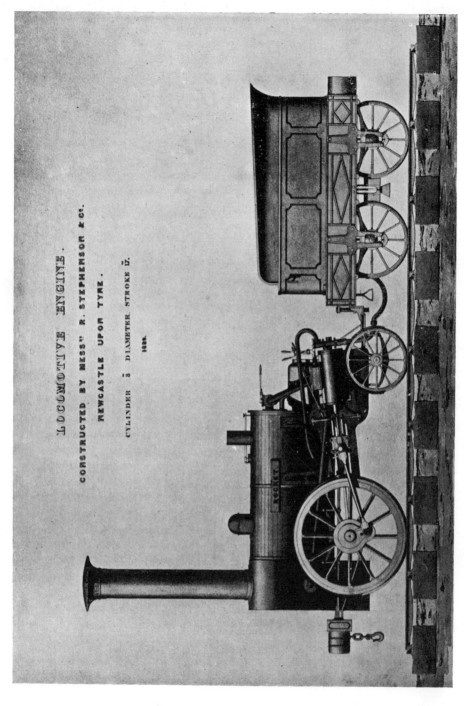

from a drawing in the Crewe offices of the London Midland and Scottish (formerly London and North Western) Railway Company.

THE 'ROCKET'

as rebuilt after the Rainhill Trials and when still in service on the Liverpool and Manchester Railway

(A)

'Rocket' after the cylinders had been lowered and the smokebox added, but they are obviously early; the first of these drawings (which we designate A) is now preserved at Crewe [1]; it bears date 1829, obviously not the date of the drawing itself, but we have a minute of the Liverpool and Manchester Railway Company's directors which records that on 22nd June 1836 :—

The treasurer stated that he had an application for the purchase of the Rocket engine if the Company was disposed to sell her. The Directors agree to sell the Rocket if a fair price could be got and ordered that a good drawing should be made of her to exhibit the form and construction of the first engine employed on the Railway.

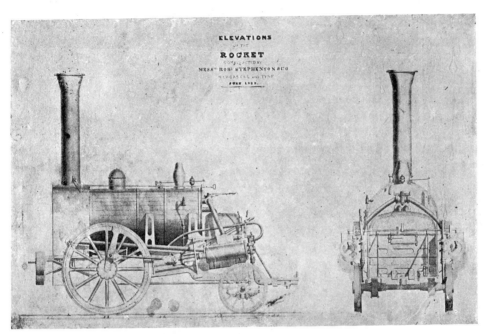

from a drawing (undated) in possession of Robert Stephenson & Co.

(B)

It seems reasonable to suggest that the Crewe drawing (A) may have been made as a direct consequence of this order, and if this assumption be correct we have valuable evidence on the question under discussion, the draughtsman having evidently recorded the engine as actually in service in 1836 and made no attempt to restore the cylinders to their original position.

Another drawing (which we designate B) still in the possession of Robert Stephenson & Co. offers further valuable evidence ; this drawing also bears date 1829, obviously again not that of its execution. Though generally in the same style it has evidence of having been made at a later date than the Crewe drawing (A) ; a whistle is shown of a type which we have not found appearing

[1] In the Drawing Office of the London, Midland & Scottish (formerly London & North Western) Railway Company, by whose permission it is now published.

on the makers' drawings of other engines before 1838, and there are some notable differences in detail from the Crewe drawing, as for instance in the chimney and safety valve casing. The driving wheel is shown with a crank strap extending from the boss to the rim; this is not shown on the Crewe drawing nor are there any evidences of such straps on the still existing wheels, though they are shown on the original drawings of the engines which followed the 'Rocket.' The padded leather buffers of the Crewe drawing have been removed and solid blocks of wood fastened below the buffer beam to engage with waggon buffers having different heights from the rail. The front end of the frame is shown with a special attachment to suit these additions, and the draw hooks and chain of the Crewe drawing are replaced by a simple fixed loop. These additions and alterations were no doubt required to render the engine suitable for the colliery service for which she was bought by James Thompson, of Kirkhouse, Carlisle, in 1836.[1]

These differences show that drawing B, now in the possession of Robert Stephenson & Co., is of a later date than drawing A, *but so far as the two drawings show the working parts of the engine, and notably the outline of the firebox in side elevation, they are in almost exact agreement with each other, and the view on the back of the firebox given on drawing B exactly represents this part of the engine as it may be seen to-day.* This drawing appears therefore to have been based, partly on facts obtained from the rebuilt engine itself, and partly on information obtained from the drawings of the engines which followed the 'Rocket'; only on this supposition can we now account for the portrayal of a crank strap on the driving wheels. It seems probable that drawing B may have been made by Phipps, some time after 1829, in the circumstances related by him.

Now if we accept the illustrations in the *Mechanics' Magazine* of 1829, and Wood's *Treatise* of 1831, as generally correct in outline they, together with drawings A and B, appear to show that, both in an early, and in the last stage of her working life on the Liverpool and Manchester Railway, the 'Rocket' had a firebox with a vertical back plate similar to, or identical with that still in existence, and that whatever alterations may have been made before the trials none was made to the form of the firebox when the cylinders were lowered to their present position.

As additional evidence on this point we have the fact that the placing of the valve shaft across the back of the firebox, as a result of lowering the cylinders, made it necessary to close the upper portion of the firedoor as originally made, and the means taken to effect this are still evident on the engine. But most notable is the fact that both drawings A and B, show the ogee finish at the top corners of the firebox which would be obtained by a reconstruction on the lines of the drawing prepared by the Museum Authorities, taking the existing back plate as a basis.

The drawings we have described above are all that are known, or may be assumed, to have been made during the working life of the 'Rocket'; we have

[1] Liverpool & Manchester Railway Directors' Minute, 24th October 1836.

now to consider three drawings made subsequently for Robert Stephenson & Co. and still in their possession ; these are :—

1. A drawing of the engine alone, in outside elevation, with dimensions.

2. A drawing of the boiler and firebox, in section.

These appear to be the two drawings referred to in the manuscript '*Particulars*' from which we have already quoted in a previous chapter.

3. A drawing of the engine and tender together in outside elevation.

This latter drawing was published in 1880 [1] *with a statement that it was the drawing which had been made by Phipps.* It has since been widely reproduced and generally accepted as showing the 'Rocket' in its original state, but a more critical examination in later years has led to some doubts on this point. Robert Stephenson & Co. have now written evidence that this drawing showing the engine and tender in outside elevation was made in 1859 by their then chief draughtsman [2], 'from a copy of certain particulars of the building and delivery of the 'Rocket,' from a few rough sketches hunted up in the works, and from the engine as standing in the works yard.'

It will be observed that drawing 3 closely follows drawings 1 and 2 referred to in the '*Particulars*,' and it becomes important to try to fix a date for the compilation of this document. A slight clue is offered by the statement in regard to the blast pipe, that 'no alterations were made in these pipes from the time the engine left the works until it won the prize.' [3] There may be some reference here to a controversy which took place after the publication of Smiles', *Life of George Stephenson*, in the course of which it was contended that the idea for the blast pipe which contributed so greatly to the efficiency of the multi-tubular boiler had been borrowed from Hackworth's engine on the eve of the Rainhill trials. This statement, as we shall show, is disposed of by contemporary evidence recorded before the controversy arose, but the reference in

---

[1] *The Engineer*, 1880, Vol. L., p. 217. 'Many years ago Mr. G. Phipps, long member of the Institution of Civil Engineers, who was very well acquainted with the 'Rocket', was employed by Messrs. Stephenson to make a drawing of the engine. This drawing was it appears compiled from such drawings as could be found in the office aided by his own knowledge of the engine ; our engraving is an accurate reproduction to a reduced scale of this drawing.'

[2] The late Mr. J. D. Wardale, who in a letter to Robert Stephenson & Co. dated 11th July 1913, refers to :— 'a framed drawing of the Rocket engine of 1829 which I made in 1859 . . . from a copy of the original particulars *re* building and delivery of the Rocket given to me by the late Mr. Weallens the then manager of the South Street Works.' On 15th September 1913 Mr. Wardale writes further :—'the original drawing which I made had a tender attached which was sketched from a colliery waggon ; to the best of my recollection I made the drawing in 1859 and when Mr. Weallens instructed me to restore the missing parts and make a drawing of the engine he told me that Mr. Robert Stephenson intended to send it to the South Kensington Museum.'
The Rocket was in fact later presented to the Museum by the owners, Messrs. Thompson Brothers. It is to be regretted that in preparing the engine for South Kensington in 1862 a partial restoration was made which attempted to give the 'Rocket' something of its original appearance, and at the same time to follow an early drawing, which bears the title 'Rockett' (*sic*) but refers in fact to the succeeding engines of the so-called 'Rocket' type. To this drawing we shall refer later. In other respects the restoration provided a chimney of the original form at the top, and height from the rail, but placed *on* the smokebox. The exhaust pipes were carried into the base of this chimney, thus giving a combination of parts which had never existed, since, when the smokebox was fitted the chimney was altered both in design and height of top, and when the cylinders were lowered the exhaust pipes were taken into the lower sides of the smokebox, as shown by the Crewe drawing and by existing holes in the smokebox.

[3] Compare Robert Stephenson's Narrative of his Father's Inventions, Smiles, *Lives of the Engineers*, 1862, Vol. III., p. 503. 'The 'Rocket' worked perfectly well with the double blast-pipe, and to the best of my recollection the prize was won without any alteration having been made in that part of the engine.'

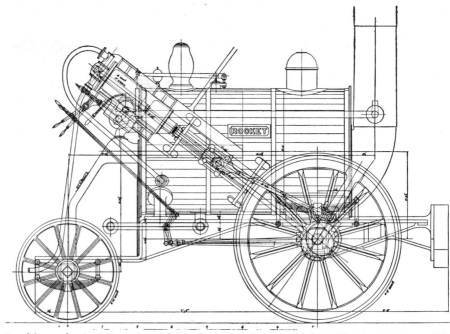

(1)

traced from a drawing in possession of Robert Stephenson & Co., signed J. D. Wardale, 25th January 1858.

(2)

BOILER FOR THE ROCKET LOCOMOTIVE ENGINE

1829

traced from a drawing of uncertain date in possession of Robert Stephenson & Co.

A RE-CONSTRUCTION OF THE 'ROCKET'

the '*Particulars*' to circumstances which need not otherwise have been emphasised, suggests that an answer was intended to the allegation, and that the document may have been prepared between the years 1857 and 1859, and the relative drawings 1 and 2 during the same period, when the controversy was at its height.

When we come to compare these with the earlier drawings, A and B, and with the existing engine, we find a remarkable difference in the form of the firebox ; the later drawings (1 and 2) show a steeply sloping back and a

(3)

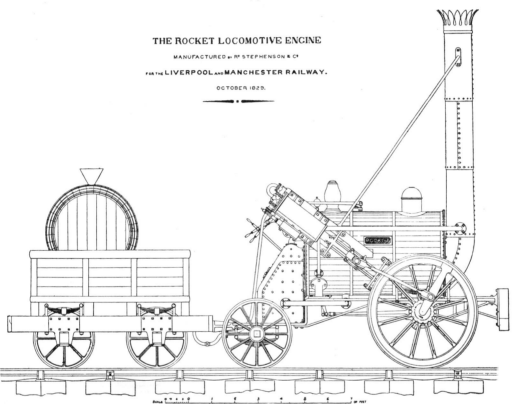

THE ROCKET LOCOMOTIVE ENGINE

MANUFACTURED ʙʏ Rᵗ STEPHENSON & Cᵒ

ꜰᴏʀ ᴛʜᴇ LIVERPOOL ᴀɴᴅ MANCHESTER RAILWAY.

OCTOBER 1829.

from a drawing by the late Mr. J. D. Wardale, 1859.

continuous water space, while the earlier drawings show, and the back plate now on the engine actually has, a vertical self-contained water space, structurally independent of the top and side water spaces, but with provision for connection by means of pipes. It would seem therefore that those responsible for the preparation of drawings 1, 2 and 3, must have had what appeared sufficient reasons for showing a firebox back differing in so remarkable a manner, and we must conclude that there was at the time some tradition, or documentary evidence, to support the representation with a sloping back purporting to show the 'Rocket' in its original state. When in 1880 an attempt was made to reconstruct the 'Rocket' on its original lines Phipps, who was consulted, wrote [1] :—

I have before me Mr. Nicholas Wood's *Treatise on Rail Roads* published in 1831, in which will be found on page 382 a good description of the 'Rocket' with its principal dimensions.

This statement was published, together with editorial comment that drawing 3, which we now know to have been made by the late Mr. J. D. Wardale in 1859, had been made Phipps. To-day we can only regret the failure of those who were investigating the matter to notice the great discrepancy between Wood's illustration which was cited by Phipps, between drawing 3, published as being by himself, and between the back plate on the existing engine. A thorough comparison of the two designs would have shown too that the sloping box, having the inner top and side plates flanged *inwards* to make the water space, provides a grate area of only about $4\frac{1}{4}$ square feet, while Wood gives for the box which he illustrates a grate area of 6 square feet, which is approximately the area actually obtained by the reconstruction proposed, in which the top and side plates are flanged *outwards* to give the water space.

It seems to be now impossible to determine at what period the sloping box was actually fitted, or even to be satisfied that it was actually so made ; the very completeness of the drawings 1 and 2 which show it suggests a more or less artificial reconstruction, based largely on late reminiscence. It must be admitted too that a drawing which purports to represent the 'Rocket' as in 1829, but shows a steam whistle which was not invented until some years later, cannot be accepted in other respects as indisputable evidence. Constructively, as a stage in the evolution of the firebox, that with the sloping back and continuous water space appears to be a stage later than that built up of separate parts. On the other hand we must remember that according to Robert Stephenson's letters the firebox sent from Liverpool was of copper, a material which would have been more suitable for working into the shape required by the sloping back ; the rectangular form might have been adopted later, as more suitable to the use of iron plates, the material of which the existing back is made.

But there would hardly have been time between the arrival of the firebox from Liverpool and the despatch of the engine to have made an entirely new box. We mention the suggestion as one of the many theories which have presented themselves in a consideration of the whole question.

The balance of the evidence seems to show that the sloping firebox was not on the engine seen by Vignoles at the time of the trial ; as an engineer he would hardly have failed to notice and record its peculiar outline. Another theory suggests that it may have been fitted some time after the trial, as an experiment, and abandoned later ; an account of the construction of the engines at work in September 1830, including the 'Rocket,' states that 'most of them were on principles somewhat similar,' and thus describes the boiler [2] :—

[1] *The Engineer*, 1880, Vol. L., p. 217.

[2] James Scott Walker, *An Accurate Description of the Liverpool and Manchester Railway*, 13th September 1830.

The boiler, a cylinder placed horizontally and longitudinally, and cased with wood or copper, occupies nearly the whole length and bulk of the machine. In front of it rises a short round chimney, and behind, and rivetted to it, is the furnace, a small compartment, with a sloping front, (sic) in the middle of which is the little door by which it is fed with fuel.

The value of this evidence is partly discounted by the fact that the writer publishes an illustration of the 'Rocket' in which the firebox has a straight back; moreover one of the engines seen, the 'Northumbrian,' is known to have had a firebox of an entirely different type; on the other hand a later aquatint [1] shows the 'North Star,' one of the engines particularly mentioned, with a firebox door which appears to slope.

The particular opportunity to clear up the mystery, which occurred some forty years ago, cannot recur, all those directly concerned in the design or construction of the 'Rocket,' and of its immediate successors, having passed away. Recent wide spread enquiry has so far shown that the only indis-

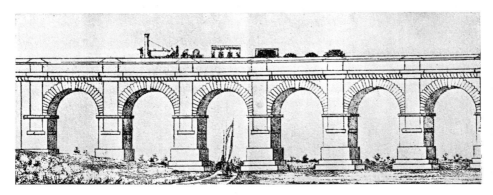

(part) from a lithograph by J. B. Baird for J. S. Walker's Description of the Railway, Sept. 13th 1830.

SANKEY VIADUCT

putably early evidence for our guidance is to be found in the illustrations of 1829 and 1830, already mentioned; in another drawing published in 1830, showing the 'Rocket' on the Sankey Viaduct[2]; in the Crewe drawing, of probably 1836; and in the remains of the engine now at South Kensington. We are thus left in a dilemma between the more or less crude approximation of the early illustrations, and the meticulous exactness of the much later drawings (1, 2 and 3), showing the sloping box.

We have shown that it would be easily possible to reconstruct an approximately rectangular box which would exactly suit the existing engine; it would be equally possible to construct a suitable sloping box. There is still to be seen, in the plate forming the back end of the boiler, a row of studs, nutted on the inner ends but cut off flush with the outer face of the plate, which would

---

[1] *Travelling on the Liverpool and Manchester Railway,* drawn by I. Shaw, aquatint by S. G. Hughes, published by Ackermann & Co, January 1833. See p. 236, Chapter XVII. following.

[2] Lithograph, drawn by Wm. Smoult, Civil Engineer, 3rd February 1830. Binn's Collection, Liverpool Public Library. See p. 210, Chapter XIII. *ante.*

suit such a sloping box, and a model was accordingly made at the Science Museum some years ago, based on the information afforded by drawings 1 and 2 and by the original boiler.   But it would appear now that only the discovery of a further contemporary sketch, such as that which has recently been brought to light in connection with the early locomotives of the Stockton and Darlington Railway, can satisfactorily settle the question which we have been considering.

So far as the evolution of the firebox is concerned, either of the alternatives we have described shows great ingenuity in providing the common combustion chamber which had become necessary with the multitubular boiler ; either of these fireboxes contained indeed the essential elements, though not the form, of the present firebox, and offered a far simpler arrangement than that adopted by Séguin for his multitubular boiler.   The firebox afterwards universally adopted for the locomotive was in fact derived directly from that of the 'Rocket.'

CHAPTER XV

THE BLAST PIPE

He that complies against his will
Is of his own opinion still.
Butler's 'Hudibras.'

We can now no longer evade a question which has provoked in the past, and can still provoke, much controversy ; in its very name the 'Blast Pipe' has a provocative sound. Some writers frankly avoid the subject, perhaps fearing a fate depicted with some humour by a local caricaturist[1], who found in 1875, during the celebrations of the first Railway Jubilee at Darlington, that a controversy which had been at its height in the late 'fifties had lost

from a drawing by S. T. Richardson, Darlington, 1876.

THE BATTLE OF THE BLAST PIPE

little of its violence. The disputants may be roughly divided into three camps—those who hold that the 'Blast Pipe' was 'invented and first applied by George Stephenson to his early engines at Killingworth'—those who ascribe its invention to Timothy Hackworth and its first application by him to the 'Royal George' in 1827—and those who claim that it was first applied by William Hedley, or Timothy Hackworth, to the Wylam engine in 1813, and borrowed from that engine by George Stephenson ; most writers ignore or dispute any claim on behalf of Trevithick.

The controversy appears to have commenced only after the Rainhill trials ; there is definite evidence of it in an article[2] published in 1836, in which

[1] S. T. Richardson, *The World's First Railway Jubilee*, Bailey, Darlington, 1876. The principal figures depicted are George Stephenson, Smiles, and Jeans, with John Wesley Hackworth in the upper centre.

[2] Lecount, Article 'Railways,' *Encyclopædia Britannica*, Seventh Edition, 1836.

the relative claims of Stephenson and Trevithick are discussed. So far as Trevithick's claim is concerned we have the evidence of John Farey, who in 1831, referring to means for obtaining an increased production of steam, states [1] :—

> The waste steam was very commonly discharged into the bottom of the chimney in Trevithick's high pressure engines many years ago, in order to mix with the smoke ascending in the chimney, and thus get rid of the waste steam. . . . It improved the draught in that way, by rendering the smoke more buoyant; but the waste steam was not discharged through a contracted orifice to give it velocity, nor was it directed upwards as is now done by Mr. Stephenson.

No claim to the invention of steam blast, as afterwards generally applied, appears in the evidence given by Trevithick himself two days later, and his own letter of 20th February 1804 [2] supports the view that while he had observed, apparently as an accidental circumstance, the stimulating effect of steam exhausting into the chimney, he had not pursued the opportunities he had of applying to locomotives the principles so discovered. In his evidence in August 1831 he refers to his locomotive of 1804 as 'the first ever seen, which had performed its work to admiration and been the model of all the engines since introduced on rail-roads', adding that he had been abroad for a good many years and 'had nothing to do with steam carriages' until shortly before the time at which he was speaking.

The whole controversy seems to have revived after the publication of the *Life of George Stephenson*, in which Smiles claimed for him the 'invention' of the 'blast,' unfortunately without giving the early authorities on whose evidence this statement was based; some writers appear in consequence to have assumed that Smiles was the first to make the claim, but it had in fact been made more than twenty years earlier. This claim was challenged in the columns of *The Engineer* [3] on behalf of Timothy Hackworth, then deceased, but there was so much confusion of the point at issue by the introduction of personalities into the discussion, as to provoke editorial comment that 'one proof is worth a hundred ill-tempered arguments.' Proofs from contemporary documents were indeed conspicuously lacking.

Now we may note that the word 'blast,' though used in connection with bellows, as in the case of the 'Lancashire Witch,' does not appear to have been generally, if at all, applied to the action of exhaust steam until some time after the Rainhill trials. The pipe by which the steam was carried into the chimney was previously known as the 'eduction' or 'exhaust' pipe, a fact which offers a clue, and may perhaps help to a cooler consideration of the question which we shall now consider—*i.e., Whether, of those workers on the locomotive who succeeded Trevithick, George Stephenson in his early engines had consciously applied the exhaust steam to stimulate combustion, or whether he was entirely ignorant*

---

[1] Evidence before the Select Committee on Steam Carriages, *Mechanics' Magazine*, Vol. XVI., p. 463.

[2] Quoted on page 13, Chapter II. *ante.*

[3] *The Engineer*, 1857, Vol. II., p. 286. 'Personal abuse is a bad substitute for argument and some time ago Mr. [J. W.] Hackworth asserted he had proofs behind. Why not produce them?'

*of its possibilities in this way until after the performance of the ' Sans Pareil '
at Rainhill.*

On the method adopted for Hedley's first |Wylam engines in 1813 we
have found no convincing evidence ; the claim on behalf of Hedley in this
respect appears to have been first made by his son, many years later [1], and
based on hearsay.   Wood, speaking in 1860 on this claim [2], called attention
to the lack of contemporary evidence ; it is clear however that by 1825, when
the drawing of the modified Wylam engines was published by him, their
exhaust was turned into the chimney, but after passing through a silencer,
and the contemporary description by Wood shows that this was with the object,
not of producing a draught, but of reducing a noise to which serious objection
had been taken.   His account suggests that the exhaust on these engines had
previously escaped into the air direct, but he is ambiguous on this point ; we
have however his distinct and indisputable record in 1825 [3] :—

Mr. Stephenson thought that by causing the steam to escape into the chimney through a
pipe with its end turned upwards the velocity of the current would be accelerated, and such
was the effect.

Later Robert Stephenson himself, comparing locomotive with stationary
engine boilers, wrote in 1830 of the locomotive that [4] :—

To compensate for the loss of heating surface it was necessary to augment the temperature
of the fire.   This was effected, shortly after the first locomotive Engine was tried on the Killingworth Colliery Railway, by conveying the steam into the chimney, where it escaped in a perpendicular direction up the centre, after it had performed its office in the cylinders.   The
velocity of the steam on entering the chimney being much greater than that due to the ascending
current of air from the natural draft of the furnace, the effect was to increase the draft and
consequently the temperature of the fire.

Wood showed in 1825 that the result was an objectionable noise, and that,
by enlarging the flue to obtain greater heating surface, it had been found
possible to dispense with this method of accelerating combustion, which
he considered greatly to the advantage of the engine.   Bearing in mind the
use made by their opponents of every possible objection to the locomotive,
in particular the puffing noise, we can understand George Stephenson, after
experimenting on the 'Lancashire Witch' in 1828 with a forced draught
produced by bellows, writing to Timothy Hackworth—'the engine works
beautifully . . . . . there is not the least noise.'   This remark may quite as
well express the writer's satisfaction with an apparent improvement as prove
his ignorance of the action of exhaust steam in stimulating combustion.

The bellows blast for burning coke on the ' Lancashire Witch ' was abandoned
and in August 1829 George Stephenson wrote definitely of experiments with the
' exarsting pipe' of the ' Coke Engine' [5] which was ' doing extremely well.'

[1] O. D. Hedley, *Who Invented the Locomotive ?* 1858.

[2] 'Address on the two late Eminent Engineers,' 1860.

[3] See page 26, Chapter III. *ante,* for facsimile from Wood's *Treatise on Rail Roads,* 1825, p. 293.

[4] Robert Stephenson and Joseph Locke, *Observations on the Comparative Merits of Locomotive and Fixed
Engines,* 1830.

[5] The ' Twin Sisters.'   See pp. 155, 156, Chapter X. *ante.*

P

From Wood's contemporary evidence it is indisputable that the stimulating effect of exhaust steam turned into the chimney was known to George Stephenson at least as early as 1825, and we have a definite statement then published that the principle had been applied by him ten years before ; it is further clear that with the single flue boiler then in use such means were either not necessary or were required only in moderate degree. But with the multitubular boiler of the 'Rocket' conditions were completely altered, and Wood in his account of the Rainhill trials [1] has shown that this engine depended from the first on the exhausting power of the steam, and that it, as well as the 'Sans Pareil,' was provided with some form of blast, though the latter engine exhibited a far more powerful application of the principle.

It is however clear that in the 'Rocket' the principle was applied sufficiently to enable that engine to produce an ample supply of steam for the purposes of the trials, and later Wood records :—

Mr. Stephenson has also improved the working of the 'Rocket' engine and by applying the steam more powerfully into the chimney to increase the draught was enabled to raise a much greater quantity of steam than before.

We gather from these accounts that it was only after Rainhill that this essential feature of the multitubular locomotive boiler became generally known as the 'Blast Pipe,' and for some years it seems to have been accepted rather as a natural development than as a subject for conflicting claims. With a full knowledge of the facts and, no doubt, many others not available to us Robert Stephenson himself replied in 1858 to the controversy in *The Engineer* by a statement [2] which appears to have been little noticed by subsequent writers ; we now quote from it at some length since it appears to be conclusive on the particular question we have been considering.

ROBERT STEPHENSON'S NARRATIVE.

Certainly not many weeks had elapsed after the first travelling engine was placed on the Killingworth waggon-way in 1814, before the steam-blast was introduced by my father into the chimney, and it was uniformly employed in every subsequent engine that was built; but the orifice of the blast-pipe was, I believe, in no instance contracted so as to give a less area than that of the steam-ports.

The Stockton and Darlington Railway was opened in 1825, but as I was absent from England, at the time, I cannot state whether the engines constructed in Forth-street or at the factory, for that line, had contracted blast-pipes or not. Shortly after my return from America, I was frequently in the habit, as a matter of business, of visiting the line alluded to, the superintendence of the locomotive engines being then under Timothy Hackworth, with whom I was constantly in the habit of discussing the remarkable effects produced by the blast in the chimney. It was about that time, I believe, Mr. Hackworth had found that an increased effect was obtained by contracting the orifice of the blast-pipe. Considerable doubt was, however, then entertained whether such contraction would be attended with any actual economy in the working of the engine, for, although the combustion was a little more excited, and a more copious amount of steam was generated, it was believed that the negative pressure produced on the piston counterbalanced in a great measure the advantages mentioned.

[1] *Treatise on Rail Roads*, Second Edition, 1831, p. 382, see p. 200 *et seq.*, Chapter XIII. *ante.*
[2] Smiles, *Lives of the Engineers*, 1862, Vol. III., p. 501.

THE BLAST PIPE

During the construction of the 'Rocket' a series of experiments was made with blast-pipes of different diameters, and their efficiency was tested by the amount of vacuum that was formed in the smoke-box (*sic*). The degree of rarefaction was determined by a glass tube fixed to the bottom of the smoke-box and descending into a bucket of water—the tube being open at both ends. As the rarefaction took place the water would of course rise in the tube, and the height to which it rose above the surface of the water in the bucket was made the measure of the amount of rarefaction. These experiments certainly showed that a considerable increase of draught was obtained by contracting the orifice, and accordingly the two blast-pipes in the 'Rocket' were contracted slightly below the area of the steam ports,—and before she left the factory the water rose in the glass tube three inches above the water in the bucket.

I was quite aware at the time that Mr. Hackworth's 'Sans Pareil' was being constructed in the same manner, with the exception that the two eduction-pipes were brought into one blast-pipe in the centre of the chimney. The two engines might therefore be considered as precisely alike in principle. With respect to the objection which has been made in *The Engineer*, to two separate orifices, I must affirm that no remark could possibly be more unfounded. The writer states that when two separate orifices are employed, the blast produced by one is neutralized by the other. The 'Rocket' worked perfectly well with the double blast-pipe, and, to the best of my recollection, the prize was won without any alteration having been made in that part of the engine.

The experiments already mentioned proved that the double blast-pipe in the 'Rocket' was capable of producing a considerable rarefaction in the chimney, and the alteration from two blast-pipes to one was made by myself rather with a view of lessening the space occupied by them in the chimney. The writer in *The Engineer* completely ignores the fact of the single steam-blast having been in existence eleven years prior to the opening of the Stockton and Darlington Railway, and seems to argue that the 'Sans Pareil' was the first engine to which the steam-blast was ever applied with effect; whereas it had actually been in regular use since the year 1814, and the only alteration which it underwent, was the contraction of the orifice made on the Stockton and Darlington Railway some time between the years 1825 and 1827.

Whatever merit or value may attach to this alteration I believe to be due to Timothy Hackworth, but nothing beyond it, I am quite certain; and even this was decidedly much overrated by him; in fact, he carried the contraction to such an extent that nearly half of the fuel was thrown out of the chimney unconsumed, as many can testify who witnessed the experiments at Rain Hill.

But surely such an alteration is not to deprive George Stephenson of the merit of the invention of the steam-blast. Moreover the contraction in many of our best locomotive engines is totally unnecessary and rather disadvantageous than otherwise, for, since the speed of the engines has been increased, the velocity of the eduction steam is quite sufficient to produce the needful rarefaction in the chimney without any contraction whatever. In the early engines, when the speed of the piston was slow, the contraction was undoubtedly advantageous, but now that the boilers have been increased in size—the heating surfaces thereby being extended—a less intense blast is required. The orifices of the blast-pipes of many engines running at the present day are as large as the steam ports.[1] Consequently they cannot be said to be contracted at all. In fact the greater apparent efficiency of the steam-blast, as at present used, is entirely due to the greater velocity of the piston.

We will conclude this chapter in the hope that a consideration of the above narrative, by a man distinguished as much for his generosity of mind as for the sobriety of his statements, supported as it is by the earlier evidence of contemporary witnesses, may lay to rest a controversy which has disfigured the history of the locomotive by its extravagances.

---

[1] For actual examples see D. K. Clark, *Railway Machinery*, 1855, pp. 119, 133.

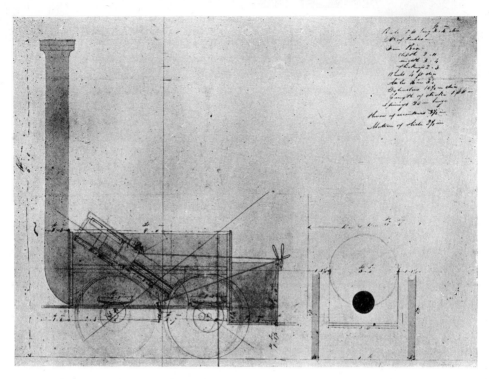

from the original drawing dated February 1830.

CANTERBURY LOCOMOTIVE ENGINE

from a coloured lithograph by T. M. Baynes, Canterbury, in the collection of Sir David Salomons, Bart.

VIEW OF CANTERBURY AND WHITSTABLE RAILWAY

taken from Church Street on the opening day May 3rd 1830

CHAPTER XVI

THE CANTERBURY AND WHITSTABLE RAILWAY

The third public railway to employ the steam locomotive, the second of such to be opened for public use, was a short line of six miles from Canterbury to Whitstable, for which an Act had been obtained in 1825. This railway was one of the many in which William James had been interested, and he had surveyed for it, but it eventually came under the influence of George Stephenson. Construction was commenced on his behalf by John Dixon, whose note-book records that, after the opening of the Stockton and Darlington Railway he went to Canterbury, and began cutting the new line in December 1825 ; the tunnel was commenced in April 1826, and finished in June 1827. Dixon left for Liverpool before the line was finished, and was succeeded at Canterbury by Robert Stephenson, who wrote to Longridge on 1st December 1828[1] of his expectation that the directors of the Canterbury Railway would shortly consider at a general meeting, and decide on, certain proposals prepared by him and put forward in his father's name, the question of locomotive *versus* stationary engines being apparently one of those to be considered. Later, after the publication of Walker's *Report* to the Directors of the Liverpool and Manchester Railway Company on a similar question, we find Robert Stephenson writing to Thomas Richardson under date 17th December 1829[2] :—

I am now engaged in preparing an answer to James Walker's Report on Locomotive and Stationary Engines. I am induced to do this from the industrious manner with which he has been circulating his Report in every quarter in England. He left one with Kingsford, the solicitor at Canterbury, doubtless with some object.

The gradients on the line between Canterbury and Whitstable, rising 200 feet in the first two miles, and falling 220 in the last three, made the adoption of fixed engines inevitable for the greater part of the distance and the locomotive was adopted for use only on a portion, of a little more than one mile in length.

THE 'INVICTA' The two original drawings of the engine still in the possession of Robert Stephenson & Co. show clearly the influence on its design of the 'Rocket,' which it followed. As originally built the 'Invicta' was fitted with a separate firebox generally resembling externally that of the 'Rocket' as shown by Wood[3] ; the working drawings unfortunately give no details, but they show the firebox with a vertical back plate, and apparently continuous water space. What remains of the original engine is now preserved at Canterbury[4], but the separate firebox has at some time been removed, and the tubes replaced by a single flue, the boiler barrel being

---

[1] Jeaffreson, *Life of Robert Stephenson*, Vol. I., p. 122.

[2] Jeaffreson, *Life of Robert Stephenson*, Vol. I., p. 151.

[3] Wood, *Treatise on Rail Roads*, 2nd edition, 1831, see p. 200, Chapter XIII. *ante.*

[1] The preservation of this engine is due to Sir David Salomons, Bart.

extended to suit ; this alteration, with the addition of a smokebox, has considerably changed the appearance of the engine. The cylinders, inclined and with direct drive on to the crank pins, are placed at the smokebox end, and the drawings show the engine with four wheels of equal diameter, as on the engine to-day ; the existing wheels are coupled but have spokes of different patterns, and we may note that an early artistic illustration [1] shows the front pair of smaller diameter than the driving wheels. The makers' records give no information on this engine other than that given on the drawings.

On 6th May 1830 Robert Stephenson was able to write to Richardson [2] :—

The opening of the Canterbury Railway went off remarkably well, without a single mishap. The paper will be forwarded to you....I have not seen any detailed account published.

We have the account of a contemporary journal [3], and an artistic representation of the scene in two contemporary aquatints :—

On Monday, May the 3rd 1830, according to announcement, the opening of the Railway took place. The day being remarkably fine, the whole City seemed to have poured forth its population, and company from the surrounding country continuing to augment the throng, by eleven o'clock, the time appointed for the procession to start, the assemblage of spectators was immense. The fields on each side of the line of road being crowded by well-dressed people of all ages, presented one of the most lively scenes we have witnessed for some time. The arrangements were so judiciously made, that by a quarter past eleven the procession was set in motion, the signal for starting having been given by Telegraph. The bells of the Cathedral rang merrily, and guns were fired from Westgate Tower at intervals during the day. Flags were displayed on the public buildings and Railway, with various inscriptions, such as 'Prosperity to the City,' &c. The following is the order of the procession.

1. Carriage with the Directors of the Railway Company, wearing white rosettes, and the Engineers wearing crimson rosettes.

2. A coach with the Alderman, and other Members of the Canterbury Corporation.

3. A carriage with ladies.

4. A carriage with a band of music.

5. A carriage with ladies.

6. to 20. Carriages containing the Proprietors of the Railway, their friends, &c., in all amounting to upwards of 300. A convoy man, with a crimson riband round his hat, upon which 'Railway' was printed, was placed behind each carriage.

The procession, on starting, was loudly cheered by the assembled multitude, and was drawn forward in two divisions, until it arrived at the first Engine Station, in which manner it also entered Whitstable, preceded by the Locomotive Engine. The various carriages contained upwards of 300 persons, consisting of the principal gentry, citizens, and inhabitants of Canterbury and its neighbourhood. At Whitstable, an excellent lunch was provided for the company by the Directors at the Cumberland Arms. On returning, the procession was joined at the Engine Station, and the whole went forward into Canterbury together.

The motion of the carriages is particularly easy and agreeable, and at first starting, the quiet power with which the vast mass was set in motion dispelled every fear in the passengers. The entrance into the tunnel was very impressive—the total darkness—the accelerated speed—the rumbling of the cars—the loud cheering of the whole party echoing through the vault, combined to form a situation almost terrific—certainly novel and striking. Perfect confidence in the safety of the whole apparatus however seemed to prevail, and the company emerged from the dismal tunnel into 'the warm precincts of the cheerful day' in high spirits. The passage

---

[1] *View of Canterbury and Whitstable Railway from Church Street*, published by **Henry Ward, Canterbury.**

[2] Jeaffreson, *Life of Robert Stephenson*, Vol. I., p. 154.

[3] *Kent Herald*, quoted in *The Railway Magazine*, new series, Vol. I., p. 134.

through the woods was very pleasing, and the views at different points are picturesque in the extreme. The whole procession after finally mustering at the Engine Station glided rapidly and majestically into Canterbury at about six o'clock, greeted by, if possible, a more numerous assemblage of spectators than hailed its outset. The journey altogether was a delightful one. Not the slightest accident occurred.

An account of some experiments on the railway in 1833[1] gives the speed of the engine on the level as 8 miles an hour, with a train load of 16 tons 16 cwt., but this cannot be taken as a criterion of its maximum performance since the load may have been determined by the capacity of the fixed engines on the severe inclines of 1 in 31 and 1 in 46. The locomotive on the Canterbury and Whitstable Railway appears to have been abandoned before 1840[2]; local conditions were indeed unfavourable for its use, and it is difficult to account for its adoption by George Stephenson in the present instance, unless with a view to its introduction to the south of England. But both the Canterbury and Whitstable Railway and its locomotive are worth notice here as evidence of the ubiquity of the two Stephensons as railway engineers; indeed we cannot escape their traces.

from the Railway Magazine, new series, Vol. I.

THE TUNNEL

on the Canterbury and Whitstable Railway

[1] *Mechanics' Magazine*, Vol. XVI., p. 314.
[2] Whishaw, *Railways of Great Britain and Ireland*, 1840, p. 51.

CHAPTER XVII

THE 'ROCKET' TYPE

'METEOR,' 'COMET,'
'DART,' 'ARROW'

The success of the 'Rocket' at Rainhill was immediately reflected in a decision by the Liverpool and Manchester Railway Company on 26th October 1829 to order four locomotives from Robert Stephenson & Co.—'to be constructed on the principle of the 'Rocket,' not to exceed five tons in weight each, and to be delivered in Liverpool in three months.' In the following December Robert Stephenson was able to write to Richardson of rapid progress with these four engines which he was 'confident would exceed the 'Rocket' in powers.' On 1st February 1830 it was decided by the railway company's directors that the first of the four engines should be named 'Meteor,' the second

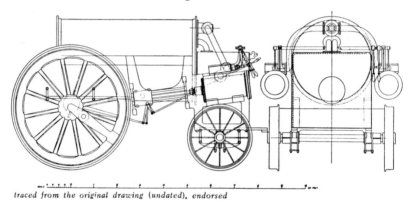

traced from the original drawing (undated), endorsed

PLAN OF 'ROCKETT' ENGINE.

'Comet'; the remaining two it was decided later to call 'Dart' and 'Arrow.'

Robert Stephenson & Co. fortunately have still in their possession an early original drawing endorsed as for 'Rockett' (*sic*) which appears to be the preliminary design for these four engines. The word 'Rockett' has evidently been used as generic only, since the engine represented is neither the original 'Rocket' itself, as first built, nor as afterwards altered, but this design drawing is in close agreement with the working drawing of the four engines above mentioned, the outline of the plate frame which carries the cylinder being practically identical, and it clearly embodies the plan on which the 'Rocket' itself was subsequently altered.

BOILER

In the new engines further advantage was taken of the multitubular system, by reducing the diameter of the tubes to 2 inches, and increasing their number to 88, thus obtaining, in a boiler of the same diameter and length, a large increase in heating surface over that of the 'Rocket.'

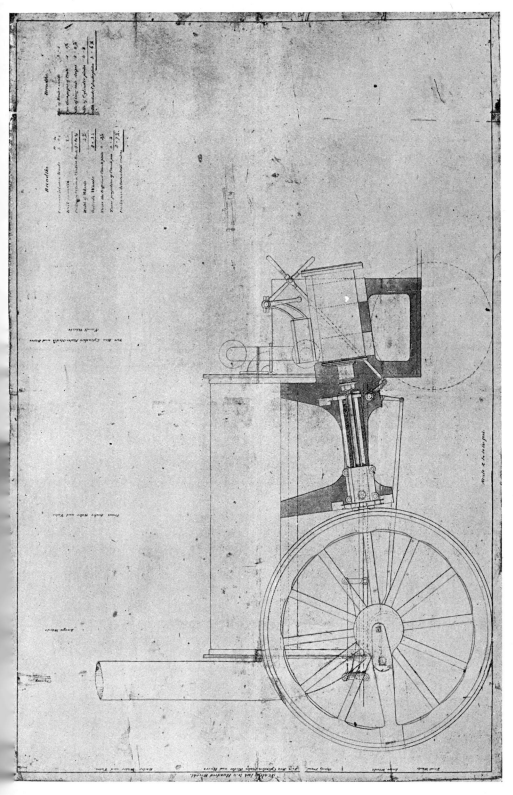

from the original (undated) drawing endorsed

LOCOMOTIVE ENGINES

Plan of the first after the 'Rocket'

(The drawing shows a scale of weights at the left hand side and a graphic method for calculating the centre of gravity of the engine)

FIREBOX The original drawings show an apparently rectangular firebox with a vertical back, but unfortunately give no indication of its internal construction.

CYLINDERS The principal and most obvious improvement on the 'Rocket' is to be seen in the position of the cylinders, now placed almost horizontal. The disadvantages of steeply inclined cylinders placed outside the wheels, though less than those of vertical cylinders in this position, had been made more obvious by the greatly increased speed at which the locomotives were now being run, and the second important step from the vertical to the horizontal was now definitely taken by the Stephensons. The larger heating surface in the new engines made it possible to increase the diameter of the cylinders to 10 inches, and so to 'exceed the 'Rocket' in powers,' although the stroke had been reduced to 16 inches.

The weight of the 'Arrow' exceeded that specified; it is recorded in the makers' books as 5 Tons 14 cwt. 2 qrs. or about 1½ tons heavier than the 'Rocket'; its increased power is shown too by a railway company's record of its performance two months later, on a journey of inspection and trial, made on 14th June 1830, 'to prove the capabilities of the locomotive engine' :—

The Moving Power was the 'Arrow,' built by Robert Stephenson & Co., and the load *drawn* was about 33 tons, viz.:—

80 stone blocks, in 7 waggons	20 Tons.
Weight of seven waggons	7 ,,
Tender with water and coal and six persons	3 ,,
Two Coaches, viz.: the Bolton Close Coach, and an open carriage with 20 Persons	3 ,,
	33 Tons.

The train started from the Engine House, Edgehill, at 20 minutes before nine, and proceeded to the bottom of the Whiston Inclined Plane, being met a Quarter of a Mile on this side, by the 'Dart' Locomotive, which was attached to the 'Arrow' for the purpose of assisting the train up the Incline. The whole ascent was effected in 12 minutes; the speed for the first quarter of a mile being 17 miles per hour, which however, gradually decreased to about 4 miles per hour, before reaching the top. On the summit level at Rainhill, where the line is straight and level, the Arrow proceeded with her load at the rate of sixteen miles per hour. She arrived at Oldfield Lane Bridge, Salford, Manchester, 5 minutes past eleven, having stopped at Parkside, and again near Eccles, to take in water. On the journey homeward, the Load consisted of the Engine, Tender, and two Carriages and Passengers. The train started at 6 minutes before five, and arrived at the Liverpool Station 20 minutes before seven, being one hour and 46 minutes on the road, including two stoppages; one at Bury Lane to set down Mr. Hulton, and one at Parkside to take in water. The ascent up the Sutton Inclined Plane was effected at an average speed exceeding 15 miles per hour, and the rate of movement on other parts of the road was frequently 25 miles per hour and upwards, the engine working below her power a great portion of the way.

'PHŒNIX,' 'NORTH STAR' After the second engine of the 'Arrow' type had been delivered the railway company decided, on 1st February 1830, 'to contract with Robert Stephenson & Co. for two additional locomotives, the weight and price to be fixed.' In the following June the arrival was reported of the first of these two engines from

(part) from a coloured lithograph by W. Crane Chester, in the collection of Mr. C. F. Dendy Marshall.

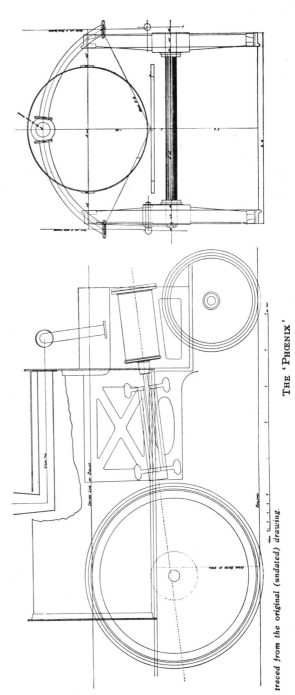

THE 'PHŒNIX'

traced from the original (undated) drawing.

Newcastle, 'which it was agreed should be named the 'Phœnix'; the arrival of the second, the 'North Star,' was reported about two months later. The working drawings of the 'Phœnix' and the 'North Star' show that they generally resembled the four preceding engines, but were somewhat larger; the diameter of the cylinders was increased to 11 inches, and the length of the boiler by 6 inches. There does not appear to have been any increase to the size of the firebox, which remained a separate construction; the drawings show it as still rectangular in form, but give no internal details; the makers' records give no information on the number and diameter of the tubes, but in these respects there was probably not much difference from the four preceding engines.

(part) from an aquatint by S. G. Hughes, drawn by I. Shaw, published by Ackermann & Co., January 1833.

THE 'NORTH STAR'

The drawings of the 'Phœnix' and 'North Star' generally agree with contemporary artistic representations, but the picture we reproduce shows the 'North Star' with the sloping firehole which we have already mentioned.

The most notable and important improvement in these two SMOKEBOX engines is the provision of a smokebox, as shown in the contemporary pictures of both the 'Phœnix' and 'North Star,' though it does not appear on the makers' drawings. In the 'Rocket,' and the four succeeding engines, the base of the chimney itself had been swelled to cover the tube area and was provided with a loose plate, removable as required to give access for inspection and cleaning; this must soon have been found insufficient for the purpose, and the new smokebox, with an upper door opening on to the tubes, and a chamber below for the ashes, having separate doors for cleaning, no doubt added both to the efficiency of the engine and to convenience in operation. Generally however the 'Phœnix' and 'North Star' did not embody any new principles of vital importance, and their recorded performances show no marked differences from those of the 'Arrow' type. Owing to their large increase in tube heating surface these engines were all more powerful and more economical of fuel than the 'Rocket,' but in spite of their superiority the demands of a rapidly increasing traffic within two or three years rendered them too light for general service on the Liverpool and Manchester Railway.

We have a record of engine performances which shows that during 1831 the 'Phœnix' ran about 15,400 miles, the 'North Star' over 15,600 miles; but their mileages in the first seven months of 1832 amounted to only about 2,000 and 6,900 respectively.[1]

---

[1] From a contemporary statement preserved among the papers of Thomas Ellis; communicated to Robert Stephenson & Co. by Mr. C. W. Ellis, 8th July 1921.

from the Mechanics' Magazine, October, 1830, Vol. XIV., p. 113.

THE 'NORTHUMBRIAN.'

from the original drawing (undated), endorsed

Liverpool Locomotive 'MAJESTIC,' similar to the ' Northumbrian.'

CHAPTER XVIII

THE 'NORTHUMBRIAN'

This engine, whose arrival at Liverpool was reported on 9th August, 1830, represents the highest development of the 'Rocket' type ; the general principles of its design were the same, but so greatly had their application been extended that both in fact and in appearance there was small resemblance between the proto-type 'Rocket' of September 1829 and the 'Northumbrian' of less than a year later, and there was as marked a difference between their respective powers. The makers' records show that the multi-tubular system in the boiler had been carried to its logical extreme, by a further reduction in diameter of the tubes to $1\frac{5}{8}$ inches, and an increase in their number to 132, so that with a boiler barrel having still the same diameter as that of the 'Rocket' and only 6 inches longer, the tube heating surface had been increased from 117 to 379 square feet. The firebox was also made larger, giving about $36\frac{1}{2}$ square feet of heating surface instead of the 25 square feet of the 'Rocket.'

The cylinders remained as in the 'Phœnix' class, 11 inches diameter by 16 inches stroke, giving a tractive power of over 1,100 lbs. as compared with about 725 lbs. of the 'Rocket' calculated on the same basis. The total weight was increased from about $4\frac{1}{4}$ tons to 7 tons 7 cwt. ; the weight on the driving wheels alone is recorded as about 4 tons.

EVOLUTION OF THE FIREBOX

In the design of the firebox and its shell the improvement on the preceding engines was greatest ; from a separate construction bolted to the back of the boiler barrel the firebox had become by a brilliant stroke an integral part of the boiler ; the firebox of the 'Northumbrian' determined in fact the lines on which the normal locomotive firebox has since been made. If we wish to appreciate the extent to which the Stephensons had realised essential requirements we have only to study the phases through which this part of the boiler has passed at the hands of later designers, particularly between 1850 and 1860, to come back eventually to the simple form introduced in the 'Northumbrian' as being the best whenever circumstances might permit.

The appearance of the 'Northumbrian' created something of a sensation ; it was described by a contemporary periodical [1] as 'one of the latest made and best of Mr. Stephenson's engines, distinguished from his other engines by having its boiler and chimney of copper instead of iron.' What parts of the boiler or firebox were actually made of copper we have not ascertained, but it appears that in July 1830 the Liverpool and Manchester Railway Company were informed by the makers that :—

.... after the next Locomotive Engine, which they expected shortly to despatch from Newcastle, and which it was proposed should be called the 'Northumberland' (*sic*) the price, in consequence of the increased quantity of copper, and superior workmanship of the engines, as now made, would be £650 each.

[1] *Mechanics' Magazine*, Vol. XIV., p. 114.

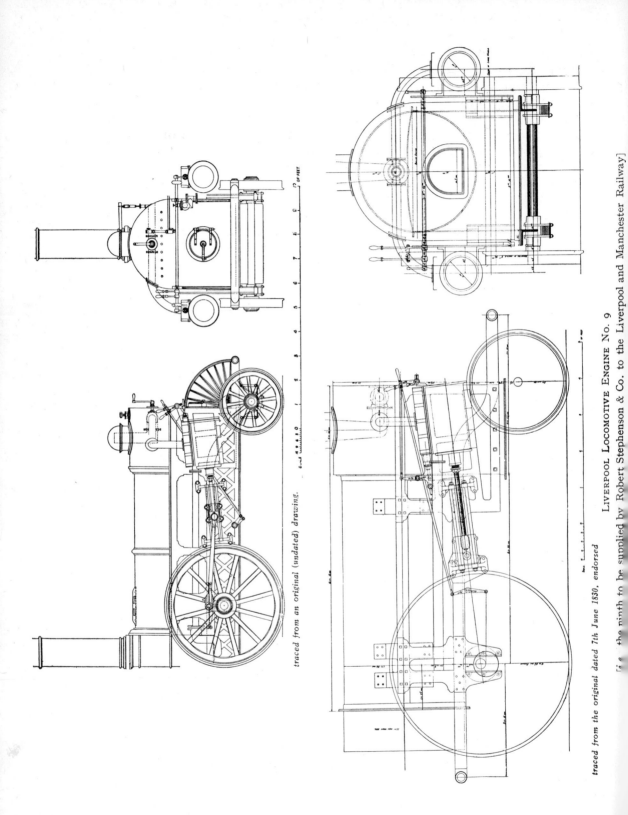

traced from an original (undated) drawing.

traced from the original dated 7th June 1830, endorsed

LIVERPOOL LOCOMOTIVE ENGINE No. 9

[i.e. the ninth to be supplied by Robert Stephenson & Co. to the Liverpool and Manchester Railway]

The original drawings of this engine are still in the possession of Robert Stephenson & Co. and leave us in little doubt as to the most important details of its design ; there are also many contemporary published illustrations which well record the general appearance ; the earliest of these shows a rectangular smokebox which does not appear on the later pictorial representations ; there is however some indication of such a smokebox on one of the original drawings in the makers' possession. But it must be borne in mind that we cannot be sure that any of the original drawings of this period show the engines exactly as made, and it may be well to emphasise here the impossibility of reconciling all such drawings, published illustrations, and descriptions. The figures and dimensions we have given, and shall give, for these early locomotives, are those which the balance of evidence available to us suggests in each case as most probably correct, and they must be accepted with this reservation.

FRAME   After the firebox, the most notable feature of the 'Northumbrian' is the frame, constructed throughout of plate, or bars in the form of plates, arranged vertically. This type of frame appears as a logical development from the plates introduced to carry the cylinders of the 'Lancashire Witch.' In the engines which followed the 'Rocket' the plate used to carry the cylinders was extended forward to the front end of the slidebars, but the main frame, to which this plate was partly attached, remained as before, a flat bar extending the whole length of the engine. This flat bar was now abandoned by Robert Stephenson & Co. for a vertical construction of bar and plate combined, the origin of the inside plate frame.

One other locomotive of the 'Northumbrian' type was built, the 'Majestic,' put to work in January 1831[1] ; an original drawing of this engine has been preserved among the makers' records. No more of the type were built, for, great as had been the improvement on their predecessors, these two engines were almost at once outclassed by the 'Planet,' which we shall describe in a subsequent chapter. The permanent interest of the 'Northumbrian' lies in the fact that in this engine the Stephensons had stabilised the design of the firebox, and embodied a considered policy in boiler design from which they do not appear to have ever departed.

The 'Northumbrian' also enjoyed a passing celebrity from its rivalry with the 'William the Fourth' and 'Queen Adelaide,' the two large engines of the 'Novelty' type which had been ordered from Braithwaite and Ericsson at a cost of £1,000 each, and of which such great performances had been promised by their makers, and hoped for by the railway company. This rivalry, which has been graphically recorded by a contemporary print, led to a heated and amusing newspaper controversy. The *Mechanics' Magazine*, still convinced of the superiority of the 'Novelty' type which it had maintained so vigorously at the time of the Rainhill trials, now asserted that Stephensons' engines were of no use for carrying goods ; to this charge the *Manchester Guardian* retorted [2] :—

---

[1] *Mechanics' Magazine*, Vol. XIV., p. 415.   [2] Quoted in *Mechanics' Magazine*, Vol. XIV., p. 189.

What the practical difficulties are which Mr. Stephenson has had to encounter with his engines, we do not know; but we understand the difficulty which Messrs. Braithwaite and Ericsson had, and have still to encounter (and it is 'practical' enough) is, that their engines will not work—at all events, not to any useful purpose, whilst those of Mr. Stephenson perform their allotted tasks in the admirable manner which most of our readers have, no doubt, witnessed.

In the course of the discussion the moral and professional reputations of the disputants did not escape aspersion. The *Manchester Guardian* having referred to the 'system of petty detraction so long and insistently levelled at Mr. Stephenson's engines by a little knot of pseudo-mechanics,' was met by the retort :—

The *Mechanics' Magazine* has its own—perhaps a peculiar opinion of Mr. Stephenson's merits as an engine-maker, but sticks to truth in support of it; the *Manchester Guardian* has somewhat of an opposite opinion, and thinks an adherence to truth in maintaining it exceedingly superfluous.

The writer then proceeds to quote the current gossip which supplied later much of the material for the attack by the *Edinburgh Review*, in 1832, to which we have already referred at some length[1]; but 'truth' was against him, and the editor of the *Mechanics' Magazine* referring later to the official trials of the 'William the Fourth' and 'Queen Adelaide' had to admit[2] :—

. . . whether the trial was final or not, we are free to confess that it is of a nature well calculated to cast down the hopes which people have been led to entertain of Messrs. Braithwaite and Ericsson's engine. It may not have started to do its best, but the circumstances which arose were such as to call for its best exertions. It had been greatly damaged by the accident which befel it last September, but had since undergone a complete repair, and when last on the road had been pronounced by Mr. Ericsson to want only the addition of an expansion-slide—which addition had been subsequently made to it—to be all that he could desire. That after all this delay and preparation it should, under any circumstances, have performed so ill, surprises us not a little. Indeed, were we to judge by results merely, we should be induced to say there was an end of the affair. But we refuse to despair of the success of this engine, because we feel so well persuaded of the correctness of the principles on which it is constructed, that we are certain its present failure can only have arisen from some defect in the details of the machinery, admitting of a remedy; or from some unskilfulness in management, which ought not to have occurred. The report states, that the engineer could not keep up the steam !

It is important to keep in mind, that the point on which the success of Messrs. Braithwaite and Ericsson's carriage turns, is simply the efficiency of the boiler. Wheels of equal diameter are common both to Mr. Stephenson and them; so also is the application of the power to the axle; and whether the cylinders are above or below the boiler, in the front or in the rear, is (we apprehend) a matter of much indifference. Now, that Messrs. Braithwaite and Ericsson's boiler is a very excellent boiler, is a fact, which it is fortunately not left to these railway experiments to determine; a number of the most eminent engineers and men of science of the day, have concurred in pronouncing it to be, in respect of rapidity and economy of production, the very best ever invented; and many are the boilers of this description, which are already in successful use in distilleries, breweries, sugar refineries, &c., in and about the metropolis. It is at the same time, remarkable for the very small space it occupies. Why then should it fail in its application to locomotive machinery? We see no reason, and can imagine none.

Whether the *Mechanics' Magazine* ever appreciated the reasons we do not know, but the 'William the Fourth' and 'Queen Adelaide' were a failure ; 'it

[1] See p. 79 *et seq.*, Chapter VI. *ante.*
[2] *Mechanics' Magazine*, Vol. XV., p. 39.

was impossible'—wrote Hardman Earle afterwards—'to imagine a more signal failure, she could not make steam,' while on 23rd February 1831 Robert Stephenson was able to state that [1] :—

The 'Northumbrian' drew 50 tons up the inclined plane at Rainhill at the average rate of $7\frac{1}{2}$ miles per hour; pressure of steam 50 lbs. on the square inch, inclination of the ground at Rainhill 1 in 96.

But here we are anticipating events, and we must now return to take a general view of the engines on the Liverpool and Manchester Railway on the eve of the public opening. We have accounted for the 'Rocket,' 'Meteor,' 'Dart,' 'Arrow,' 'Comet,' 'Phœnix,' 'Northumbrian,' and 'North Star,' all

from an aquatint by S. G. Hughes, published by R. Ackermann, 1832.

VIEW OF THE INTERSECTION BRIDGE
crossing the Liverpool and Manchester Railway near the foot of the Sutton Inclined Plane

built by Robert Stephenson & Co.; and we have fortunately an excellent contemporary description [2] of these engines, which, though not strictly applicable to each one, is generally correct, and confirms what is shown by the early illustrations and drawings :—

Most of the engines now on the road, are on principles somewhat similar to that of the 'Rocket,' but so applied and with such improvements in the machinery, and increase in dimensions of cylinder, that they are of greater velocity and power. The appearance of these admirable pieces of mechanism is singular and simple. The engine and boilers are mounted on four

[1] Statement before the Institution of Civil Engineers, quoted in *Report from the Select Committee on Steam-Carriages. Mechanics' Magazine*, Vol. XVI., p. 474.

[2] James Scott Walker, *An Accurate Description of the Liverpool and Manchester Railway*, 13th September 1830, p. 28 *et seq.*

upright wheels, about the size of those of a coach, and of great strength, the two in front being the largest. The boiler, a cylinder placed horizontally and longitudinally, and cased with wood or copper, occupies nearly the whole length and bulk of the machine. In front of it rises a short round chimney, and behind, and rivetted to it, is the furnace, a small compartment, with a sloping front (*sic*), in the middle of which is the little door by which it is fed with fuel. All of the machinery that is visible, are a few pipes, bright iron rods, and valve handles, and the two cylinders (about 12 inches diameter each), affixed to the sides, in a sloping direction, pointing, as it were, to the nave of the front wheels. The piston-rods are steadied by working on two parallel square rods, and to the extremities of each is jointed a rod, the further end of which is attached to a strong spoke of the front wheel, at a short distance from the centre of the

from an etching by I. Shaw, Junr., published by I. Shaw, Liverpool, 1831.

THE NORTHUMBRIAN ENGINE

nave, and communicates the power on the principle of a crank, or, in other words, at every stroke of the engine, forces the wheel once round, as a common reel of yarn is turned by a handle fixed to one of the spokes. The engine tender, for the supply of fuel and water is a separate carriage closely attached to the other, with either an iron tank, and a space for coke, or in lieu of the former, a large water butt, mounted behind. In front of these tenders, stands the engineer, and his assistants, who feeds the furnace with an occasional spadeful of fuel. The water is conveyed from the cistern in leather pipes, and is thrown into the boiler by forcing pumps, worked by the engine. These machines, which are about 9 horse-power, are finished in a very superior manner, and have been much admired by men of science, as well as by ordinary observers. The engines of Messrs. Braithwaite and Ericsson, are different in principle and appearance, as are those of Mr. Berry (*sic*), and of several eminent engineers, now on the line, but our limits do not, were it requisite, permit us to notice them in detail. Suffice it to say, that discoveries are daily made of new principles applicable to these machines, and, extraordinary as they now are, in their power and velocity, great improvements may yet be reasonably anticipated, both in power and in economy of fuel. It is stated that in the first instance, the journey will be announced to be accomplished in two hours.

The writer tells us that in addition to these eight Stephenson engines, 'and another expected,' there were also the 'Dreadnought' and 'Liverpool' by Mr. Berry (*sic*) and 'a large engine called 'The Sisters',' but that 'no London engine was prepared to run.' Of the 'Dreadnought' which was the first engine built by Bury to work on the Liverpool and Manchester Railway no contemporary drawings are known; it is said to have been on six wheels, and has been described by a competent witness [1] as 'a clumsy machine with a chain to an accelerating wheel.'

The 'Liverpool,' which had first started work on the 22nd July 1830, being employed in the construction of the line, appears to have been the first rail locomotive to have the cylinders placed horizontally, between the frames, and driving on to a crank axle. Another qualified witness [2] tells us that 'the boiler was not multitubular like that of the 'Rocket' but contained a number of convoluted flues. The furnace was urged by a blast from a pair of bellows working under the tender. This engine after having been tried for some time was not purchased by the Liverpool and Manchester Railway Company, probably from their not being satisfied with its performance or construction.' The 'Liverpool' afterwards became the subject of a dispute between Bury and Stephenson, and in this connection we shall refer to it later.

'The Sisters' was the 'Liverpool Coke Engine' which we have already described; it too had been employed on the construction of the line since it had been first put to work in July 1829, but neither this engine, nor Bury's engines, were to take part in the opening ceremony, for which the following programme was announced :—

On the day of opening, the Northumberland (*sic*) will take the lead on the North Line of Rail-way,—drawing the fine triumphal chariot of his Grace the Duke of Wellington, between whom, and the engine tender, will be placed a band of music, and following him, the carriage of the Directors.

On the other line of Rail-way, the lead will be taken by the Phœnix, followed by the other Engines, each with its complement of carriages in its wake,—so that the Noble Duke and his friends may view the flying procession at several points, and without interrupting its progress, pause, to examine the Viaducts and other interesting objects on the line.

[1] Hardman Earle, letter to Dr. Lardner, 16th July 1832.

[2] Edward Woods (sometime Locomotive Superintendent of the Liverpool and Manchester Railway), *Proc. Inst. Civil Engineers*, Vol. XVI., p. 24.

CHAPTER XIX

THE OPENING OF
THE LIVERPOOL AND MANCHESTER RAILWAY

All the world's a stage.—Shakespeare.

We can hardly have failed by this time to feel something of the attraction of the early locomotives on the Liverpool and Manchester Railway, or to appreciate the extraordinary personality of the man, who, more than any other, had been responsible for their introduction into general use. We have seen George Stephenson striding across the scene, hoping and pleading, but finally convincing by facts rather than words. During the two critical years just passed he had been helped by his son, to an extent which has perhaps not even yet been sufficiently appreciated. But 'old George' still filled the stage, with a touch of both the heroic and dramatic which appears to have made a strong appeal, when the occasion offered, to the talented girl who, in 1829, had scored a great success in her own profession. Frances Anne Kemble, the young actress, like many another felt the attraction of both the engineer and his work, and her picture of the new world which was opening under her eyes can help us to appreciate again the wonders of that time.

from the portrait by Sir Thomas Lawrence, P.R.A.

FRANCES ANNE KEMBLE

1809—1893

Writing in later life the memoirs of her girlhood[1] she tells us that, while she was acting in Liverpool in 1830, an experimental trip on the railway was proposed by some of the proprietors, who invited her father to accompany them ; the invitation was extended to herself, and her subsequent experiences are recorded in a letter written from Liverpool on 26th August 1830 :—

And now I will give you an account of my yesterday's excursion. A party of sixteen persons was ushered into a large court-yard, where, under cover, stood several carriages of a peculiar construction, one of which was prepared for our reception. It was a long-bodied vehicle with seats placed across it back to back ; the one we were in had six of these benches, and it

---

[1] Frances Anne Kemble (afterwards Mrs. Butler), *Record of a Girlhood*, 1878, Vol. II., p. 158. 'Fanny' Kemble's first appearance at Covent Garden on 5th October 1829 was an overwhelming success, and was the beginning of a career which saved her father from financial ruin. *Dictionary National Biography.*

was a sort of uncovered *char à banc*. The wheels were placed upon two iron bands, which formed the road, and to which they are fitted, being so constructed as to slide along without any danger of hitching or becoming displaced, on the same principle as a thing sliding on a concave groove. The carriage was set in motion by a mere push, and, having received this impetus, rolled with us down an inclined plane into a tunnel, which forms the entrance to the railroad. This tunnel is four hundred yards long (I believe), and will be lighted by gas. At the end of it we emerged from darkness, and, the ground becoming level, we stopped. There is another tunnel parallel with this only much wider and longer, for it extends from the place we had now reached, and where the steam carriages start, and which is quite out of Liverpool, the whole way under the town, to the docks. This tunnel is for waggons and other heavy carriages; and as the engines which are to draw the trains along the railroad do not enter these tunnels, there is a large building at this entrance which is to be inhabited by steam engines of a stationary turn of mind, and different constitution from the travelling ones, which are to propel the trains through the tunnels to the terminus in the town, without going out of their houses themselves. The length of the tunnel parallel to the one we passed through is (I believe) two thousand two hundred yards. I wonder if you are understanding one word I am saying all this while.

We were introduced to the little engine which was to drag us along the rails. She (for they make these curious little fire horses all mares) consisted of a boiler, a stove, a platform, a bench, and behind the bench a barrel containing enough water to prevent her being thirsty for fifteen miles,—the whole machine not bigger than a common fire engine. She goes upon two wheels, which are her feet, and are moved by bright steel legs called pistons; these are propelled by steam, and in proportion as more steam is applied to the upper extremities (the hip-joints, I suppose) of these pistons, the faster they move the wheels; and when it is desirable to diminish the speed, the steam, which unless suffered to escape would burst the boiler, evaporates through a safety valve into the air. The reins, bit, and bridle of this wonderful beast, is a small steel handle, which applies or withdraws the steam from its legs or pistons, so that a child might manage it. The coals, which are its oats, were under the bench, and there was a small glass tube affixed to the boiler, with water in it, which indicates by its fullness or emptiness when the creature wants water, which is immediately conveyed to it from its reservoirs. There is a chimney to the stove but as they burn coke there is none of the dreadful black smoke which accompanies the progress of a steam vessel. This snorting little animal, which I felt rather inclined to pat, was then harnessed to our carriage, and Mr. Stephenson having taken me on the bench of the engine with him, we started at about ten miles an hour.

The steam horse being ill adapted for going up and down hill, the road was kept at a certain level, and appeared sometimes to sink below the surface of the earth and sometimes to rise above it. Almost at starting it was cut through the solid rock which formed a wall on either side of it, about sixty feet high. You can't imagine how strange it seemed to be journeying on thus, without any visible cause of progress other than the magical machine, with its flying white breath and rhythmical, unvarying pace, between these rocky walls, which are already clothed with moss and ferns and grasses; and when I reflected that these great masses of stone had been cut asunder to allow our passage thus far below the surface of the earth, I felt as if no fairy tale was ever half so wonderful as what I saw. Bridges were thrown from side to side across the top of these cliffs, and the people looking down upon us from them seemed like pigmies standing in the sky.

After describing the passage through the Olive Mount cutting, the crossing of Chat Moss, and a walk with George Stephenson down into the valley spanned by the Sankey Viaduct, Miss Kemble proceeds:—

He explained to me the whole construction of the steam engine, and said he could soon make a famous engineer of me, which, considering the wonderful things he has achieved, I dare not say is impossible. His way of explaining himself is peculiar, but very striking, and I understood, without difficulty, all that he said to me. We then rejoined the rest of the party, and the engine having received its supply of water, the carriage was placed behind it, for it

from an etching by I. Shaw, Junr., published by I. Shaw, Liverpool, 1831.

THE VIADUCT OVER THE SANKEY CANAL

from an etching by I. Shaw, Junr., published by I. Shaw, Liverpool, 1831.

OLIVE MOUNT

248

cannot turn, and was set off at its utmost speed, 35 miles an hour, swifter than a bird flies (for they tried the experiment with a snipe). You cannot conceive what that sensation of cutting the air was; the motion is as smooth as possible, too. I could either have read or written; and as it was I stood up, and with my bonnet off 'drank the air before me.' The wind, which was strong, or perhaps the force of our own thrusting against it, absolutely weighed my eyelids down. When I closed my eyes this sensation of flying was quite delightful, and strange beyond description; yet strange as it was, I had a perfect sense of security, and not the slightest fear.

At one time, to exhibit the power of the engine, having met another steam-carriage which was unsupplied with water, Mr. Stephenson caused it to be fastened in front of ours; moreover, a waggon laden with timber was also chained to us, and thus propelling the idle steam engine and dragging the loaded waggon, which was beside it, and our own carriage full of people behind, this brave little she-dragon of ours flew on. Farther on she met three carts, which, being fastened in front of her, she pushed on before her without the slightest delay or difficulty; when I add that this pretty little creature can run with equal facility either backwards or forwards, I believe I have given you an account of all her capacities.

Now for a word or two about the master of all these marvels, with whom I am most horribly in love. He is a man from fifty to fifty-five years of age; his face is fine, though careworn, and bears an expression of deep thoughtfulness; his mode of explaining his ideas is peculiar and very original, striking, and forcible; and although his accent indicates strongly his north country birth, his language has not the slightest touch of vulgarity or coarseness. He has certainly turned my head.

Four years have sufficed to bring this great undertaking to an end. The railroad will be opened upon the fifteenth of next month. The Duke of Wellington is coming down to be present on the occasion, and, I suppose, that with the thousands of spectators and the novelty of the spectacle, there will never have been a scene of more striking interest. The whole cost of the work (including the engines and carriages) will have been eight hundred and thirty thousand pounds; and it is already worth double that sum. The Directors have kindly offered us three places for the opening, which is a great favour, for people are bidding almost anything for a place, I understand.

The enthusiastic writer of this account was present at the opening and nearly witnessed the fatal accident to William Huskisson, Member of Parliament for Liverpool, which has become for historians the central event of the day's proceedings. Few indeed could fail to notice the tragic stroke of fate by which the Duke of Wellington's foremost political antagonist had been struck down just after the exchange of a formal courtesy, the accident being the consequence of Huskisson's having left his own carriage in order to shake hands with the Duke.

There had been many vague forebodings of disaster on the opening day, due largely to the political conditions prevailing. A well known diarist [1] had recorded a few days previously 'a long conversation' with his brother-in-law —'who takes a gloomy view of everything, not a little perhaps tinctured by the impending ruin which he fears to his own property from the Liverpool Railroad, which is to be opened with great ceremony on the 15th; moreover, he thinks the government so weak that it cannot stand and expects the Duke will be compelled to resign.' To such private anxieties were added great public anxieties; times were bad, great distress had given rise to great discontent, and the country was already, as Longridge wrote some months later, 'in a state of high excitation as to the fate of the Reform Bill,' and 'fearing the

[1] Greville, *Memoirs*, Vol. II., p. 43.

dreadful consequences' if it should not be passed. The Duke, then Prime Minister, representing the party in opposition to the Bill, was a most unpopular figure, and there was every reason to expect that his visit to Liverpool might lead to serious disturbances. On this account the greatest precautions had been taken to prevent accident of any kind, and all points and crossings between the two lines of rail had been removed except at one place. The special train with the Duke's state coach, hauled by the 'Northumbrian,' was to run on one of these lines, while the seven other trains were to follow on the other line at intervals of six hundred yards between them. But even these precautions did not prevent the accident to Huskisson which nearly led to an even greater disaster.

from an etching by I. Shaw, Junr., published by I. Shaw, Liverpool, 1831.

THE OPENING OF THE LIVERPOOL & MANCHESTER RAILWAY, SEPT. 15TH 1830, WITH THE MOORISH ARCH AT EDGE HILL AS IT APPEARED ON THAT DAY

A few years earlier the publicity given to such an event might have retarded the development of the railway system, but this was now too firmly established, and the tragedy, though it marred what might have been a day of unbroken triumph for George Stephenson and his locomotives, had in fact less political effect than the completion of the engineer's great work.

The day's proceedings were intended to be a repetition, though on a national and more magnificent scale, of such events as had taken place previously at Darlington and Canterbury. A full account of them is beyond the scope of these notes, and we must leave description of the opening scene to the pen of a contemporary artist; our principal interest lies in the fact that all of the engines which took part in the ceremony had been supplied by Robert Stephenson & Co. The 'Northumbrian,' which led the procession, was driven by George Stephenson himself, and this engine with some others of the earlier types, and the arrangements by which the trains were to run on independent lines, have been well shown by the artist.[1]

from the collection of Mr. C. F. Dendy Marshall.

[1] The early history of the Liverpool and Manchester Railway has been generously illustrated in many beautiful aquatints and etchings by contemporary artists. For a valuable catalogue and monograph see Dendy Marshall, 'The Liverpool and Manchester Railway.' *Trans. Newcomen Society*, Vol. II.

CHAPTER XX

THE 'PLANET'

On the 4th October 1830 it was reported to the Liverpool and Manchester Railway Company that a new locomotive built by Robert Stephenson & Co. had arrived from Newcastle ; this engine 'was ordered to be called the 'Planet',' and on the 29th November following it was decided by the directors :—

That a trial of the power of the 'Planet' Engine be made with a load to be conveyed from Liverpool to Manchester. Mr. Stephenson to make the necessary arrangements.

from an etching by I. Shaw, Junr., published by I. Shaw, Liverpool, 1831.

'PLANET' ENGINE

Subsequently, at a board meeting on 6th December 1830 :—

Mr. Earle reported that the first Load of Merchandise by the railway from Liverpool to Manchester had been sent by the 'Planet' Locomotive in 18 Waggons, on Saturday the 4th instant, consisting of :—

> 200 Barrels of Flour.
> 34 Sacks of Malt.
> 63 Sacks of Oatmeal.
> 35 Bags of Cotton.
> 100 Bales   do.
> —
> 432 Packages.

The Nett Weight chargeable with freight was 51 Tons 1 cwt; the Gross Weight drawn by the Engine, including Waggons, Tender and Passengers, being about 80 tons. The journey was accomplished in 6 minutes less than 3 hours, including three stoppages for watering and oiling, and being assisted up the Inclined Plane by additional Engines.

An account of the trial in a contemporary journal [1] states that :—

The train was assisted up the Rainhill Incline plane by other engines, at the rate of 9 miles an hour, and descended the Sutton Incline at the rate of 16½ miles an hour. The average rate on the other parts of the road was 12½ miles an hour, the greatest speed on the level being 15½ miles an hour, which was maintained for a mile or two at different periods of the journey. The road, we understand, will be opened for the general carrying business in the course of a few weeks, when a further supply of engines is expected; the above experiment having been made in the mean time, for the purpose of ascertaining the powers of the present engines, and of removing some doubts which have been most unaccountably entertained, as to the practicability of transporting cotton and other bulky articles along the railway. Taking this performance as a fair criterion, which there is no reason to doubt, four engines of the same class as the 'Planet' (with the assistance of one large engine, constructed for the purpose, up the inclined plane) would be capable of taking upon the railway all the cotton which passes between Liverpool and Manchester. We understand that the journey on Saturday would have been performed in less time, had not the engineer, when passing over Chat Moss, allowed the fire to burn too low, and afterwards, when he found the steam was falling off, thrown a large quantity of coke upon it, which greatly reduced the temperature, and caused the loss of a considerable time, before the proper speed could be regained. The consumption of coke was, we believe, about two-thirds of a pound per ton per mile.

Another account states that the 'Planet' had previously, on 23rd November, travelled the thirty miles from Liverpool to Manchester in one hour, of which two minutes were taken up in examining and oiling the machinery about mid-way; there were no carriages attached to the engine. The performance of the 'Planet' on 4th December 1830 is evidence of an extraordinary increase in both the power and efficiency of this locomotive, as compared with its predecessors. The explanation is to be found in the design of the engine, and principally in the position of the cylinders, now placed at the front end, between the frames and under the smokebox, where they were kept warm, and some thermal losses were prevented. The boiler was multi-tubular, of the type now standardised by Robert Stephenson & Co., but the marked superiority of the 'Planet' over all locomotives previously constructed lay in the particular combinations we have described, not in an increased boiler capacity. The boiler of the 'Planet' had, in fact, practically the same dimensions, and approximately the same heating surface, as the boiler of its immediate predecessor, the 'Northumbrian.'

The cylinders, 11 inches diameter by 16 inches stroke, were also of the same size as in the preceding engine, but the drive was through a cranked axle, placed in front of the firebox, where it carried a larger proportion of the total weight. The weight of the 'Planet' was about 8 tons, of which rather more than 5 tons were carried on the driving wheels alone, an increase of 25 per cent. over the weight carried by the driving wheels of the 'Northumbrian.' The effective tractive power of the engine was increased correspondingly.

[1] *Mechanics' Magazine*, Vol. XIV., p. 284.

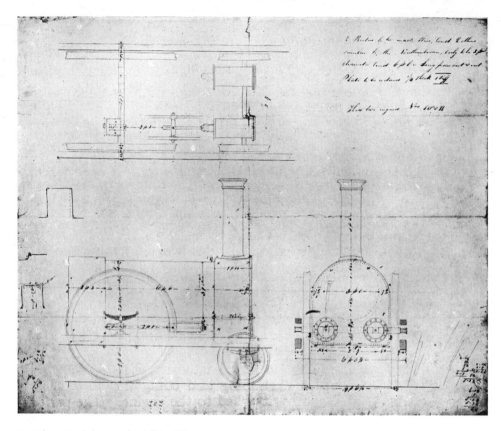

from the original drawing dated July 1830, endorsed

'LOCOMOTIVE ENGINES, DESIGN FOR NOS. 10 & 11'

(*i.e.* the tenth and eleventh to be supplied to the Liverpool and Manchester Railway,
afterwards called 'Planet' and 'Mercury')

from a drawing by G. H. Phipps, Wood's Treatise on Rail Roads, 1831.

THE FIRST 'PLANET' TYPE

FRAME
AND
WHEELS

An original drawing, still in the possession of Robert Stephenson & Co., records what is possibly the first design for the 'Planet,' and the date, July 1830, shows that it was being considered while the 'Northumbrian' was under construction. There are several notable features in this design. The driving wheels are drawn with a diameter of 6 feet but dimensioned 5 feet ; the leading wheel is drawn with a diameter of 2 feet 6 inches, and the frame, which is carried *outside* the wheels, is shown passing *below* the driving axle and above the leading axle, which is placed towards the front end of the smokebox. A modern drawing of a locomotive so constructed has been widely published, and hitherto generally accepted, as representing the 'Planet,' but we have no evidence to show that this engine was ever so built. Indeed such an arrangement of the frame would have been possible only with driving wheels of 6 feet, and leading wheels of 2 feet 6 inches diameter, as shown by *scale* in the design ; with these sizes the vertical relation between the two axles would have made it possible

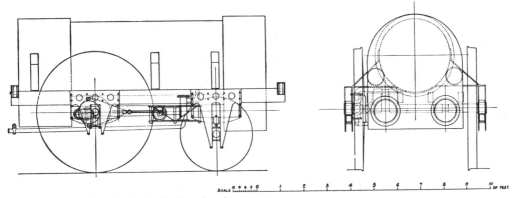

traced from an original drawing (undated), endorsed

No. 10 L'POOL LOCOMOTIVE, MR. R. STEPHENSON'S

to carry the frame below the driving axle, and above the leading axle, at the same time leaving sufficient space for the arrangement of the horns and axle-boxes, with their necessary clearances above and below.

Now, that the driving wheels of the 'Planet' were actually made 5 feet, instead of 6 feet diameter, can be definitely established by the records of a dispute on this very point ; and we have corroborative evidence from two original working drawings of the frame, preserved among the makers' records. These drawings show the driving wheels with a diameter of 5 feet, the leading wheels with a diameter of 3 feet 1 inch, and the frame is shown passing *above* both axles. Several contemporary drawings and artistic representations of this celebrated engine confirm that this was the arrangement actually adopted by Robert Stephenson & Co., though the 'design' of July 1830 shows that a diameter of 6 feet for the driving wheels had been considered by them.

The success of the new combination embodied in the 'Planet,'—*i.e.* inside cylinders below the smokebox, outside frames, and multitubular boiler, was beyond question, and the design was immediately adopted by the Liverpool and Manchester Railway Company as a standard, being the first contractor's design to be so adopted, and to be subsequently imposed on other makers. Within two years one of the railway company's directors could write [1] of the 'Planet.'—'She came nearer to what was considered perfection, relatively of course, than any which had succeeded her.' But the adoption of Robert Stephenson & Co's. locomotive as a standard led to a dispute with a rival engine builder, Edward Bury, whom we find complaining to the railway company in November 1830 that no trial had yet been made of his own engine.

It appears that George Stephenson was subsequently instructed to make a trial, but of this event we have found no record; a directors' minute seven months later records, on 20th June 1831 :—

Read a letter from Mr. Edward Bury requesting that his Engine the 'Liverpool' might be employed in the Conveyance of Goods between Liverpool & Manchester and a fair comparison made between it and one of the most approved Engines constructed by Robert Stephenson & Co.

Mr. Stephenson attended and stated that he had no objection to the trial as applied for—but he had to state to the Directors that he considered the 6 feet wheels of Mr. Bury's Engine injurious to the Road, and less safe than 5 feet wheels, which he was of opinion were as large as they ought to be made.

The Committee of Management were requested to consider the subject and to make the necessary arrangements for the trial of Mr. Bury's engine, if they should be of opinion it could take place with propriety—and Mr. Stephenson was requested to report in writing to the Sub-Committee, the advantages and disadvantages of 6 feet wheels as compared with 5 feet wheels for Locomotive Engines. First considered mechanically, second—as affecting the Road, whether injuriously or otherwise: and Thirdly—as to safety in working.

A minute of 27th June 1831 records that the directors :—

Read Mr. Stephenson's Report on the size of wheels for Locomotive Engines—after which a discussion took place with reference to Mr. Bury's request that his engine might be allowed to work on the Liverpool & Manchester Railway in competition with the best of Mr. Stephenson's Engines with a view to ascertain the comparative powers of each—When it was Resolved, That Mr. Bury's Engine be allowed to run with Goods between Liverpool & Manchester taking such loads as Mr. Bury may deem expedient. That the directors do not think it desirable to load the Company's Engines differently from what they are now doing for the purpose of comparison with other engines; but that Mr. Bury shall be allowed the opportunity of ascertaining the performance of the Company's Engines during the period Mr. Bury's Engines shall be at work, namely for two months, should that time be agreeable to Mr. Bury. As matter of arrangement with reference to the number of journeys, it will be expected that Mr. Bury's Engine will take its turn with the engines of the Company.

We have been unable to obtain any copy of George Stephenson's report, or particulars of the reasons for his objection, but these minutes establish beyond doubt that the driving wheels of the 'Planet' were made to a diameter of 5 feet, and that they determined the standard which prevailed for some years on the Liverpool and Manchester Railway. It has been shown however [2] that the trials of Bury's engine, the 'Liverpool,' were not ruled out on account

[1] Hardman Earle, letter to Dr. Lardner, 16th July 1832. See p. 84, Chapter VI. *ante.*
[2] *Proc. Inst. Civil Engineers*, Vol. XVI., p. 24.

of her 6-foot wheels, but because of accidents, including a broken crank axle, and inability to make steam with her first boiler, and that on these accounts she was not bought by the railway company.

In August 1831 Bury attended a directors' meeting and stated 'that he was desirous to make an engine for the railway company if they were in want.' A fresh controversy then arose as to the merits of inside and outside bearings and a minute of 15th August records :—

Read draft of agreement with Mr. Edward Bury for the building of two Locomotive Engines for £730 each. Mr. Bury attended and strongly recommended inside bearings instead of outside, as stipulated in the agreement. After Mr. Bury retired, Mr. Stephenson attended and stated that he considered outside bearings necessary, for safety, to Locomotive Engines having cranked axles. Ordered that Mr. Bury be informed that in any contract for engines the directors cannot dispense with the stipulation for outside bearings.

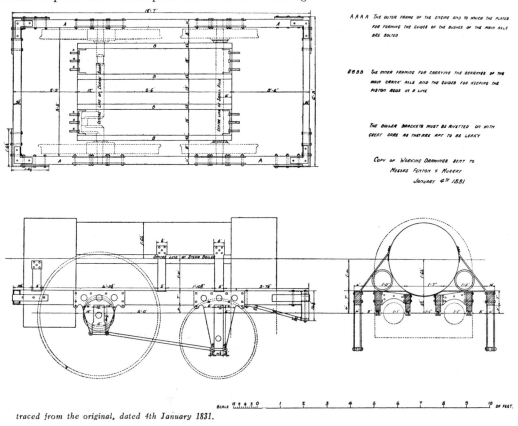

traced from the original, dated 4th January 1831.

'PLANET' TYPE FRAME

copy of working drawing sent to Messrs. Fenton & Murray

The reasons for this dispute are no doubt to be found in George Stephenson's fears of broken crank axles, based upon his own experience of such axles fifteen years earlier and justified by difficulties in their manufacture which had yet to be overcome. To minimise the ill effects of the breakages which were inevitable in the circumstances, Robert Stephenson had adopted outside frames for the 'Planet,' with a series of internal frames, providing no less than six supports for the axle in a vertical direction, which in the event of breakage might prevent the wheels leaving the rails. These internal frames were also intended to relieve the axle from stresses in a horizontal direction due to the steam pressure on the pistons; they were not intended to carry any of the engine weight, and in a vertical direction they came into operation only in case of a fractured crank axle.

The directors of the Liverpool and Manchester Railway Company accepted their engineer's recommendation, and the locomotives ordered from Bury were consequently 'precisely on Mr. Stephenson's plan, with the exception of having a round instead of a square firebox. He was not confined to any particular plan, excepting that his wheels were not to exceed five feet and the bearing of the axle was to be on the outside, both which it is thought contribute to the safety of the engine upon the road.' [1] It appears that George Stephenson was asked later to inform the directors whether he had found any reason, since his report of the 22nd June 1831, to change his opinion as to the largest size of engine wheels to be admitted on the railway; to this Stephenson replied that his objections to a larger diameter than 5 feet remained unabated, adding that, in the particular case of an engine made by another maker, with wheels 5 feet 6 inches diameter, the resulting evil would be less if it was restricted to a slow speed. As a result of this opinion it was resolved at a board meeting on 29th October 1832 :—

That it be a bye law of the Company that in future no Engine shall be allowed to be introduced on the Rail Way with wheels of larger diameter than 5 feet.—A circular containing this regulation to be sent to all Engine makers who have furnished Engines for the Rail Way.

Of the two engines ordered from Bury, one was sold by arrangement to the Bolton and Leigh Railway, the other, retained for the Liverpool and Manchester Railway was called the 'Liver.' [2] Of this engine we have no contemporary drawing, but the evidence given above, and a complete list of sizes for the various inside and outside bearings, preserved among the records of Robert Stephenson & Co., prove conclusively that the usual representation of the 'Liver' with inside bar frames only, of Bury's standard type, is incorrect, and that in respect of the frame it probably closely resembled Stephenson's 'Planet.'

There was however a marked difference in the boiler, for which Bury adopted a firebox of D section in plan, with the spherical domed top which was for many years characteristic of his designs. The form of Bury's firebox, usually, though incorrectly, known as circular, also became the subject of controversy with George Stephenson, and at a board meeting of the Liverpool and Manchester Railway Company on 10th September 1832 was :—

[1] Hardman Earle, letter to Dr. Lardner, 16th July 1832.

[2] Pronounced *Liver*; the name of a mythical bird from which the name *Liverpool* is erroneously supposed to be derived.

Read a Report from Mr. Stephenson as to the Plan of Circular Fire places in Locomotive Engines. Mr. Stephenson was of opinion that they were objectionable and dangerous because, as they could not be advantageously strengthened by Cross stays as the square sided Fire-Boxes were, when an accident by bursting took place the effects would be extremely disastrous.

Considering the importance of the point to be determined, and that there was a decided difference of opinion on the subject between Mr. Stephenson and Mr. Bury several of whose Engines with Circular Fire places were now working on the railway, The Board Resolved, To request the Professional opinion of John Farey Esq. of London on the point at issue, and it was thought desirable that Mr. Bury on the one side and Mr. Stephenson on the other should state their views in writing with the grounds of their different opinions.

Later, at a board meeting on 14th January 1833 was :—

Read Mr. Farey's and Mr. Joshua Field's Report on the comparative advantages and disadvantages of Round and Square Fire places for Loco-Motive Engines; and giving a decided preference to the Square Fire-Box, principally on the score of superior safety. The Consideration of the Measures to be adopted in consequence of this Report was postponed till the Directors could communicate with Mr. Stephenson on the subject. The Treasurer was instructed to acknowledge the receipt of the report and to enquire of Mr. Farey whether there would be any objection to printing a few copies for distribution, occasionally, at the discretion of the Directors. The Treasurer was further instructed to inform Mr. Bury that the Report was arrived, and that he was welcome to peruse the same at the Railway Office.

A week later, on 21st January :—

Mr. Bury attended the Board and stated that he had made an alteration and improvement in the form of his circular fire box for Loco-Motive Engines; and he thought, if Mr. Farey had known of it he might have given a different Report upon the comparative merits of Circular and Square sided Fire-Boxes. Mr. Bury was informed that if he would furnish his statement in writing, the Directors would transmit it to Mr. Farey with request to be informed whether the perusal of it would induce him to alter his decision in respect of the description of Fire places as contained in his Report.

Subsequently, at a board meeting on 28th January 1833 :—

Mr. Edward Bury attended and stated that he had called in the assistance of 10 Engineers who he expected would be unanimous in preferring the Circular Fire-Box to the Square one. Mr. Bury stated that it was evident from Mr. Farey's Report that the drawing of the 'Liver' Fire place sent to London had been incorrect. The Board recommended to Mr. Bury to adopt the Plan before suggested namely to state clearly in writing in what particulars the drawing appeared to have been incorrect. This statement when furnished the Board would transmit to Mr. Farey with request to be informed whether, in consequence thereof, he should be induced to alter his opinion respecting the comparative merits of Square and Round Fire-Boxes. Mr. Bury said he must have time to consider whether it would be expedient for him to adopt the course recommended by the Board.

These minutes suggest that Bury had so far admitted some of the objecttions as to modify the design of his firebox, but it appears that in spite of further discussion and correspondence George Stephenson's opinion on 'the superiority of square over round fireboxes in point of safety' remained unchanged, and the railway company, not being in immediate want of engines, Bury's proposal to supply them with two for the conveyance of merchandise was declined. But his 'Liver,' which they had previously bought, was a good engine, and the round firebox, though it later became a limiting feature, at the time of its adoption provided the engine with a larger grate area than was obtained with the square firebox of the 'Planet.'   A report laid before the directors on 2nd July 1832 shows the following comparative consumption of coke by the two engines during an experiment of six days with trains of merchandise :—

The 'Liver'   ....   0·49 lbs. per ton per mile.
The 'Planet'   ....   0·54 lbs. per ton per mile.

The 'Liver' is mentioned in 1833 as one of the ten best engines then in use on the Liverpool and Manchester Railway [1]; of the remainder, eight had been built by Robert Stephenson & Co. and one by Fenton, Murray & Co. to Stephensons' designs and under their superintendence.   All these engines were

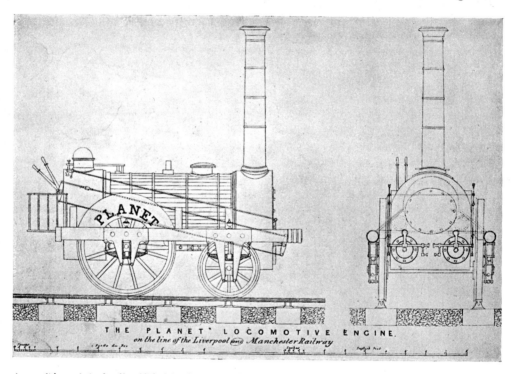

THE 'PLANET' LOCOMOTIVE ENGINE.
on the line of the Liverpool and Manchester Railway

from a lithograph (undated) published by Geo. Smith, Liverpool; in the Liverpool Public Library

of the 'Planet' type as we have described it, or of the modified type with four wheels coupled, which we shall describe in our next chapter.

The 'Planet' was not the first rail locomotive to have inside cylinders driving on to a crank axle, this arrangement, as we have mentioned, having been previously adopted by Bury for his engine the 'Liverpool.'   Inside cylinders, and a crank axle, had also been adopted by Hackworth, in the design of an engine ordered from Robert Stephenson & Co. for the Stockton and Darlington Railway in February 1830, but this engine, the 'Globe,' was not completed by the makers until October 1830, and we shall therefore describe it later in its sequence of construction.   We mention it here because it has been claimed

[1] De Pambour, *A Practical Treatise on Locomotive Engines upon Railways*, 1836, p. 334.

that it gave to Robert Stephenson the idea for the engine arrangement of the 'Planet.'

But Hackworth's engine in fact differed as much in general design from the 'Planet' as did Bury's 'Liverpool,' and the idea of inside cylinders placed below the boiler had been derived by Robert Stephenson from a much earlier source. Immediately after his return from South America in 1827 he had written a letter to the Liverpool and Manchester Railway Company 'explanatory of Mr. Gurney's locomotive engine for coaches and passengers'[1], and on 1st January 1828 he had, as we have already seen, written to Longridge of the 'desirability of applying the engine on the side of the boiler or beneath it entirely,' and he had referred in this letter not only to Gurney's but to other steam coaches then running.

It was in the 'Lancashire Witch' that Robert Stephenson had taken the first step towards the contemplated improvement, that of placing the engine on the side of the boiler. Hackworth had previously adopted a similar arrangement in the 'Royal George,' though retaining a vertical position for the cylinders ; in both cases a great simplification and saving in the amount of machinery and other parts had been effected, this being one of the improvements which Robert Stephenson had in view. We may wonder why the second step, that of placing the engine underneath the boiler, had not been taken by him when building the 'Rocket' in 1829 ; but it seems reasonable to suggest that previous experience with cranked axles, first used by George Stephenson at Killingworth for the purpose of coupling the wheels only, may have made his son chary of adopting the crank axle for driving an experimental engine on which so much was to depend. There was indeed experiment enough in the construction of the 'Rocket's' boiler, and we can understand why it should have been decided for the engine arrangement to follow that of the 'Lancashire Witch,' already a great improvement on anything preceding it.

In support of such a view we have various evidences that Robert Stephenson's designs preceded by steps, each of which was a logical development from that preceding. On his return from America his attention had been first directed to the improvement of the engine, then to that of the boiler ; this effected he again turned his attention to the engine, the result being the 'Planet.'

When, many years later, other designers claimed priority of idea, Robert Stephenson himself replied[2] :—

... that the working drawings of the 'Planet,' which was admitted to have been the type of the engines employed on the Liverpool and Manchester line, had been made, and the engine constructed under his direction, without reference to, or knowledge of, the 'Liverpool.' These facts could be fully confirmed by those who were confidentially employed upon the engine at the time. Neither was there any analogy between the two machines, for the 'Planet' had

[1] Liverpool and Manchester Railway Directors' Minute, 17th December 1827. See also p. 72, Chapter VI. *ante*.

[2] *Proc. Inst. Civil Engineers*, Vol. XVI., p. 23.

Lecount, Article 'Railways,' *Encyclopædia Britannica*, 7th Edition, 1836, states that Robert Stephenson's adoption of the crank axle 'was suggested by a conversation which Mr. Stephenson had with Trevithick when they were on their passage from South America. Trevithick stated there was 40 per cent. increase in the duty of Watt's engine (worked expansively) in Cornwall, from putting a jacket on the cylinders.' Lecount's article was afterwards published as *A Practical Treatise on Railways*, 1839, in which see p. 376 *et seq.*

a multitubular boiler, the fire being urged by a blast-pipe, and the cylinders, which were as nearly horizontal as their position would permit, were fixed inside, or between the frames, because it was only by such an arrangement that they could be placed within the smoke-box, where it was considered desirable to fix them, in order to prevent the condensation of the steam in the cylinders, and the consequent loss of power. This had been resolved upon, from information given to himself by the late Mr. Trevithick, who, in the course of some experiments, had built a brick flue round the cylinder, and had applied the heat of a fire directly to the metal, with very beneficial results, as regarded the economical use of steam. With the cylinders in the smoke-box, a cranked axle was indispensable, and there was not anything new in its use in locomotives, for the 'Novelty,' by Braithwaite and Ericsson, had one in 1829. Horizontal cylinders and cranked axles had also been commonly employed long previously, in Trevithick's, Gurney's, and almost all the other locomotives for turnpike roads.

Phipps himself, who had been employed in the makers' drawing office at Newcastle while the 'Planet' was under consideration and construction, stated that 'with regard to the position of the cylinders, repeated conversations were held between Mr. Stephenson, the late Mr. Hutchinson, and himself, with respect to the saving of fuel that would be effected by placing the cylinders within the smokebox; they also had a great desire to fix the cylinders in a horizontal position, as it was found necessary when an engine travelled at a quick speed, that the vertical motion of the springs should be eliminated from the cylinders, and this naturally led to the horizontal arrangement.'

BURY AND STEPHENSON

We may gather from this discussion and other evidences that in 1830 Bury & Co. were the only serious rivals to the Stephensons as designers and manufacturers of locomotives. It is usual to refer to Edward Bury himself in this connection, but James Kennedy, who later became his partner, himself claimed the credit for the design of the 'Liverpool,' and was probably largely responsible for some of the other designs of Bury & Co. Having been engaged in locomotive designing under George Stephenson so early as 1824, he was in 1830 one of the few engineers having much experience in such matters. It is worth noting that, though Bury & Co. became known as the champions of the inside frame, this construction had been introduced on the Liverpool and Manchester Railway in the first instance in the 'Twin Sisters,' built by Robert Stephenson & Co., who however afterwards abandoned it for the outside frame, which they introduced in the 'Planet' for the reasons stated. The alternative merits of the two arrangements were, and must remain, largely matters of opinion, but, as we shall see later, the combination of Bury's 'circular' firebox with a satisfactory bar frame eventually became impossible.

The dispute between Bury and Stephenson on these questions had far reaching effects, to some of which we have already referred in our notes on the development of Robert Stephenson & Co.; but it becomes clear later that, in spite of the vigour with which both makers advanced their theories, the designs of neither could eventually escape the influence of the other. In 1836 Braithwaite, who had built the 'Novelty,' stated that his firm was constructing a great many locomotives for Cuba and that 'they were making engines on the model laid down by the Liverpool and Manchester Railway Company,

Mr. Stephenson's improved by Mr. Bury.' [1]   It might perhaps be more strictly correct to invert the sequence, but it is clear that *on the vital question of cylinder arrangement* both makers were in accord at a time when others were still obsessed by the vertical cylinder of the 'Novelty'; among these were Sharp Roberts & Co., whose 'Experiment' supplied to the Liverpool and Manchester Railway was a failure.   A contemporary illustration of a similar engine of the same type, supplied to the Dublin and Kingstown Railway, shows an arrangement which did not long survive.   Sharp, Roberts, with other

from the Mechanics' Magazine, Vol. XXII., p. 289.

THE DUBLIN STEAM CARRIAGE 'HIBERNIA'

built by Sharp, Roberts & Co. for the Dublin and Kingstown Railway

makers, subsequently, accepted the standard which the Stephensons had laid down, and they themselves introduced various improvements when designing the details of their own locomotives.

But it was the design of Robert Stephenson & Co's. 'Planet' of 1830 which determined the main features of the British steam locomotive for many years.

[1] Evidence before a Select Committee on *The Tolls on Steam Carriages Bill*, Session 1836.   *Mechanics Magazine*, Vol. XXVI., p. 90.

CHAPTER XXI

THE 'PLANET' TYPE AND SOME MORE EXPERIMENTS

The critical portions of the Liverpool and Manchester Railway, so far as operation by locomotives was concerned, were the inclined planes at Whiston and Sutton, having gradients of 1 in 96. These inclines had been designed intentionally for operation by fixed engines, and at the time it had been considered that no locomotive could be usefully employed upon them. But while the Rainhill trials were in progress the 'Rocket' had disposed of this theory by such exhibitions of its powers as we have had recorded by John Dixon in the letter written to his brother in October 1829.[1]

'SAMSON' AND 'GOLIATH' — The inclines were however a severe tax on the locomotives, and it was decided, at a meeting of the railway company's board on 20th September 1830, to order two locomotives 'of a more powerful description' than the 'Phœnix,'—'to be used on the inclined planes.' The first of these engines, delivered early in 1831, was eventually called 'Samson,' and a second 'large locomotive engine' reported on 14th March was 'ordered to be called the "Goliath".' An original design, and an exceptionally complete working drawing of this engine, still in possession of Robert Stephenson & Co., show that it was an enlarged edition of the 'Planet,' and generally did not embody any new principles, being an extension on lines already determined.

The diameter of the boiler was increased from 3 feet to 3 feet 6 inches, the length from 6 feet 6 inches to 7 feet, and the firebox was increased in both length and breadth. There were in the 'Samson' 140, and in the 'Goliath' 132 tubes, $1\frac{5}{8}$ inch diameter in each case. By the increases in dimensions noted above, total heating surfaces of about 457 and 447 square feet respectively were obtained, instead of the 407 square feet of the 'Planet.' The grate area was increased from $6\frac{1}{2}$ to $7\frac{1}{2}$ square feet. The cylinders were made 14 inches diameter, instead of 11 inches diameter, the stroke remaining as before, 16 inches. The diameter of the driving wheels was reduced to 4 feet 6 inches and they were coupled to the leading wheels.

The weight of the 'Samson,' with the iron wheels which were later fitted, is recorded in the makers' books as about 10 tons, all of which was available for adhesion, the capacity of the engine in this respect being nearly double that of the 'Planet,' which had a total adhesive weight of about 5 tons on the driving wheels.

[1] See p. 208, Chapter XII. *ante*.

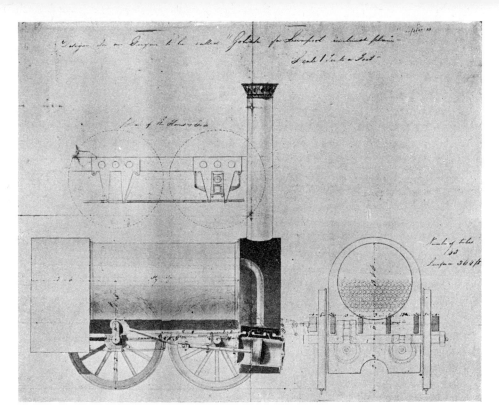

from the original (undated) drawing

DESIGN OF AN ENGINE TO BE CALLED 'GOLIAH' FOR LIVERPOOL INCLINED PLANE

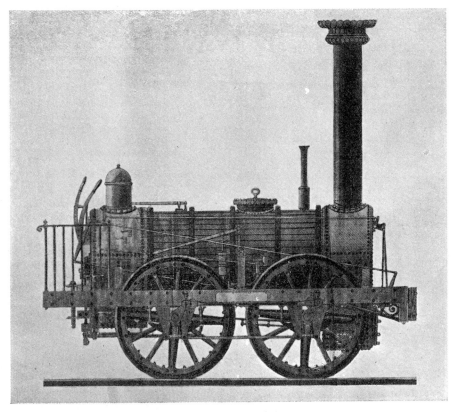

from D. O. Hill's Views of the Glasgow and Garnkirk Railway, 1832

The result of these modifications and increased dimensions is to be seen in the account given by a contemporary journal[1] of :—

THE EXTRAORDINARY PERFORMANCE OF MR. STEPHENSON'S ENGINE, 'SAMSON.'

Yesterday morning [25th February 1831], Mr. Stephenson's engine, the Samson, started from the station at Liverpool with 30 waggons, carrying the following load :—

	Tons.	Cwt.
23 waggon load of oats	82	10
7 Waggon load of merchandize	24	15
Total nett weight	107	5
Tares of the 30 Waggons	42	15
15 persons (chiefly directors and their friends)	1	0
Making the gross weight of	151	0

(besides the weight of the tender, with its coke, water, &c.)

With this enormous load, the Samson moved off at ten minutes past eight, and proceeded to the foot of the inclined plane, at the rate of about twenty miles an hour. It was assisted up the inclined plane by three other engines (the Mars, the Mercury, and the Arrow), and arrived at the top in 38 minutes after leaving the station. As the assisting engines pushed behind the load, whilst the Samson tugged in front, it was easy, by observing where the connecting chains were tight, and where slack, to ascertain what portion of the work was done by each, and it was found that the Samson generally drew sixteen waggons, the gross weight of which would be about 80 tons; on arriving at the top of the inclined plane, the Samson stopped five minutes to take in water, and then proceeded to Park-side, where it arrived at 29 minutes past nine, stopped there eight minutes to water, and arrived at Manchester at sixteen minutes before eleven. The whole time of the journey was, consequently, two hours and thirty-four minutes, and deducting the thirteen minutes employed in taking water, the nett time of travelling was two hours and twenty-one minutes. From the performance of the Samson on the inclined plane, no doubt is entertained that it would draw 200 tons on a perfectly level railway. The quantity of coke consumed by the Samson in this extraordinary journey was 1,376 lbs. (12 cwt. 1 qr. 4 lbs.), being not quite one-third of a pound per ton per mile. Adding to this, the coke consumed by the three engines which assisted up the inclined plane, the whole expense of the fuel would not amount to twenty shillings.

It was subsequently stated of this engine that[2] :—

On 19th April, 1831, the 'Samson' drew up the inclined plane at Rainhill about $44\frac{1}{2}$ tons gross of goods and waggons, at the rate of about 8 miles an hour. Weight of the engine $8\frac{1}{2}$ tons (sic); weight of tender, which was full of water, 4 tons; making the total weight of goods, waggons, engine and tender, 57 tons; and calculating the speed of the engine eight miles per hour, she was exerting a force equal to 39 horse-power.

A later account[3] of the engines on the Liverpool and Manchester Railway in 1835 refers to the 'two bank engines, the Goliath and Samson,' which were used for assisting the trains with passengers and luggage up the inclined planes at Whiston and Sutton, and describes them as of 'about 50 horse-power.'

Though these engines differed from the proto-type in respect of the particulars given above, they were commonly known as of the 'Planet' type.

---

[1] *Manchester Guardian*, 26th February 1831 ; quoted in *Mechanics' Magazine*, Vol. XV., p. 36.

[2] Appendix to *Report from the Select Committee on Steam Carriages* ; quoted in *Mechanics' Magazine*, Vol. XVI., p 475

[3] *Trans. Scottish Society of Arts* ; quoted in *Mechanics' Magazine*, Vol. XXIII., p. 272.

They marked the maximum development of the four-wheeled, four-coupled locomotive by Robert Stephenson & Co., whose improvements in design between 1825 and 1831 can be best appreciated by a comparison of the 'Samson'

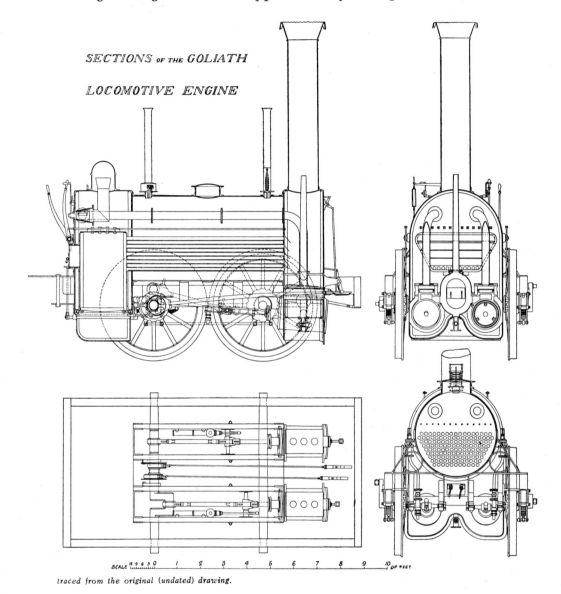

SECTIONS of the GOLIATH

LOCOMOTIVE ENGINE

SCALE *traced from the original (undated) drawing.*

and 'Goliath' with George Stephenson's patent engine as used at Killingworth and Hetton. The particulars and dimensions given in the following table are approximate, but they show sufficiently the marvellous advance which had been made in five years :—

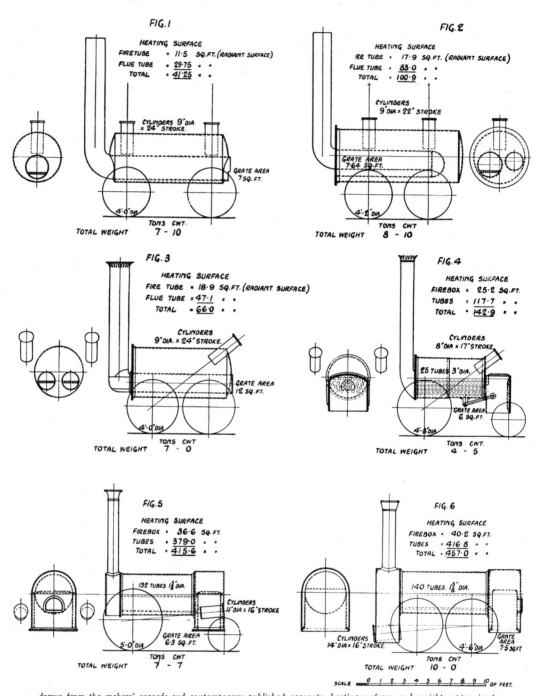

drawn from the makers' records and contemporary published accounts, heating surfaces and weights approximate.

EVOLUTION AND DEVELOPMENT OF THE MULTI-TUBULAR LOCOMOTIVE BOILER, 1825-1830

Fig. 1. Killingworth and Hetton type, 1825   Fig. 2. Stockton & Darlington type, 1827
Fig, 3. 'LANCASHIRE WITCH'   1828   Fig. 4. 'ROCKET'   1829
Fig. 5. 'NORTHUMBRIAN'   1830   Fig. 6. 'SAMSON'   1830

(*Erratum* Fig. 2. Cylinders 24″ stroke)

	Weight of Engine. Tons.	Horse-Power.	Horse-Power per ton of Engine Weight.	Heating Surface. Square Feet.	Heating Surface per ton of Engine Weight.	Evaporation. Cubic Feet of Water per hour.
1825 ..	7½	7½	I	41	5·6	16
1831 ..	10	50	5	457	45·7	60

'PLANET' TYPE IN SCOTLAND

Among the locomotives which followed soon after the 'Planet' and 'Goliath,' were two built for the Glasgow and Garnkirk Railway, the fourth public railway to be opened by Robert Stephenson & Co.'s locomotives. These are described in a contemporary account[1] as having 'fully sustained the high character acquired for their engines by these eminent engineers. They are quite similar in their construction to those on the Liverpool and Manchester Railway, with all the improvements up to the date of their making.'

These engines, the 'St. Rollox,' with single driving wheels, and the 'George Stephenson,' with coupled wheels, were built to suit the rail gauge of 4 feet 6 inches which had been adopted for the Glasgow and Garnkirk Railway. Both were lighter editions of the proto-types, which, however, they closely resembled in external appearance, and in the design of details, as shown by the makers' original drawings which have been preserved. These locomotives have been well recorded by a contemporary artist[1] in a series of views commemorating the opening of the railway, and in the same publication are given particulars of their performances :—

The ordinary load drawn by the 'St. Rollox' is sixteen waggons, each containing three tons of coal, and weighing itself one ton. This is about twelve times its own weight, with half a ton of water in boiler. Several times it has drawn twenty waggons, equal to eighty tons; and on one occasion twenty-three waggons, equal in all to ninety-two tons, and this for eight miles in fifty minutes, being eighteen times its own weight; this, however, is quite beyond what it was ever intended for, and such an overload is very injurious, by straining the working parts. With a load, it generally travels at the rate of ten miles an hour, and when drawing passengers alone, at sixteen to eighteen miles.

The next engine which came on the road, was the *George Stephenson*. This weighs six and a half tons, without water in the boiler. The cylinders are eleven inches diameter, stroke sixteen inches, showing a power of 29 horses. They are placed horizontally as in the 'St. Rollox' and act similarly on the axle of the hind wheels; but here the hind and fore wheels are connected by a rod placed on the outside; so that the adhesion arising from the whole weight of the engine is obtained, which is found of great use when the rails are in a slippery state between wet and dry; the wheels of the engines are then often liable to slip, and spin round a half or a whole revolution without dragging the load, and which besides occasions a very violent action of the engine, tending to strain and often break some of the working parts. The boiler is three feet three inches diameter, and seven feet long. The construction of the fireplaces and of the air tubes is quite the same as in the 'St. Rollox,' and the number of tubes is 102. No regular

[1] D. O. Hill, *Views of the Opening of the Glasgow and Garnkirk Railway*, 1832 (Mitchell Library, Glasgow).

from D. O. Hill's Views of the Glasgow and Garnkirk Railway, 1832.

VIEW NEAR PROVEN MILL BRIDGE

from D. O. Hill's Views of the Glasgow and Garnkirk Railway, 1832.

VIEW OF THE GERMISTON EMBANKMENT

account has yet been kept of the quantity of fuel and water required by these engines. It is much the same, however, as others of a similar construction.

The usual load drawn by this engine, is twenty waggons, equal to eighty tons; but it has frequently drawn twenty-eight, equal to 112 tons, at the rate of ten or twelve miles an hour; and on the day of the opening of the railway, drew thirty-three, besides two more filled with passengers. This engine generally makes three trips a day of eight miles, each way; frequently four, and on several occasions has made five, and thus delivered at the depots about 200 tons of coal in one day. With passengers, the speed of the engine varies from twelve to twenty miles an hour; and, if it were desirable or prudent, could be increased far beyond this. On one occasion, this engine, with sixteen empty waggons, of a ton weight each, and a carriage with nine passengers, travelled a mile in one minute and a quarter, being at the rate of fifty miles an hour. With such powers of locomotion and draught for heavy goods, and of speed, where that may be required, such engines as the above, without even considering the future improvements which may yet be anticipated in their construction, appear capable, on well constructed railways, of effecting almost anything, in point of dispatch or power, that may be desired, in regard to the internal traffic and intercourse of the country.

Since the railway commenced, in September, the chief trade on it has been in coals, of which a very great quantity has been already sent down the line, averaging about 350 tons daily, or at the rate of 100,000 tons annually; and the quantity is expected to be much greater, when additional engines arrive, and things get into their regular train. A carriage for the conveyance of passengers also leaves Coat Bridge and Leaend every morning for Glasgow, and returns in the evening. Each time, also, the engine starts with a load of coals from the upper part of the line, or with empty waggons returning, a small passenger waggon is attached, not being regulated by any hour; and a considerable number of stragglers find their way in this manner along the line.

This railway promises to realize fully the great object of its promoters, and to become, at the same time, a work of vast benefit to the city of Glasgow, as well as to the districts through which it passes. Such is the facility of transport on it, that coals from Kipps Colliery for example, which were formerly carted one and a half miles to the Monkland Canal, and by it conveyed to Glasgow at an expense in all of 3s. 6d. a ton, can now be sent by the railway for less than 1s. 3d. In fact, the expense of carting them that one mile and a half to the canal, amounted to two-thirds of the whole expense of sending them by the railway to Glasgow.

DESIGN
OF
DETAILS

Although the locomotives of the 'Planet' type built by Robert Stephenson & Co. between 1830 and 1835 remained much the same in general arrangement and outline, many changes were made in the design of parts. Our record of these engines would be incomplete without a reference to some of these modifications, and to the reasons for their introduction from time to time. Most of them were attempts to prevent, or mitigate, troubles which have remained with railwaymen to this day, the same in essence, though not in degree.

For the purpose of the following notes information has been obtained, except where otherwise mentioned, from the official records and published *Reports*, of the Liverpool and Manchester Railway Company; from De Pambour's *Practical Treatise on Locomotive Engines*, first published in England in 1836, and from the early order books of Robert Stephenson & Co. These books record various communications from John Dixon, who 'immediately on the opening of the railway was entrusted with the care and management of the locomotive engines under Mr. Stephenson's directions.' Dixon records that he 'not only tried many experiments with locomotive engines, but witnessed their daily and hourly performances,' and we have evidence that several modifications to design were introduced by the makers on his recommendation. The various engines mentioned by name in his communications were all of the 'Planet' type, and, with the exception of the 'Liver,' all had been built by Robert Stephenson & Co., or to their designs and under their directions. The illustrations from contemporary drawings and publications, which we reproduce here, show clearly the principal features and many of the details, some of which appear to deserve special notice.

BOILER
JOINTS
The number of joints, each a possible source of trouble, was determined then, as now, by the size of the plates obtainable, and these were no doubt limited by the capacity of the rolling mills at the Bedlington Iron Works, which supplied the plates and in many cases the boilers required by Robert Stephenson at this period.

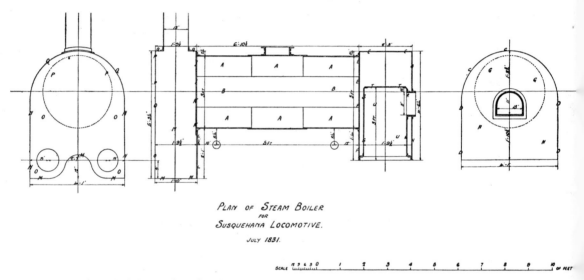

PLAN OF STEAM BOILER
FOR
SUSQUEHANA LOCOMOTIVE.
JULY 1831.

SCALE

traced from the original drawing dated July 1831.

The available sizes of the plates are well shown in the drawing of a boiler for a 'Susquehanna Locomotive,' dated July 1831. In a barrel 3 feet diameter, by 5 feet long, having a firebox 2 feet 3 inches long, by 4 feet 1 inch wide, are no less than twenty-two plates ; the largest size mentioned in the accompanying specification being 4 feet 1 inch, by 3 feet 1 inch, by $\frac{3}{8}$ inch thick.

The drawing shows that most of the junctions were made by means of angle irons. The joints of the firebox to its shell, particularly at the fire hole and at the bottom of the box, were soon found to be critical parts, and we have various suggestions for modifying the methods of connection. A sketch in July 1832 shows 'a solid hoop of iron round the door, fastened with screwed rivets,' with the remark—'if the holes in the plate were made opposite one another and long rivets put in hot, we think it would make a good job.'

Another sketch shows a solid firehole ring with rivets taken right through the plates and ring as suggested; but though this method afterwards became general some others were tried. In May 1832 Robert Stephenson 'wishes all the boilers now in hand to have the fire doors altered'—to a sketch which shows a modification of the arrangement on the Susquehanna boiler, the various plates themselves being flanged to make the joints and the use of angle irons thereby avoided—'he thinks it would be a good plan to cut the hole in the door after the firebox is finished and to make it circular.'

Attempts were also made to avoid the use of angle irons at the bottom by flanging the inside firebox plate outwards, on to the shell plate, and fixing by a double row of rivets. A later sketch, in January 1833, shows the inner firebox plate again brought straight down as on the Susquehanna boiler, but with the joint made by a plate bent into the form of a channel iron. Another sketch shows a solid ring for the bottom joint of the firebox, as afterwards, though not immediately, adopted almost universally.

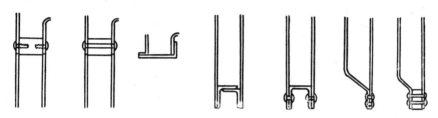

re-drawn from rough sketches in an original works order book, 1832-1836.

FIREHOLE AND FIREBOX BOTTOM JOINTS

BOILER STAYS The longitudinal stays appear to have been usually in the form of rods, as adopted by Robert Stephenson for the boiler of the 'Rocket'; they were taken through from the smokebox tube-plate to the firebox back plate, and screwed and nutted on the outside. In some cases the stays were made with jaws at the ends, to take T-irons inside the firebox back and smokebox tube plates.

FIREBOX TUBE PLATE We have several references to tube-plate trouble and in March 1832 a note from John Dixon—'it is a good plan to put angle iron into the boiler just under the bottom tubes to get some stays into.' The accompanying sketch shows an early, possibly the first, use of a belly stay in a locomotive boiler.

FIREBOX Definite information as to the materials employed for the fireboxes of the first 'Planet' type locomotives is lacking from the makers' records, but a note in May 1832 records—'no more inside fireboxes to be made of iron as we think of trying copper.' This suggests that previously the general practice had been to use iron. A report of the Liverpool and Manchester Railway Company for the last six months of 1832

S'

refers to the excessive expenditure on account of repairs during this period, principally 'from the frequent renewals of tubes and fire-places, which in most of the engines have been found to burn very rapidly away.' It is however added that 'to this general result there have been some exceptions of engines which had run between twenty and thirty thousand miles with very inconsiderable repairs to these parts'; but the material of which the fireboxes were made in each case is not specified by the report.

In 1833 John Dixon writes that the 'Fury' by Fenton & Co., after having run 21,330 miles 'then got a new box at Galloway & Co.'s, the plates being ordered from Low Moor, intending to have good ones, but they alas proved

from an original works order book in possession of Robert Stephenson & Co.

false and only lasted 6,060 miles, and we are now at work with the third !! 'Milo' got a new box of Forster and Griffin, L'pool, but it has shown symptoms of blistering &c. before it has worked a month. I have great hopes that copper will do us some service.'

The makers' records subsequently specify copper fireboxes in individual cases, and a railway company's report for the last six months of 1833 refers to the 'purchase of copper and brass plates for the renewal of fireboxes and tubes.'

TUBES It was soon found that copper tubes wore out very rapidly. John Dixon writes in May 1833—'he thinks the use of coke from the gas works has caused the tubes to give lately. The 'Venus' which has a new firebox and tubes by Bury ran only 8,000 miles before she began to burst tubes by three or four a day.' A railway company's enquiry for new locomotives in December 1833 specifies brass tubes, and these were afterwards largely adopted. This substitution of brass for copper is usually ascribed to Dixon's recommendation. A note in December 1833 records—'Mr. Stephenson says iron tubes should be $\frac{1}{16}$ $\frac{1}{32}$ thick'—and shows that experiments were being made with this material, which was also adopted in some cases.

The fixing of the tubes in the tube plates was no doubt by means of ferrules, as adopted by Robert Stephenson for the 'Rocket,' and there is some suggestion that the tubes may also have been beaded over. We have a note in February 1833—'the holes for the copper tubes in the locomotives need not be counter-sunk so much as they used to be.'

There appears to have been a diversity of opinion as to the most desirable thickness of the tubes, and we find Dixon writing to Hardman Earle in 1832 on the superiority of light tubes over heavy ones[1] :—

The Jupiter was the first to get an entirely new set of tubes in her (12 lbs. instead of 6 lbs.). It took 600 lbs. Copper and several tubes have burst and the extra weight has been useless. Heavy tubes cost £60 extra, add 1,000 lbs. to the weight and do no good, and I consider that they injure the boiler ends.

To this Earle replies :—

I was in favour of heavy tubes, but am changing my mind and you add confirmation to my opinion. The Planet first shook my faith in heavy tubes. She has light ones (6½ lbs., some I find now shrunk to 4 lbs.) but she has done double what the Jupiter has. I consider she is better because she has a large boiler, has more tubes and a larger firebox and blast pipe.

After referring to injury to the tubes from intensity of blast he proceeds :—

We must have greater space between tubes, or larger boiler, more tubes and less blast, I prefer the latter. Let us transfer Phœnix into the Planet class, put copper ends to her boiler, copper into her firebox, and 140 tubes, one half copper, the rest iron with copper ends.

The makers' records confirm that there were variations both in the number, and the diameter, of boiler tubes in the engines which followed the 'Planet,' and show that many experiments were being made in attempts to obtain the best results. A note in May 1832 records,—'the tubes in boilers in future to be 2 in. diameter inside and $\frac{1}{16}$" thick.'

FIREBOX STAYS The inner and outer plates of the firebox and its shell were connected by stays screwed into both plates, with nuts on the inside, and riveted over on the outside plate. These stays were at first of iron, and we have no evidence in the makers' records to show the use of other material until early in 1836.

---

[1] *Handbook on the Rise and Development of the Railway System,* Edward Baker, 1893. Ref. No. **324b**.

The roof stays were simple angle irons, bolted to the crown plate to stiffen it, and not slung in any way to the outside shell.

ASHPAN AND FIREGRATE An ashpan appears on the drawing of the 'Goliath,' but on some of the drawings of later engines it is not shown. In May 1832 'Mr. Stephenson wishes to have the top of the fire bars 3 inches above the bottom of the firebox.'

SMOKEBOX AND CHIMNEY The smokebox was prolonged downwards at the sides, and its bottom carried underneath, so as to enclose the cylinders, with a view to their complete protection against thermal losses. The earliest known illustrations of the 'Planet' show that the design of its chimney was conceived in the classical spirit of contemporary Georgian architecture, and suggest that it must have been made of cast iron. The elaborate design shown on the drawing by Phipps may probably be explained by the intention that the 'Planet' should take part in the ceremony of opening the Liverpool and Manchester Railway. Such a design was no doubt soon found to be as unnecessary for practical purposes, as it was æsthetically unsuitable to a locomotive. The later chimneys appear to have been made mostly of plate, at first with some variety of top, but eventually with a simple inverted cone, which continued in use by Robert Stephenson & Co. for some years.

BLAST PIPE The blast nozzle was sometimes placed above the top of the smokebox, well inside the chimney ; in other cases it was placed rather lower, and the chimney prolonged downwards into the smokebox. The size and position were then, as now, the subject of constant experiment. De Pambour, as the result of his investigations, recommended an adjustable exhaust orifice.

SPARK ARRESTER The need for some form of spark arrester was discussed between George Stephenson and the directors of the Liverpool and Manchester Railway so early as July 1830, and various devices were tried, usually without entirely satisfactory results. In some of the engines the bottom of the smokebox was made to hold water into which the cinders, which had passed through the tubes, were thrown down by baffles, similar to venetian blinds. Such baffles are shown on the drawing of the 'Goliath,' but it was stated afterwards by Robert Stephenson[1] that 'the most effectual method' was that of covering the orifice of the chimney with a cap of very rough gauze.

REGULATOR The regulators were at first simple plug valves, and this pattern was used until superseded by the 'butterfly' valve. This appears to have been introduced when the regulator, which had been at first placed over the firebox, was moved forward to a position behind the smokebox tube plate. In March 1832 an order from America asks for '4 steam cocks of the old kind instead of the steam regulators.'

---

[1] Evidence before the Select Committee on the Danger of Locomotive Carriages in narrow streets. *Mechanics' Magazine*, Vol. XXVI., p. 175.

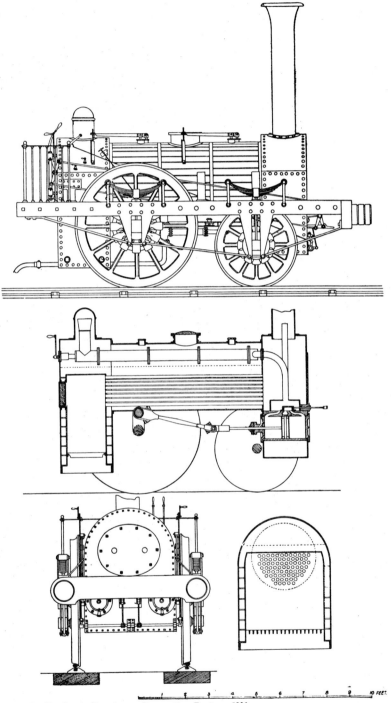

from De Pambour's Treatise on Locomotive Engines, 1836.

'PLANET' TYPE

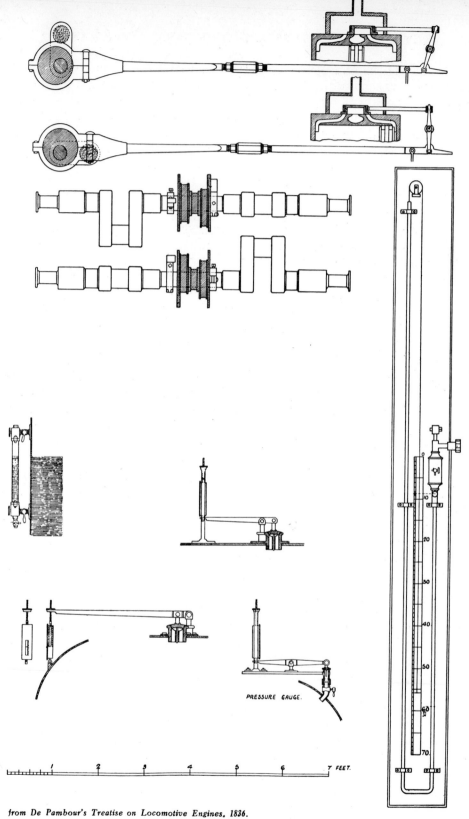

PRESSURE GAUGE.

7 FEET.

from De Pambour's Treatise on Locomotive Engines. 1836.

DETAILS OF 'PLANET' TYPE

SAFETY VALVES — These engines were fitted with two safety valves, of which one was sometimes enclosed in a lock-up casing to prevent tampering by the engine-men. The drawings of the 'Goliath' show the front safety valve as of this description, having a nest of small, separate, flat springs placed back to back. This ingenious design, due to Hackworth, is shown on Rastrick's sketch of the 'Royal George.'[1] The rear valve of the 'Goliath' is shown with a coiled spring and lever balance; in some cases both valves were of this latter type.

De Pambour observes that—'the levers and valves used by the different constructors vary considerably in their proportions. But, among those proportions there is one, first used by Mr. Edward Bury, of Liverpool, which possesses an uncontested advantage over all other combinations of that sort. It consists in taking for the proportions between the two branches of the lever the ratio of the area of the valve to the unit of surface. By that means the weight suspended gives immediately the pressure produced on the valve per unit of surface.' A note in Robert Stephenson & Co.'s order book records a request on 24th May 1832 to fit safety valves of this type.

PRESSURE GAUGE — The working pressure was nominally 50 lbs., but De Pambour finds that to depend on the '*nominal* pressure' might lead to great mistakes—'for it sometimes happens that, with a view to give a locomotive engine the appearance of executing more than others, though at the same pressure, its pressure is declared to be 50 lbs. per square inch, whilst it really is 60 or 70 lbs. Moreover, the calculation of the pressure is generally so incorrectly made, that scarcely any dependance can be placed upon it.'

He explains that estimations of the actual pressure could at first be made only from the behaviour of the safety valves, but that the mistakes resulting from this method could be avoided by the use of the mercurial gauge—'an expensive instrument, as yet so scarce, that in all the factories and on all the railways except the Liverpool one, there is at present no other mode of ascertaining the pressure than those explained.' To obviate these difficulties, De Pambour proposed, and himself designed, a convenient manometer to replace the mercurial gauge.

BOILER FEED — Generally two feed pumps were fitted, worked from the crossheads; in the later engines the valves were 'ingeniously made with a small metallic sphere resting on a circular seat on which it always exactly fits.' It is recorded that the pumps, 'which in the beginning were continually out of order are free from that difficulty since Mr. Melling of Liverpool first introduced that sort.' John Melling was at the time foreman in the railway company's workshops and appears to have been a man of much ingenuity.

In some cases a hand pump was fitted, to be worked by the engine-man as required. Such a pump is shown on contemporary drawings and illustrations.[2]

[1] See p. 124, Chapter VII. *ante.*   [2] See p. 265 *ante.*

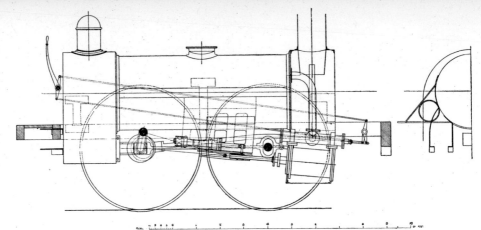

traced from the original (undated) drawing.

LOCOMOTIVE WITH CIRCULAR SLIDE VALVES AND AXLE-RODS

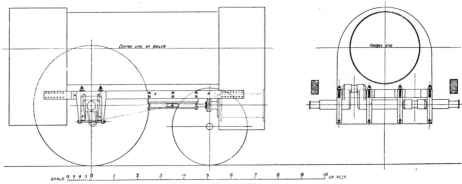

(part) traced from the original drawing, dated 28th March 1832.

' The alteration proposed consists in the substitution of bars A A for the axle-rods and also in the particular manner of tightening the brasses on the axle when they require it from wear '

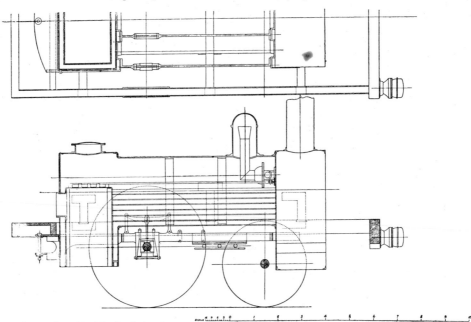

traced from the original (undated) drawing.

SOLID IRON INSIDE FRAMES WITH ADDITIONAL SPRINGS ON TWO INSIDE BEARINGS

FRAMES The main frames of the 'Planet,' which were outside the wheels and formed a complete rectangle, were made of wood, bound at the corners by iron plates and angles. The four intermediate frames, also of wood, were attached at the front end by angle irons and screws to the cylinders, and similarly at the back end to the firebox. The method of fixing is clearly shown on the 'copy of a working drawing sent to Fenton and Murray' by Robert Stephenson & Co. in January 1831.[1]

The principal function of the inner frames, as already mentioned, was to support the crank axle in the event of breakage, and to relieve it of stresses in a horizontal direction. These inner frames also served to carry the slide bars, but they were not at first used for the transmission of weight, and the whole of the engine weight carried by springs was borne by the outside frames. When we consider the loads hauled by these locomotives, and the speeds at which they ran, it is not surprising to find that in 1832 the necessity for re-newing and strengthening the frames is mentioned as one of the principal reasons for heavy charges in maintenance.

The inner wooden frames were first replaced by iron 'axle-rods,' and we have a record in July 1832 that 'they seem to answer very well.' These rods were arranged at one end with a jaw, fitted with brasses to take the inside bearings on the crank axle ; these brasses were held in place by a cotter, the whole arrangement resembling that of a locomotive connecting rod big-end. No weight was transmitted through these bearings, and the axle-rods had a hinged attachment to the smokebox which permitted vertical move-ment at the firebox end to correspond with the movement of the outside axle-boxes in their guides, the jawed ends of the axle-rods which contained the bearings being free to move in vertical guides fixed on the firebox.

These axle-rods were later replaced by solid iron frames in the form of vertical bars, wrought to form guides for the crank axle bearings, and fixed to both smokebox and firebox. The guides were fitted with adjustable wedges. Like the axle-rods, these inside iron frames do not at first appear to have been intended to carry any weight.

AXLEBOX GUIDES The horns, or guides, for the axleboxes were at first formed by double plates, bolted to the wooden outside frames. In later engines the plates out of which the horns were formed were extended for the whole length of the outer wooden frame, the result being the 'sandwich frame,' which became general in English practice, though particularly associated with the work of Robert Stephenson.

SPRINGS In the 'Planet' the springs were below the frames, and were fitted only to the outside bearings on the axles, *i.e.* those on the outside of the wheel. In later engines these springs were placed above the frame, and in some cases others were provided also on the inner frames, transmitting part of the engine weight to the bearing between the crank and the wheel. Various arrangements were adopted, including a double spring known as a 'grasshopper,' which we find first mentioned in

---

[1] See p. 257, Chapter XX. *ante.*

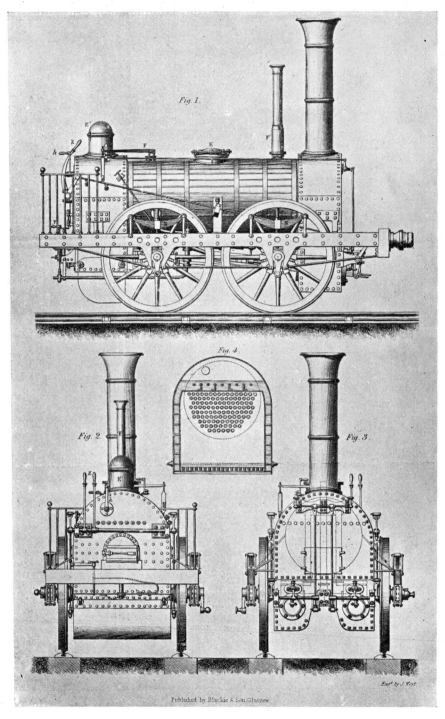

Fig. 1.

Fig. 4.

Fig. 2.

Fig. 3.

Eng.ᵈ by J. West

Published by Blackie & Son, Glasgow

from Grier's 'Mechanics' Pocket Dictionary,' published by Blackie & Son, Glasgow, 1838.

FOUR-COUPLED 'PLANET' TYPE

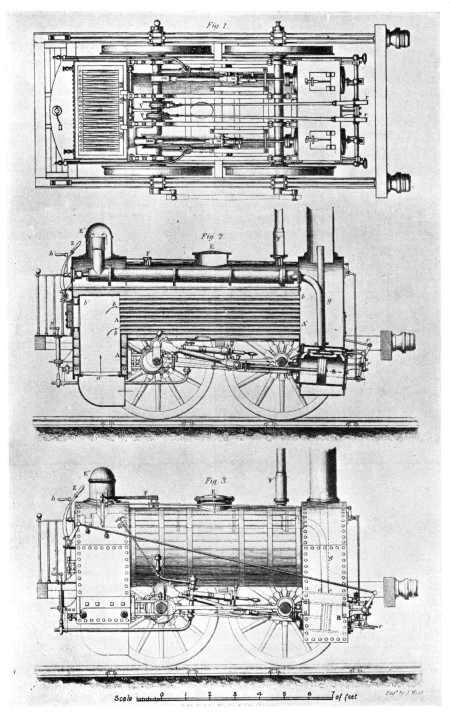

Scale |⊣⊣⊣⊢⊢⊢| 0 1 2 3 4 5 6 7 of feet   Eng.ᵈ by J West

from Grier's 'Mechanics' Pocket Dictionary,' published by Blackie & Son, Glasgow, 1838.

FOUR-COUPLED 'PLANET' TYPE

See p. 287, for details, from *'Locomotives Stephenson circulant en Angleterre et en France'*

March 1832. But the use of springs on the inside bearings does not appear to have been entirely satisfactory, and in September of the same year Robert Stephenson ordered that no more need be fitted.

WHEELS   Spokes and rim of wood, as first adopted by Robert Stephenson & Co. for the 'Lancashire Witch' in 1828, were still used by them, with various modifications, until 1832 when they introduced an iron wheel, having gas pipe spokes. In April of that year it is recorded that these 'patent' wheels are doing well, but in 1833 the railway company write of several 'complete failures,' and later, referring to the 'failure of several of the spokes of the 'Fire Fly's' wheel,' they recommend that engines then being made at the Vulcan Foundry should have Bury's or Roberts' wheel. A letter from Charles Tayleur, junior, recommends nevertheless a

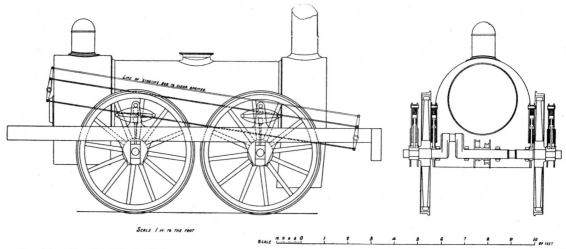

SCALE 1 IN. TO THE FOOT

SCALE   1   2   3   4   5   6   7   8   9   10 OF FEET

traced from the original (undated) drawing.

GRASSHOPPER SPRINGS

'trial of their engine wheels on the principle of Mr. Stephenson's patent' and offers to guarantee their stability.

CYLINDERS   An original drawing of spare cylinders sent to America for AND VALVES   engines of the 'Planet' type, shows the valve chest as a separate casting bolted on, a feature which survived in American practice for many years.[1] This drawing shows double slide valves with short steam ports, but in May 1832 it is decided that 'locomotive cylinders in future are to work with single slides.' Drawings have been preserved which show that piston, or 'circular slide valves,' were to be fitted to a locomotive for the Liverpool and Manchester Railway but we have no evidence as to their behaviour, or that they were actually fitted. The straight ports are particularly noteworthy.

[1] This practice had perhaps been introduced to America with the cylinders supplied by Robert Stephenson & Co. in 1828. See p. 159, Chapter X. *ante.*

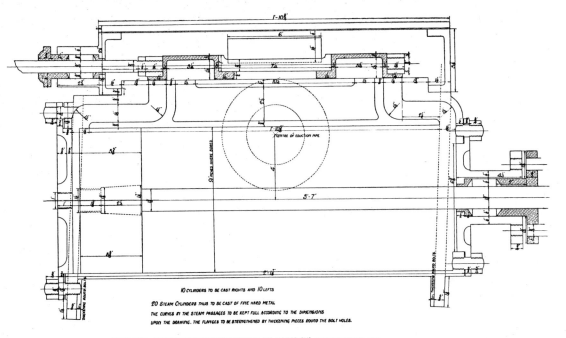

10 CYLINDERS TO BE CAST RIGHTS AND 10 LEFTS

20 STEAM CYLINDERS THUS TO BE CAST OF FINE HARD METAL

THE CURVES IN THE STEAM PASSAGES TO BE KEPT FULL ACCORDING TO THE DIMENSIONS
UPON THE DRAWING. THE FLANGES TO BE STRENGTHENED BY THICKENING PIECES ROUND THE BOLT HOLES.

LONGITUDINAL SECTION OF STEAM CYLINDER & VALVES FOR MR STEVENS. MARCH 26TH 1832. D⸗M/M

traced from the original drawing, dated 26th March 1832.

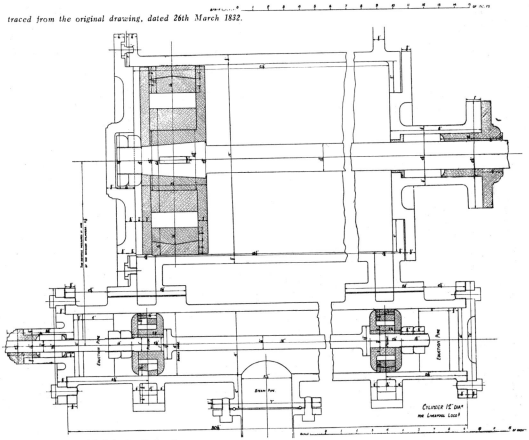

CYLINDER 12" DIA
FOR LIVERPOOL LOCO

traced from the original (undated) drawing.

CYLINDER 12" DIAMETER FOR LIVERPOOL LOCOMOTIVE

There were two excentrics only, attached to each other to form a single piece, which was free to slide sideways on the driving axle within determined limits. On the outer face of each excentric was fixed a plate having a small slot and on the axle were fixed two straps, one on either side of the loose piece, and determining its total side movement. Each of these straps had a projecting lug, so arranged as to engage with the slot in the side plate of the relative excentric. The twin excentric could be moved sideways as desired by means of a treadle worked from the footplate, the movement being sufficient to allow engagement with the lug on one or other of the axle straps accordingly as the backward or forward motion of the engine was desired. Since it was usually necessary for some movement of the driving wheel wheels to take place before the projecting lug could enter the slot, provision had to be made for starting the engine by other means. A hand lever and rods were therefore provided for lifting the excentric rods clear of the pin on the slide valve operating lever. Other levers were provided

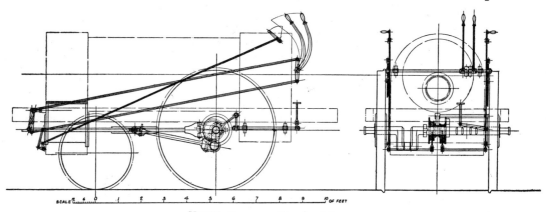

SCALE 0   1   2   3   4   5   6   7   8   9   10 OF FEET

VALVE GEAR OF 'PLANET' TYPE

to enable the valves themselves to be moved by hand in order to admit steam to either end of the cylinder sufficiently to start the engine in the desired direction. After the required movement of the driving wheel had been obtained, the excentric rods were allowed to engage again with the pin on the valve driving lever. This arrangement continued in general use by Robert Stephenson & Co. until the adoption of four fixed excentrics.

Inventors of 'patent fittings' were not slow to avail themselves of the new field offered by the locomotives of the Liverpool and Manchester Railway, whose directors' minutes show their willingness to allow experiments of all kinds, with a view to the improvement of their existing locomotives, or to the introduction of new or more efficient types. We find Perkins, whose earlier experiments with high pressure steam in 1823 we have already noted[1], engaged during 1833 'in adapting his invention for improving the circulation of the water in the boiler to one of the Company's engines which they have

[1] See p. 60, Chapter VI. *ante*.

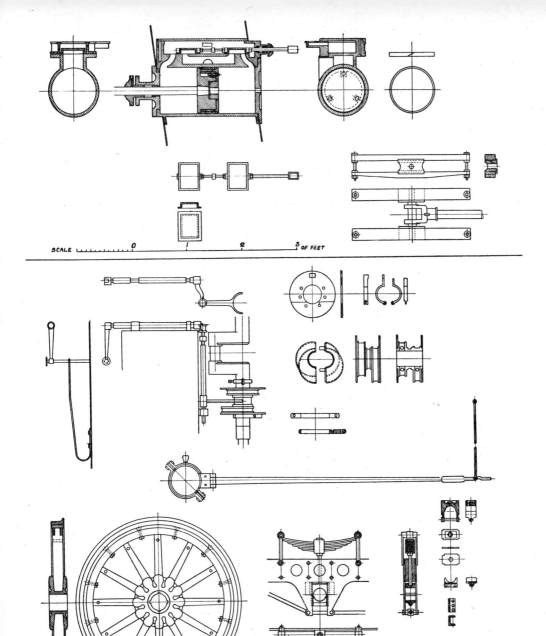

SCALE |......|......| 0   1   2   3 OF FEET

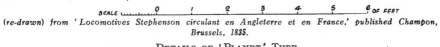

SCALE |......|......| 0   1   2   3   4   5   6 OF FEET

(re-drawn) from 'Locomotives Stephenson circulant en Angleterre et en France,' published Champon, Brussels, 1835.

DETAILS OF 'PLANET' TYPE

cheerfully placed at his disposal for the purpose of experiment.' It was afterwards claimed that during 360 successive journeys the locomotive to which his lining, or circulator, had been introduced had run 'upwards of 20,000 miles without the slightest appearance of wear and tear ; the tubes of the boiler at the end of the journey being as free from corrosion as at the first moment of their use, and with a saving of fuel to the extent of 40 tons when contrasted with the ascertained consumption of any locomotive engine drawing equal weight.'

These extravagant claims were in due course contradicted [1], and Perkins' circulator appears to have shared the fate of many similar inventions subsequently applied to the locomotive.

So far as the general design of their locomotives was concerned, we find that although the railway company had adopted the 'Planet' as a standard, they subsequently allowed experiments with, and in some cases eventually purchased engines which differed considerably from it.

from a ' Descriptive Catalogue of the Padorama of the Manchester and Liverpool Rail Road,' drawn by G. H. West, printed by E. Colyer, 1834.

THE 'CALEDONIAN'

In September 1832 the directors ordered that 'a fair trial be made under Mr. Dixon's superintendence' of a new locomotive constructed by Galloway, Bowman & Co., of Manchester. This engine, called the 'Caledonian,' was afterwards purchased by the railway company for £800, but, in view of a subsequent objection by George Stephenson to vertical cylinders, they ordered that a copy of his report be sent to the makers, 'with a notice that in future the directors would object to any new engines with vertical cylinders being put to work on the Liverpool and Manchester Railway.'

In spite of this decision the company later ordered 'a comparative trial of the merits' of a new locomotive, called the 'Experiment' [2], about which the makers, Sharp, Roberts & Co., had been in correspondence for some time,

---

[1] *Mechanics' Magazine*, Vol. XVIII., p. 448.   [2] See p. 263, Chapter XX. *ante*.

and now offered to sell to the company for £1,000. A directors' minute of 22nd August 1831 records :—

Read a letter from Sharp, Roberts & Co. with their ideas on Locomotive Engines. The Treasurer having stated he had seen Mr. Roberts who mentioned that part of his plan for a Locomotive was to have upright cylinders, was instructed to inform Messrs. Sharp & Co. that the directors had a decided objection to upright cylinders as injurious to the road as well as causing an objectionable motion to the engine.

Subsequently on 29th August was :—

Read a letter from Sharp, Roberts & Co. stating that they should proceed with building a Locomotive Engine with vertical cylinders, but with such arrangements of the connecting parts as would obviate the objectionable motion complained of. The Treasurer to reply that if the objection that was apprehended were removed, and the engine were satisfactory in other respects, the Company would be glad to receive it.

Dixon's report on the 'Experiment,' made after the comparative trial which had been ordered, showed that 'her consumption of coke was about 40 per cent. more than some of the company's engines, and that there were besides other objections.' It was therefore resolved that 'it would not be expedient to purchase the 'Experiment '.' But the makers continued to urge acceptance, and eventually accepted an offer of £700 for the engine.

The 'Caledonian' and the 'Experiment' appear to have been the last serious attempts to reintroduce a vertical arrangement of cylinder on the Liverpool and Manchester Railway ; both engines were failures.

A ROTARY ENGINE — We have now to record, in its chronological order, an experiment of peculiar interest made at the instance of a remarkable man—Thomas Cochrane, 10th Earl of Dundonald—who, after retirement from a brilliantly adventurous, if chequered, career, 'devoted his leisure to mechanical inventions and especially to improvements of the steam engine in its adaptation to marine purposes.'[1] At the same time he appears to have applied his fertile mind to the problems of steam loco-motion, and a Liverpool and Manchester Railway directors' minute of 3rd October 1834 records :—

Lord Dundonald stated that, having observed the construction of the Company's Loco-Motive Carriages, he was of opinion that a trial of his revolving Engine might be made on the *Rocket* in a manner that would sufficiently prove the power of his Engine; and so convinced was His Lordship that the expense would not exceed £30 that he was willing himself to pay any additional cost.

After discussion the Board agreed to expend as far as £30 in making the proposed experiment; any additional cost beyond that sum to be defrayed by Lord Dundonald.

The minutes subsequently record, on 20th October 1834, that the cost of fitting up and fixing this rotary machine to the 'Rocket,' already amounted

---

[1] Thomas, Lord Cochrane, 1775 to 1860, succeeded to the Earldom 1831, Admiral in the English Navy, sometime Commander-in-Chief of the Chilian Navy. 'As early as 1843 he urged on the Admiralty the necessity of adopting steam power and screw propellers to ships of the line.' *Dictionary of National Biography.*

As Lord Cochrane he was co-patentee, with Alexander Galloway, of a boiler, and co-plaintiff in the action for infringement of patent brought against Braithwaite and Ericsson, which we have mentioned in a previous chapter. *Mechanics' Magazine*, Vol. XIII., p. 308. See p. 205, Chapter XIII. *ante.*

T

'to near £80' and that the arrangements were not sufficiently completed to allow of any satisfactory and conclusive trial. A subsequent letter from Lord Dundonald, upon his leaving Liverpool, 'thanks the directors for the facilities afforded him of making a trial of his rotary engine, and expresses his unabated confidence in the efficiency of his engine provided some unobjectionable plan were discovered of applying its powers to a locomotive carriage.' The rotary engine was eventually taken off the 'Rocket' and laid up to await its inventor's further orders, and we have no further news of it until, many years later, a reference was made by George Stephenson himself to this experiment.[1] Speaking on the 'fallacies of the rotary engine' he related that 'he was invited on one occasion to see it tried on the Liverpool and Manchester Railway, but he refused to go because he was convinced that a failure would be the result, and so it was—for the engine could not be made to draw a train of empty carriages.'

It was on engines of the 'Planet' type that De Pambour PERFORMANCES carried out the exhaustive experiments recorded in his AND book. He tells us that he owed the opportunity to make WORKING COSTS these experiments to his friendship with Hardman Earle, who as a director permitted him to use the engines and waggons of the Liverpool and Manchester Railway :—

The beauty of these engines, their number, which is not less than thirty, the care with which they are kept, and the immense trade on that line, which gives the facility, without interfering with the business of the railway, to select loads for experiments as considerable and as light as one wishes, make that place the only one, perhaps, in the world, where experiments on a great scale may be made with the same precision as in general can only be obtained by a small apparatus. It is for that reason we preferred that railway to any other at present in activity, either in France or in England.

De Pambour's experiments were directed to the investigation of engine and train resistances, to ascertaining the steaming capacity of boilers, to recording the mean effective pressures obtainable under different conditions, and to determining the most desirable proportions for steam pipes, port areas and blast pipes. These investigations led to a revision of the figures for engine and train resistances previously arrived at by Wood, and the results obtained bear witness to the great improvements which had taken place in the construction of both locomotives and carriages between 1831 and 1836.

De Pambour also records the facilities for experiments offered to him by the directors of the Darlington Railway, who 'obligingly communicated interesting documents concerning the repairs and expenses of all sorts.' His analyses of the expenses of working and maintenance on the Liverpool and Manchester, and Stockton and Darlington Railway respectively, are of interest as showing how profoundly such expenses are affected by the nature of the service required. After pointing out that 'on the Liverpool and Manchester Railway at an average velocity of 16·73 miles per hour the total expense of haulage by locomotive engines amounts to 1·75d. *per gross ton carried to a distance of one mile on a level,*' De Pambour records of the Darlington Railway :—

---

[1] Address at Birmingham, 26th July 1848, *Proc. Inst. Mechanical Engineers*, 1848. For details of Lord Dundonald's 'Revolving Steam Engine,' see *Mechanics' Magazine*, Vol. XXII., p. 194.

Their expenses amount only to two-thirds of those of the Liverpool Railway for the same object. The difference is owing to the rapid motion of the engines and carriages that pass on the latter railway. But it is chiefly in the expense for repairs of engines that this effect of velocity is felt.

It must not however be supposed that the considerable difference observed in that respect, between the engines of the two companies, is exclusively owing to the velocity of the motion. That velocity enters, indeed, for a great part in it, but the conditions attending each sort of business have a no less considerable influence on it. What we mean is, that passengers forming the chief business on the Liverpool line, their safety requires that a much greater care be taken of the engines than when the load is composed only of coals, as on the Darlington Railway. The consequence is, that the Liverpool engines are kept with a degree of care, we might even say of luxury, to which the Darlington ones can by no means be compared. In order to explain completely our idea, we shall say that the business of the Darlington Railway is a business of waggonage, and that of the Liverpool Railway a business of stage coaches.[1]

The data laid down above must therefore be taken each in their speciality, that is to say, the one as suitable to a slow motion, with engines of a certain construction and intended for the draft of goods, and the other to a rapid motion with engines of a different construction, and intended for the draft of passengers.

To these causes he says 'must also be added the considerable difference in the price of fuel ; the Darlington Company employing coals which cost only 5s. per ton, instead of 23s. 6d., the price of the coke used by the Liverpool Company.'

Comparisons which have been sometimes made between the costs of locomotive power on the two railways, to the apparent discredit of the locomotives on the Liverpool and Manchester Railway, ignore such considerations as those to which De Pambour has called attention, himself pointing out that, under conditions of working so entirely dissimilar such comparisons are of little more value than they would be between the costs of a racing stable and of a carter's establishment respectively.

from a drawing by G. H. West, printed by E. Colyer, 1834.

PARK SIDE STATION ON THE LIVERPOOL AND MANCHESTER RAILWAY

[1] The locomotives on the Liverpool and Manchester Railway were provided and maintained by the Railway Company at their own expense; while at the time of De Pambour's visit those on the Stockton and Darlington Railway were being maintained by Hackworth as a contractor.

CHAPTER XXII

HACKWORTH AND STEPHENSON LOCOMOTIVES

ON THE

STOCKTON AND DARLINGTON RAILWAY

1830—1840

We have seen how the difference in the requirements and working conditions of the two railways is reflected in the costs of operating, and repairing, the locomotives on the Liverpool and Manchester, and the Stockton and Darlington Railway respectively. A visitor to the latter railway in 1830 would have found the influence of these factors on the design of its locomotives to be no less marked. Indeed, if we wish to appreciate the remarkable advance made by Robert Stephenson & Co. in locomotive design between 1828 and 1832, we cannot do better than suppose ourselves making such a visit.

At the end of 1830 we should have found nine locomotives in service on the Stockton and Darlington Railway. Of these, the first eight comprised the following :—the four engines, railway company's Nos. 1, 2, 3 and 4, which had been supplied by Robert Stephenson & Co. in 1825 and 1826—Hackworth's 'Royal George,' No. 5—Stephenson's 'Experiment' of 1827, No. 6, now rebuilt—Stephenson's 'Rocket,' No. 7, the six-wheeled engine built in 1829, and Hackworth's 'Victory,' No. 8, a locomotive designed and built by him on lines generally following the 'Royal George,' i.e. with vertical cylinders.

Most remarkable perhaps is the fact that the first four of the above mentioned engines, of which such hard things have been said, and which were, we are told, to have been abandoned in 1827, were still at work, and hauling a fair proportion of the coals, which still constituted the principal traffic on the Stockton and Darlington Railway.

HACKWORTH'S 'GLOBE' — The ninth engine was the 'Globe,' ordered in accordance with a railway company's sub-committee minute of 12th February 1830, which records :—

It appearing to this Committee that the introduction of a locomotive engine on construction better adapted to a swift motion than those already in use, for the conveyance of passengers and merchandise at regular hours daily, would prevent many interruptions to the Coal Trade in the course of the ensuing Summer &c. Resolved that as the expense is represented to this Meeting as likely not to exceed £400, that T. Hackworth be authorised to take such steps as may enable him to start such an Engine on the first of 5 month (May) next.

The 'Globe' had been designed by Hackworth after his return from the Rainhill contest, and the order was subsequently placed with Robert Stephenson & Co. The original working drawings are no longer in existence, but a drawing dated 1831[1] sufficiently shows the general arrangement of the engine.

---

[1] In possession of a grandson of Timothy Hackworth, Mr. Robert Young, by whose permission it is now reproduced on page 296 following.

The boiler is said to have had a single straight flue, having the fire-grate at one end—'a number of small tubes were also passed transversely through the diameter of the main flue, so as to form a species of spiral, the water being allowed to circulate through them.'[1] It appears that these, like other water tubes previously tried in locomotive boilers, were found to be unsatisfactory, 'they soon choked with matter deposited from the water,' and were subsequently removed.[2]

Although this engine had been ordered in March 1830 it was not completed and tried until the following October, when Harris Dickinson, on behalf of the makers, wrote to Edward Pease, as we have seen[3], that it had been 'tried, and worked very well,' but that they considered it likely to be deficient in steaming power. We have, however, no evidence that this was found to be the case in service, and the 'Globe' appears to have performed what duties were required of it for nine years, until an explosion of its boiler put an end to its active life.

We have already alluded to the suggestion that the design of Robert Stephenson's 'Planet' was based upon that of the 'Globe,' but a comparison between the two will show that, beyond the common use of a crank axle, there was no resemblance in either general arrangement of parts, details of construction, or appearance.[4] The 'Globe' was indeed the first and last of its type. From a railway company's sub-committee minute of November 1830 it would appear that this engine cost £515.

The next locomotives bought by the Stockton and Darlington Railway Company are referred to in a sub-committee minute of 27th August 1830, which records :—

Resolved that 2 Locomotive Engines be ordered of R. Stephenson & Co. and that they be confined not to exceed 5 Tons each including water, one to be completed and delivered at Darlington on or before the end of October, and the other before the close of the year.

These engines appear to have been of the single and coupled 'Planet' types respectively, but neither drawings nor descriptive particulars now exist among the makers' records. If they were of the type stated we may assume that drawings prepared in recent years purporting to represent them, and showing the frame below the driving axle, are incorrect. These two engines were called 'Planet' and 'North Star,' names which had already become popular in railway circles.

On 26th October 1830 Robert Stephenson & Co., having offered to build two more locomotives for the Stockton and Darlington Railway Company, the sub-committee resolved that Hackworth should produce at their next meeting 'a drawing or drawings of such engines as he could recommend, with the view of making a considerable addition to the number of engines on the railway.'

Subsequently, a sub-committee minute of 4th December 1830 records that :—

[1] *A Chapter in the History of Railway Locomotion*, p. 11.

[2] Zerah Colburn, *Locomotive Engineering, etc.*, 1871, p. 31.

[3] See page 74, Chapter VI. *ante.* [4] See page 260, Chapter XX. *ante.*

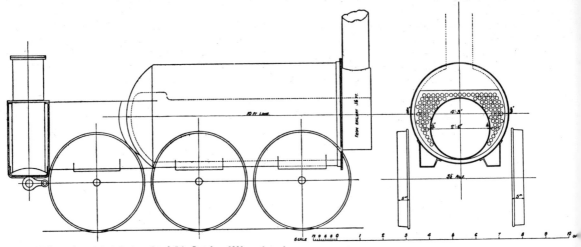

traced from the original design, dated 7th October 1831, endorsed.

'ROUGH PLAN OF ENGINE DRAWN AT SHILDON'

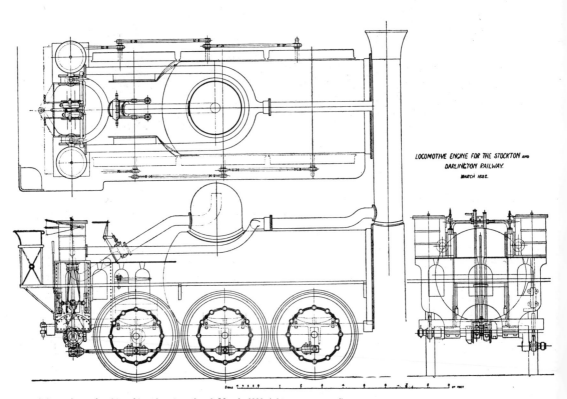

traced from the makers' working drawing, dated March 1832 (chimney assumed)

THE 'DIRECTOR'

built to Hackworth's design by Robert Stephenson & Co, 1832

Timothy Hackworth having laid before this Meeting a plan of a Locomotive Engine which in his judgment is the best suited to this Company's purpose. Resolved that Joseph Pease, Junr. and William Kitching be appointed to take the same into their best consideration and receive from different Engine Manufacturers proposals for making this Company a given number of Engines according to such plan and specification as they may agree upon.

NAPIER'S BOILER Of the engines subsequently ordered, three, called 'Director' 'Adelaide,' and 'Lord Durham,' were supplied by Robert Stephenson & Co., among whose records is an original drawing endorsed 'Rough Plan of Engine drawn at Shildon, Oct. 7th 1831,' this being evidently Hackworth's own design for the new engines. The first notable feature is the boiler, having a single straight fire tube containing the grate at one end and opening at the further end into a chamber, from which small tubes return in two groups, one on either side of the flue, to a smokebox in the form of a saddle over the fire-place. **On 8th November**

(part) from an original in possession of Messrs. Harrison & Sons, Darlington.

STOCKTON AND DARLINGTON RAILWAY TIME TABLE, SUMMER OF 1837

1831 Robert Stephenson & Co. advised Hackworth that his new locomotive boiler which they were making was 'a patent of Napier's of Glasgow'[1], and that they could not proceed with the tubes until they should hear further on the subject; meanwhile they had communicated with Mr. J. Pease, Junr. It appears that a satisfactory arrangement of matters between Hackworth and the patentee subsequently made it possible to proceed with the construction.[2]

The makers' finished drawing, still in the possession of Robert Stephenson & Co., shows the details of the engine, of which the most remarkable feature is the vertical cylinder driving on to a dummy crank shaft. The introduction of this intermediate shaft made it possible to use springs for the driving axle, and so to avoid the disadvantage of the 'Royal George' in this respect.

These peculiar engines, and others of similar type built by Hawthorns' of Newcastle, worked the traffic successfully for some years. By the use

---

[1] Letter from Robert Stephenson & Co. to Timothy Hackworth, in possession of Mr. Robert Young. Napier's Patent (No. 6,090) is dated 4th March 1831.

[2] *A Chapter in the History of Railway Locomotion*, p. 33. *Appendix* by J. W. Hackworth.

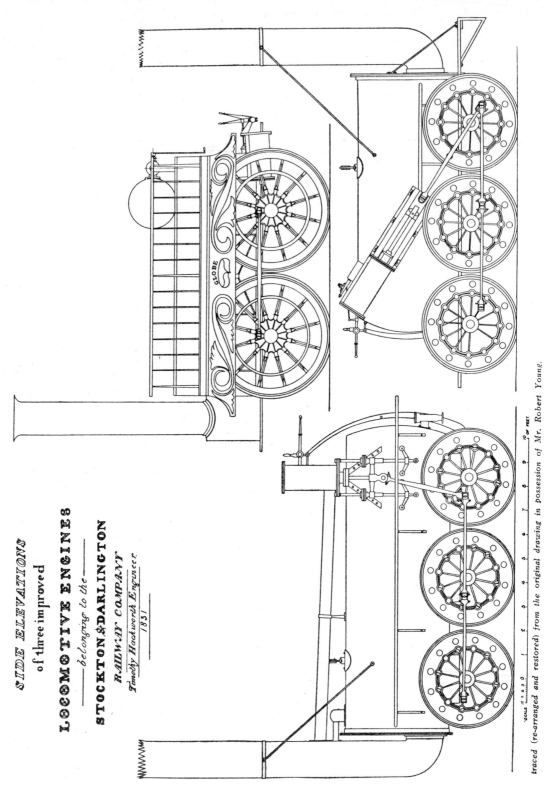

SIDE ELEVATIONS
of three improved
LOCOMOTIVE ENGINES
belonging to the
STOCKTON&DARLINGTON
RAILWAY COMPANY
Timothy Hackworth Engineer.
1831

THE 'VICTORY'
designed and built by
Hackworth, 1829

THE 'GLOBE'
designed by Hackworth
built by Robert Stephenson & Co., 1830

THE 'ROCKET'
designed and built by
Robert Stephenson & Co., 1829

traced (re-arranged and restored) from the original drawing in possession of Mr. Robert Young.

of the Napier boiler their steaming capacity was very much greater than that of the older engines, of which the first four, by Robert Stephenson & Co., with a single flue, 'had about 63 superficial feet of heating surface, evaporating about 100 gallons of water per hour and took a load of 30 or 40 tons at 8 miles per hour. Next the return or double flue was adopted, which about doubled the evaporating power and consequently also the work done, the heating surface being about 125 square feet. In the 'Adelaide' by Stephenson, and the 'Wilberforce' by Hawthorn, the Napier boiler was fitted, with one flue through it 2 feet 2 inches diameter, and about 100 return tubes $1\frac{3}{4}$ inch diameter, the heating surface was increased to nearly 500 superficial feet and the evaporative power to 500 gallons per hour, being five times as much as the 'Locomotion.' These engines could haul five times the load at 10 miles an hour.'[2]

But the official records of their performance show that, in comparison with the older and simpler engines they did not perform in practice a duty proportionate to their much greater capacity, size and cost. We find for instance from a '*Statement of the work done by the locomotive engines from 1st July to 1st December 1833*[3],' that No. 1 engine, 'Locomotion,' built in 1825, had been in activity 80 days during which it had travelled 5,300 miles, performing a duty equal to 146,011 tons of coals carried to one mile going down by the engine, while the 'Director' which had been in service for 91 days and travelled 5,860 miles, had hauled the equivalent of 202,492 tons, and most of the other engines of the same type considerably less.

Number of the engine.	Date.	Name of the engine.	Total number of miles travelled by the engine.	Tons of coals carried to one mile going down by the engine.	Gross tons carried to one mile on a level including the waggons and return.	Number of days that the engine was		Amount of the repairs made to the engine during that time.	Amount of the repairs per gross ton carried to 1 mile on a level.	Observations
						Inactivity.	In repair.			
			miles.	tons.	tons	days.	days.	£ s. d.	d.	
1	1825	LOCOMOTION	5,300	146,011	287,896	80	52	41 19 7	0.035	Boiler with a flue and two returning tubes.
2	1825	HOPE	3,100	82,305	162,281	63	69	57 5 5	0.085	——with a single flue.
3	1826	BLACK DIAMOND	1,000	26,920	53,078	27	105	14 0 5	0.063	——with a single flue.
4	1826	DILIGENCE	80	1,906	3,758	2	130	13 18 3	0.889	Engine taken to pieces.
5	1827	ROYAL GEORGE	700	23,733	46,794	11	121	161 7 8	0.828	Boiler with a flue and one returning tube.
6	1828	EXPERIMENT	4,400	122,442	241,420	70	62	53 1 2	0.053	ditto.
7	1829	ROCKET	3,940	109,512	215,925	64	68	57 0 9	0.063	ditto.
8	1829	VICTORY	10,600	349,150	688,418	107	25	58 3 10	0.020	ditto.
9	1830	GLOBE	3,120	70,683	139,365	60	72	36 4 6	0.062	Boiler with 120 returning tubes.
16	1832	DIRECTOR	5,860	202,492	399,253	91	41	107 19 11	0.065	Boiler with tubes on the model of Napier's patent.

[1] Zerah Colburn, *Locomotive Engineering, etc.*, 1871, p. 31.

[2] John Dixon, *Traction on Railways and the Alleged Loss of Power at High Speeds practically considered*, (printed for private circulation) 1864

[3] De Pambour, *Treatise on Locomotive Engines*, 1836 (Appendix), p. 343.

De Pambour calls attention to the sufficiency of the old engines for coal traffic—'when a speed of 8 miles per hour only is required and for an average train of 24 waggons the most convenient boilers have been found to be those with one return tube. They generate a sufficient quantity of steam for the work required of them and have the advantage of being cheap in regard to prime cost and repairs, as their form is simple and they are entirely made of iron, whilst the tube boilers require the use of copper.'

It is recorded that in 1837 the railway company decided to dispose of some of their heavy engines of the 'Director' class and replace them by others of an earlier type. One of the most successful and useful of the earlier engines was Hackworth's 'Victory,' generally resembling the 'Royal George,' and to this design he now returned. But it appears that the later engines of this type supplied to the Stockton and Darlington Railway had no springs, and it was pointed out to the directors by their engineer that 'in adopting this springless type of engine they had omitted to take into account the greater wear and tear of the rails which it caused, and that the resultant expense would more than counterbalance the saving in prime cost. Timothy Hackworth then introduced another type of engine with cylinders placed obliquely, that position enabling springs to be used with advantage.' [1]

It appears that Hackworth in fact now adopted the cylinder arrangement which had been first applied by Robert Stephenson to his 'Lancashire Witch' in 1828.[2] We therefore find on the Stockton and Darlington Railway in 1838 a return to a design which had elsewhere become obsolete; such a return was possible only because working conditions had remained much as they had been when the line was first opened. So late as 1840 it is recorded that 'the coal-engines are limited in speed to six miles an hour, and if the engine-men are found driving at a velocity exceeding eight miles, they are invariably fined. At night a fire-lamp is suspended both in front and in the rear of each coal train, and the approach of a train of coal waggons is distinguished from that of a passenger train by a bell . . . . the passenger engines being furnished with a steam whistle according to the modern system.[3]

The requirements of the Stockton and Darlington Railway had no such permanent influence on the design of the locomotive as had those of the Liverpool and Manchester Railway, where the stimulating influence of a large passenger traffic, and rapidly increasing demands for speed, had made impossible the survival of such primitive types as could be seen still at work at Darlington for some years after 1840.

---

[1] Tomlinson, *The North Eastern Railway*, 1914, p. 389.

[2] Some of the engines built to Hackworth's design of 1838 resembled generally Stephenson's 'Darlington Engine A' built for the Stockton and Darlington Railway in 1829 and called 'Rocket.' See page 153 Chapter X. *ante*, and page 296 *ante*.

[3] Whishaw, *Railways of Great Britain and Ireland*, 1840, p. 422.

CHAPTER XXIII

THE STEPHENSON LOCOMOTIVE IN AMERICA
1831—1836

It was observed by an English writer [1] in 1833, that the railway system in the United States of America appeared, at that time, to be making much greater progress than in Great Britain :—

In almost every state there are railways either commenced or about to be commenced; and nothing less is anticipated than that in a few years the whole of the vast territory of the American Republic will be in possession of the benefits of this superior mode of communication. With us, on the contrary, the Liverpool and Manchester Railway is still the only considerable line for general traffic; for, thanks to the interdicting and discouraging influence of our House of Lords, not only has the execution of the projected line between Birmingham and the metropolis been postponed for the present, but the public taste for speculations of this kind has so much abated, that though there are many other promising railway schemes on foot—such as the Brighton, the Greenwich, and the Southampton (perhaps the best of all)—none of them seem to be taken up with the adequate degree of spirit.

An American writer [2] has said that 'while Stephenson was fighting the battle of the locomotive, America, as if in anticipation of his victory, was building railroads'; with the consequence 'that the country was not only ripe to accept the results of the Rainhill contest, but was anticipating them with eager hope. Had George Stephenson known what was going on in America he would not, when writing to his son in 1829 have limited his anticipation of orders for locomotives to at least thirty.' [3]

We have seen that in 1828 two locomotives had been sent by Robert Stephenson & Co. to America, one on four wheels, the other on six, but both following generally the design of the 'Lancashire Witch.' No more engines of this type followed, the Rainhill trials had rendered them obsolete, and the next locomotive sent by Robert Stephenson & Co. to America was of the 'Planet' type, to the order of the Mohawk and Hudson Railroad. Original drawings of the engine, and of the frame, dated April, and May, 1831, show that it was a small edition of the four-wheeled 'Planet,' having cylinders 10 inches diameter by 14 inches stroke, and coupled wheels of 4 feet diameter. There do not appear to have been any new features in construction, and the engine probably closely resembled the 'George Stephenson,' built for the Glasgow and Garnkirk Railway.

Other engines of this type, or with single driving wheels as in the 'Planet' itself, were supplied later by Robert Stephenson & Co. to other American railroads; they embodied the modifications introduced by the makers from time to time, and were in fact generally the same as the engines supplied to the Liverpool and Manchester Railway, for which some of them appear to have

[1] *Mechanics' Magazine*, Vol. XVIII., p. 9.

[2] Adams, *Railroads : Their Origin and Problems*, 1888 (Revised edition), p. 9.

[3] Jeaffreson, *Life of Robert Stephenson*, Vol. I., p. 120.

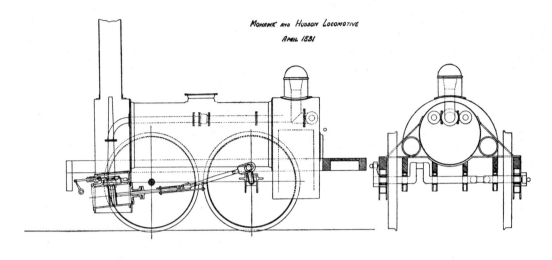

traced from the original drawing dated April 1831.

MOHAWK AND HUDSON LOCOMOTIVE 'JOHN BULL'

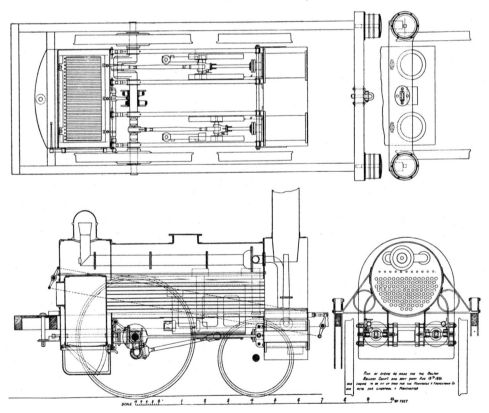

traced from the original drawing dated August 15th 1831.

NEWCASTLE AND FRENCHTOWN LOCOMOTIVE
'one engine to be set up thus for the Newcastle and Frenchtown Co.; one thus for Liverpool & Manchester'

been originally intended, and on which some were apparently tried before being sent to America. The makers' records show that such engines were supplied to the Newcastle and Frenchtown, Baltimore and Susquehanna, Saratoga and Schenectady, Charlestown and Columbia, Philadelphia Germantown and Norristown, and other railroads. Some were sent to agents ; it is difficult to trace the ultimate destination of these latter engines. It appears [1] that one of the first engines of the 'Planet' type sent to America was carefully examined by Matthias W. Baldwin, who had himself previously built, in 1831, a miniature locomotive, based on 'the imperfect published descriptions and sketches of the locomotives which had taken part in the Rainhill competition in England.'

As a result of his success with this model Baldwin received an order from the Philadelphia, Germantown and Norristown Railroad Company for whom he built an engine, known afterwards as 'Old Ironsides,' which was tried successfully on 23rd November 1832. A contemporary American account remarks that :—

The principal superiority of the engine over any of the English ones known consists in the light weight—which is but between four and five tons—her small bulk, and the simplicity of her working machinery. We rejoice at the result of this experiment, as it conclusively shows that Philadelphia, always famous for the skill of her mechanics, is enabled to produce steam engines for railroads combining so many superior qualities as to warrant the belief that her mechanics will hereafter supply nearly all the public works of this description in the country.

We may perhaps assume that some of the success of this engine was due to its close imitation of Stephenson's 'Planet' type. But there were differences ; the 'Old Ironsides' had cylinders $9\frac{1}{2}$ inches diameter by 18 inches stroke, with driving wheels 4 feet 6 inches diameter, and it differed in other respects. Its total weight is recorded as 'something over 5 tons,' *i.e.*, about the weight on the driving wheels of the 'Planet.'

Contemporary with the engine built by Robert Stephenson & Co. for the Mohawk and Hudson Railroad was another, described in the makers' books as 'Mr. Stevens' Locomotive, New York, America.' This engine was for the Camden and Amboy Railroad and Transportation Company. An original drawing of the boiler, dated 18th May 1831, shows that it had a circular firebox, with domed top. In view of George Stephenson's objection to Bury's similar, though not identical, design, it seems probable that this particular construction was specified by the purchaser. In the engine built for Stevens there were other departures from the makers' standard 'Planet' design, notably in the cylinders, which had a diameter of 9 inches with a stroke of 20 inches.[2]

This engine, which is now preserved in the Smithsonian Institution at Washington, the National Museum, is the oldest complete locomotive in America, having been put into service on 12th November 1831 at Bordentown, New Jersey. After being for many years out of service it emerged from retirement on 17th April 1893, leaving New York City under steam to haul the 'John

---

[1] *History of the Baldwin Locomotive Works*, 1920, p. 9, communicated by the Baldwin Locomotive Co., 1923.
[2] See working drawing of 'Steam Cylinder and Valves for Mr. Stevens'; p. 285, Chapter XXI. *ante.*

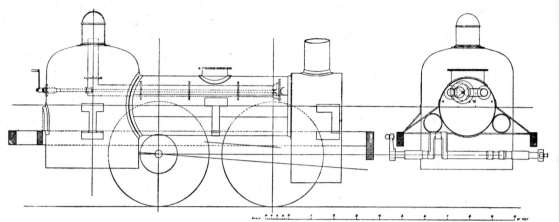

traced from an original (undated) drawing, without description.

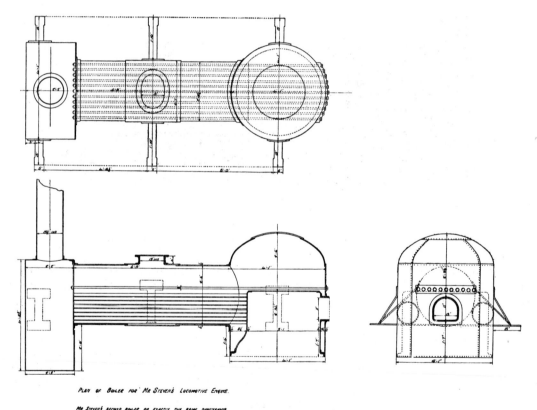

Plan of Boiler for Mr Stevens' Locomotive Engine.

Mr Stevens' second boiler of exactly the same dimensions.
as the above ordered at Bedlington May 18th 1831.

traced from the original drawing dated 18th May 1831.

BOILER FOR MR. STEVENS' LOCOMOTIVE

Bull' train to Chicago. The train consisted of two Camden and Amboy passenger coaches of the type used in 1836, one of these being an original car which had in the meanwhile filled the humble but useful rôle of a chicken coop. The 'John Bull' completed the journey of 920 miles without assistance, arriving at Chicago on 22nd April 1893, having met with a continuous ovation throughout her journey.[1]

A noticeable feature of the engine as now to be seen is the leading truck and cow catcher, which was fitted after its arrival in America to make it suitable for the road on which it had to run. Other differences from the original engine are to be seen in the removal of the coupling rods, to allow the fitting of the truck, the substitution of cast iron, for the original wooden, wheels, the fitting of a regulator and steam pipes outside the boiler, and the addition of a bell, and other fittings which are obviously not contemporary with the original engine.

from a photo by the Pennsylvania Railroad Company.

THE 'JOHN BULL'

built for Mr. Stevens in 1831, now in the Smithsonian Institution, Washington, U.S.A.

From Robert Stephenson & Co.'s order books it appears that many single, and four-coupled, locomotives of the 'Planet' type were supplied by them to America between 1831 and 1836. In 1832 it is recorded of the Newcastle and Frenchtown Railroad that [2] :—

A locomotive engine of the latest pattern (made by Robert Stephenson, of Newcastle-upon-Tyne, England), has been imported by the Company. The spokes of the wheels are wrought iron *tubes*, bell shaped at their extremities; the rim and hub cast on them—the union being effected by means of borax. The wheels are encircled by a wrought iron tire and flange—the latter is very diminutive, and will require enlargement. The weight of the engine is not adapted to a railway of slender proportions, composed of timber and light rails.

[1] Letter to Robert Stephenson & Co., 17th February 1921, from Mr J. T. Wallis, Chief Superintendent of Motive Power, Pennsylvania System.

[2] Wood, *Treatise on Rail Roads* (American Edition), 1832 (communicated by Mr. J. Snowden Bell, 26th Nov. 1920).

A contemporaneous account of the Baltimore and Susquehanna Railroad records that [1] :—

The cars on this road are drawn by a beautiful and very efficient imported locomotive steam engine, which affords a very pleasant and delightful mode of travelling.

But it is added that :—

The locomotive engine called the 'Herald,' received last summer from Liverpool, which is a beautiful piece of mechanism, costing the company $4,000, being calculated to run on a straight track, would not suit this meandering road.

from a photo in the collection of Mr. B. Thomas, Boston & Maine Railroad.

STEPHENSON LOCOMOTIVE ON THE BANGOR, OLD TOWN AND MILFORD RAILROAD
formerly the Bangor and Piscataquis Canal and Railroad

About the same time an English traveller wrote from America [2] :—

The immediate obstacle to the use of the locomotives in this country arises from their great weight, which crushes the iron rails into the wooden runner which supports it. These wooden runners will all be gradually exchanged for stone as they decay, which material can now be bought at a moderate rate, when they do not anticipate any difficulty in making locomotives equal to the English. Other railroads are forming in all directions; and both in these as well as canals, this infant country already far surpasses us in the extent of their application. There is no want of capital for any undertaking.

A report by an American engineer in 1835 referring to engines manufactured by Robert Stephenson & Co. remarks [3] :—

They are not as efficient as those manufactured in this country; the workmanship is good, but the most important parts of the machinery too light to enable them to encounter (with a heavy load) the high grades and severe curves, in consequence of which frequent repairs are required upon them.

[1] Charles Varle, *A Complete View of Baltimore, and Statistical Sketch,* 1833. (Communicated by Mr. J. Snowden Bell, 22nd Aug. 1921).

[2] *Mechanics' Magazine,* Vol. XVIII., p. 208.

[3] Quoted in *The Portable Boats of Early Railroad Practice,* Snowden Bell. Baldwin Locomotive Works Record, 1920, No. 97, p. 19.

From such reports it would seem that the American railroads must have been inferior in both lay-out and construction to those in England, and the need for some modification in the wheel arrangement of the engine to meet local conditions had become apparent to American engineers.

THE
BOGIE

The principle of the swivelling carriage, truck, or bogie, as it came to be called[1], had been known in the north of England since 1812, when it had been proposed and described by William Chapman.[2]

It has been stated[3] that Robert Stephenson himself recommended to a deputation of American engineers visiting Newcastle in 1828, that they should adopt such a truck for working the curves of 400 feet radius which they

from an undated drawing, formerly in possession of the makers; but differing from their design and working drawings.

FIRST STEPHENSON BOGIE LOCOMOTIVE

had in mind for the Baltimore and Ohio and other lines projected in the States, but we have no contemporary evidence in confirmation of this statement, and Robert Stephenson & Co.'s records show that they did not build an engine with a bogie until 1833.

This engine was to the order of the Saratoga and Schenectady Railroad Company for 'a locomotive to go upon six wheels, the greatest weight upon

[1] The derivation of the word 'bogie' is obscure.
[2] W. & E. W. Chapman's Patent Specification, 21st April 1812 (No. 3,632).
[3] Zerah Colburn, *Locomotive Engineering, etc.*, 1871, p. 96.

U

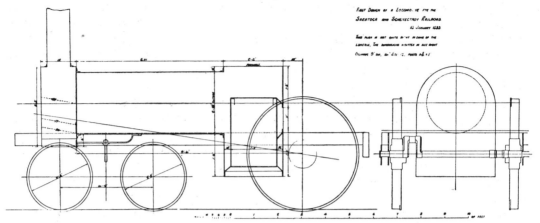

traced from the original drawing dated 16th January 1833.

FIRST DESIGN OF A LOCOMOTIVE FOR THE SARATOGA AND SCHENECTADY RAILROAD

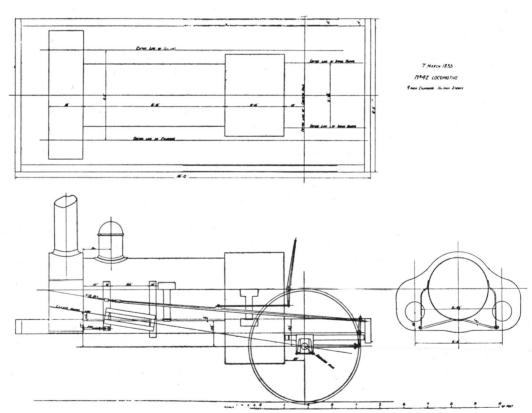

traced from the original drawing dated 7th March 1833.

a pair being 2½ tons.'   A 'first design' dated 16th January 1833, and a working drawing of this engine, have been preserved; they show that it had a pair of driving wheels 4 feet 6 inches diameter, placed behind the firebox, and a leading bogie with four wheels 2 feet 8 inches diameter.   The arrangement of the driving crank is notable, being identical with that previously adopted by Robert Stephenson & Co. in 1832 when rebuilding the engine for Forman which we have illustrated in a previous chapter.   It appears that Baldwin subsequently modified this arrangement, in the locomotives which he built, by removing the outer arm of the crank and fixing the crank pin directly into the wheel, so forming the well-known 'Baldwin half-crank.'   Another American maker, Dunham, returned to the complete crank in 1842, and this design, though it had been applied by Stephenson ten years previously, was afterwards patented in England with but slight modification. [1]

Another interesting feature of these early English and American bogie engines is the anticipation of the driving wheel arrangement afterwards adopted and patented by Thomas Crampton.

The valve gear of the first Stephenson bogie engine for America is also worthy of notice, since the excentric rod drives in a backward direction on to a rocking lever placed below the footplate, and therefore easy of access to the engineman.   This arrangement is however mentioned by an American account in 1835 [2] as one of the improvements on the English engines which had been introduced by Baldwin.   In his adoption of the single fixed excentric, with double gabs on the rod, Baldwin appears to have anticipated Stephensons' use of this arrangement.

In 1834 Robert Stephenson & Co. built another remarkable bogie loco-motive, for the Mohawk and Hudson Railroad; the maker's original drawing, dated January 1834, shows horizontal cylinders placed below the smokebox. The drive is transmitted to the outside crank pins through a rocking shaft, so avoiding the use of a crank-shaft, which had been found by this time to be 'by far the most troublesome and expensive part of the machine to be kept in repair.'

The writer of another account [3] refers in 1835 to 'two English engines from the workshop of their most celebrated maker, R. Stephenson,' as being at work on the Pennsylvania State Road, and claims that 'the power of the American engines is about 35 per cent. greater than that of the English,' and 'the cost of repairs is altogether in favour of the American engines.'   He adds however :—

It is here proper to observe, that the Pennsylvania road is almost a continued series of curves, ranging from 500 to 700 feet radius, and so severe is it upon the wheels of an engine, that one of the English engines (the other having been out of repair most of the time) has within two months used up or destroyed a part of the wheels of both engines, and is now using a set of Mr. Baldwin's wheels.

[1] Zerah Colburn, *Locomotive Engineering, etc.*, 1871, p. 46.
[2] *Mechanics' Magazine*, 27th June 1835, Vol. XXIII., p. 240, quoted from *Journal of the Franklin Institute.*
[3] *Mechanics' Magazine*, Vol. XXIII., p. 319.

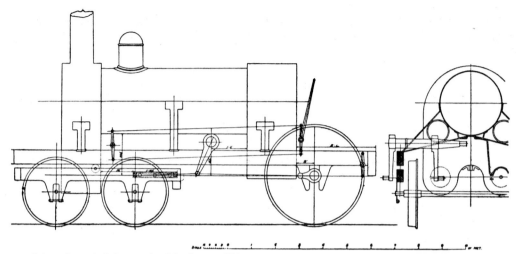

traced from the original drawing dated 1st January 1834.

LOCOMOTIVE FOR THE MOHAWK AND HUDSON RAILROAD

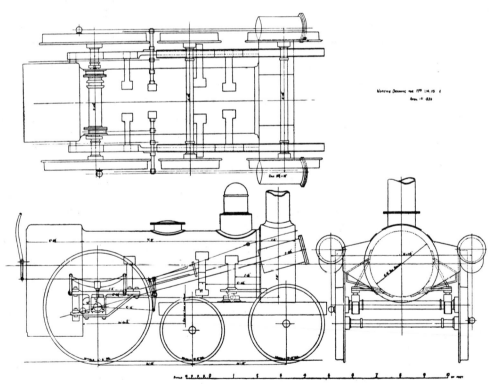

traced from the original drawing dated 1st April 1835.

LOCOMOTIVE FOR THE SOUTH CAROLINA RAILROAD

We nevertheless find the Baltimore and Susquehanna Railroad Company writing to Robert Stephenson & Co. in 1850, of certain engines built by the firm in 1831 and 1836 :—

These five locomotives are still running on our road, but have all been rebuilt. Our Driving wheels from 4 to 5 feet diameter are entirely of *Cast* iron, with chilled treads, as our Passenger & Burden Car wheels 33 in. in diameter are cast. Our preference is the *Cranked* axle Locomotive, but [from] the repeated breaking of the axle, every locomotive having broken one or more, we were induced to try *Cast Iron,* and after an experience of five years, we have adopted them entirely, never yet having broken a *Cast Iron Crank Axle.*

In spite of this astonishing and apparently successful use of cast iron, crank axles of any kind were eventually abandoned by American builders, and although the Locks and Canals Company, of Lowell, began in 1834 to build locomotives after the model of the 'Planet' [1], it is evident that by this time American designs had assumed a character of their own, and begun to show increasing divergence from those of Robert Stephenson & Co. But the Stephenson wooden frame with outside bearings was used by both Baldwin and Rogers for some years. An American periodical [2] referring in 1839 to locomotives seen under construction at the Rogers' works states that :—

The truck frames, whether of wood or iron, were admirably stiffened by diagonal braces, and where the crank axle is used, the large frame is very strongly plated in the manner of Stephenson's engines, the neglect of which till very lately has been, we are informed, a constant objection to the Philadelphia engines on the Long Island and Troy railroads.

American locomotive builders eventually adopted the bar frame, which had been introduced by Stephenson in 1828 and subsequently developed by Bury, who sent engines of his standard construction to America. In 1835 Robert Stephenson & Co. built for the South Carolina Railroad Company three six-wheeled locomotives with four-wheeled bogies ; the makers' drawing, dated 1st April 1835, shows obviously the influence of American requirements.

For their boilers both Baldwin and Rogers adopted the circular, or D shaped firebox, which continued in use by Rogers until 1857 and we find that many of the features which up to this time, and until to-day, have differentiated American from British locomotive design, are survivals of the early practice of the two English builders, Stephenson and Bury.

After 1836 Robert Stephenson & Co. built few locomotives for the United States, but this perhaps is to be attributed rather to the increasing capacity of the American builders than to the superiority in workmanship claimed at the time for their work.[3]

---

[1] Zerah Colburn, *Locomotive Engineering, etc.,* 1871, pp. 31, 34.

[2] *American Railroad Journal,* 15th Dec. 1839, quoted in *Locomotives and Locomotive Building of the Rogers Locomotive and Machine Works,* 1886, p. 14.

[3] A publication by the U.S. Congress, *Document No. 51,* 1839, contains a list of locomotives then in the United States, recording thirty-five as made by Robert Stephenson & Co. ; twenty-one by Bury ; four by Braithwaite ; seven by Tayleur & Co., and a few by other makers. (Communicated to Robert Stephenson & Co., 6th June 1923, by Mr. C. B. Chaney).

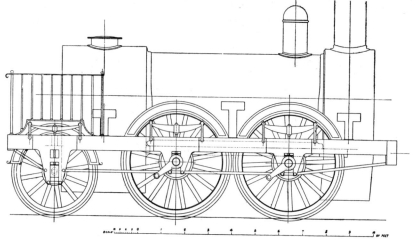

traced from the original drawing dated October 1832.

PROPOSED LOCOMOTIVE ENGINE FOR THE STANHOPE RAILWAY

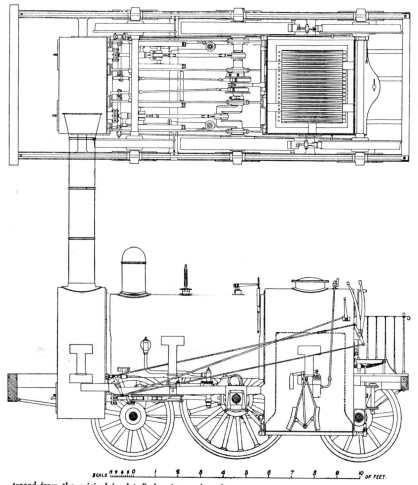

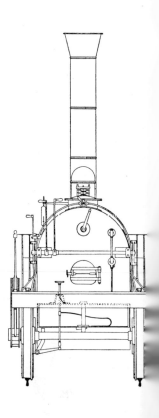

traced from the original (undated) drawing, endorsed

'PATENTEE' LOCOMOTIVE ENGINE

CHAPTER XXIV

THE SIX-WHEELED LOCOMOTIVE
ROBERT STEPHENSON'S PATENT
1833-1841

We have seen that the weight of the four-wheeled engines on the Liverpool and Manchester Railway had increased, between 1829 and 1831, from the $4\frac{1}{4}$ tons of the 'Rocket' to the 10 tons of the 'Samson,' which had more than $5\frac{1}{2}$ tons on the driving wheels alone. These astonishing and, as they must have seemed, alarming increases no doubt gave serious cause for reflection to both the railway company and their engineer. On 5th November 1832 a discussion took place 'as to the weight of the locomotive engines,' and George Stephenson, who was in attendance, was requested to report to the board 'upon the most desirable size and weight of locomotive engines for the business of the Company, and the loads it would be expedient they should draw.'

Stephenson's report recommended the adoption of six wheels, an arrangement which had indeed become inevitable, and had moreover been foreseen in the report which he had made to the directors four years previously. It is worth noting too that so early as 1825 he had recommended to Strickland the use of six wheels, and had himself built a six-wheeled engine before 1815. Moreover, the first engine supplied by Robert Stephenson & Co. to work on the construction of Liverpool and Manchester Railway, the 'Twin Sisters,' had been carried on six wheels.[1]

A working drawing dated October 1832 shows that the addition of a third axle to an engine of the four-coupled 'Planet' type had been considered by Robert Stephenson & Co. before the discussion at Liverpool mentioned above.

The derivation from the proto-type is obvious, and the advantage of the additional wheels is apparent in the increased length of firebox. This drawing is described as a design for the Stanhope and Tyne Railway, but it appears from the makers' records that the first engine built with the wheel arrangement shown was transferred to the Leicester and Swannington Railway, a line in which George Stephenson was at the time peculiarly interested, and which is interesting to historians to-day as the oldest portion of the Midland Railway.

A later drawing, dated 3rd January 1833, shows a development of the 'Planet' type with single driving wheels, and further advantage taken of the additional trailing wheels by another increase to the length of the firebox. This type of locomotive was patented by Robert Stephenson on 7th October 1833.[2] The special features of the patent design, which include the fitting of a steam brake, are recorded by an original, but undated, drawing still

---

[1] See p. 169, Chapter XI. *ante.* p. 32, Chapter III. *ante.* p. 155, Chapter X. *ante.*

[2] Robert Stephenson's Specification 7th October 1833 (No. 6,484). *Repertory of Patent Inventions,* 1834, new series, Vol. II., p. 261.

preserved among the makers' records. In the design of its details the engine follows generally the 'Planet' type.

The principal modifications and improvements, and the reasons for their introduction, are described by Robert Stephenson's specification :—

My said improvement consists in making the main-wheels of the locomotive-engine on the ends of the cranked-axis, with plain tires to run upon edge-rails without any projecting flanges on their tires, and applying two additional small wheels, with flanges on their tires, beneath the hinder end of the engine, to cause that end of the engine by means of those flanges to keep straight upon the rails, and also to bear up part of the weight of the furnace-end of the boiler.

It is claimed that by the removal of the flanges from the driving wheels the most severe 'strain' to which the cranked axles had hitherto been subjected would be avoided, and the tendency to bend or break greatly diminished. The object of this improvement was to 'obviate or diminish some inconveniences which had been experienced in the use of engines for the quick conveyance of passengers and goods on the Liverpool and Manchester Railway ' :—

The cranked axles of the great wheels have been found liable to break, and then the engines run off the rails, and sometimes overturn, or are otherwise injured. They have also in some cases run off the rails when the cranked-axle has been only strained, without being actually broken.

Referring to the wheel arrangement Robert Stephenson remarks :—

The additional small wheels which I apply beneath the hinder end of the boiler, will sustain the extra weight of a larger boiler than heretofore used, without distressing the rails; and bearing-springs are to be used for the extra small wheels, the same as is now done for other wheels in the ordinary engines, and the said springs will cause all the six wheels to apply and bear fairly on the rails, and ease all jolts and concussions; the relative weights or portions of the whole weight of the engine, which shall be borne by each of the six wheels being regulated by the strength and setting of their respective bearing-springs. The main-wheels which are to be impelled by the power of the engine being in all cases left loaded with as much of the weight of the engine as will cause a sufficient adhesion of those wheels to the rails to avoid slipping thereon.

Attention is then called to the important advantages offered by the larger boiler which can be used with the new wheel arrangement :—

When by virtue of my improvement, a larger boiler is used, containing more heating-surface than heretofore, a less intense excitement of the combustion will be required in order to produce the necessary quantity of steam for the supply of the engine, and that diminution of the intensity of the combustion will be advantageous to the performance of the engine for another reason, as well as by avoiding the heretofore rapid burning out of the metal of the boiler, because the jet of waste steam (which is thrown into the chimney to produce a rapid draught therein, and a consequently intense combustion of the fuel), may be greatly diminished in its velocity, and thereby the waste steam will be allowed to escape more freely from the cylinders than heretofore, when a very sharp and sudden jet of the waste steam up the chimney is found absolutely necessary to excite that intense violence of combustion which can alone enable the present boilers to yield the requisite supply of steam, but that very sudden jet can only be obtained by throttling the eduction-passage, and thereby impeding the free discharge of the steam from the working-cylinders, so as to impair the force of the pistons; and at the same time the excessive combustion which is excited (by so impairing the force of the pistons), also destroys the metal of the boiler in a short time. Increasing the magnitude of the boiler, giving a larger extent of heating surface thereto, and working the enlarged boiler with a more moderate intensity of fire, is the true remedy, and will save fuel as well as avoid the rapid destruction of the boiler, because the steam will be allowed to escape more freely from the cylinders The adoption of larger boilers in the said locomotive-engines, with all the advantages to be derived therefrom as aforesaid, depends upon the application of the two additional small wheels beneath the furnace end of the boiler, because the present engines are already too heavy on the rails, and require a diminution of weight, instead of an augmentation.

STEAM BRAKE   The specification also describes a steam brake:—

. . . . . which consists in applying the force of small extra steam-pistons fitted into suitable cylinders, which by turning a cock can be supplied when required with steam from the boiler, in order to act upon a double brake, or pair of clogs, which are applied to the circumferences of the tires of the said main-wheels without flanges and of the two additional small wheels.

On 28th April 1834 Robert Stephenson & Co. offered to the Liverpool and Manchester Railway Company their six-wheeled engine embodying the specified improvements, and after a trial on the railway, and a discussion by the board on its merits, the treasurer was authorised to offer £1,000 for the engine. This offer was accepted, and it was decided later that the engine should be called the 'Patentee.' This was the first locomotive built under Robert Stephenson's patent but the last supplied by his firm to the Liverpool and Manchester Railway Company. The type was however adopted elsewhere as a standard, both at home and abroad, and in fact determined eventually the general design of the British passenger locomotive for about fifty years.

The 'Patentee' had cylinders 11 inches diameter by 18 inches stroke; the boiler 3 feet 6 inches diameter by 7 feet long, contained 106 tubes, $1\frac{5}{8}$ inch diameter. The total heating surface was about 364 square feet, and the grate area nearly 10 square feet. The heating surface was actually rather less than in some of the earlier engines of the 'Planet' type, and the advantage of the new wheel arrangement is shown rather in the larger grate area now obtainable. The reduction in nominal heating surface was in accordance with the increasing tendency to adopt the larger water spaces between the tubes which had already been found to be desirable.

The weight of the 'Patentee' is recorded in the makers' books as 11 tons 9 cwt., distributed as below :—

Leading.		Driving.		Trailing.	
Tons.	Cwt.	Tons	Cwt.	Tons	Cwt.
4	10	4	6	2	13

These six-wheeled patent engines, which had developed naturally from the Planet' type by the addition of a carrying wheel behind the firebox, were subsequently built in four types :—(1) with single driving wheels, like the 'Patentee'—(2) with the leading wheels coupled to the centre pair—(3) with the small wheels leading and the coupled wheels behind the firebox—(4) with all six wheels of the same diameter, and coupled.

A drawing dated September 1833 shows a six-coupled locomotive for the Leicester and Swannington Railway, the fourth to be built under the new patent. Its dimensions, as given by the makers' records, mark an extra-

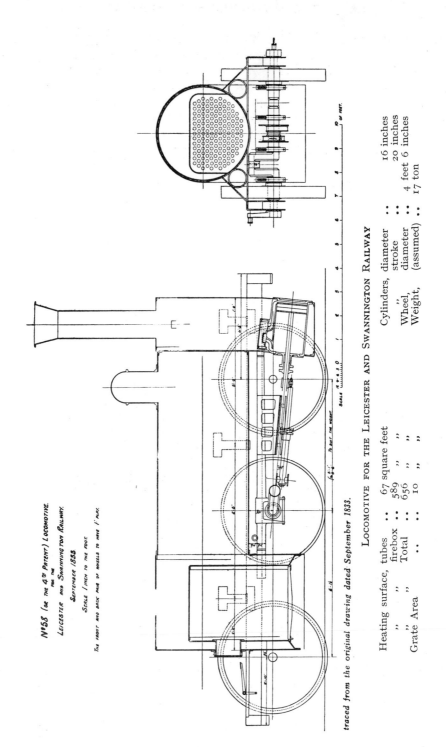

No. 58 (or the 4th Patent) Locomotive.
for the
Leicester and Swannington Railway.

September 1833.

Scale 1 inch to the foot.

This front and back pair of wheels to have 1" play.

traced from the original drawing dated September 1833.

Locomotive for the Leicester and Swannington Railway

Cylinders, diameter	::		16 inches
" stroke	::		20 inches
Wheel, diameter	::		4 feet 6 inches
Weight, (assumed)	::		17 ton

Heating surface, tubes	::	67 square feet
" " firebox	::	589 " "
" " Total	::	656 " "
Grate Area	::	10 " "

ordinary advance in size. The boiler has a diameter of 3 feet $11\frac{1}{2}$ inches, with a length of 8 feet 6 inches ; the firebox shell is made flush at the top with the barrel and brought straight down the sides at the maximum width permitted by the wheels. There are 154 iron tubes, $1\frac{5}{8}$ inch diameter, at $2\frac{1}{2}$ inch pitch, giving a water space of $\frac{7}{8}$ inch. The total heating surface is increased to 656 square feet, but the grate area remains about the same as in the 'Patentee,'— 10 square feet. The increased boiler capacity of the Leicester and Swannington engine made it possible to adopt a diameter of 16 inches for the cylinders, with a stroke of 20 inches. The six-coupled wheels had a diameter of 4 feet 6 inches, with a total wheel base (as built) of about 11 feet 8 inches. The engine is described in the makers' books as of 60 horse power but the weight is not given.[1]

from Simms' Public Works of Great Britain, 1838, Vol. I., p. 69.

LOCOMOTIVE FOR THE STANHOPE AND TYNE RAILWAY, 1834

This locomotive for the Leicester and Swannington Railway, built in 1834, may be justly called the proto-type of the English six-coupled goods engine which has been—and is to-day—the maid-of-all-work of the British railway. Particulars of more than six hundred locomotives, obtained from various builders and railway companies, and published in 1840 [2], show that up to that time the dimensions of this engine had been exceeded in a few instances only, to some of which we shall refer later.

[1] The weight of the three six-coupled locomotives on the Leicester and Swannington Railway in 1845 is recorded as 17 tons. *Gauge Commissioners' Report*, 1846. Appendix p. 504.

[2] Whishaw, *Railways of Great Britain and Ireland*, 1840, p. xxxiv.

DESIGN
OF
DETAILS

As with the 'Planet' type, various modifications and improvements were introduced from time to time in the design of details, notably in the valve gear. As the result of these improvements, some of them introduced by other makers, but developed by Robert Stephenson & Co., the various handles for starting and reversing the engine were eventually replaced, towards the end of 1835, by a single lever. These improvements we shall describe later in dealing with the development of the link motion.

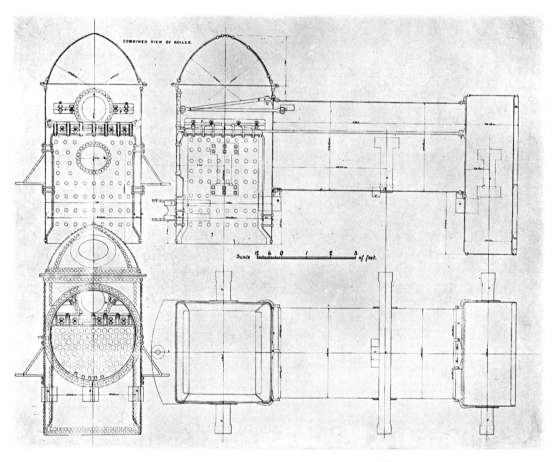

COMBINED VIEW OF BOILER.

Scale of feet.

from the original drawing, signed Robert Stephenson, June 12th 1840,' preserved in the Horwich Drawing Office
of the London Midland and Scottish Railway Company

FIREBOX

In 1838 Robert Stephenson and Co. adopted a domed firebox of rectangular section in plan. There appear to have been two, concurrent, forms of construction ; in the one case the side plates of the firebox were prolonged upwards to the vault of the dome producing what were known in England as 'haystack' boilers. In the other a joint was introduced and the dome assumed a pointed shape, aptly described as the gothic, or 'arc-de-cloître.' The construction of the pointed dome is shown by a drawing, dated 1840, and signed by Robert Stephenson. This drawing exhibits the highest development of his six-wheeled patent engine of 1833.

FRAME In 1835 the two innermost iron frames were united in front of the crank axle and continued in one piece to the firebox, thus providing a central bearing for the crank axle. But neither these nor the other remaining inside frames were at first used for the transmission of the

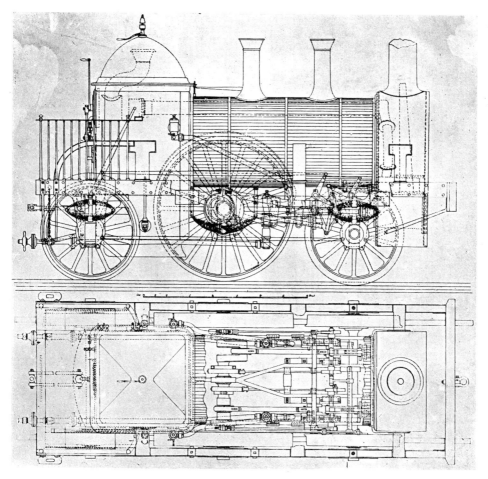

from the original drawing, signed ' Robert Stephenson, June 12th 1840,' preserved in the Horwich Drawing Office of the London Midland and Scottish Railway Company.

weight, which was still carried entirely by the bearings outside the wheels. In some of the later engines however springs were applied to the inside bearings of the driving wheels as well, but not to the central bearing ; later again this central bearing was omitted in some cases.[1]

[1] See drawing dated 17th September 1841, p. 361 Chapter XXVII. following.

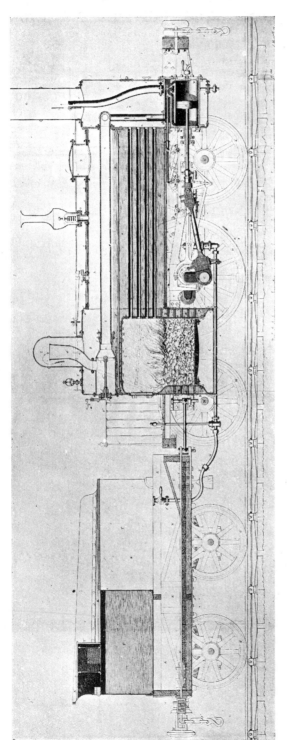

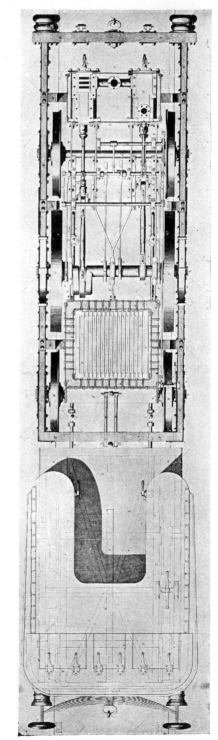

from Marshall's Description of the Patent Locomotive Steam Engine of R. Stephenson & Co., Newcastle-upon-Tyne, 1838.

ROBERT STEPHENSON'S PATENT LOCOMOTIVE

THE 'HARVEY COMBE'

In a drawing, dated 15th April 1841 we find a remarkable innovation; this drawing shows the sandwich frames placed inside the wheels; both the outside and the central bearings are abandoned. In another drawing, undated but apparently contemporary, the inside sandwich frames have given place to

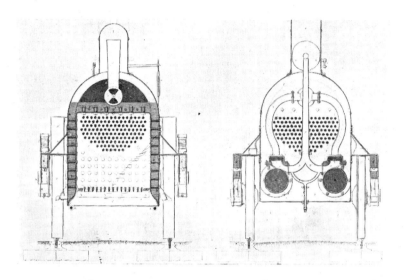

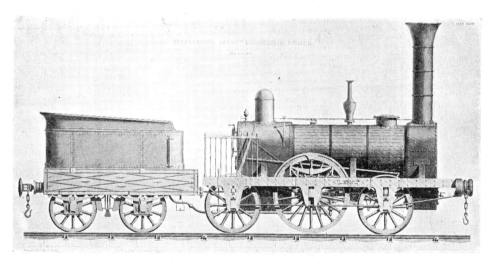

from Marshall's Description of the Patent Locomotive Steam Engine of R. Stephenson & Co.

THE 'HARVEY COMBE'

simple iron plates. These two drawings are of peculiar interest as marking the transition from Robert Stephenson's six-wheeled engine of 1833 to his long-boiler engine of 1841. With his reasons for this drastic change in construction we shall deal in a later chapter.

In 1838 Robert Stephenson authorised the publication of a complete and elaborately illustrated description of his patent locomotive.[1] The engine selected for illustration was the 'Harvey Combe,' built in 1835 for William Cubitt, the contractor then engaged in the construction of the London and Birm'ngham Railway. This engine had cylinders 12 inches diameter by 18 inches stroke. The total heating surface was about 389 square feet, with a grate area of 10 square feet; the weight was about 11 tons 17½ cwts. Their designer claimed for these engines an evaporation of 77 cubic feet of water per hour, but far higher results were recorded in practice, showing an average of 89 cubic feet per hour for engines 'whose dimensions and proportions correspond very nearly with those of the 'Harvey Combe'.' [2]

In 1837 Robert Stephenson recommended locomotives of these dimensions as the most suitable for passenger trains at high speeds; the driving wheels to be 5 feet diameter, carrying wheels 3 feet 6 inches diameter; he states the price as about £1,450 sterling.[3]

The particulars to which we have already referred as published in 1840 show that out of 630 engines running on British and foreign railways, more than two-thirds were six-wheeled engines, of which 159 had been built by Robert Stephenson & Co. The wide spread acceptation of the type may be realised from the following notes on some of the continental railways to which such locomotives were supplied.

STEPHENSON LOCOMOTIVES IN BELGIUM

'The true creators of the Belgian railway system'—says a French writer—'were King Leopold and Charles Rogier, a monarch and a prime minister who suffer no humiliation if placed beside such men of genius as George Stephenson.' [4] The first studies for this system were, it appears, entrusted to a Belgian engineer, Albert Simons, but George Stephenson himself was called in later to advise. This early and important connection with the Belgian railways led to an order, in 1834, for three locomotives from Robert Stephenson & Co., who transferred the order for one of the engines to Tayleur & Co., and themselves built the two others. All three engines were of the new standard six-wheeled type. 'L'Éléphant,' the largest, built by Tayleur & Co., had four coupled wheels, and a small pair of leading wheels; while 'La Flèche' and 'Stephenson,' built at Newcastle, had single driving wheels. These three engines were employed at the opening of the line from Brussels to Mechlin on 6th May 1835.

A contemporary account of this ceremony records that [5] :—

At a quarter past twelve o'clock, the King being at the station, near the Boulevards, to witness the ceremony, the departure of the steam-carriage train was announced by a salute

---

[1] Marshall, *Description of the Patent Locomotive Steam Engine of Robert Stephenson & Co.*, 1838; also Tredgold, *The Steam Engine*, 1838, Vol. I., pp. 407-469.

[2] Lardner, *The Steam Engine*, 1840, p. 406.

[3] Perdonnet, *Chemins de Fer*, 1865, Vol. III., p. 96.

[4] Perdonnet, *Chemins de Fer*, 1865, Vol. IV., p. i.

[5] *Mechanics' Magazine*, Vol. XXIII., p. 128 (from Brussels paper). A delightful account is also to be found in *Olla Podrida* by Captain Marryat, R.N., author of *Mr. Midshipman Easy*.

of artillery. Immediately three files of ten carriages, each carrying nearly a thousand persons, began to move, drawn by the 'Flèche,' the 'Stephenson,' and the 'Elephant.' The passage from Brussels to Mechlin occupied fifty-three minutes. On their return the 'Elephant' took in tow all the thirty carriages that had been drawn by the three locomotives, and would probably have reached Brussels in half an hour, had it not been obliged to stop at Vilvorde for a fresh supply of water. In the evening the Minister of the Interior gave a public dinner to 200 of the principal persons, natives and foreigners, who were present at the ceremony.

Many other locomotives were subsequently built by Robert Stephenson & Co. for the Belgian railways ; we have already referred to the honours conferred by King Leopold on both George and Robert Stephenson in recognition of their services in the development of railways and improvement of the locomotive.[1]

STEPHENSON LOCOMOTIVES IN GERMANY
The first locomotive sent to Germany was built by Robert Stephenson & Co. in 1835, for the Nuremberg-Fürth Railway, for which a project had been first published in May 1833. It appears that the railway company had then entered into correspondence with Robert Stephenson with a view to the supply of materials for their line, but that communications were eventually broken off 'in consequence of his demands, which, owing to the great difference in the value of money in the two countries, seemed to the directors too high to be conceded in justice to their constituents.' The order for the locomotives was therefore placed with a firm at Aalen who had guaranteed to deliver an engine 'equal to the best English engines and not requiring more fuel.' The contract for delivery not being fulfilled, the engines were subsequently ordered from Robert Stephenson & Co. at a price calculated at equal to £1,750 on the line. It was estimated that an engineman, who had been sent out with the engine, and was paid at the rate of £2 per week on condition of teaching another man, would receive a wage amounting to nearly double the pay of the manager of the railway.' [2]

The first locomotives for the Nuremberg-Fürth Railway were small editions of the 'Patentee,' having a weight in working order of only 6 tons 12 cwts. A modern model of the first locomotive 'Der Adler' is to be seen in the Eisenbahn Museum at Nuremberg.[3] Similar engines were supplied by Robert Stephenson & Co. to the Berlin and Potsdam, and later to other German railways, and many of the same type were also built for the continent by Tayleur & Co., to Stephensons' designs.

FIRST LOCOMOTIVES IN RUSSIA
We have seen that the working of Blenkinsop's locomotive had been witnessed by the Grand Duke Nicholas of Russia in 1812, and that a model of this engine had been subsequently sent to Russia. Some years later, in 1824, it was stated by the promoters of the Liverpool and Manchester Railway that the Emperor of Russia actually had at the time ' a professional agent investigating the railways of the North,'—an example which was urged as one that might well be imitated by the British Government.[4] We have also a

[1] See p. 87, Chapter VI. *ante.*   [2] *Railway Chronicle*, 11th October 1845.
[3] See p. 78, Chapter VI *ante.*
[4] Sandars, *A letter on the Subject of the projected Rail Road between Liverpool and Manchester,* 1824.

v

enlarged from the medal in the collection of Mr. C. F. Dendy Marshall, see page 94 ante.

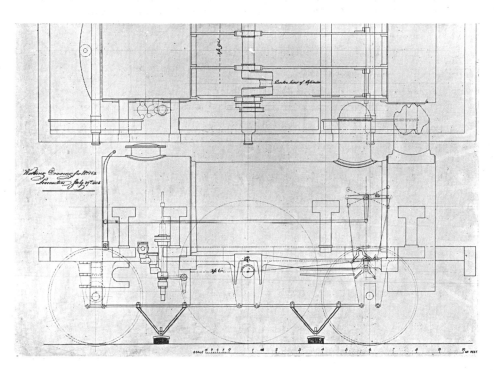

from the original drawing dated 29th July 1836.

THE FIRST STEPHENSON LOCOMOTIVE IN RUSSIA

record in 1831 that William Read, of the Peterhoff Paper Mill, 'had nearly finished a miniature locomotive steam-carriage made of silver for the purpose of better explaining the operations on the Liverpool and Manchester Railway'; this model would weigh 3 lbs. and be 'nearly a copy of Mr. Braithwaite's engine.'[1]

The Grand Duke Nicholas had been in fact so much impressed by what he had seen of the locomotive that subsequently, when Tsar, he gave every encouragement to its introduction into Russia. While the first schemes for railways in England had had to struggle against an opposition which threatened to strangle them, the first railway in Russia may be said to have sprung full fledged from the decree of an autocrat, who had to consider neither the recommendations of a parliamentary committee, nor the opposition of his ministers. The builder of this first Russian railway was Franz Gerstner[2], a Czech, who obtained in England the whole of the material required for the railway, the first three locomotives being ordered from Timothy Hackworth, Robert Stephenson & Co., and Tayleur & Co., respectively.

We find some echoes of an old rivalry in the contemporary accounts of the locomotives built by the two makers first mentioned. A local journal records on 17th September 1836[3] :—

A locomotive of a most superior workmanship has just been constructed for the Petersburgh and Pavlovsky Railway, at the manufactory of Messrs. R. Stephenson & Co., of Newcastle. It was tried lately, and exceeded the extraordinary speed of 65½ miles an hour.

This was shortly afterwards followed by a notice that[4] :—

On Thursday, the 15th of September, a large and powerful locomotive-engine, built by Mr. Timothy Hackworth of New Shildon, for the Emperor of Russia, was shipped on board the 'Barbara,' at Middlesbro'. This engine is constructed on an improved principle, and finished in the best manner. She has been tried on the premises, and propelled at the rate of 72 miles per hour. It is said that this machine, and the similar one built at Newcastle, will, on their arrival at St. Petersburg, have cost the Emperor upwards of £2,000 each. Who, a few years ago, would have dreamed of the exportation of machinery from the river Tees. This engine is for travelling on the railroad from St. Petersburg to Pavlovsky, where stands one of the country palaces of his Imperial Majesty.

The original drawing of Robert Stephenson & Co.'s locomotive has been preserved, and we have also a striking memorial in the Russian medal which commemorates the opening of the railway and records that :—

Nicholas I., worthy heir of Peter the Great, introduced railways into Russia.
First railway from St. Petersburg to Pavlovsk opened on 30th October 1837.

A contemporary record states that[5] :—

[1] Mechanics' Magazine, Vol. XVI., p. 208. See p. 82, Chapter VI. ante.

[2] Von Gerstner was born at Prague, 1795; died at Philadelphia, U.S.A., 1840; he is usually described as an Austrian; the commemorative Russian medal records however that he was 'by birth a Czech, of the same race as the Russians.' (Translation by Dr. C. Hagberg Wright of the London Library).

[3] Mechanics' Magazine, Vol. XXV., p. 432 (from Durham Advertiser).

[4] Mechanics' Magazine, Vol. XXV., p. 464. For an account of this engine in Russia see Railway Magazine Vol. II., new series, p. 136.

[5] Mechanics' Magazine, Vol. XXVIII., p. 48 (from a Hamburg paper).

from an early (undated) drawing in possession of Robert Stephenson & Co.

LOCOMOTIVE FOR THE ALAIS AND BEAUCAIRE RAILWAY

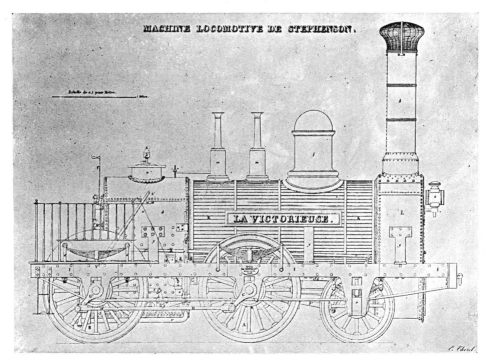

from 'Atlas du Mineur et du Metallurgiste,' 1838.

The first public trial of the Iron Railroad to Tsarkoeselo was made on Oct. 7th [1837]. It was five versts in length, and begun in the middle of the city, near the Church and parade of the Semenoff Guards.

The price of 2½ Roubles for seats in the first and second class carriages is considered to be much too high for such a short distance. A private trial of the two engines received from England was made on Tuesday. Though but a short notice was given, and only to the police, many thousand persons had collected to see this novel sight. Many persons crossed themselves at the sight of these gigantic machines as if they had been demons.

The commemorative medal and the makers' drawing show a locomotive of Stephenson's standard six-wheeled type, but notable for the fact that it was built for a gauge of six feet, which had been adopted by Gerstner for the first Russian railway.

STEPHENSON SIX-WHEELED LOCOMOTIVES IN FRANCE Robert Stephenson's patent locomotives, with one or other of the wheel arrangements which we have described, were also supplied to France; amongst them, built in 1837, was the celebrated engine 'La Victorieuse' of the Versailles Railway, one of the most notable engines of its day. It had the least common wheel arrangement, in which the trailing wheels were coupled to the driving wheels, and in dimensions and capacity exceeded the average of its time. The cylinders were 15 inches diameter by 18 inches stroke, the total heating surface was about 595 square feet, with a grate area of about 11¼ square feet, the weight in working order was about 13 tons. 'La Victorieuse' has been described and illustrated by most French writers on the locomotives of the period.

But in spite of the universal acceptance of the type as most suitable to the requirements of the time, Robert Stephenson's six-wheeled locomotives were, as we have already mentioned[1], precluded from the London and Birmingham Railway, now one of the most important in England.

A *Report* to the shareholders of that railway dated 5th August 1836, records that[2] :—

> The Directors have entered into a contract, under the guarantee of two responsible sureties, with Mr. Edward Bury, of Liverpool, an able and experienced builder of locomotive engines, for the conveyance of passengers and goods, on the railway, by locomotive power, to whatever extent may be required, at a fixed rate of remuneration; the company providing engines of Mr. Bury's specification, and Mr. Bury, on his part, maintaining and keeping them in repair; the contract to be in force for three years from the opening of the railway. The company have thus assured to themselves the advantages of locomotive power at a uniform and moderate rate and under a system of management which it is the interest of the contractor to render mutually beneficial to the Company and himself.

Edward Bury became in effect the locomotive superintendent of the London and Birmingham Railway, while he was at the same time a contractor for the supply of its locomotives—a combination of offices which it is hard to reconcile with an earlier decision of the directors to preclude the use of Robert Stephenson & Co.'s locomotives so long as Robert Stephenson was their engineer-in-

---

[1] See p. 87, Chapter VI. *ante.*

[2] *Mechanics' Magazine*, Vol. XXV., p. 356.

chief. The irony of the new situation did not escape notice. 'How is it,' wrote a railway journal a few years later, 'that we now find the engines to be the property of the company and Mr. Bury the servant of the company as resident engineer. . . . The great talents of Mr. Bury's family may be gathered from their multifarious connection with the company. In addition to 'Edward Bury' being engineer of the line, there is an 'Edward Bury' contractor for building their locomotives. That 'Mr. Edward Bury' of the line is, at the same time, the consulting engineer as to the merits of all new plans, springs, wheels, or other matters.' [1]

A strange echo this of the similar charges laid against the Liverpool and Manchester Railway Company some years previously, when George Stephenson had been their engineer and the Newcastle firm had supplied their locomotives.

from Bourne's 'London and Birmingham Railway,' drawn and lithographed by J. C. Bourne, 1838.

STEPHENSON LOCOMOTIVE ON THE CONSTRUCTION OF THE LINE IN BERKHAMPSTEAD CUTTING

TWO SCHOOLS
OF
LOCOMOTIVE
DESIGNERS

Bury, as we have already seen, was an engineer who had pronounced theories on design; he appears too to have been in some respects less open to conviction by the logic of facts than was Robert Stephenson. At a time when demands for increased power, and the limitations of the existing permanent way, had made the use of six wheels advisable, indeed inevitable, Bury adopted, and subsequently persisted, in a policy which equipped the London and Birmingham Railway with four-wheeled locomotives. Whether supplied by his own or by other firms, these engines were built to his design, with inside bar frames and 'circular' firebox, which had been rejected by the Liverpool and Manchester Railway Company on George Stephenson's recommendation.[2]

[1] *Railway Times*, 1840, Vol. III., p. 966.   [2] See p. 257 *et seq.*, Chapter XX. *ante*.

The critic whom we have quoted above refers to Bury's pleading the cause of his locomotive with the directors of the London and Birmingham Railway, to 'his final success in chasing away the six-wheeled competitors, and to his out-manoeuvring of Mr. Stephenson in a most masterly manner with his own discarded engine.'

We have already shown that, in respect of their different designs for frames and boiler, Bury and Stephenson represented two schools in locomotive construction ; they now became further differentiated as advocates of four-

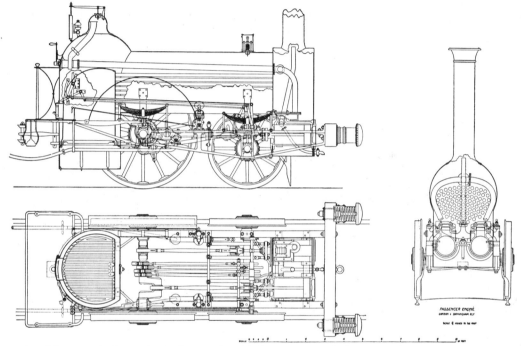

traced from a contemporary drawing in possession of Robert Stephenson & Co.

BURY'S STANDARD LOCOMOTIVE ON THE LONDON AND BIRMINGHAM RAILWAY

wheeled and six-wheeled engines respectively. An engineer, commenting on the controversy which raged for some years on this question, remarks [1] :—

Amongst the advocates of each there are men of talent and experience ; and amongst the locomotives made on each plan there are many of a highly efficient character ; and all seem to be constructed with so much solid beauty of workmanship, as to render them very imposing examples of mechanical skill. The fabrication of these splendid machines can only be conducted with due ceremony in large works, where the self-acting machinery is elaborate, powerful, and of the highest quality. Hence the manufacture of railway locomotive engines is confined to comparatively few establishments, amongst them there is a rivalry for producing the best engines. And when any accident occurs to an engine, it is too often attributed by a rival to a defect in its construction, which may not have contributed to it in the slightest degree.

[1] Hebert, *Engineers' and Mechanics' Encyclopædia*, new ed., 1849, Vol. II., p. 455.

To this controversy Bury's firm contributed a *circular*, in which they set forth their reasons for preferring the four-wheeled to the six-wheeled engine, and in particular the inside frame to the outside frame. They claimed the superiority of their four-wheeled engine on account of certain inherent virtues of its design—less first cost, less space occupied, greater economy in working due to fewer parts in motion, less cost in repairs, less risk of accident and greater safety in the event of such accident. The first of their claims were indisputable ; but that the four-wheeled engine was less liable to accident, and that the inside frame provided greater security in the event of an axle breaking, were matters of opinion on which many disagreed. Edward Bury had however the courage of his convictions, and we have a report by him of an experiment made with one of his engines, in which the leading axle had been partly cut through, in order to produce fracture when running. He writes from Wolverton to R. Creed, secretary to the London and Birmingham Railway, on 25th May 1842 :—

I send, for the information of the Board, the particulars of an experiment which was made on Monday and Tuesday last, at this station on engine No. 18 ; and as the result proves that a fracture may occur in the fore-axle, without any serious consequence to engines of the description used by the Company, I doubt not that it will be found exceedingly interesting at a time when the public mind is so much excited by the recent accident on the Paris and Versailles Railway.

I must premise, that engine No. 18 was selected for the experiment because she had been sent to Wolverton to undergo a thorough repair ; and it was further decided to substitute for her fore-axle one which, having been erroneously made a quarter of an inch less in diameter than the prescribed dimensions, had been long since laid aside.

The axle thus selected was cut circularly through, by a tool three-eighths of an inch wide, close to one of the journals, and to within half an inch of the centre of the diameter, leaving, therefore, an intervening thickness of one inch of metal connecting the partially severed parts.

The engine, in this state, was sent from the station towards Roade ; the fore-axle broke in two as intended, at the point where it had been divided, but the occurrence had no apparent effect on the movement of the engine, which continued its course till it reached Roade, when it was crossed from the down to the up line, and returned in safety to Wolverton.

Bury's four-wheeled engines did in fact work the whole of the traffic on the London and Birmingham Railway for nearly ten years after its opening. Bury carried his policy so far beyond the economical point that in 1845 it was stated as 'a well-known fact that the London and Birmingham Railway had been conveying their traffic with engines of inadequate power, and that greater economy would result to them by the adoption of larger engines.'[1] How far Bury's persistence in the use of four-wheeled engines was influenced by the limitations imposed by his circular or D shaped firebox, we cannot say ; certain it is that when he had eventually to design a six-wheeled engine having a pair of wheels behind the firebox, the vital objection to this circular form became evident, since increased grate area could only be obtained by a proportionately increased width, which made it necessary to bend the frame round the firebox to a degree which became undesirable, if not impossible.

[1] *Gauge Commissioners' Report*, 1846, p. 16.

By 1845 the directors of the London and Birmingham Railway Company could no longer be blind to the mistaken policy of their locomotive engineer, and Robert Stephenson & Co. were approached, as we have seen, with a view to devoting their whole output to the supply of locomotives for this railway. In August 1845 the locomotive committee was empowered to order 10 engines 'on the principle of Mr. Robert Stephenson,' and later to advertise for proposals for 20 passenger and 10 goods engines 'of the greatest power that might be advantageously employed, and to have not less than 1,000 square feet evaporative surface.'

(part) from an original in the Newcastle Public Library.

BURY LOCOMOTIVE WITH TRAIN, 1838

It was evident that such engines could not be carried on four wheels. Bury & Co. had to accept the inevitable and commence building six-wheeled engines. This change in their policy perhaps marks the beginning of the end for the 'unpleasant beetles—with shiny green-and-gold backs,' which annoyed Mr. Weller senior, on his dangerous journey from Euston to Birmingham with the widow.[1] To the eyes of a less prejudiced observer, Bury's little engines as they now seemed, must have had a charm, as they had a distinct character of their own, and to engineers they appealed by their excellent workmanship.[2]

The principal features of the design, the 'circular' firebox and the bar frame, eventually disappeared under the stress of circumstances, but certain deductions from the performance of Bury's locomotives on the London and Birmingham Railway influenced Robert Stephenson when designing his 'long boiler' engine of 1841 which largely replaced them. With this new Stephenson design we must deal in a succeeding chapter; we have now to consider the influence of another remarkable personality who was to cause much searching of heart among locomotive designers and to shake the railway world to its foundations.

[1] Dickens, 'Mr. Weller, senior, on Railways,' in *Master Humphrey's Clock*.

[2] One of these interesting engines which was in service on the Furness Railway until 1898 has fortunately been preserved at Barrow-in-Furness. See *Proc. Inst. Mech. Engineers*, July 1901, p. 727.

(part) frontispiece to Bourne's History of the Great Western Railway, 1846.

THE GREAT WESTERN RAILWAY

The artist shows one of the standard engines designed by Gooch.
The design is typical of Stephenson's practice in 1839 being based on the later engines of the 'Star' class
built by Robert Stephenson & Co.

CHAPTER XXV

BRUNEL AND THE BROAD GAUGE

Who, greatly daring in implacable logic, swept ruthlessly away all that had gone before, planning to raise a structure complete and harmonious all through, the absolute expression of one overmastering ideal of future perfection, but bound to remain incomplete at the last from the weakness of all human aims and means.—WEST (on the French builders), *Gothic Architecture in England and France.*

A CHALLENGE
TO THE NORTH

By 1835 the two Stephensons were recognised as the leading railway engineers of their time, the reputation of the elder securely founded on his accomplishment of the Liverpool and Manchester Railway, that of the son being built up on the London and Birmingham Railway, now under construction ; while, as a designer and builder of locomotives, Robert Stephenson enjoyed a world-wide reputation, though there were now many competitors with Robert Stephenson & Co.

Among the important lines in progress at this time was the Grand Junction Railway, under Joseph Locke, himself a pupil of the elder Stephenson ; this railway was to form a junction between the Liverpool and Manchester, and the London and Birmingham lines, which would eventually bring the 4 foot 8 inch gauge of the Killingworth waggon-way to London, or, to be more exact, the 4 foot 8½ inch gauge, which it had now become. For some other railways a smaller gauge had been adopted, but a contemporary list, recorded in an early description book in the possession of Robert Stephenson & Co. gives only one instance by 1835, and that in America, of a gauge so wide as 5 feet, though a year later we have the 5 foot 6 inch gauge of the New Orleans Railway and the 6 foot gauge of the first Russian railway.

WIDTH OF RAILWAYS. 1830-1835.

These are the distances between inside of Rails.

ENGLAND.	Ft.	Ins.	FRANCE.	Ft.	Ins.
Killingworth	4	8	Loire	4	9
Stockton and Darlington	4	8	St. Etienne	4	9
Liverpool and Manchester	{4	8			
	{4	8½	AMERICA.		
Canterbury	4	8			
Leicester and Swannington	4	8½	New York	4	3
Warrington	4	8½	Baltimore and Ohio	4	6
Newcastle and Carlisle	4	8½	Baltimore and Susquehanna	4	9¼
			Camden and So. Amboy	4	9¾
SCOTLAND.			Mohawk and Hudson	4	9
Garnkirk and Glasgow	4	6	Saratoga and Schenectady	4	9
Monkland	4	6	Newcastle and Frenchtown	4	8½
Ballockoney (sic)	4	6	Charlestown and Columbia	5	0

By 1836 wrought iron was in general use for the rails, which were either fish-bellied between the supports, or of the parallel section adopted by Robert

Stephenson for the London and Birmingham Railway as the result of experiments carried out on his behalf.[1] The rails, which depended for their rigidity on their depth, were usually carried on chairs, which were fixed to stone blocks, or to cross sleepers of wood as used upon the Chat Moss section of the Liverpool and Manchester Railway and on embankments generally. The weight of the rails on the Liverpool and Manchester line, at first 35 lbs. per yard, had been progressively increased to meet the constant increases to the loads which they had to carry. The permanent way, though still far from perfect, was capable of carrying loads at speeds which six years earlier would have been considered fabulous.

At a moment when George Stephenson as a railway engineer was approaching that period in a man's life when his own past accomplishment may well be the limit to his theories for further progress, there appears upon the scene a young engineer, unfettered by the limitations of the past, to whom the gauge of the Killingworth waggon-way meant nothing in sentiment or practice. The 4 foot $8\frac{1}{2}$ inch gauge might be good enough for the men of the North, content with their twenty to twenty-five miles an hour, but it would not suffice the man who had to lay out a great new trunk line to connect London with Bristol and the west country; and with the Far West overseas by the great steamships which he was planning.[2]

from the painting by J. C. Horsley, R.A

ISAMBARD KINGDOM BRUNEL

1806-1859

Isambard Kingdom Brunel[3] was the son of Sir Marc Isambard Brunel, a distinguished engineer of Norman-French extraction, who is best known for his construction of the Thames Tunnel. Young Brunel was born in 1806,

[1] By Professor Peter Barlow of the Royal Military Academy, Woolwich.

For an outline of the development of the permanent way, see E. Wood's Presidential Address, *Proc. Inst. Civil Engineers*, 9th November 1886, also Nicholas Wood, *Treatise on Rail Roads*, 3rd edition, 1838.

The history of the evolution of the rail and the permanent way, closely related to that of the locomotive itself, offers a fascinating study which is beyond our present scope. Some of the earlier forms of rail and sleeper in use are however shown in our reproductions from contemporary drawings.

[2] Brunel's steamship, the 'Great Western,' which took only 15 days on her first voyage to America in 1838, far surpassed any existing steamship of the time. She was the first to be employed in regular ocean service between England and America. He subsequently built the 'Great Britain,' the first large vessel to use a screw propeller, and later the celebrated 'Great Eastern.'

[3] The original of our picture is in the National Portrait Gallery, London (copyright photo Emery Walker).

and was thus contemporary with Robert Stephenson, who was to be both his greatest personal friend and keenest professional opponent.   In 1829 young Brunel became known in Bristol in connection with his design for the proposed Clifton Suspension Bridge, and in 1833 he was appointed to survey a railway from Bristol to London. We have his own statement that, between this date and the passing of the first Great Western Railway Bill in 1835, he had made up his mind to depart from the accepted railway practice of the day.

This practice had been established principally by the work of George Stephenson, in the 'stolid acceptance of existing facts which preserves all that has gone before, however imperfect . . . . adding to here, and changing there . . . . a structure incapable of perfection because begun and ended incessantly.' This practice Brunel now challenged.   With the vision of genius, the valour of inexperience, and 'implacable logic,' he defied the opinion of the Stephensons, claiming that both a wider gauge and a different construction of road were essential if the loads and speeds which he had in view were to be obtained.

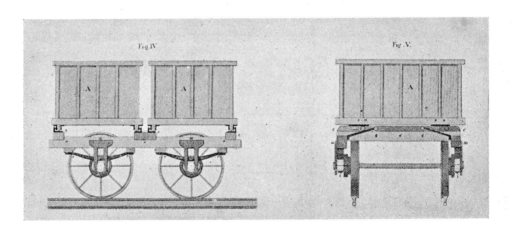

(part) from Wood's Treatise on Rail Roads, 1831, Pl. III., Figs. IV., V.

GEORGE STEPHENSON'S COAL CARRIAGE WITH OUTSIDE BEARINGS
FOR THE 4 FOOT 8 INCH GAUGE.

THE
BROAD
GAUGE

Any mention of these intentions was purposely omitted from the Bill, and it was not till 1835 that Brunel declared his proposal for a 7 foot gauge, with rails carried throughout their length on longitudinal timbers, these again to be carried on piles.   Brunel's decision was based both on known facts and on theory.   Stone blocks as sleepers had been found unsatisfactory in many ways, as too rigid, and difficult to keep properly bedded and in alignment.   In some cases they were being replaced by transverse wooden sleepers, and in America longitudinal wooden sleepers had been used, and in some few instances at home.

On the Glasgow and Garnkirk Railway a combination of both was in use.[1] Indeed the longitudinal continuous sleeper was in a sense but a return to the original square wooden rail, to which a flat bar, to take the wear, had eventually been nailed, rigidity being still dependent on the wood. In 1845 the comparative merits of the two systems remained with some engineers a matter of opinion [2], but the greater cost of Brunel's road was a matter of fact.

So far as the width between the rails, or the gauge, was concerned, it had been found on the Liverpool and Manchester Railway that the distance between the wheels on the 4 foot 8 inch gauge, while sufficient for the body of a coal waggon, was inadequate for that of a coach ; but this difficulty had been overcome by George Stephenson's adoption of the outside bearings which he had introduced in the tender of the 'Rocket,' and by carrying the floor of the vehicle over the wheels. As for the engines, some builders were already wishing for more space between the wheels, or frames, for the arrangement of the machinery and had begun to speculate whether the 4 foot $8\frac{1}{2}$ inch gauge was the best for their purposes. Their views were further affected by a theory then generally held, that a low centre of gravity was essential to smoothness and safety in running. With the inside cylinders, generally accepted at this time as most desirable, the minimum height of the boiler was determined by the clearance required between the cranks of the driving axle and the underside of the boiler barrel, and it was obvious that no increase in the diameter of the boiler would be possible without raising its centre, unless alternatively the distance between the cranks could be increased, and this would only be possible by widening the gauge.

The need of more room for the arrangement of the machinery subsequently became one of the most prominent issues in the gauge controversy, and indeed so early as 1838 we have a report on the subject to the directors of the Great Western Railway by John Hawkshaw, who writes [3] :—

Impressed with the importance of having other opinions on this subject than my own, I addressed a letter to two of the largest manufacturers of locomotives in this country, requesting from them to know what in their opinion were the practical disadvantages of the 4 feet $8\frac{1}{2}$ inches gauge as effecting the manufacturer.

The opinions of both these parties in my view are peculiarly valuable, for they were not only amongst the early locomotive manufacturers, but have also had much more experience as to the working of their engines on railways than any other manufacturers I know; and without this latter kind of experience, manufacturers are, to a certain extent, only theorists, as to the question in hand.

Their answers are below:—

Liverpool, Sept. 29th 1838.

Dear Sir,—In reply to your letter of the 27th inst. referring to the question of the right gauge which at this time is so much agitated.

[1] *Mechanics' Magazine*, Vol. XV., p. 333, from *Glasgow Evening Post*, 16th July 1831.
'Here [*i.e.* on the Glasgow and Garnkirk Railway] an entirely new and admirable plan has been adopted for the fixing of the rails, by longitudinal sleeper beams, supported on double transverse ones, placed on beds of brush and ballasting, the success of which application is momentarily experienced on the carriages entering it, from the additional smoothness and agreeableness of their motion.'

[2] Evidence before the Gauge Commissioners, *Report*, 1846. J. Hawkshaw, p. 286 ; J. Gray, p. 133.

[3] *Railway Times*, 1837, Vol. II., p. 3 *et seq.*

I beg to state that though we do not labour absolutely under great difficulties, in consequence of the want of breadth, yet there is no doubt an addition to the present width (4 feet $8\frac{1}{2}$ in.) of a few inches would enable us to make a more perfect engine. The addition of 6 inches would be ample, and I consider anything beyond that would tend to increase the difficulties beyond what we now experience, rather than otherwise.

Yours truly,
Edward Bury.

John Hawkshaw, Esq.

Hawkshaw also wrote to Robert Stephenson & Co. who replied:—

London, Oct. 1 1838.

Sir,—The extent of inconvenience we experience in the construction of locomotive engines of moderate power (say 14 inch cylinder) for a gauge of 4 feet $8\frac{1}{2}$ inches, is very small indeed. In our early engines an additional width of 3 or 4 inches would have facilitated the arrangement of the working gear and eccentrics; but this has since been simplified, and our latest arrangement of those parts leaves scarcely this small increase of width to be wished for. The construction of engines for Russia for a *six feet* gauge, leads us to believe that a considerable increase of expense is attendant upon increased width; more especially if the power of the engine is considered to bear any relation to the width of the gauge. If the power or dimensions of the engine be kept the same, the additional expense consequent upon increase of gauge will not be very considerable.

We are, Sir, &c.,
Robert Stephenson & Co.

Hawkshaw concludes his quotation with the remark:—

With respect to Mr. Bury, it may be observed, that if any manufacturer in England has felt inconvenience from the 4 ft. $8\frac{1}{2}$ in. gauge, he must have done so; for, from the peculiar construction of his engines, it is a principle with him to use inside bearings only, which necessarily leave less room for the working gear than when outside bearings are used.

The advocates of the 'broad gauge' afterwards made full use of the locomotive builders' wish for a greater width, but this had not been Brunel's principal reason for proposing a gauge of 7 feet. His declared reason was the desire to place the body of the coach between the wheels. 'He had never'—he said later—'recommended the gauge for the purpose of having larger engines.' [1]

To such technical arguments as he used in regard to the construction of the road and rolling stock, Brunel added another of a different kind; he claimed that, since the Great Western Railway would serve a large district entirely untouched by railways, and so far removed from the existing lines of the north as to make contact unlikely, it was unnecessary to consider the interchangeability of rolling stock. This assumption was strongly opposed by the Stephensons, particularly by Robert Stephenson, who had adopted the 4 foot $8\frac{1}{2}$ inch gauge for the London and Birmingham Railway, not because there was any intrinsic virtue in a dimension which had been arrived at in a more or less fortuitous way, but rather because the new railway was intended to link up to already existing railways.

[1] *Railway Times*, 1839, Vol. II., p. 55, Report of Special Meeting, Great Western Railway Company.
The shareholders present at this meeting supported Brunel's policy by an overwhelming majority, but they eventually had to pay for the costly success of the broad gauge. Others paid dearly later for Brunel's costly experiment with the atmospheric system on the South Devon Railway; this, unlike the broad gauge, was a complete failure, as George Stephenson had foretold.

Robert Stephenson's advice, and an original intention to unite the two lines in a common terminus at Euston was rejected by the directors of the Great Western Railway, who accepted Brunel's views, and the first section of the line laid on the 7 foot gauge was opened from Paddington to Maidenhead on 4th June 1838. Experience soon showed that Brunel's method of supporting the longitudinal sleepers on piles must be abandoned, since it made the road far too rigid ; and the rails were soon found to be too light. In other respects the line appeared to justify the theories of its engineer ; more trains ran regularly at high speeds than on the northern lines, some perhaps a few miles an hour faster ; and there was some evidence of greater security in case of accidents. But as the much greater cost, and other implications of the broad gauge began to be better understood by traders and engineers connected with the narrow gauge lines of the north, a public agitation arose which led the directors of the Great Western Railway to reconsider Brunel's theories and to ask other well-known engineers to report on the desirability of continuing their railway on the broad gauge.

On 15th August 1838 Brunel wrote to the directors [1] :—

As the endeavour to obtain the opinions and reports of Mr. Walker, Mr. Stephenson, and Mr. Wood, prior to the next half-yearly meeting, has not been successful, I am anxious to record more fully than I have previously done, and to combine them into one report, my own views and opinions upon the success of the several plans which have been adopted at my recommendation in the formation and in the working of our line.

After pointing out that the exceptionally favourable gradients and curves obtainable on a line from London to Bristol offered the possibility of unusually high speeds, Brunel proceeds :—

The attainment of high speed appeared to involve the question of the width of gauge, and on this point, accordingly, I expressed my opinion at a very early period. It has been asserted that 4 feet 8 inches, the width adopted on the Liverpool and Manchester Railway, is exactly the proper width for all railways, and that to adopt any other dimension is to deviate from a positive rule which experience has proved correct ; but such an assertion can be maintained by no reasoning.

Brunel then refers to the report of a Commission which had recommended a gauge of 6 feet 2 inches for the Irish railways, this width having been determined with the particular object of increasing the diameter of the carriage wheels without raising the bodies of the carriages, and he proceeds to show that with the same object in view he required a gauge of 7 feet to allow of an ordinary coach body 6 feet 6 inches in width being placed between the wheels. The inconveniences of a carriage body placed between the wheels were however quickly realised, the principle was soon abandoned, and by 1840 at any rate the standard carriages of the Great Western Railway had outside bearings as on the northern lines and were carried over the wheels as in the 'narrow' gauge. [2]

Dealing with the question of cost, Brunel in his report makes another

---

[1] We are indebted to the Great Western Railway Company for a correct transcription from this report.

[2] Whishaw, *Railways of Great Britain and Ireland*, 1840. plate 10.

statement of great interest in relation to the assumption that the 7 foot gauge would require an increased width for bridges, tunnels, etc., he states :—

Yet such is not the case within the limits we are now treating of; a 7 feet rail requires no wider bridge or tunnel than a 5 feet; . . . . and on the London and Birmingham railway with 11 feet, a 7 feet gauge might be placed just as well as a 5 feet, leaving the bridges, tunnels, and viaducts exactly the same.

It may be observed that had this theory been accepted and put into practice, as was urged subsequently, by a conversion of the 'narrow' gauge lines to a broad gauge, the diameter of an outside cylinder would have been even more limited in England than it is to-day.

FIRST LOCOMOTIVES ON THE BROAD GAUGE After dealing with the construction of the line, and carriages, with the advantages felt in the increased lateral steadiness of both carriages and engines, and the greater space provided for the works of the locomotives, Brunel, in his letter of 15th August 1838, proceeds :—

The next point I shall consider is the construction of the engines, the modifications in which, necessary to adapt them to higher speeds than usual, have, like the increased width of gauge, been condemned as innovations.[1] I shall not attempt to argue with those who consider any increase of speed unnecessary. The public will always prefer that conveyance which is the most perfect, and speed within reasonable limits is a material ingredient in perfection in travelling.

A rate of 35 to 40 miles an hour is not unfrequently attained at present on other railways in descending planes, or with light loads on a level, and is found practically to be attended with no inconvenience. To maintain such a speed with regularity on a level line, with moderate loads, is therefore quite practicable and unquestionably desirable. With this view the engines were constructed, but nothing new was required or recommended by me; a certain velocity of the piston is considered the most advantageous.

The engines intended for slow speeds have always had the driving wheels small in proportion to the length of stroke of the piston. The faster engines have had a different proportion, the wheels have been larger, or the strokes of the piston shorter. From the somewhat clamorous objections raised against the large wheels, and the construction of the Great Western Railway engines, and the opinions rather freely expressed of my judgment in directing this construction, it would naturally be supposed that some established principle had been departed from, and that I had recommended this departure. The facts are, that a certain velocity of piston being found most advantageous, I fixed this velocity so that the engines should be adapted to run 35 miles an hour, and capable of running 40—as the Manchester and Liverpool Railway engines are best calculated for 20 to 25, but capable of running easily up to 30 and 35 miles per hour; and fixing also the load which the engine was to be capable of drawing, I left the form of construction and the proportions entirely to the manufacturers, stipulating merely that they should submit detail drawings to me for my approval.

This was the substance of the circular, which, with your sanction, was sent to several of the most experienced manufacturers. Most of these manufacturers of their own accord, and without previous communication with me, adopted the large wheels as a necessary consequence of the speed required. The recommendation coming from such quarters, there can be no necessity for defending my opinion in its favour; neither have I now the slightest doubt of its correctness. As it has been supposed that the manufacturers may have been compelled or induced by me to adopt certain modes of construction or certain dimensions, in other parts by a specification—a practice which has been adopted on some lines—and that these restrictions may have

[1] The reference is presumably to the engines with 10-foot driving wheels, built by Mather Dixon & Co. and to the geared engines built by R. & W. Hawthorn to the designs of T. E. Harrison. See Wood, *Treatise on Rail Roads*, 3rd ed., 1838, p. 721, Plate XII. See also under 'North Star' p. 338 following.

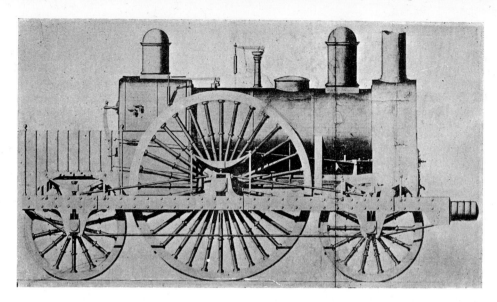

(part) from an original (undated) drawing in possession of Robert Stephenson & Co

LOCOMOTIVE WITH EIGHT-FOOT DRIVING WHEELS FOR THE GREAT WESTERN RAILWAY
built by Tayleur & Co.

from a photo by the Great Western Railway Company

THE 'NORTH STAR'

as in service on the Great Western Railway till 1870 after being rebuilt, with new boiler, in 1854.

'And lastly let me call your attention to the appearance. We have a splendid engine of Stephenson's it would be a beautiful ornament in the most elegant drawing room and we have another of Quaker-like simplicity carried even to shabbyness but very possibly as good an engine, but the difference in the care bestowed by the engineman, the favour in which it is held by others and even oneself not to mention the public, is striking—a plain young lady however amiable is apt to be neglected—now your engine is capable of being made very handsome and it ought to be so.'—*I. K. Brunel* to *T. E. Harrison*, March 6th 1838.

embarrassed them, I should wish to take this opportunity to state distinctly that such is not the case. I have, indeed, strongly recommended to their consideration the advantages of having very large and well-formed steam passages, which generally they have adopted, and with good results; and with this single exception, if it can be considered one; they have been left unfettered by me (perhaps too much so) and uninfluenced, except, indeed, by the prejudices and fears of those by whom they have been surrounded, which have by no means diminished the difficulties I have had to contend with.

The principal proportions of these engines being those which have been recommended by the most able experimentalists and writers, and these having been adopted by the most experienced makers, it is difficult to understand who can constitute themselves objectors, or what can be their objection. Even if these engines had not been found effective, at least it must be admitted that the best and most liberal means had been adopted to procure them; but I am far from asking such an admission. The engines, I think, have proved to be well adapted to the particular task for which they were calculated, namely, high speeds—but circumstances prevent their being beneficially applied to this purpose at present, and they are, therefore, working under great disadvantages. An engine constructed expressly for high velocity cannot, of course, be well adapted to exert great power at a low speed; neither can it be well adapted for stopping frequently and regaining its speed. But such was not the intention when these engines were made, neither will it be be the case when the arrangements on the line are complete; in the meantime our average rate of travelling is much greater than it was either on the Grand Junction or Birmingham Railway within the same period of the opening.

The locomotives referred to by Brunel had been ordered from various makers, but the first to be delivered were built by Tayleur & Co. and Robert Stephenson & Co. respectively. Tayleur's engine, with its 8 feet driving wheels, was a striking departure from any previous design and shows very markedly the attempt to meet Brunel's requirements for speed. A particularly interesting feature of the design is the placing of the driving axleboxes above the frame, the arrangement which had been considered, but not adopted, by Robert Stephenson & Co. for the 'Planet' in 1830.

Of these engines, built at the Vulcan Foundry, and of the first Stephenson engines for the Great Western Railway, Gooch wrote many years later [1]:—

The 'North Star' and the six from the Vulcan Foundry Company were the only ones on which I could rely. The 'North Star' was the most powerful one, and in other respects the best. She was my chief reliance.

The engines built by the Vulcan Co. did not survive in their original form—their boilers were too small. Most of the engines built by other makers were failures from the first.

STEPHENSON'S 'NORTH STAR'

We have now to consider who was responsible for the design of the 'North Star,' bearing in mind Brunel's disclaimer which we have quoted above. We have shown from Robert Stephenson & Co.'s records that during 1836 two engines had been made by them for a Russian railway with a gauge of

[1] *The Diaries of Sir Daniel Gooch*, 1892, Kegan, Paul, Trench & Co. Until we come to the entries relating to the year 1856 this book is rather an autobiography, written many years after the events, than a transcription from the diaries.

Daniel Gooch was born at Bedlington 1816, his mother was a Longridge of Newcastle; he records—'George Stephenson was frequently at my father's house, and used to take a great deal of notice of me, taking me on his knee and talking to me about pits, &c. At that time he was much engaged in advising on colliery matters, and had just commenced his glorious career.'

Gooch, who had been appointed locomotive superintendent when only twenty-one years of age, became chairman of the Great Western Railway Company. He was created a Baronet in 1866, and died in 1889.

6 feet, and with driving wheels of 6 feet diameter. During the same year two engines were ordered for the New Orleans Railway of America, with a gauge of 5 feet 6 inches, and driving wheels 6 feet 6 inches diameter. The drawings show that but for the larger wheels, and the differences in gauge, all these engines were typical examples of Stephenson's patent six-wheeled locomotive of 1833. Now it appears from the reminiscences of Sir Daniel Gooch that when a young man of about twenty he was employed in Robert

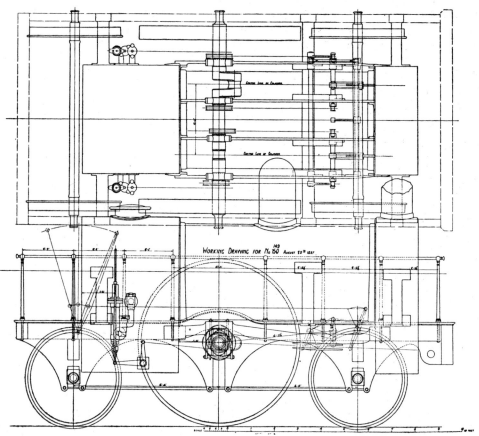

traced from the original drawing dated 10th August 1837.

The drawing shows the alterations intended to engines Nos. 149, 150 to suit the 7 foot gauge ; these engines became the 'MORNING STAR' and 'NORTH STAR' but the drawing does not appear to represent exactly either engine as actually made

Stephenson & Co.'s drawing office, from January to October 1836, during which period the first of the Russian engines had been designed and built. Forty-four years later, in 1880, Gooch wrote on a drawing of the Russian engines which was then in his possession, the following statement :—

These engines were built by Messrs. R. Stephenson & Company, Newcastle, for a Russian order, 6 feet gauge, but were not delivered. The Great Western bought them for £3,000 each. The 'North Star' in 1837, the 'Morning Star' later, the gauge being altered to 7 feet.

We have already illustrated the original drawing for these engines, dated July 1836[1]; it is identical with that signed by Gooch[2], and it is quite possible that Gooch himself may have made both these drawings during his engagement with Robert Stephenson & Co. He certainly had a duplicate in his possession in 1884; but on one important point his memory at that time was at fault; for, as we have shown, the engines designed by Robert Stephenson & Co. for Russia were sent to that country. On the other hand we have Robert Stephenson's statement[3] that owing to a financial panic at the time the two engines built for America were left on his hands, and that it was these two engines which were converted, by widening the frames and lengthening the axles, to suit the 7 foot gauge, becoming the 'North Star,' and the 'Morning Star' of the Great Western Railway.

In the 'North Star' the diameter of the driving wheels was increased by Robert Stephenson & Co. to 7 feet, obviously to meet Brunel's requirements; but the driving wheels of the 'Morning Star' remained as designed for the American railroad, 6 feet 6 inches diameter. The original drawings showing one or other of these engines before and after alteration record certain differences in the spacing of the wheels which suggest that more considerable alterations were made when adapting the 'North Star' to the broader gauge, but speaking generally both engines were of the same type and capacity; both had frames with the peculiar outline which was characteristic of succeeding broad gauge engines until their abolition. Otherwise, except that their boilers were larger and their fireboxes rather wider, these two engines were generally typical of Robert Stephenson's patent locomotive of 1833.

The 'North Star' had cylinders 16 inches diameter by 16 inches stroke; the boiler barrel was 4 feet in diameter, by 8 feet 6 inches long, containing 167 tubes, $1\frac{5}{8}$ inch diameter; the firebox had a width of 4 feet 6 inches, with a length of 4 feet 3 inches outside, giving a grate of $13\frac{1}{2}$ square feet; the total heating surface was about 711 square feet. The weight was possibly 21 tons.[4] It should be noted that the boiler dimensions only slightly exceed those of the six-coupled patent engine built by Robert Stephenson & Co. for the Leicester and Swannington Railway in 1833, but they exceeded considerably the average for their makers' standard six-wheeled engine of the period 1833-1840.

The performances of the 'North Star' were at once remarkable; Nicholas Wood records an experimental trip by the directors on 1st June preparatory to the opening of the line on 4th June 1838[5] :—

The engine employed on this occasion was No. 150 (the makers' number), the 'North

---

[1] See p. 322, Chapter XXIV. *ante.*

[2] Published in *The Engineer*, Vol. LXXIII., p. 447. 'The Conversion of the Gauge on the Great Western Railway.'

See also *The Engineer*, Vol. CX., Supplement 16th December, 'The Great Western Railway,' p. **xix.**

[3] Evidence before the Gauge Commissioners, *Report*, 1846, p. 7, Answer 107.

[4] The records of the weights of these early engines are unsatisfactory; comparison with other recorded weights suggests that the 'North Star' in working order must have weighed about 21 tons.

[5] Wood, *Treatise on Railroads*, 3rd edition, 1838, p. 727.

Star,' to which was attached a train of carriages containing nearly 200 passengers; with this train the engine performed a journey in 47 minutes the distance being 22½ miles, which is at the rate of 28 miles an hour.

A later experiment carried out in the same year at the request of the directors showed that 'the 'North Star' drawing a load of 110½ tons gross, engine and tender inclusive, at 30½ miles a hour, evaporated 200 cubic feet of water per hour, and when drawing 45 tons at 38½ miles an hour evaporated 198 cubic feet of water per hour,' which Lardner, one of the observers, reckoned 'to give a power of four hundred horses.' [1]

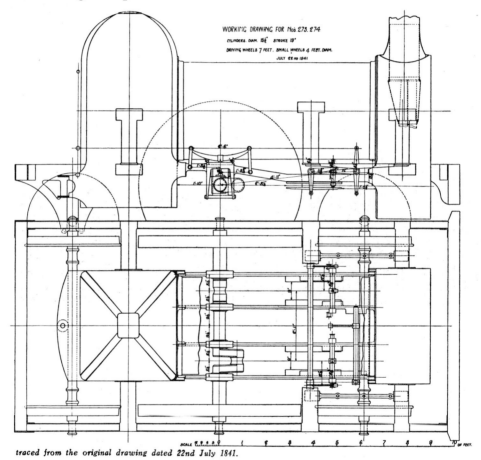

traced from the original drawing dated 22nd July 1841.

ENGINES OF THE 'STAR' CLASS
built by Robert Stephenson & Co. in 1841

Subsequently, between 1837 and 1841, Robert Stephenson & Co. supplied ten other engines called by the names of various stars. These engines, known as the 'Star' class, differed from the 'North Star', and from each other, in various respects. Some of the later engines were fitted with the gothic or

[1] Lardner, *The Steam Engine*, 1840, p. 406.

the haystack, firebox which the makers had adopted in 1838, and there were variations in the diameter of the boiler, and variations in the tubes, diameters of 2 inches and $2\frac{1}{4}$ inches being adopted for the later engines, which consequently had a reduced nominal heating surface. There were also variations in the cylinder dimensions, originally 16 inches diameter by 16 inches stroke, they are shown on the drawings for some of the later engines, as $15\frac{1}{2}$ inches diameter by 19 inches stroke.

DANIEL GOOCH   In 1837, after the first locomotives had been ordered by Brunel, Daniel Gooch was appointed locomotive superintendent, and it appears that he was subsequently instructed by his directors to make a report on each of the engines under his care, and to

from a lithograph by J. Beecham, published I. Ann, Swindon, in the collection of the Great Western Railway Company.

NEW SWINDON, 1847
The drawing shows the 'FIREBRAND' one of Gooch's standard engines

prepare designs for future rolling stock ; in his reminiscences he wrote :—

These drawings I took great pains with giving every detail much thought and consideration, and the result was designs for two classes of engines—one with a 7 feet driving wheel, 15-inch cylinder, and 18-inch stroke, and another with 6 feet wheel, 14-inch cylinder, and 18-inch stroke, both with ample boiler power ; and I may with confidence, after these engines have been working for twenty-eight years, say that no better engines for their weight have since been constructed either by myself or others. They have done, and continue to do, admirable duty ; advantage has been taken of new cylinders being required to give them an extra inch in diameter and 4 inches more in stroke, and expansion gear has been added ; in other respects the engines are the same.[1]

When I had completed the drawings, I had them lithographed and specifications printed, and thin iron templates for those parts it was essential should be interchangeable, and these were supplied to the various engine-builders with whom contracts were made. One hundred and forty-two engines were let, and all the makers did their work well. The best were built

[1] For Gooch's design with 7 foot driving wheels, see p. 384, Chapter XXVIII. following.

by Fenton, Murray & Jackson, of Leeds, but the great durability of the engines has proved that all did their work well. I very frequently visited the various works where they were built. My chief draughtsman at that time was a clever fellow, and he has made a good position for himself since as a contractor. His name is Thomas Crampton; he died April 1888.

Gooch adds that, of the engines ordered to his drawings the 'Firefly,' started in March 1840, was the first, and that 'they all gave every one general satisfaction.' These engines had a boiler 4 feet diameter with a barrel 8 feet 6 inches long. A consideration of Gooch's statement, with an examination of his design and the principal dimensions, shows that in all essentials the 'Firefly' was a development from the previous engines of the 'Star' class, all of which had been derived in the first instance from Stephenson's 'North Star.'

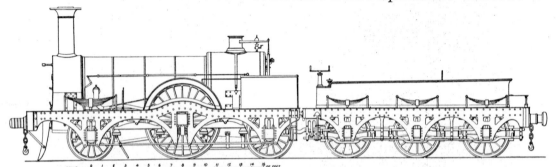

from an original drawing by the makers, Messrs. Beyer, Peacock & Co.

GOOCH'S FIRST DESIGN FOR THE 4 FOOT 8½ INCH GAUGE
built for the Great Western Railway by Beyer, Peacock & Co. in 1855

It has been sometimes stated that it was only the 7 foot gauge which made possible the 'North Star' and the engines of the same type which immediately succeeded it on the Great Western Railway; but, so far from Brunel's requirements and Gooch's designs having produced a new and improved type of locomotive, the fact is that the needs of the Great Western Railway were satisfied for many years by engines of Stephenson's standard type which had been designed some years previously, and in this particular case constructed actually for an American railway.

By a curious and striking irony the influence of one of Robert Stephenson's most successful early designs lasted longest on the line of his great professional antagonist, and the development of the type by Gooch into the 'Great Britain,' 'Lightning,' and 'Lord of the Isles,' carried down to 1892 the early Stephenson tradition of outside frames and bearings, with additional inside bearings for the crank axle. Some of Gooch's first 4 foot 8½ inch, or standard gauge, locomotives built [1] for the Great Western Railway Company have the outside frames of the 'North Star,' with inside frames as well, and indeed in outside appearance closely resemble it. Though Gooch himself, and succeeding locomotive superintendents, departed at times from the Stephenson tradition which they had inherited, they as frequently returned to it.[2]

[1] Built in 1857 by Messrs. Beyer, Peacock & Co., to whom we are indebted for the drawing.

[2] *The Locomotive*, Vol. XX., p. 215, 'Early Great Western Standard Gauge Engines'; also *The Engineer*, Vol. CX., Supplement 16th December, p. xxi.

A traveller on the Great Western Railway in 1892 could see, as on few other lines, locomotives at work embodying those theories of frame design which Robert Stephenson had first applied in the 'Planet,' and subsequently developed in his six-wheeled patent engine of 1833. Considerations of cost in the first instance, and later the unsuitability of the design for modern types, have rendered the outside frame obsolete to-day, except for engines of the metre and other narrower gauges. But its continued use on the broad gauge, and subsequently on the narrow gauge of the Great Western Railway, points to some intrinsic advantage which made it worth while to continue a construction that was undoubtedly more costly than that of the inside frame. It seems not unreasonable to suggest that the immunity from the worst effects of certain accidents which has frequently been ascribed to the long tudinal sleeper, may have been partly due to the outside frame, one of the reasons originally put forward for its adoption.

from a photo by the Great Western Railway Company.

THE LAST BROAD GAUGE TRAIN, 1892

Stephenson's outside frame is passing, and the longitudinal sleeper has gone from the Great Western Railway, except in a few country sidings where it may still be seen by the curious. Brunel's fine bridges and his immense earthworks remain to remind us of his original great design ; the broad gauge remains only as the treasured memory of a passing generation. Time has falsified some theories, as it has justified others ; we know now that it is less rail-gauge than load-gauge which matters. There is nothing in the outside appearance of the modern Great Western Railway locomotive to suggest the Stephenson locomotive of 1837—but could they watch on the narrow gauge the passing of a Great Western express train to-day, the shades of Isambard Kingdom Brunel and Robert Stephenson might find a final reconciliation for a professional rivalry which during their lifetime was not inconsistent with a lasting personal friendship.

CHAPTER XXVI

THE 'LONG BOILER' LOCOMOTIVE
ROBERT STEPHENSON'S PATENT

1841—1845

We have already recorded in our notes on the development of the firm [1], that on 13th October 1841 Robert Stephenson & Co. were awaiting with interest and confidence the results from a trial of their 'Patent Engine,' the first of which had been sent away on the previous day to Darlington, to be tried on the Great North of England Railway. Robert Stephenson, who had expressed himself as 'well satisfied with it,' was to be present at the trial of this engine, which had been designed to meet certain definite conditions and requirements, and marked a radical departure from the previous practice of its makers, embodying many improvements which are described by Robert Stephenson's specification or shown in detail by the drawings attached thereto. Engines of the Long-Boiler type, as they were at once called, became involved later in the competition for speed, and in certain experimental trials which resulted from the gauge controversy, known as the 'Battle of the Gauges.' It is therefore well to note here that they were not designed with any such contest in view, but—to quote Robert Stephenson's words—'for the purpose of obtaining an economical consumption of fuel, which at that time was considered of paramount importance,' and 'when the size of turntables was such as to offer an inducement to keep the wheels as close together as possible.'

We have seen that during the period of about five years prior to Brunel's challenge in 1835, the weights of locomotives on the 4 foot $8\frac{1}{2}$ inch gauge had been more than doubled, and that Robert Stephenson's patent six-wheeled engine of 1833 had been so generally adopted as to have become in fact a standard type. An examination of the dimensions of some hundreds of such engines running in 1839 shows that they had cylinders ranging from 11 inches diameter by 16 inches stroke, to 15 inches diameter by 18 inches stroke, and in one or two exceptional cases 16 inches diameter, by 16 inches and 20 inches stroke respectively. The boilers had barrels which varied in diameter from 3 feet to nearly 4 feet, though the latter was an exceptional size ; the length of the barrel rarely exceeded 8 feet 6 inches, and the total heating surface, including that of the firebox, had reached a maximum of 650 square feet with a grate area of about 10 square feet ; except in the case of the engines for the broad gauge, in which these figures had been exceeded.[2]

The maximum wheel base appears to have been about 11 feet 8 inches on the narrow gauge, about 13 feet 6 inches on the broad gauge. There was still room within the limits of the narrow gauge to increase the diameter of the boiler, but the straight sided firebox had nearly reached its limit of width. Greater heating surface could have been obtained in engines of this type by

[1] See p. 95, Chapter VI. *ante.*   [2] See p. 341, Chapter XXV. *ante.*

increasing the diameter of the boiler and the length of the firebox, and it would in fact have been possible to put on to the narrow gauge, engines having the same heating surface as the 'North Star' of the Great Western Railway, whose boiler dimensions had been closely approached by those of the narrow gauge engine built by Robert Stephenson & Co. for the Leicester and Swannington Railway in 1833.[1]

But any increase to the diameter of the boiler barrel with a view to obtaining a larger tube heating surface would have increased the tendency of the type to be heavy on the leading wheels, while any increase to the length of the firebox, which was placed between the driving and trailing axles, would have rendered necessary a corresponding increase to the wheel base. The fireboxes moreover had already been increased without a proportionate increase in tube heating surface or length of tube, with the result that smokebox temperatures were excessive. To meet these objections, and to obtain such increase in tube surface as he considered desirable, Robert Stephenson in his patent engine of 1841 placed all three axles in front of the firebox, so that the long boiler barrel which was an essential part of his intended improvement would not involve any increase to the wheel base, and it would therefore be possible to accommodate new and more powerful engines on existing turntables. This was a practical advantage, in many cases probably a necessity, which was one of the principal factors determining the design.

In his specification of 1841 [2] Robert Stephenson claims :—

It is an advantage in a six-wheeled locomotive engine which is constructed according to my first improvement that the cylindrical part of the boiler and the small tubes within it will be longer than usual, because with that greater length the heating surface in the straight tubes may be more advantageously proportioned to the heating surface in the furnace, and at the same time the whole extent of heating surface will be greater than usual in the boilers of locomotive engines, whereby the boiler will be qualified for producing more steam if required so as to enable the engine to exert more power than usual; or if no more power than usual is required, then the fuel consumption will be less in proportion to the steam that is produced.

In his long-boiler engine Robert Stephenson in fact attempted to obtain a better ratio of tube length to diameter. Replying to adverse criticism he was able to say some five years later [3] :—

Upwards of 150 engines of this description have been in daily use in this country, and on the continent for the last two or three years; the long boiler has, by every experienced and impartial locomotive manager with whom I have communicated been received as a decided improvement, so much so that since this class of engine was first introduced, the boilers of old engines have been in several cases within my own knowledge very considerably lengthened, thus offering the most incontestable proof that the old engine is admitted to be deficient in length of boiler.

In considering the proportions adopted for the long-boilers, in particular the reduced grate area provided, it must be borne in mind that they were intended to burn coke.

---

[1] See p. 314, Chapter XXIV. *ante.*   [2] Patent Specification, 23rd June 1841 (No. 8,998).
[3] *Report to the Directors of the Norfolk Railway,* 21st Jan. 1846.

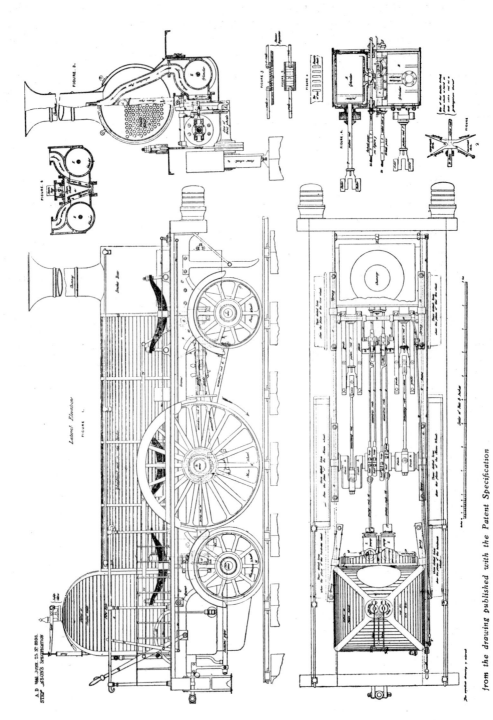

ROBERT STEPHENSON'S LONG-BOILER ENGINE, 1841, TYPE I
(Narrow Gauge 'NORTH STAR' type)

from the drawing published with the Patent Specification

VALVE
GEAR Robert Stephenson's specification claimed other improvements of considerable importance, such as the provision of a common steam chest between the cylinders, the arrangement of the slide valves as shown on the drawings, in particular their vertical, or slightly inclined, position, and a great simplification of the valve gear. To this we shall refer in our next chapter when describing the evolution of the link motion which directly followed, partly it would appear as a logical result of these improvements. Another improvement claimed was the operation of the feed pumps from the excentrics provided for the backward gear.

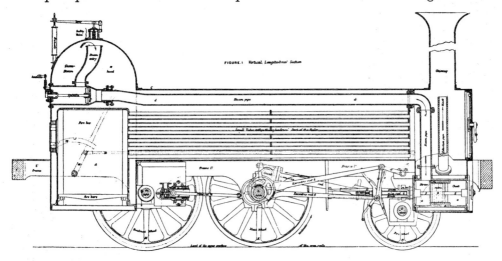

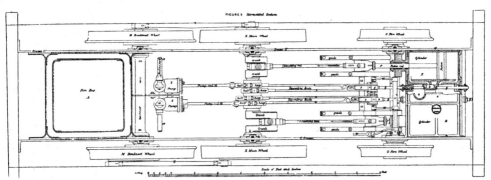

from the drawing published with the Patent Specification

ROBERT STEPHENSON'S LONG-BOILER ENGINE, 1841, TYPE II

REGULATOR Another innovation shown by the drawings was the 'gridiron' valve for the regulator, and the placing of this valve immediately over the steam chest in the smokebox. This arrangement, which was applied to some of the first engines built under the patent, does not appear to have survived long, but the 'gridiron' valve afterwards came into general use. Drawings of later Stephenson long-boiler engines show it fitted

349

to a vertical standpipe and placed over the firebox; some makers continued to place it in the smokebox, but arranged in the steam T pipe, above the tubes.

CONNECTING
ROD

The first long-boiler engines built under the patent appear to have been fitted with a connecting rod large end of marine type, as shown on the drawings offering interesting evidence of the makers' activities in another sphere of construction. In later long-boiler engines the design was modified into a form which was, however, soon abandoned in English practice, but has remained in common use on the continent. Robert Stephenson & Co. themselves returned generally to the use of the strapped end for engines with inside cylinders.

WHEELS

The drawings show a new type of wheel in which the boss is of cast iron, as on the Stephenson patent locomotive of 1833, but the spokes are made of bent angle iron. Robert Stephenson & Co. appear to have been one of the last firms to adopt the more costly solid wrought iron wheel. Opinions differed as to the merits of Stephenson's built-up wheel, but whatever its defects it must have possessed some virtues, for we find original wheels of this type in use in 1905 on the long-boiler goods engine 'Mammoth' supplied to the Paris Orleans Railway in 1846.

FRAME

One of the most notable departures from Robert Stephenson's previous practice was the adoption for his long-boiler engine of the single plate frame, placed inside the wheels, which eventually became, and remains to-day, the standard for normal British designs. The abandonment of the outside frame and bearings, with the additional inside frames and supports for the crank axle, appears as a complete reversal of the principle introduced in the 'Planet' and developed in his patent engine of 1833. Equally remarkable is the return to an overhanging firebox. In reply to subsequent criticisms of this overhanging firebox, combined with a comparatively short wheel base, Robert Stephenson stated that he had been influenced by his observations of the four-wheeled locomotives on the London and Birmingham Railway which for eight years had worked an unparalleled traffic with engines having overhanging fireboxes, without any accident which could fairly be attributed to such a peculiarity of construction.[1]

I originally objected to this projection of the firebox beyond the axle; but after an experiment continued uninterruptedly for a series of years, with an enormous traffic, it would be absurd to reject such practical evidence, and to hold such an opinion. It was this evidence that led me to the construction of the new long-boiler engine, and the abandonment of the objection I originally entertained and acted upon.

It may be that the same evidences contributed to his decision to adopt an inside frame, but we have the statement of a French engineer with whom he was well acquainted, that [2] :—

The inside frame was adopted by Mr. Stephenson with the object of reducing the cost of construction.

[1] Robert Stephenson's *Report to the Directors of the Norfolk Railway*, 21st Jan. 1846.
[2] Perdonnet, *Chemins de Fer*, Vol. III., p. 84.

The same authority observes :—

Some persons consider that engines with inside frames, in case of fracture of an axle, are less dangerous than those with outside frames. This is an error which it is important to combat.

Further, regarding the cost, we have the makers' statement in 1843 that 'the cost of the patent engines was less than of those upon the old plan.' [1] In view of the keen competition among locomotive builders at the time, and in consideration of the evidence we have quoted, it appears that this reduction in cost may have been the primary reason for Robert Stephenson's decision to abandon the outside frame and inside support, and that what he had considered to be a counsel of perfection in design had to be sacrificed to commercial considerations. On the other hand there is evidence that the risk of broken axles was now much reduced, at any rate in England. But, whatever the relative value of the several reasons, the effect of Bury's influence on the design of the long-boiler engine generally is not only apparent, but admitted, for Robert Stephenson never failed to give credit where it was due.

In their *Circular*, from which we have already quoted [2], Bury, Curtis & Co. advert with 'some satisfaction' to the fact that :—

In the latest invention of an eminent engineer the outside frame is now being abandoned, or at least that the inside framing has been adopted in that instance, and the large firebox dispensed with.

Robert Stephenson & Co.'s hopes of their long-boiler engines were soon realised ; many engineers testified to their more economical performance, and their lower cost was an advantage to both makers and buyers. A contemporary periodical records the result of the trials of one of the first of the new engines [3] :—

The alteration in the construction of the boiler and tubing gives a heating surface of 800 superficial feet, whereas in the ordinary engine it rarely exceeds 450 feet, being for the new plan a superiority of fully 350 feet. Such is the effect produced by this addition, that the temperature of the air escaping in the chimney scarcely exceeds the temperature of the water in the boiler; a circumstance which has a further beneficial effect beyond the economy of fuel, for it has been found, by increasing the extent of heating surface, and employing usefully the whole of the heat generated in the fire that a less violent draught of air is required; the consequence is that very few hot ashes are thrown out of the chimney; this peculiarity is quite remarkable in the engine now running. A few days since, a journey of 90 miles was performed by this engine, during which no ashes were thrown out of the top of the chimney, and at the same time the accumulation in the smokebox was very trifling, not exceeding a fourth of the usual quantity. As the tendency to eject ashes from the chimney is dependent upon the speed, it is necessary to state, that the speed was never below 20 miles per hour, generally exceeding 30, and for several miles a speed of 48 miles per hour was uniformly attained, with five loaded coaches.

The consumption of fuel during the above experiment was 19·2 lbs. per mile with a load of 8 coaches over half the distance (45 miles), and five coaches over the remaining half. This consumption includes the whole of the fuel used in lighting the fire and raising the steam.

[1] Cook, for Robert Stephenson & Co., letter to Edward Pease, 11th Dec. 1842. See p. 97, Chapter VI. *ante.*

[2] See p. 328, Chapter XXIV. *ante.* See Herbert's *Engineer's and Mechanic's Encyclopaedia*, 1849, Vol. II.

[3] *Railway Times*, 1842, Vol. V., p. 388, from *The Civil Engineer and Architect's Journal.* We have omitted some of the dimensions given as we have been unable to reconcile them with other records.

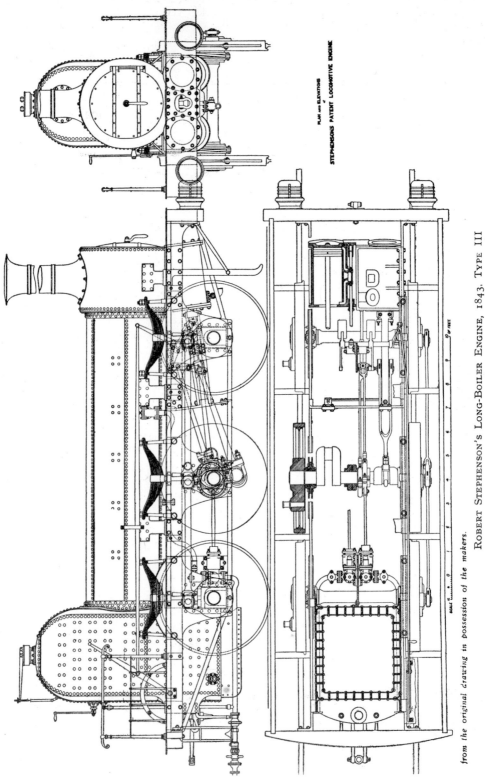

PLAN and ELEVATIONS

STEPHENSON'S PATENT LOCOMOTIVE ENGINE

from the original drawing in possession of the makers.

Robert Stephenson's Long-Boiler Engine, 1843. Type III

(The 'Mammoth' type see p. 102 *ante*)

(*Erratum*—p. 102, for 1844 read 1845)

The following are the principal dimensions of the engine now working on the York and North Midland Railway:—

Diameter of cylinder	....	....	....	....	....	14 inches.
Length of stroke	....	....	....	....	....	20
Diameter of driving wheels		....	....	....	....	5½ feet.
Diameter of small wheels	....	....	....	....	....	3

LONG-BOILER FIRST AND SECOND TYPES — Two types are described in the patent specification, the first to have single driving wheels, 5 feet 6 inches diameter, leading and trailing wheels 4 feet 6 inches diameter, with a wheel base of 10 feet 9 inches; the boiler barrel to have a diameter of 3 feet 1 inch, with a length of 11 feet 9 inches, and to contain 150 tubes 1⅝ inch diameter. One of the first engines to be built under the patent was called by the still favourite name 'North Star.' This particular engine was built for the 5 foot gauge of the Northern and Eastern Railway, but was the proto-type of its class for the 4 foot 8⅓ inch gauge. Its dimensions differ from those given in the patent specification.[1]

The second type described has the driving and trailing wheels coupled, 4 feet 6 inches diameter.[2] The cylinders in both types are given as 14 inches diameter by 20 inches stroke.

LONG-BOILER THIRD TYPE — In 1843 the principle of the long boiler was applied to a six-coupled engine having wheels 4 feet 9 inches diameter, and cylinders increased to 15 inches diameter by 24 inches stroke. The dimensions of the boiler were considerably increased and engines of this type were the most powerful of their time. The performances of a typical engine the 'Hercules,' of the York and North Midland Railway have been recorded at length in the report on the 'gauge experiments,' to which we shall refer in a succeeding chapter.

OUTSIDE CYLINDERS — Early in 1843 Robert Stephenson modified the design of the first long-boiler type by placing the cylinders outside the frame and increasing the stroke to 22 inches. This change in position, which he afterwards regretted, was made to meet difficulties experienced on the continent with broken crank axles, 'where'—he said speaking in 1849—'it was still very difficult to make a good crank axle, but the same objection did not exist in England.' He further observed that since high speeds were not then required on continental railways the tendency to oscillation which would result from the use of outside cylinders did not appear of immediate importance at the time of their adoption.[3] Towards the end of 1843 he reduced the diameter of the cylinders to 13 inches and further increased the stroke to 24 inches, in a 'Pattern' engine built for the Marseilles-Avignon Railway. This engine had a total heating surface of about 860 square feet and the weight is recorded as about 22 tons.

[1] The makers record of this period present some internal discrepancies which cannot be reconciled with each other, or with other known records. Engines ordered for one railway were frequently transferred to another, and the maker's consecutive numbers do not necessarily show sequence of construction. The dimensions and particulars which we give must be accepted with this reservation, and the identity suggested for particular engines may be open to question. The information we have given is however sufficient to illustrate on broad lines the development of the locomotive by Robert Stephenson & Co. between 1840 and 1846.

[2] For a late engine of this type, built in 1856, see p. 110, Chapter VI. *ante.*

[3] *Proc. Inst. Civil Engineers,* 1849, Vol. VIII., p. 242.

from a model by Clair, 1848, in the Conservatoire des Arts et Métiers, Paris.

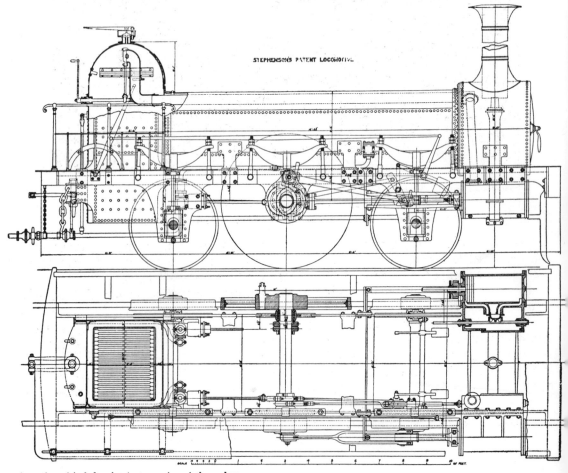

STEPHENSON'S PATENT LOCOMOTIVE

from the original drawing in possession of the makers.

ROBERT STEPHENSON'S LONG-BOILER ENGINE, 1843, TYPE I MODIFIED

'Pattern Engine,' with outside cylinders

LONG-BOILERS IN FRANCE Many long-boiler engines of the original and the succeeding modified types, were supplied by Robert Stephenson & Co. to continental railways, and in France particularly they had an influence on design which was both immediate and lasting. In December 1843 all the locomotives on order from Robert Stephenson & Co., including fifteen for the Marseilles-Avignon Railway, were to be of the 'patent' type. Two long-boiler engines of the new 'North Star' type, with inside cylinders and single driving wheels, supplied to the Paris-Orleans Railway in 1843, had a long career, and were copied at the railway company's works at Ivry and elsewhere.[1] Long-boiler engines of the second type, with four wheels coupled, and outside cylinders, were also widely adopted and became in France the

from a photo in the collection of Mr. E. L. Ahrons.

LONG-BOILER ENGINE ON THE GREAT EASTERN RAILWAY
built by Robert Stephenson & Co. in 1847, rebuilt in 1867 as shown

classic design for mixed traffic, large numbers being built by various companies until towards 1880.[2] The four-coupled type with outside cylinders was also supplied to other continental and to home railways.

THE 'MAMMOTH' Of the six-wheeled long-boiler engine with inside cylinders, a classic example, the 'Mammoth,' supplied to the Paris-Orleans Railway in 1846, was followed by every French builder,'with some variations in the design of details, and a notable increase in evaporating power.' In 1886 there were in France alone more than 600 such engines in service, which, after having had their boilers renewed, were frequently worked on mixed trains at speeds of 50 kilometres per hour.[3] Engines having

[1] Deghilage, *Origine de la Locomotive*, 1886, p. 37.
[2] Communicated to Robert Stephenson & Co. by M. Ferdinand Achard, 6th Feb. 1923.
[3] Deghilage, *Origine de la Locomotive*, 1886, p 42, see p. 102, Chapter VI. *ante.*

from a photo taken in 1875, now in possession of the makers.

LONG-BOILER ENGINE, 'HERCULES' TYPE
built by Robert Stephenson & Co. in 1845

from a photo in the collection of M. Ferdinand Achard.

LONG-BOILER 'STEPHENSON GOODS ENGINE' ON THE 'NORD' RAILWAY, FRANCE
as built by various French makers in 1846

this wheel arrangement were also built by Robert Stephenson & Co. with outside cylinders. Some of this type, built by French makers in 1846, and subsequently fitted with new boilers, are at work to-day. Our illustration shows one of these engines in its primitive state.[1]

The six-coupled long-boiler goods engine has persisted everywhere in its primitive form, and within the limits of its capacity it is still to-day, as it was when designed, one of the most useful types of locomotive anywhere at work; its equable weight distribution and short wheel base making it specially suitable for operating goods traffic in sidings and station yards. So late as 1866 engines of this type were built by Robert Stephenson & Co. for the North Eastern Railway. Their outside frames give them a peculiar interest.[2] On the continent thousands of long-boiler engines have been put into service since the 'Mammoth' was supplied to the Paris-Orleans Railway, and the Stephenson long-boiler engine remains the standard six-coupled locomotive in Europe to-day.

from a contemporary print in the collection of Mr. Isaac Briggs.

NORTH VIEW OF CAMDEN STATION
ON THE LONDON AND NORTH WESTERN RAILWAY, 1849

[1] Communicated to Robert Stephenson & Co. by M. Ferdinand Achard, 6th Feb. 1923. See also *Railway Gazette*, June 13th 1923, Vol. XVIII., p. 727.
[2] See p. 412, Chapter XXIX. following.

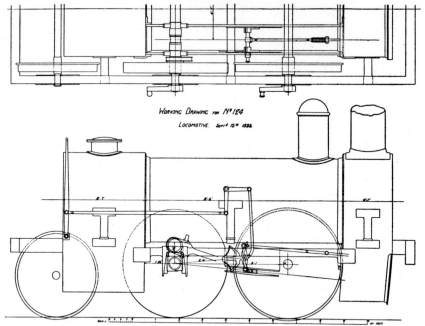

traced from the original drawing dated 15th September 1835.

ENGINE NO. 124 WITH TWO FIXED EXCENTRICS AND SINGLE REVERSING LEVER

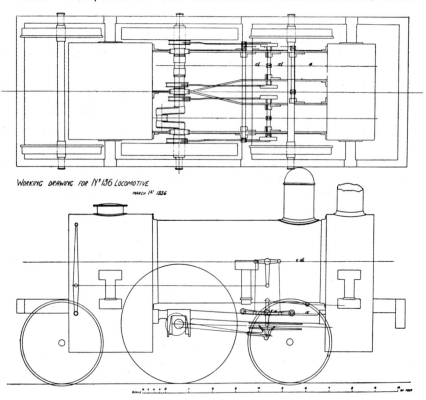

traced from the original drawing dated 1st March 1836.

ENGINE NO. 136 WITH FOUR FIXED EXCENTRICS AND SINGLE REVERSING LEVER

CHAPTER XXVII

EVOLUTION OF THE 'STEPHENSON' LINK MOTION
1835—1842

The Link-Motion, the valve gear which, since the adoption of high pressure steam by Trevithick, has contributed more to the development of the steam engine than any single improvement introduced between the time of Watt and our own day, embodied, like the locomotive of 1840, the inventions and ideas of many engineers. It was the culmination of various efforts, if not to obtain expansive working of steam, at least to improve upon, and finally to eliminate, the loose excentric and a multiplicity of reversing handles. It is impossible within our present limits to deal with all these attempts, to give credit to all who were concerned in them, or to determine their exact chronological order.

We shall confine ourselves here to describing such attempts as are recorded by drawings still in the possession of Robert Stephenson & Co., showing the sequence in which some of these improvements were adopted, or introduced, by this firm.

TWO FIXED EXCENTRICS We have described the loose excentric gear applied by Robert Stephenson & Co. to the 'Rocket,' then to the 'Planet' class, and to succeeding engines of the type, until 1835. The first drawing still in the possession of the firm to record a different arrangement is for Locomotive No. 124, dated 15th September 1835. It shows that by that date Robert Stephenson & Co. had adopted two fixed excentrics, with an arrangement of double gabs [1], with spreading jaws, at the end of each excentric rod, one or other of which gabs, could be made to engage with one or other of the two arms on the rocking lever which operated the valve. In the one combination the motion of the valve was derived directly from that of the excentric, in the other combination it was reversed by means of the rocking lever. The provision of the jaws, which as they were moved into position embraced the pin in the valve lever and guided it into the gab, made it possible to reverse the valve by means of a single lever.

The arrangement now adopted was an adaptation of a valve gear which had been applied by Carmichael, of Dundee, in 1818.[2] Its advantages appear to have been immediately recognised by Robert Stephenson & Co., and a note in their records, dated 26th October 1835, specifies that the 'new hand gear' is to be fitted ; a later note referring to a locomotive on order, records on 19th January 1836 that 'the new reversing gear might be put on if agreeable to the company's engineer.' For another engine it is specified that :—

[1] Gab—of obscure origin—cf. Flemish *gabbe*, notch, gash. *New English Dictionary*.

[2] D. K. Clark, *Railway Machinery*, 1855, p. 21 Matthias Baldwin in America anticipated Stephenson's use of this gear. See *Mechanics' Magazine*, June 27 1855. Vol. XXIII., p. 240 (from *Journal of Franklin Institute*).

The Excentrics may be made to shift on the crank axle in the manner hitherto generally adopted, or fixed on the axle, provided the method of 'changing the gear' and the other conditions requisite for placing the slide valve correctly when the engine travels backwards or forwards are approved by the Company's Engineer.

FOUR FIXED EXCENTRICS

The next important step taken by Robert Stephenson & Co. was the adoption of four fixed excentrics, which are shown on a drawing for locomotive No. 136 dated 1st March 1836.

The first use of four fixed excentrics in England has been ascribed to Forrester & Co. of Liverpool, in 1834, and to R. & W. Hawthorn, in 1835, respectively. These claims for priority, and others, have been, as in so many other cases, the subject of controversy.[1] That the controversy is no new one is shown by a letter written to Robert Stephenson & Co. by the Baltimore and Susquehanna Railroad Company on 8th March 1850 :—

In 1836, this Company and the Wrightsville York & Gettysburg R.R. Co., contracted with you through the agency of A. & G. Ralston & Co., for two Locomotives each. This Company working the latter road purchased the two imported for them. Each locomotive had four excentrics and the Company is now threatened with a suit for an alleged infringement of a Patent right issued to Col. Stephen H. Long 17th Jany. 1833 amongst other things, the use of four *excentrics*. Will you please inform me when you commenced using 4 excentrics and whether it was patented in England and if so when?

You built for this Company in 1831 a small locomotive with four wheels which had but two excentrics.

Unfortunately no record of the reply to this letter has been preserved. We shall not attempt to answer here the question asked by the American railroad company, and recently again under discussion ; the first adoption of four fixed excentrics does not appear to have been claimed at any time for Robert Stephenson & Co. and our present purpose is to simply record the date of the first use of four such excentrics by this firm, so far as it can be determined by their existing records. It appears that Hawthorns' in their first adoption of four fixed excentrics did not at once take full advantage of them. A contemporary drawing of a celebrated locomotive [2] to which this gear was fitted, shows that the old method for engaging the excentric rods with the valve operating lever had been retained, requiring as it did the use of several handles.

But Robert Stephenson & Co.'s drawing of 1st March 1836 shows that they had improved the gear by providing jaws on the excentric rods, making it possible to use a single lever for reversing. With the new four-excentric gear it was no longer necessary to engage the excentric rods alternatively with pins at the opposite ends of the lever, since each rod had its motion determined by its own excentric, set for forward or backward motion. Each excentric rod had to engage in its turn with the same pin on the valve operating lever accordingly as backward or forward gear was required. It was therefore necessary, when engaging the gab of one rod with the pin, to disengage the other

---

[1] See correspondence in *The Engineer*, Vol. CXXXI., p. 594 *et seq.*

[2] Hawthorn's 'Comet' for the Newcastle and Carlisle Railway. See Simms, *Public Works of Great Britain*, 1836, Vol. I., p. 69. Plate LXXVII. See also '*The Locomotive*,' Vol. XXVII., p. 127, for description and drawings.

gab ; one rod had to be raised into the desired position, the other had to be lowered, and various arrangements were adopted to effect this movement.

In Robert Stephenson & Co.'s first four-excentric gear these opposite movements to the excentric rods were obtained from the opposite arms of a bell-crank on the side of the boiler, the arms of the bell crank being connected to the arms of two independent shafts between the frames. Later the bell-crank was abolished, and the two shafts below the boiler were themselves directly connected by a link and controlled by a lever on one shaft, which was connected to the reversing lever. The two shafts were so arranged that when the lifting arm of the one was lowered, the lifting arm of the other was raised, with the excentric rod attached to it in each case.

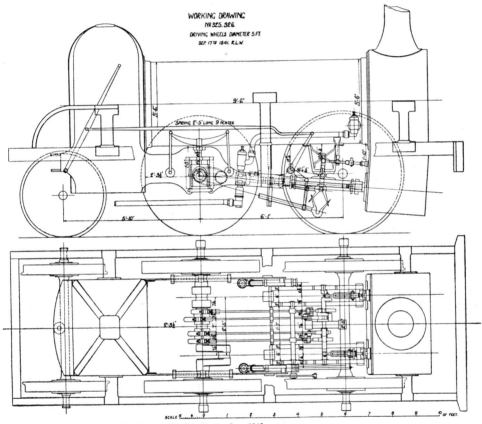

traced from the original drawing dated 17th September 1841.

FORKED GABS ON THE EXCENTRIC RODS AS APPLIED BY BUDDICOM

(see next page)

The gear just described was fitted to the 'Harvey Combe' in 1835[1] and subsequently to many other Stephenson locomotives, including the broad gauge 'North Star' for the Great Western Railway[2] ; it appears to have been as simple as most, and better than some, of those in use at the time, since the shafts were

[1] See p. 318, Chapter XXIV. *ante.*   [2] See p. 340, Chapter XXV. *ante*

self-balancing. The objection to this, and other contemporary arrangements as a whole, was in the considerable space required for the various shafts and levers.

It will be observed that in the gears we have just described the gabs for both rods are directed upwards ; in the engine built by Robert Stephenson & Co. for Russia, Locomotive No. 163, the gabs are directed downwards.[1]

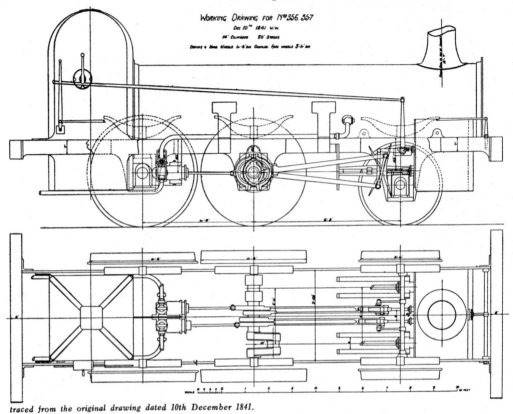

traced from the original drawing dated 10th December 1841.

FIXED COMBINED GABS UNITED ON THE VALVE SPINDLE
by Robert Stephenson in his patent Long-Boiler Locomotive, 1841

OPPOSITE
GAB MOTION

In a later gear, sometimes ascribed to Sharp, Roberts & Co.[2], the gabs on the rods point towards each other. This arrangement, with some improvements, was used by Buddicom in France, and a drawing for Locomotive No. 325, dated 17th September 1841 shows that it had been adopted by Robert Stephenson & Co. at this date in a very simple form. It is worth noting as a step towards the link, which is obvious enough in the light of later developments.[3]

Although the use of four excentrics had made it unnecessary to reverse the motion at the valve by means of a rocking lever, this lever had been re-

---

[1] See p. 322, Chapter XXIV. *ante.*   [2] D. K. Clark, *Railway Machinery*, 1855, pp. 22, 23.

[3] See previous page 361.

tained in the arrangements we have above described and the slide valves were still placed on top of the cylinders.

FIXED COMBINED GABS AND DIRECT DRIVE — The next great improvement adopted by Robert Stephenson is described in the specification for his long-boiler engine of 1841. In his new arrangement the gabs instead of being on the ends of independent rods are combined in X form, as in the adaptation of Carmichael's gear applied by Robert Stephenson & Co. in 1835. The combined gabs are however no longer attached to a movable excentric rod, raised or lowered as required to engage with the pin on the valve rod, but they are fixed directly to the valve rod and are consequently capable of movement in a horizontal direction only. The ends of the excentric rods are again made movable up and down, as in the two last gears we have described, but in this case the rods are themselves fitted with pins at their extremities to engage, as the case may be, with the upper or lower fixed gab on the valve rod.

A great simplification and reduction in the number of parts has been effected, the valves are now placed between the cylinders, and the valve rocking lever is no longer required. The new arrangement still permitted of only one point of cut-off for the steam in the cylinder, but had the great advantages we have mentioned [1], and with the previous gear marks an important stage in development and improvement. This stage has however been little noticed, since it was almost immediately followed by another of greater importance.

THE LINK MOTION — It is recorded that in 1841 Robert Stephenson, visiting Derby, said to the locomotive superintendent of the North Midland Railway, who had been experimenting for him with different valve gears—'there is no occasion to try any further at scheming valve motions ; one of our people has now hit upon a plan that beats all the other valve motions.' [2] This invention was the link motion, ever since known as the 'Stephenson Link.' Looking at the drawings to which we have referred, it is easy now to imagine a process of thought by which either the fixed combined forked gab, just introduced by Robert Stephenson in his long-boiler patent, or the opposing forked gabs of Buddicom, might develop into a slot, and it is probable that the link motion was the result of some such inspiration. But whatever the actual circumstances or process of thought in the minds of the men whose names have since been associated with it, it is indisputable, that certain advantages of the link motion soon became apparent, and within a few years the credit for its invention became, as in the case of other improvements, a subject of public controversy.

In 1846 a statement was published [3] ascribing the invention to William Williams, a young draughtsman [4] in the employ of Robert Stephenson & Co. This statement was shortly afterwards challenged by William Howe, then

---

[1] See p. 349, Chapter XXVI. *ante.*

[2] W. P. Marshall, *Evolution of the Locomotive Engine. Proc. Inst. Civil Engineers*, Vol. CXXXIII., p. 277.

[3] *Practical Mechanic and Engineers' Magazine*, 1846, Vol. I., pp. 167, 168, 192.

[4] Williams is decribed by Howe as 'a young gentleman apprentice.'

employed by the same firm as a patternmaker. Howe in his claim conceded to Williams the 'original *idea* of employing a species of link, as an expansive gear '[1], but stated that as first proposed by Williams, with its ends attached directly to the excentrics, the arrangement would have been unworkable. Howe further stated that it was only the addition by himself of rods between the link and the excentrics which made the arrangement workable. The controversy is in some respects more painful, but at the same time more justifiable than some others with which we have had to deal, though it does

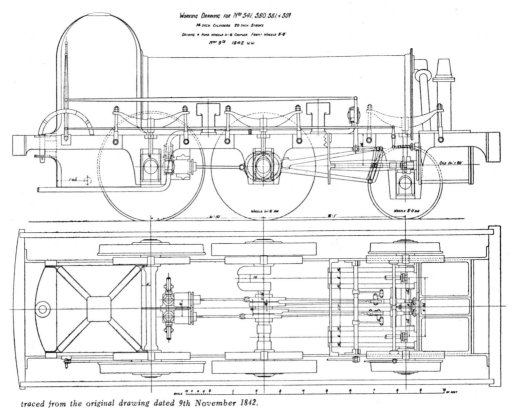

traced from the original drawing dated 9th November 1842.

THE FIRST LINK MOTION AS APPLIED TO ENGINE NO. 359

not appear at any time to have excited the same general interest or to have engendered the same heat. But, painful as it is, it cannot be entirely ignored in our pages, since it has been raised again in recent years by a statement published in 1904 [2] on the authority of Ralph Little Whyte, whose indentures show that he was apprenticed to Robert Stephenson & Co. in April 1837, and by his own statement was in charge of their drawing office in 1842. His initials appear on several of the firms' original drawings to which we have just referred.

[1] *Practical Mechanic and Engineers' Magazine*, 1846, Vol. I., p. 192.
[2] *American Machinist*, 11th Feb. 1904, Vol. XXVII., p. 178.

Whyte in his statement disputes Howe's claim to any original share in the invention. The publication of Whyte's statement in 1904 brought to light an earlier written statement by George K. Douglas, who had been a contemporary with Whyte, Williams and Howe, and afterwards became general manager of Robert Stephenson & Co.'s works.[1] From this statement it appears that in 1870 there was a proposal to promote a testimonial to Howe as inventor of the link motion.[2] To this proposal Douglas objected on the grounds that the whole of the credit was due to Williams. Though in this contention he is in agreement with Whyte, his account differs considerably in detail, and, since both statements are based on late reminiscence, little is to be gained by an attempt to reconcile them in every respect.

The case revolves largely round the circumstances concerning a sketch, or model, made by Williams to demonstrate his discovery, and the sequence of events connected with these, but *on one point Howe, Whyte and Douglas agree*—and it is a vital point—that *the idea of the link itself was due to Williams*. There is also general agreement that the first sketch or model made by Williams showed this link attached directly to the excentric straps ; but in regard to the sequence of events connected with the sketch or models the statements are widely at variance. The published sketches purporting to show Williams' first suggestion show that he was in a fair way to the discovery of the stationary link, as it was afterwards evolved by Gooch in modification of the 'Stephenson link,' and that Howe, by introducing excentric rods and taking the link forward to a block on the valve spindle, (a position which may well have been suggested by the combined fixed gabs just adopted in the long-boiler patent,) completed the inevitable evolution of the Link-Motion.

In 1851 a claim for infringement of patent was brought against the London and North Western Railway Company on account of their locomotives fitted with the ' Stephenson ' link motion. John Gray, the plaintiff, had himself invented an expansion gear in 1839.[3] Among the witnesses was Howe, who it appears had been asked by Robert Stephenson & Co. to give evidence in a case which they considered to be ' of the utmost importance not only to railway companies but to manufacturers.'[4]

Howe under examination claimed to be the ' inventor of the link motion.' When asked whether, and why, he had not been able to get a patent for it, he replied—'I do not think there was ever one applied for. There seemed to be a doubt whether it would act effectively or not at the time.' Howe added, in reply to a further question as to his pecuniary circumstances, that 'he had not been in a condition to take out a patent.' When examined as to his knowledge of experiments made about the same time to obtain expansive working

---

[1] *American Machinist*, 14th July 1904, Vol. XXVII., p. 924.
Letter from the late Mr. W. H. Crow, then works manager for Robert Stephenson & Co.

[2] *The History of the Invention of the Link Motion*. N. P. Burgh. *The Engineer*, Vol. XXVIII., p. 346.

[3] A complicated gear known as the 'Horse Leg' Motion. For performance of engines fitted with this gear, see *Railway Gazette*, 30th March 1923, Vol. XXXVIII.

[4] Letter from W. Weallens to Howe, quoted by N. P. Burgh, letter to *The Engineer*, Vol. XXIX, p. 7.

of steam, Howe replied that 'he was not acquainted with any that were tried before that,' but 'recollected a plan of Mr. Dodds that was tried about that time.' Asked whether it had then become an important object in the performance of locomotion to work the steam expansively, Howe replied—'I cannot say . . . . I only know what was generally said to be wanted.' He added that he 'was acquainted with the working of Mr. Dodds' motion, and it was understood to effect the point which was really wanted,' and that he 'tried to effect that point more simply. It was the reversing the engine in combination with working it expansively.'

Whyte in his published statement says that the sufficiency of Williams' idea for all these purposes was fully realised and demonstrated by himself in the drawing office at the time, to the satisfaction of William Hutchinson, then works manager. In considering this statement we must remember that attempts to arrange for the expansive working of steam in locomotives were no novelty. Robert Stephenson & Co. had indeed made their first crude attempt on the 'Lancashire Witch' in 1828, and we have just mentioned Gray's valve gear of 1839. The desire for an improvement in the means for reversing was due to the fact that although it was possible to reverse with the gab motion at forty miles an hour ' it was a very awkward thing to do, and many engines had been broken down by doing it.'[1] Williams, as a draughtsman, must have been well aware of the attempted improvements, and conversant with the various arrangements which immediately preceded the link motion; he no doubt had before him the identical drawings which we now reproduce, indeed the working drawing showing the parts of the first link motion as actually made bears his initials, and they appear on other drawings of the period.

Howe's qualifications as an engineer were no doubt considerable; we have already noted that he became engineer at George Stephenson's Clay Cross collieries in 1846[2], and his subsequent work there gives evidence of his capabilities; we have further evidence of these in the design for a three-cylinder locomotive patented by him jointly with George Stephenson in 1846, and in various applications of the link motion. Many writers, possibly on these accounts, have hitherto ascribed to Howe the whole of the credit for its invention, but evidence has been preserved to show that such a view was not held by the late Mr. George Robert Stephenson who, referring to the proposed testimonial to Howe which was then under consideration, wrote the following letter under date 2nd November 1870[3]:—

I have refrained from answering yours of last month, enclosing a letter from Mr. Binns[4] relating to the invention of the Link Motion, for the simple reason that it is not a pleasant matter to deal with.

---

[1] Gooch, Evidence before the Arbitrator in the *Link Motion Case, Gray v. London & North Western Railway Company*, Oct. 22nd 1855. (*MSS.* notes preserved at the Inst. Mechanical Engineers.)

[2] See p. 101, Chapter VI. *ante.*

[3] Letter from the late Mr. G. R. Stephenson to George A. Crow, 2nd Nov. 1870.

[4] Then secretary at the Clay Cross Collieries, and one of the promoters of the proposed testimonial.

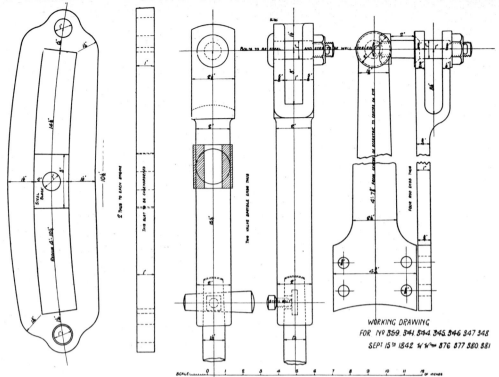

traced from the original drawing signed by W. Williams, 15th September 1842.

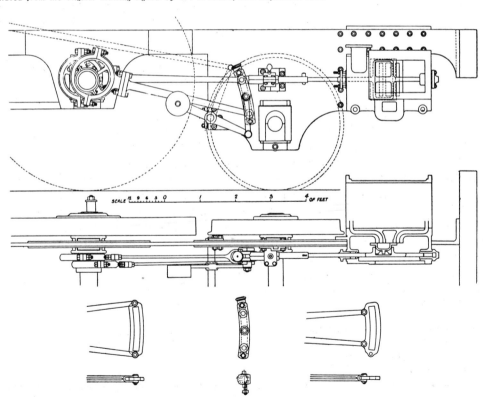

traced from an original (undated) drawing.

LINK MOTION AS FITTED BY ROBERT STEPHENSON & CO. IN 1848

Three forms of link are shown, in the sequence of adoption; the box link appears to have been first fitted about 1843. See p. 352, 354 *ante*.

It is to be regretted that Mr. Binns had not been made fully acquainted with the late Mr. Williams' professional abilities, for had this been done, my personal knowledge of Mr. Binns confirms me in the assurance that he would be the last man to say that Williams was either unpractical or vague in his mechanical ideas. Mr. Williams was well known to me, and was one of my principal assistants. He was a thorough and talented mechanic, and was connected with many of the various works under my control.

My recollections of the matter, supported by frequent conversations with the late George and Robert Stephenson, differ so much from the views expressed in Mr. Binns' letter, that in justice to the memory of the dead, I feel bound to express my strongest disapproval of giving praise wholly to the one, whilst I believe equal credit is due to them both.

I have always heard my predecessors, who best knew the rights of this question, give Mr. Howe the highest praise for the part he took in bringing out the Link Motion, but never without associating Mr. Williams' name also with the invention; and I would willingly not only have contributed to a testimonial to a man I respect, but would have made myself a partisan to its success, had I felt that the merits of both were fairly dealt with.

The promoters of the proposed testimonial to Howe, influenced no doubt by such privately expressed opinions as we have quoted above, and by opinions and statements published during 1870 [1], eventually appealed on 25th July 1871 for subscriptions to 'A Testimonial for the Invention of the Link Motion in which the names of Williams and Howe are combined.'

Their printed circular proceeds :—

The Committee formed at Chesterfield for promoting the Testimonial have recognised the claim made on behalf of the former gentleman (with the concurrence of Mr. Howe) after a strict and impartial investigation into the merits of the case, and have adopted the view expressed by Mr. D. K. Clark in his valuable work on Railway Machinery [2], and it is hoped that this will for ever decide the disputed claim to this invaluable improvement to the Locomotive and Winding Engine which have since been so generally applied.

DODDS' WEDGE MOTION

In a strictly chronological order this motion should perhaps have received mention before the link motion, but we have deferred reference to it since it appears rather as a departure from the lines of development which led eventually to the link, than as a stage in such development. Dodds' motion is shown on a drawing for Locomotive No. 358 dated June 29th 1842, and it appears that it was intended to fit it to two engines ordered from Robert Stephenson & Co. for the North Midland Railway, but that during their construction the link motion was brought out and fitted to the second of the two engines.[3] This wedge motion was patented in 1839 by Isaac Dodds, a nephew of Ralph Dodds, colliery viewer at Killingworth.[4] A letter from the inventor to William Hutchinson

[1] See correspondence in *The Engineer*, Vol. XXIX.

[2] Extract from D. K. Clark, *Railway Machinery*, 1855, p. 26.
'Nothing but an impulse of genius could have given birth to this exquisite motion; and though in its first conception by Mr. Williams it was rude, and even impracticable, the idea was there, and it had only to be cleverly worked out by Mr. Howe to render it, in conjunction with the lap of the valve, the most felicitous acquisition to the locomotive since the introduction of the blast-pipe and the multitubular flue.'

[3] Howe's evidence in case *Gray v. London & North Western Railway Company*. MSS. notes preserved at the Inst. Mechanical Engineers.

[4] Isaac Dodds was a pupil under George Stephenson at the Forth Street works, and it is stated that 'during his apprenticeship he made a model of the horizontal cylinders for the locomotive engine and advocated their adoption in preference to the vertical cylinders then made.' Memoir, *Proc. Inst. Civil Engineers*, Vol. LXXV. We have been unable to find any contemporary evidence in support of the statement quoted above, or to ascertain the date of the model.
See also *A Story of Railway Pioneers*, 1922, by Major S. Snell, M.C., to whom we are indebted for information and for the letter which we quote.

is recorded in an early description book still in the possession of Robert Stephenson & Co.

Dodds writes on 4th March 1842 :—

When Mr. Stephenson called here the other day, I was confined from attending him, and he took with him my model for expansive working of Engines, which was not finished. The wedges where the guides are placed will require to be made longer as they have all the thickness of guides less stroke of wedge, hence work further in one direction than in the opposite one, this can be remedied at once, and should it fall into your hands you will please see to this— it may be variously guided and driven, but in my opinion the model will be found very simple. I would advise the changing part to be placed as *per* very rough sketch underneath, or if not racks and arcs any other lever you may prefer. I merely offer the lever. Pick out (if anything is worth having) that which is useful, that which you deem of no use throw aside. Mr. Vickerman will call on you in a day or two, I sent a message with him to you.

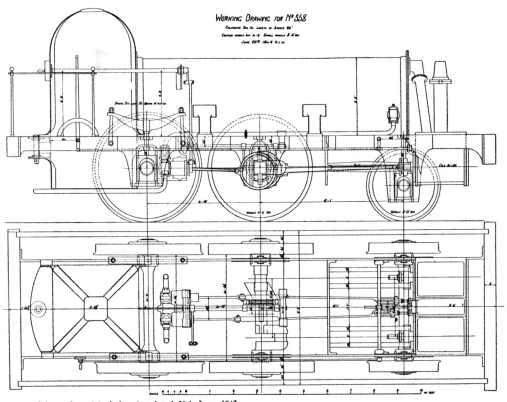

traced from the original drawing dated 29th June 1842.

DODDS' SHIFTING ECCENTRIC WEDGE MOTION

The writer gives a sketch showing his proposals for reversing the gear and adds :—

I ought to have said to Mr. Stephenson that in changing this motion one valve only moves the length of the lap, hence you have only the weight of one valve or a little more to move. I am certain it will be easy to reverse if well fitted.

We have also an interesting reference to Dodds' valve motion, and incidentally to the economy of the Stephenson long boiler, in a letter written to Dodds by the locomotive superintendent of the North Midland Railway, Thomas Kirtley, under date 4th April 1844 :—

> Yours of the 1st inst. is duly at hand, and I can assure you that you have with all willingness my opinion and testimony respecting your Patented Eccentric Motion. Your motion was put upon 3 of the last Coupled Engines this Company had made—One by Messrs. Stephenson & Co. of Newcastle and two by Messrs. Kitson & Co. of Leeds.—The Engines have been at work regularly since the latter end of the year, 1842—the trifling repairs required to the machinery have been exceedingly little, and what *has been* required I consider is owing to the position of the Pumps. The saving of fuel by these Engines is very considerable altho, it is but fair to state, the Motions are put upon Messrs. Stephenson & Co.'s *long Engines*. The motion lately supplied by you, which I intend to put on one of our ordinary Engines is not yet fixed, so that I am not able to speak to the saving effected over the common Motion. My opinion is that when tried the result will be very favourable. To apply your Motion direct, as in our case, the only machinery or joints required, beyond the Eccentric, are two Eccentric Rods connected to the Valve Spindles in a direct line; in fact, in point of simplicity it exceeds anything that I have yet seen.

Unfortunately for Dodds the introduction of his motion had coincided with the discovery of the shifting link, obviously far superior to the shifting excentric for purposes of reversing, and found to give all that could be desired in means for obtaining expansive working of steam by varying the point of cut off in the cylinder. Such were its virtues indeed that the link motion, after it became known, was to hold its own in England and America for the next three-quarters of a century.

Later, the combination of high steam pressures, with large flat valves, and the adoption of axles so large as to make it impossible to keep the diameter of the excentrics within reasonable limits, was to lead to a general use of valve gears in which such excentrics were not required. But within the limits of its capacity the Link Motion remains one of the best valve gears ever applied, and for simplicity it has never been surpassed, though even after its advantages had been established in practice innumerable attempts were made to supersede it, by devices of a more 'geometrical,' but more complicated nature, usually involving an increase to the number of parts and pin joints and often representing 'what George Stephenson used to phrase the danger of too much ingenuity.'[1]

Owing probably to the dispute as to the sequence of events connected with its development by the two men most directly concerned, the link motion has never been generally known by the name of either. It might well have been called the 'Williams-Howe' Motion, but it soon became, and is to-day universally known as the 'Stephenson Link Motion,' from the name of the firm who first fitted it.

[1] D. K. Clark, *Railway Machinery*, 1855, p. 23.

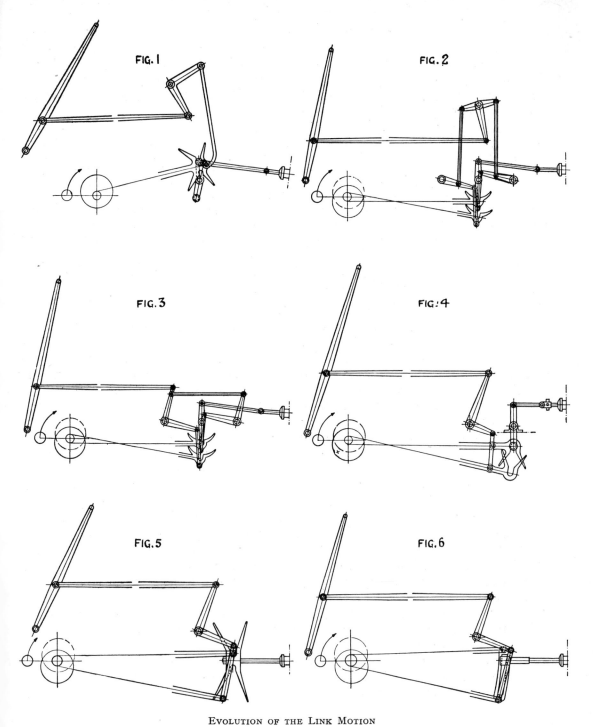

EVOLUTION OF THE LINK MOTION

The gear is shown for one side of the engine, *i.e.* for one cylinder, in each case.

Fig. 1.	Two Fixed Excentrics, Carmichael's gear as first applied by Robert Stephenson & Co., 1835.	(See p. 358).
Fig. 2.	Four Fixed Excentrics, with forked gabs and single reversing lever, as applied by Stephenson.	(,, ,,).
Fig. 3.	,, ,, ,, as before, but with reversing shafts below boiler ,, ,, ,,	(,, 317).
Fig. 4.	,, ,, ,, with forks opposed, and single reversing shaft, as applied by Buddicom.	(,, 361).
Fig. 5.	,, ,, ,, with gabs combined on valve spindle, as applied by Stephenson, 1841.	(,, 362).
Fig. 6.	,, ,, ,, united with slotted link, by Williams, and developed by Howe, 1842.	(,, 364).

[*To face page 370.*]

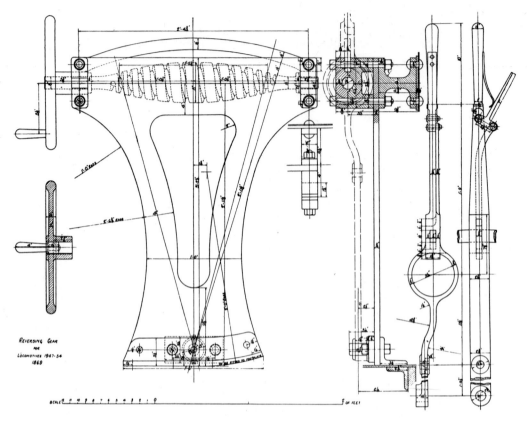

REVERSING GEAR
for
LOCOMOTIVES 1947-54
1868

COMBINED SCREW AND LEVER REVERSING GEAR
by Robert Stephenson & Co.
as fitted to locomotives built for the North Eastern Railway.

This gear was also fitted to engines for the Egyptian State Railways
of which an example was exhibited at the Paris Exbibition, 1867.
(See *Engineering*, Vol. III., p. 417.)

CHAPTER XXVIII

THE GAUGE EXPERIMENTS

AND THE

STEPHENSON LOCOMOTIVE

1845—1860

We have seen that the Stephenson long-boiler engine of 1841 was an evolution from a previous type and had been designed without reference to Brunel's challenge. But within the next few years the stimulus of this challenge was felt in a general demand for higher speeds, for which the second development of the long-boiler engine, with outside cylinders, introduced in 1843, was specially unsuitable. The tendency to unsteadiness inherent in a combination of overhanging firebox and short wheel-base, had been increased by the position of the cylinders, and this tendency was aggravated by any excessive side play which might result from wear, and, particularly in engines with single driving wheels, by any faulty adjustment of the weights. When we consider that engines of this long-boiler type weighed at the most about 22 tons, of which 10 tons might be on the driving wheels and less than 5 tons on the leading wheels, it seems remarkable that they should have been safely run, as they were, at speeds up to 45 miles an hour; and we must remember too that the permanent way of the narrow gauge lines had not been designed for such speeds.

These engines had been introduced during the controversy on the respective merits of four-wheeled and six-wheeled engines, and the Government Inspector of Railways, who objected strongly to the use of four-wheeled engines for passenger traffic, as on the London and Birmingham Railway, 'when he first saw Mr. R. Stephenson's engines with long boiler reported favourably on them.' Subsequently—according to his statement [1]—'owing to the rivalry between the railway companies, the Government was urged to restrict speeds and he was appointed to report on the subject. He had in consequence travelled on the engines of the express trains of every railway in the kingdom,' and he had concluded, as a result of his enquiries, that 'the long-boiler engine similar to the 'White Horse of Kent' was unsteady and unsafe if pushed to a speed exceeding forty-five miles an hour.' But he added, in a statement which has been generally ignored, that 'he had never made any sweeping condemnation of the long-boiler engines, on the contrary he was

---

[1] Major General C. W. Pasley, C.B., *Proceedings Inst. Civil Engineers*, Vol. VIII., p. 245. The subject under discussion was a paper by Crampton on the Construction of Locomotive Engines. The occasion was remarkable for the pointed, almost personal attack on Robert Stephenson and his long-boiler engine. It is interesting to note that Brunel with characteristic generosity supported his professional antagonist, by the statement that 'when Stephenson's Long-Boiler was designed economy of fuel was the main consideration and that machine was best adapted to attain the object.' Shortly afterwards high speeds were aimed at, and that rendered other alterations necessary in the construction of the machine.

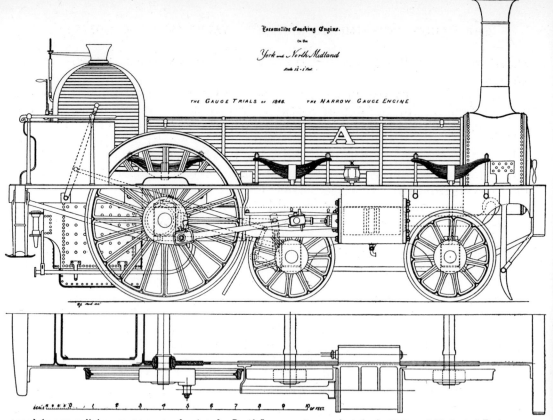

THE GAUGE TRIALS OF 1846.   THE NARROW GAUGE ENGINE

traced (re-arranged) from contemporary drawings by David Joy, now preserved at the Institution of Mechanical Engineers.

LOCOMOTIVE COACHING ENGINE 'A' ON THE YORK AND NORTH MIDLAND RAILWAY.

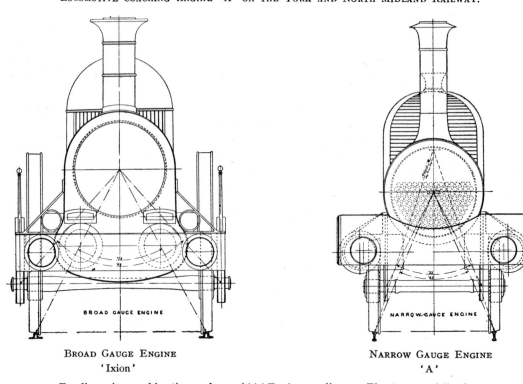

BROAD GAUGE ENGINE   NARROW GAUGE ENGINE
'Ixion'   'A'

For dimensions and heating surfaces of 'A' Engine see diagram Fig. 6, p. 402 following

inclined to think well of them, but that many accidents had happened—due to high speeds.'

The champions of the broad gauge, appreciating the unsuitability of the long-boiler engine for the higher speeds at which they were aiming, made full use of such arguments as they could obtain from the bad behaviour of a particular engine, the 'White Horse of Kent,' which had single driving wheels and outside cylinders, and though not built by Robert Stephenson & Co. was of their long-boiler design, being one of many engines of this type built by other makers to their drawings. By 1845 the unsuitability of the type for the high speeds now become fashionable, showed that some modification was required, and a consideration of this problem appears to be reflected in a letter from Robert Stephenson to the Newcastle works, dated 15th April 1845. An extract which has been preserved in the firm's order book reads:—

I have examined the two tracings and concur with Hutchinson that the one with the driving wheels next to the firebox is the best to adopt, although Hutchinson might begin with two or three swift engines upon the plan approved, with wheels 6 ft. 3 ins. or 6 ft. 6 ins. diameter, the latter I prefer, with cylinders 15 ins. diameter by 22 ins. or 24 ins. stroke.

REAR-DRIVER LONG-BOILER ENGINE 'A' The two drawings referred to cannot now be identified, but there can be little doubt that the result of Robert Stephenson's decision was a further development of his long-boiler type. The special features of the modified design were a re-arrangement of the cylinders and wheels, and the lengthening of the wheel base to 12 feet. One of the first two engines of this new type, which came to be known as Rear-Driver Long-Boiler engines, was the engine 'A,' afterwards famous for its part in the 'Battle of the Gauges,' to which we now to refer.[1]

By 1845 the meeting of the broad and narrow gauges, foreseen by Robert Stephenson, had taken place at Gloucester, and the narrow gauge party were not slow to point out the losses due to the inevitable re-loading of goods at the junction; an evil indeed which could hardly be exaggerated. To the general public they also emphasised the inconveniences to passengers which would result from a change of carriage at every subsequent point of contact between the two gauges, and by the time that the Great Western and the London and Birmingham Railway Companies submitted competing Bills for a line from Oxford to Wolverhampton, in 1845, public opinion had been thoroughly aroused and inflamed by the arguments of both parties. Gooch, in his reminiscences, has recorded this as 'the hardest gauge fight' [2]:—

I had to give evidence on the Bill, and had prepared very elaborate tables showing the speed and economy of the broad gauge. The Committee of the House of Commons sat on it rather over three weeks, and gave us the Bill on the 4th June. We met in a temporary com-

---

[1] The makers' drawing cannot now be found, and we have to rely on a contemporary drawing made by the late Mr. David Joy, inventor of the well-known valve gear. This valuable drawing is now preserved at the Institution of Mechanical Engineers, to which it was presented in 1897 by Mr. Joy, as 'reproduced from journal notes and tracings made in March 1846.' Certain dates and dimensions appear to have been added at the time of presentation and are in some cases obviously incorrect; we have therefore omitted them from the reproduction now given by permission of the Institution.

[2] *Diaries of Sir Daniel Gooch, Bart.,* 1892. See note p. 339 *ante.*

mittee room, and the crowd and heat was excessive. Sitting in this heat all day, and working most of the night in preparing evidence for the witnesses, almost broke me down. I will never forget the passion George Stephenson got into when the decision of the Committee was announced. He gave me his mind very freely for fighting the broad gauge against the narrow, in which he said I had been reared. I was not only fighting for my convictions, but also for my employers, who expressed themselves well satisfied with what I had done. The London and North Western and Grand Junction started express trains to Liverpool on the 1st May during this fight. I went by the first, so as to be able to make use in my evidence of any facts I could pick up.[1]

THE GAUGE COMMISSION The Great Western Company obtained their Bill, but the controversy had by this time become so obviously one of national importance that Cobden in the House of Commons moved for a Royal Commission, which was duly appointed[2] and proceeded to enquire into questions which may be briefly summed up as :—

(1) Whether break of gauge could be considered such an inconvenience as to call for preventive legislation.

(2) Whether such evils as might result from a break of gauge could be obviated or mitigated by mechanical means.

(3) Whether failure to devise such means would make it desirable to establish a uniform gauge throughout the country.

The Commissioners in the course of their enquiry found that an examination of this last question involved subsidiary questions of comparative safety, accommodation, speed, and economy, as between the broad and narrow gauges. A host of witnesses was examined, among them the managers, engineers, and secretaries of every important railway company in the United Kingdom ; the leading locomotive manufacturers, various traders, and competent military authorities, who had to give evidence on the strategic questions which would be involved in the event of an attempt at invasion by a foreign power. Over 6,500 questions and answers, with relative appendices, are recorded in the Commissioners' *Report*. Much of the evidence has a practical bearing on technical problems to-day, and to gauge controversies which are now acute in other countries. But for the purpose of these notes our attention must be confined to the question which immediately concerned the design and construction of locomotives, the question in short :—

Should the locomotive be designed to suit the gauge, or should the gauge be modified to suit that design of locomotive conceived to be most desirable.

In the consideration of this question three axioms were generally accepted :—

(1) That the boiler was the ultimate measure of the power.

(2) That the centre of gravity of the engine, and therefore of the boiler, must be kept low.

(3) That a low piston speed was desirable, and that a large driving wheel was therefore essential for speed.

---

[1] There is some mistake here. The amalgamation of the Liverpool and Manchester, and Grand Junction, with the London and Birmingham line, which formed the London and North Western Railway, did not take place till August 1846.

[2] The Commissioners were :—Lieut. Col. J. M. F. Smith, R.E., former Inspector General of Railways ; G. B. Airy, Royal Astronomer ; and P. Barlow, Professor of Mathematics, Royal Military Academy, Woolwich. See *Report of the Gauge Commissioners*, 1846, with Minutes of Evidence and Appendix.

ROBERT
STEPHENSON'S
EVIDENCE

The first evidence was taken on 6th August 1845, Robert Stephenson being the first witness called. His unique experience, as both a railway engineer and a locomotive builder, marked him as the most important witness for the narrow gauge party. Giving his experience as a locomotive builder he stated :—

At one time when I was called upon to construct engines of greater power than we commenced the line with, I felt some inconvenience in arranging the machinery properly; we were a little confined in space, and at that time an increase of three or four inches would have assisted us materially, and to that extent I thought an addition of gauge to five feet would have been desirable, but on no other account, looking at it as a mere engine builder. Since that time the improved arrangements in the mechanism of the locomotive engines have rendered even that increase altogether unnecessary at present with the inside cylinders, which is the class of engine requiring the most room between the rails, and the crank axle with four eccentrics; we have ample space and even space to spare.

In the arrangement of the machinery, which is the main question, having reference to the width, the working gear has been much simplified, and the communications in the most recent engines between the eccentric and the slide valve have been made direct communications; whereas formerly it was made through the intervention of a series of levers which occupied the width. But even without that which I have just now alluded to, which gives us an extra space with the engines, on the South Western and on various lines in this country by the improvements which have been made, there is quite space enough for the whole of the working gear.

Then with reference to the increase of power, the size of the boiler is in point of fact the only limit to the power, and we have increased them in length on the narrow gauge, because we have always made the boilers as wide as the narrow gauge would admit of; but we have increased the power by increasing their length both in the firebox and in the tubes; we have obtained economy, I conceive, by lengthening the tubes, and we have obtained an increased power by increasing the size of the firebox; in fact the power of the engine, supposing the power to be absorbed, may be taken to be directly as the area of the firegrate or the quantity of fuel contained in the firebox.

To a question whether any practical inconvenience resulted from the increased length of his engines, Robert Stephenson replied :—

None whatever, to the extent we have gone now. I conceive the steadiness of the engine to be very much increased by increasing the length, for the unevenness of the road is met by that; by increasing the length of the base you increase thereby the steadiness. Our present engines are made 12 feet between the front axle and the hind axle; therefore the engine may be regarded as a rectangle of 4 feet 8½ one way by 12 the other; it would in fact be 5 feet because it would be the breadth to the centre of the rail in fact by 12. They have ranged from 10 to 11 feet; we are now making them 12 feet.

I think possibly, by increasing it beyond that very much, there would be some little difficulty in their going into sidings and round sharp curves.

The reference is evidently to the rear-driver long-boiler engine 'A,' which had just been completed, but the improvements in the working gear are those introduced in the first long-boiler engine of 1841.

Referring to the first engines of the Great Western Railway and in particular to the 'North Star,' Robert Stephenson stated :—

I adopted the 7 feet wheel in making some engines for them. I may as well state that the engines which were originally made for the Great Western by me were not designed for the 7 feet gauge, they were designed for an American railroad, with a gauge of 6 feet (sic), and all the parts were proportioned to that gauge; they were made for America, and in consequence of the panic that came over the commercial world some years ago, they were not sent out, but lay on my hands; the frames were widened, and the axles were lengthened, but all the other parts of the machinery were left as they were designed, for the 6 feet gauge, and I believe the width of the boilers has remained the same to this day. Mr. Gooch will correct me if I am wrong.

To this Gooch replied that he had since increased the width of firebox from 4 feet 6 inches to 4 feet 9 inches. It should be noted that the 'North Star' had been first built for a gauge of 5 feet 6 inches, not 6 feet as stated in error by Stephenson.

Asked whether he had formerly desired to increase the gauge 'for a more convenient arrangement of the crank work or of the tubes in the boiler,' Robert Stephenson replied :—

It was for the more convenient arrangement of the crank work entirely; it had no reference to the boiler whatever.

On the question whether the 4 foot $8\frac{1}{2}$ inch gauge gave 'sufficient space to get the utmost amount of power necessary for working ordinary trains,' he stated :—

At present I believe that there are more powerful engines working upon the narrow gauge than there are upon the broad gauge lines. There are engines capable of taking 400 tons at 15 and 16 miles an hour, or more; and I do not know of any engines upon the Great Western that are equal to that task. The cylinders of those engines are 16 inches in diameter, the length of stroke is 24 inches, and the wheels vary from 4 feet 6 to 4 feet 9 in diameter. They are all six coupled; and those engines are as heavy as the present rail will bear. They weigh from 22 to 23 tons; I believe the same weight as the Great Western engines. I believe we have now as great a weight upon six wheels upon the narrow gauge as ought to be put on six wheels; and that will be, in my opinion, hereafter the limit of power, not the width of the gauge. We may build engines upon the wide gauge, no doubt heavier and larger in dimensions, and more powerful, but then you must make a road to support it on purpose.

I think the narrow gauge lines are best calculated for carrying weight, because in the one case you add to the rigidity of the rail itself, but in the other case, with a longitudinal bearing, you do not appear to add to the rigidity in the rail, but you get a great portion of that rigidity in timber.

The powerful engines to which he referred were the six-coupled long-boiler engines of the 'Mammoth' and 'Hercules' type.[1]

To a question whether locomotives could be manufactured for the narrow gauge capable of attaining as high velocities as those then running upon the broad gauge, Stephenson replied :—

I have no question about it. Every day we are running upwards of 50 miles an hour with our passenger trains, and those engines are not made with a view of attaining a maximum speed, but such a speed as we deemed them advisable to attain. We had never aimed to get our passenger trains upon the narrow gauge lines to run more than 30 miles an hour, including stoppages; therefore we had rarely if ever attempted a wheel larger than 5 feet 6 inches diameter. On the North Midland I tried some of 6 feet in diameter [2], and they are there constantly running 50 miles an hour.

There is no difficulty whatever in making an engine upon the narrow gauge to take 40 tons at 60 miles an hour; or even more than that.

The engines on the Great Western were made for the purpose of getting great speed. Mr. Brunel thought that the wide gauge would admit of getting greater speed, and he therefore

[1] See p. 352, Chapter XXVI. *ante.*
[2] These were not long-boiler engines. For typical drawing see p. 317, Chapter XXIV. *ante.*

made all his arrangements with a view of getting greater speed than was attained upon the narrow gauge lines; but he never till recently, perhaps, upon the competition arising, attained a greater speed than upon the narrow gauge.

The average speed upon the Great Western was precisely the same within a shade, I believe a little under, that of the Northern and Eastern; recently, since they have adopted the plan of express trains, they have exceeded the average on other lines, because they had on the Great Western engines prepared for those speeds.

Asked whether any accidents had occurred on either gauge attributable to an excess or a defect in the width of gauge, he replied in the negative, and when questioned on the wheel bases of the four and six wheeled engines on the narrow gauge lines, he stated :—

I think the lowest is 10 feet and the highest 12 feet 9; there have been some of 12 feet 9 built, but they are rather too long, I think. I have recently adopted the maximum of 12, and the minimum of 10. I believe, in both gauges, the centre of gravity is as nearly as possible the same height; I am speaking relatively.

Questioned on the tendency of outside cylinders to cause a 'yawing' motion and asked for the reasons, Robert Stephenson replied :—

It is exceedingly difficult to say; I cannot make up my mind about it. If you consider the action of the cylinder, it is perfectly rigid metal—engine and cylinder together. Now, when the steam presses upon the piston, it is at the same time pressing against the lid of the cylinder; the action and the reaction must be equal. Therefore, I do not believe that it is the steam that causes the irregular action, but I believe it to be the mere weight of the pistons themselves, and therefore if we could contrive to balance the pistons by the weight upon the wheel, we should get rid of that very much; but in the most recent designs of engines of that kind, I have brought the cylinder much nearer to the driving wheel and nearer to the centre of the engine; at present they hang over the wheels a good deal; now I have brought them within the wheels.

The reference here is again to the new 'A' engine then under construction by Robert Stephenson & Co. at Newcastle.[1]

To the evidence of the succeeding witnesses we can only refer very briefly, though it is of great interest and affords much information on the locomotive practice of the time.

Joseph Locke, who had been engineer of the Grand Junction, and had completed the South Western Railway, admitted that, 'if he had to begin afresh he would adopt a gauge rather wider than the narrow gauge, but certainly not so wide as 7 feet.

J. E. McConnell, locomotive superintendent of the Birmingham and Gloucester Railway, and afterwards well-known in the same capacity on the southern division of the London and North Western Railway, considered that safety did not depend so much upon width of gauge as upon other circumstances. He referred to the two schools of locomotive manufacturers[2] and to Stephenson's simplification of the arrangement and construction of the six-wheeled engine.

Edward Bury was of opinion that he would have preferred another six or eight inches; he makes an interesting reference to the finishing of parts :—

We are not obliged to make any parts too weak in consequence of limitations by the narrow gauge; but we are obliged to work very accurately to dimensions.

[1] See p. 372 *ante.*   [2] See p. 326, Chapter XXIV. *ante.*

Captain J. M. Laws, R.N., general manager of the Manchester and Leeds Railway, asked whether he had had any communication with the manufacturers of locomotives in regard to the advantages that would be derived from an increase of gauge, replied :—

I have. They are very contradictory; in fact, many manufacturers of locomotives are almost as mechanical as the instruments they use. Half the operatives (*sic*) of locomotives are boys that are set to work to order from a drawing. They hardly know the principle on which the engine is made. Mr. Robert Stephenson will tell you there is no difficulty in making an engine as powerful on a 4 feet 8½ inch gauge as can be used with safety upon any other gauge. Now his opinion and that of Mr. George Stephenson I would rather take than any other man's.

John Braithwaite, Ericsson's partner in the building of the 'Novelty,' examined as to his reasons for laying out the Eastern Counties Railway, in 1836, with a gauge of 5 feet, gave as a particular reason that he required additional water space between the tubes, and consequently an increase in the diameter of the boiler barrel, which being placed between the wheels determined the dimensions which he eventually adopted. He adds—'if the intention had been originally to run to the North we should not have added the 3½ inches, but, in common with others, have taken the chance of the very great improvements that have been made in locomotive engines.'

John Gray, resident engineer and locomotive superintendent of the Brighton Railway, as a manufacturer of locomotives would have wished a minimum gauge of 5½ to 6 feet.

William Fernihough, locomotive superintendent of the Eastern Counties Railway, and formerly a pupil of Bury, considered that, 'an engine with outside cylinders judiciously constructed may be a better engine than the inside cylinder engine on the narrow gauge, but it is very easy to make a bad engine with outside cylinders.' Asked whether he would feel disposed to adopt the four-piston principle of Mr. Bodmer, the locomotive manufacturer, he replies :—

It is a complicated way of doing what we do completely by more simple means. He seeks to balance one piston by the opposite action of another; now we balance our engine by a small weight placed at the periphery of the wheel.

John Hawkshaw, engineer of the Manchester and Leeds Railway, asked whether he was aware of Robert Stephenson's increase to the length of his boiler, stated that he had himself lengthened engines to the same extent and found it to be an improvement, the engines having done much more work since, but, he remarks :—

We have found now we have got to the extreme size and weight; the rails are crushing beneath the present size of the engines.

Richard Roberts, formerly of Sharp, Roberts & Co., had held for some time that some addition in width to the 4 foot 8½ inch gauge was desirable, but he did not approve of the long tube, observing paradoxically that nothing had been gained by it but a 'loss.'

Major General C. W. Pasley, Inspector of Railways, after quoting his uncomfortable experience on the now notorious 'White Horse of Kent,' and stating his objections to its wheel arrangement, adds :—

I travelled on another of Mr. Stephenson's long-boiler engines, which had two large pairs of wheels in rear coupled, and one small pair of wheels in front. In this engine, although the same general construction prevailed, there was not that unusual and one may almost say alarming sort of oscillation, which I observed on the 'White Horse of Kent' and others, which had only one pair of large driving wheels, and none of the wheels coupled.

He concludes, with obvious reference to the new 'A' engine :—

At Mr. Stephenson's works I found that another construction was in progress, which was to have a very large pair of driving wheels behind and two small pairs of wheels in front, which the foreman of that establishment believed to be calculated to do away with that sort of oscillation, of which I spoke to him.

GOOCH'S
EVIDENCE

We have now to consider the evidence of Daniel Gooch, the first, and so far as the question of locomotive design was concerned, the most important witness for the broad gauge party. He was now a man of well established reputation as locomotive superintendent of the Great Western Railway, who had carried out exhaustive experiments with the engines in his charge. As one of the advantages of the broad gauge he states :—

We put a spring both outside and inside the driving wheel. We do not carry all the weight upon the outer end of the crank axle; there is a spring inside, as well as outside. I believe some of the narrow gauge lines are attempting to avail themselves of that as far as the width will admit; as great safety results from it in case of accident; as of the axle breaking.

Gooch appears to have been ignorant of the fact that inside bearing springs had been fitted by Robert Stephenson to engines of the 'Planet' type and afterwards abandoned. A return was subsequently made to this practice for the reasons given by Gooch. But we have seen that the inside frames had been adopted in the first instance for safety, not to carry weight, and Gooch's definite claim that such greater safety resulted from the use of inside and outside bearings is of particular interest.[1]

But the most interesting part of Gooch's evidence, because that on which his case was largely based, deals with his conclusions on the comparative powers of locomotives on the broad and narrow gauges, as measured by their respective capacities for steam production. His arguments were derived from experiments made on the engines of the Great Western Railway, on the 'White Horse of Kent,' and on engines of the Southampton Railway, together with reports of engine performances on the Northern and Eastern Railway. From his own experiments Gooch deduced the theory that *firebox heating surface alone is the measure of boiler evaporative power*, and that such power might be calculated on the basis of 2 cubic feet of water evaporated for 1 square foot of firebox heating surface. Tube surface, he says, does not tell in anything like the proportion which might be expected.

Referring to a table which he puts in as evidence, he proceeds :—

I state this because we have heard it here that the narrow gauge engines are being constructed as powerful and efficient as the Great Western, because they make the boilers, 12, 14

[1] See p. 258, Chapter XX. *ante* and p. 317, Chapter XXIV. *ante*.

and 15 feet long, and thereby get as much heating surface, as it is called, as we get upon the Great Western; that the firebox is not the test; that by this enormous increase of tube surface, which in the 'White Horse of Kent' is 17 times the firebox surface compared with our 7, they are getting what we are getting; and that table is to show that neither by calculations nor experiment is that borne out in the least. The firebox is really the test of the power of the engine, assuming the cylinder to be made in proportion.

He refers later to the 'White Horse of Kent':—

One of the engines which the narrow gauge advocates are expecting will compete successfully with the broad gauge. It is one of Stephenson's patent engines; it is one of the long-boiler engines. The day I was on she had been running about 18,000 miles, and she was in such a state then that she was not safe; she was taken off two or three days after in consequence of the side play. When she was examined she was worn from half an inch to five-eighths sideways in the axleboxes and brasses, after running 18,000 miles. She is 21 feet 10 inches long, upon 10 feet 3¼ bearings.

Further examined as to the evaporative power of locomotives on the broad and narrow gauges, Gooch again emphasises the importance of firebox heating surface and deduces from his own experiments that owing to the length of tube the 'White Horse of Kent' condenses the steam at one end of the boiler which she evaporates at the other. He adds, as a further objection, that the 'longer the tube is the more powerful the blast must be that the engine must have to get the air through the tube; it is a disadvantage rather than a gain.' Later he emphasises the opinions which he has previously expressed, that the long-boiler engine offers no advantage in evaporation per pound of coke consumed, and that engine performance may be based on a calculated hourly evaporation of two cubic feet of water per square foot of firebox.

It is important to bear these points in mind since it was on them that the controversy as to the relative powers developed by the engines in the subsequent gauge experiments eventually turned. It was on this theory of firebox evaporative power in particular that Gooch based his case for the actual and potential superiority of the broad over the narrow gauge.

BIDDER'S EVIDENCE

The next important witness for the narrow gauge was George Parker Bidder, the engineer of the Norfolk Lines, but fully informed as to the railways with which Robert Stephenson was connected.

Bidder, who was born in 1806, had distinguished himself as a child by remarkable calculating powers; it appears that his reputation on this account led to his giving public exhibitions of these powers, greatly to his father's profit. Meanwhile however, the boy's education was being neglected, until he fortunately attracted the attention of various eminent men, who considered that the 'calculating boy' was worthy of a better career than that of an arithmetical prodigy. As the result of their interest in the boy's future he was eventually placed with a private tutor in Edinburgh, afterwards attending classes at the university, where he first met Robert Stephenson, and the two lads formed the friendship 'which afterwards became so remarkable a feature in their lives.'[2]

[1] Gooch stated that on the broad gauge, engines had run '60,000 to 70,000 miles without ever being off the wheels.'

[2] Memoir, *Proceedings Inst. Civil Engineers*, Vol. LVII.

Bidder was closely connected with Robert Stephenson in many of his important engineering works. As a witness on technical questions his powers of rapid calculation were of special value, and before the Gauge Commission he became in fact the principal opponent of Gooch, from whose theories as to the relative values of firebox and tube heating surface he completely dissented; because, he says, in reply to a question :—

Mr. Gooch has stated the evaporation on the Great Western Railway at 196 cubic feet per hour; he compared with that the evaporating power, I think, of the White Horse of Kent on the South Eastern line, which he stated at 100 feet. Now, I have tried experiments myself in which the evaporating power on the narrow gauge, even of the old boilers, was 150; the old Northern and Eastern engines could evaporate 150 feet, and have evaporated it in an hour; the small engines of the London and Birmingham have evaporated 100 feet, from experiments which I made myself; the White Horse of Kent, a similar engine to ours, has evaporated as much as 200 feet per hour; therefore I believe the experiment which Mr. Gooch must have made, was after that engine had been run off its legs; she was the only engine adequate to her duty they had at that time; they never blew her boiler out, or took any care of her whatever, and therefore it was comparing an engine literally worn out with a first rate engine, consequently the conclusion, in my opinion, is fallacious; for I know that engines of the same construction evaporated as near as can be at the rate of 200 feet per hour.

This interesting side light on the unfortunate 'White Horse of Kent' shows that she was at least a 'willing horse' which had suffered from the unchivalrous treatment of her employers, and has since suffered at the hands of those writers who harp on her failures while on her virtues they keep silence.[1]

Examined later Bidder gives the result of experiments on the Northern lines which compared favourably with any referred to in Gooch's evidence. He challenges Gooch's deductions from the temperature obtained in the smokebox of the 'White Horse of Kent,' and referring to a proposal by the Commissioners to try an experiment with one of the narrow gauge engines, in order to test the accuracy of the statements made by himself and Gooch, he observes :—

With the Great Western experiments and those which I have taken with a short boiler, I have found almost invariably as the result, that one lb. of coke evaporates 7 lbs. of water. With the long boiler we hardly ever get an effect of less than 8 lbs. of water to 1 lb. of coke, and in some of these experiments it is as much as 10 lbs.

THE GAUGE EXPERIMENTS From Brunel's evidence it is unnecessary for our present purposes to quote. It was principally a reiteration of his reasons, which we have already recorded, for adopting a gauge of 7 feet.[2] Towards the close of the enquiry, on 22nd November 1845, when asked whether he had any further observations to make, Brunel suggested that the course which the evidence had taken made it almost imperative that some experiments should be made, to test the accuracy of many of the opinions which had been given—believing, as he did, that, 'as regarded the mechanical results of the wide gauge, if experiments were made it would be found that speed, economy, and safety were attained to a much greater extent than on the narrow gauge.' He proceeds :—

[1] The 'White Horse of Kent' was of the type shown on p. 354, Chapter XXVI. *ante.*

[2] See p. 336, Chapter XXV. *ante.*

I should propose to take engines of our present power, and in making experiments with those the Commissioners will have an opportunity of observing that those engines are the engines that have been running for several years on the Great Western Railway, made from drawings prepared as long as six or seven years ago, and that we have great scope for improving and increasing the power of those engines, which, now that the public appear to require and appreciate the advantage of high speeds, we propose to do. I should suggest that the mode of trial most likely to give you the information that you wish, would be running a train of 50, 60 or 70 tons at a high speed between London and Exeter, as embracing gradients of every variety, and probably also, between London and Swindon, as having only easy gradients. I think those experiments should be repeated several times, with different loads; and probably increasing the load to about the limit of the power of the engine, at the speed of 50 miles an hour.

Bidder, asked for his observations upon this proposal dissented entirely from Gooch's proposition that engines 'constructed for a gauge of 7 feet are capable of producing a much greater quantity of power at less cost than engines of the narrow gauge.' He adds :—

We deny that most distinctly. I would not deny it with regard to the London and Birmingham engine, which is an engine which I disapprove of, and which ought never to have been put upon that line; but I do deny it with regard to the engines which are now at work upon the other narrow gauge lines, but not engines made with any view to experiments, but upon plans which have been prepared for the last year and a half or two years, and which engines are now at work.

It will be necessary, when we come to consider the results of these experiments, to appreciate the circumstances in which they were decided upon. During the sitting of the Commission the balance of the evidence had gone steadily against the advocates of the broad gauge ; the majority of the witnesses had agreed that, so far as traffic requirements were concerned, the narrow gauge was generally sufficient. For mineral traffic, involving connection with the colliery districts the narrow gauge was preferable, if not unavoidable, and no arguments could alter the fundamental fact summed up by one of the witnesses, Captain J. M. Laws, R.N. :—

We owe all our railways to the collieries in the North.

It was also agreed that a break of gauge would be fatal to the general interests of the community, and that, though it might be desirable to adopt an intermediate gauge as a solution of the problem, there would be no necessity for so extreme a width as 7 feet. There was also the indisputable fact that Brunel himself, to suit the physical features of the country, had adopted the 4 foot 8½ inch gauge for the Taff Vale Railway, and that, in his own words, he had '*never recommended the broad gauge for the purpose of having larger engines*,' but merely on account of his intention to place the carriage bodies between the wheels—an intention which had since been abandoned.[1]

The evidence before the Commissioners had shown that the majority of locomotive designers and builders would have welcomed some increase to the gauge, perhaps to the extent of a few inches, but that in the face of accomplished facts they had accepted the alternative solution—*the adaptation*

[1] See p. 336, Chapter XXV. *ante*.

of the locomotive to the gauge—and that in no case did they consider the 7 foot gauge to be either necessary or desirable.

With these facts before us it is difficult to resist a conclusion that the locomotive experiments were proposed by the broad gauge party as a counsel of despair. We have seen how largely their case had been based on the delinquencies of one particular engine on the narrow gauge, admitted even by Gooch to have been in no fit state. The trials now proposed would involve comparisons between engines of totally different constructions, designed to meet different requirements, and to suit different conditions. Such trials must obviously be to the disadvantage of one or other, depending on the question to be decided. Moreover, in emphasising the possibility for larger locomotives offered by the broad gauge, its advocates were to some extent shifting their ground. These facts give some clue to the general atmosphere in which the trials were likely to be carried out, and to the feelings of the persons involved, and in this connection the observations of the contemporary press are both interesting and illuminating.

A railway periodical referring to the proposed experiments observes on 20th December 1845 [1] :—-

At a very late period of the inquiry of the Gauge Commissioners, a proposal was received from the advocates of the broad gauge, that Experiments should be instituted as to the respective performance of the engines on the two gauges. We have to express our decided opinion of the impropriety and utter worthlessness of this wretched series of experiments, ill-contrived, and calculated to embroil inextricably a question which they could not in any event tend to clear up. Hurried individual experiments like these can, at best, only show the relative working of the particular engines selected for the experiments on the two gauges, and can form no element in the decision of the great practical question before the Commissioners—the question of *unity of gauge*. We regret, therefore, that the Commissioners have made what we regard as a false step; and we are very much mistaken in our estimate of the great tact, talent and address of the Great Western party, if they do not succeed in blowing up, as by a petard, with this very set of experiments, the entire labours of the commission, who have assisted in getting these very experiments undertaken in opposition to strong arguments laid before them on this very point.

However this opinion of ours may turn out, the facts are, that the Commissioners have ordered experiments to be made by the Great Western Company on the part of the broad gauge, and by the London and Birmingham on the part of the narrow gauge. The latter Company, have it seems, both on account of their great traffic and frequent trains on their line, their gradients, and the moderate size and weight of their engines, as well as their peculiar construction, determined that the experiments should be tried, not on their own lines, but on other lines bearing more resemblance to the Great Western in regard to gradients than their own, and with engines of a larger class than theirs, and they have requested Mr. Bidder and Mr. Harding to see to these larger experiments on their behalf.

The Great Western are anxious, on the other hand, to display the prowess of their engines with the heaviest class of passenger trains, moved at great velocities without stoppages. Some of the London and Birmingham parties, on the other hand, are understood to be of opinion that this is by no means the most desirable mode of displaying a command of locomotive power, as they hold it to be neither safe in itself, nor convenient, to convey large passenger trains at the highest velocity an engine can attain; and such trains, they say, were they frequent, would endanger and embarrass the whole traffic of any railway on which many trains ran. In accordance

---

[1] *Railway Chronicle*, 1845, Vol. II., p. 1,993.

z

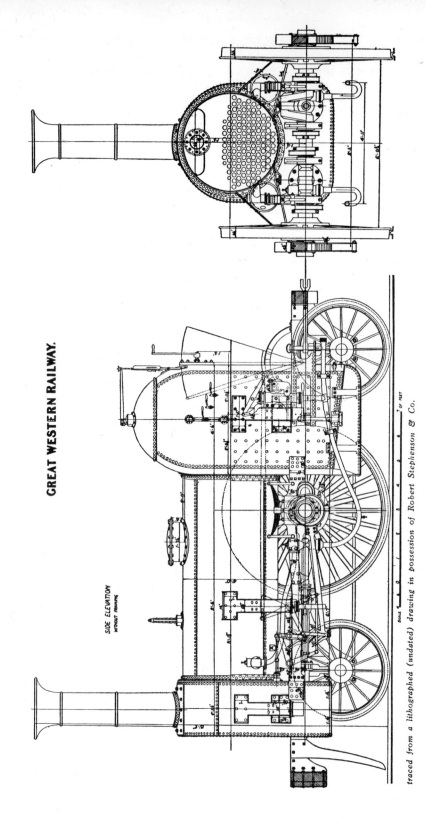

GREAT WESTERN RAILWAY.

SIDE ELEVATION
WITHOUT FRAMING

traced from a lithographed (undated) drawing in possession of Robert Stephenson & Co.

GOOCH'S DESIGN FOR THE FIRST 'STANDARD' ENGINES OF THE GREAT WESTERN RAILWAY, 1839

The 'Ixion' built by Fenton Murray and Jackson was of this design

For cylinder dimensions, and heating surfaces, see Table, p. 387 following; see also p. 343, Chapter XXV. *ante.*

with this view, they therefore prefer displaying the power at their command in drawing great loads at moderate velocities, and in maintaining a good average speed without frequent stoppages. These remarks may serve to indicate what each party consider the 'forte' of its engines as at present constructed; but they also show that even the issues of the case, thus foolishly brought to inadequate trial, are not agreed upon.

The first in the proposed series of trials on the broad gauge were carried out on the Great Western Railway generally as agreed between Bidder and Brunel. The engine employed for the passenger trains was the 'Ixion,' one of Gooch's 'Firefly' class, which we have already shown to have been an enlarged edition of Robert Stephenson & Co.'s 'Star' class.[1] By the time of the gauge trials some of these engines had been fitted with the link motion.

The results of the trials are recorded at length in the Gauge Commissioners' *Report* as observed by both parties and by the Commissioners themselves. The narrow gauge trials were commenced on the Great North of England Railway between Darlington and York, but the series was not completed. Gooch who was present subsequently reports an experiment with Robert Stephenson & Co.'s 'A' engine hauling a load of 50 tons, with which an average speed of 47·7 miles an hour was obtained ; he remarks [2] :—

At this speed I find the engine exceedingly unsteady, so much so that I doubted the safety of it and even deterred Mr. Brunel from returning upon it which he had proposed to do. This engine, which being quite new has as yet no name, stands very high and has driving wheels of 6 ft. 6 ins. diameter: it has been built by Messrs. Stephenson since the commencement of the enquiry by the Gauge Commissioners and has only been completed a few weeks. All the improvements of the day and all the alterations suggested by Mr. Stephenson have been introduced and every effort made to construct a powerful engine in as small a space and with as little weight as possible. Every contrivance has particularly been resorted to to obtain the utmost width that the gauge is capable of giving. The cylinders are placed outside and besides this a couple of additional inches have been obtained by throwing the bosses and spokes of the wheels out of the centres of the tires; it may indeed safely be asserted that in width everything has been done that can be done, and that the efforts to obtain width are apparent in every detail; while if I may judge by the yawing and pitching motion of the engine when moving at any velocity much more has been done in increasing the length of the mass in proportion to the length of the base than is at all consistent with safety, notwithstanding that the front and back pair of wheels are as far apart as Mr. Stephenson has stated in his evidence before the Gauge Commissioners they can be safely and properly placed.

Gooch complains of the manner in which the trial was conducted—the engine passing the starting post at a speed of 15 miles an hour instead of stopping and starting from a state of rest—and he comments on the artificial blast worked by a stationary engine, which was provided at Darlington for the purpose of blowing up the fire and heating the water in the tender. He reports a later experiment with a North Midland engine, 'also of the long class, but with inside cylinders,' which attained a speed of 45 to 46 miles per hour, but between the 21st and 22nd miles of her run from York, at a speed of 48 miles an hour, 'jumped off the rails, falling upon her side.' He proceeds :—

[1] See p. 344, Chapter XXV. *ante.*

[2] Gooch, Report to Directors of Great Western Railway, 24th Jan. 1846. *Gauge Commissioners' Report,* Appendix, p. 681.

The results of my observations on this line have confirmed me most fully in the views and opinions I have previously held and expressed—that to obtain practically even moderately high speed on the narrow gauge, with fair working loads, and taking the average of weather, the engines must be of such a construction to obtain the requisite power, that they become excessively unsafe. By having so great a weight overhanging the wheels, both longitudinally and transversely by the extremely long boilers and the outside cylinders, or, if inside cylinders be used, by the disproportionate height to which the whole must be raised. . . . . . . indeed a mere sketch such as the one I enclose of an end view of the two engines would lead anybody to the conclusion that the one is too high and top heavy to be fit for high speeds, whilst the other has all the appearance of breadth and stability.[1]

The official report by the Commissioners differs in some important respects from that by Gooch. They record of the trial on 31st December that :—

Professor Airy rode on the engine. The engine was less steady than that of the Great Western Railway; but the unsteadiness was unimportant. It was not related to the strokes of the piston but seemed rather to be produced by faults in the road. At one point 10 or 12 miles from York violent shock was felt.

A study of the evidence shows that the permanent way of the narrow gauge lines was inadequate to the speeds now being attempted, and the very lightness of the engines rendered them peculiarly susceptible to such shocks as described above. The combination of these conditions appears in most cases to have been the principal cause for some of the derailments which occurred about this period. The accident with the North Midland engine, of the long-boiler type, but with single driving wheels in the middle, is ascribed by the Commissioners to a 'broken joint-chair which it appeared had been fractured long before, but there was reason to believe that the engine was somewhat unsteady, and that its leading wheels had a tendency to rise from the rails as if, in the adjustment of the weights, too much weight had been thrown upon the driving wheels.'[2]

Gooch's remark, in his report to his directors, that the 'A' engine had been built by Messrs. Stephenson since the commencement of the enquiry by the Gauge Commissioners, suggests that it had been specially designed to take part in the experiments, but so far from this having been the case, the design had been considered by Robert Stephenson and approved in April 1845, some months before the Commission was appointed.

When we come to examine the records of the experiments with the passenger trains we find that in only one or two cases was there such a parity of conditions as to make a comparison easily possible. On the broad gauge the 'Ixion' hauled a load of approximately 80 tons at an average speed of 47 miles per hour. On the narrow gauge the 'A' engine hauled a load of approximately 80 tons at an average speed of 43·25 miles per hour.[3]

The great difference between the two engines is shown both by the drawings which we reproduce and by the following table, which gives also the evaporation obtained per lb. of fuel in each case.

Other experiments, with however different loads in each case, showed higher evaporations, of 7·8 lbs. per lb. of coke by the 'Ixion,' and 9·6 lbs. per lb. of coke by the 'A.'

---

[1] For comparative end views see p. 372 ante.   [2] See p. 371 ante.

[3] The 'A' Engine, with forty tons, subsequently attained sixty miles an hour. Robert Stephenson's *Report to the Directors of the Norfolk Railway*, January 21st. 1846.

Engine.	Cylinders. Diam. × Stroke.	Grate Area. Sq. Feet.	Firebox Heating Surface. Sq. Feet.	Tube Heating Surface. Sq. Feet.	Total Heating Surface. Sq. Feet.	Evaporation per hour per pound of Coke.
'Ixion' ...	15″ × 18″	13·4	97	602	699	7
'A'	15″ × 24″	9·6	58	880	939	8·8

The results show that on the whole the broad gauge engine hauled greater loads at the same speeds, or equal loads at slightly greater speeds, than were obtained by the narrow gauge engine. But there are discrepancies which baffle analysis and justify Bidder's opinion that the unknown factors, among them wind resistance, would make the trials of little practical value.

In his report on the experiments he observes :—

If I have at any time appeared over anxious in taking care that the narrow-gauge experiments should be made under tolerably fair circumstances, my anxiety must be attributed to the conviction (which a perusal of the daily papers must show to be correct), that the whole scope of these experiments would be reduced into a mere trial of speed and load between engines on the respective gauges, and would be so introduced to the public.

The velocity of a train will be influenced by a slant of wind, the slipperiness of the rails, or the necessity of shutting off the steam, arising from accidental circumstances, occurring on the line of railway.

Bidder then proceeds to examine the evaporating power of the engines, as well as the relative economy of evaporation, and efficient application of the steam evaporated. He refers to Gooch's contention that while the 'engines of the Great Western Railway could evaporate nearly 200 cubic feet per hour [1], the narrow gauge engines could only convert into steam 100 cubic feet, the comparative firebox surfaces being as 97 to 50 square feet. Bidder shows that the 'Ixion' with 97 square feet of firebox evaporated about 197 cubic feet of water per hour, while the 'A' engine, with 58 square feet, could evaporate at the rate of 178 cubic feet per hour. He claims that the results of the experiments do not confirm Gooch's assertion, and moreover that the long-boiler engine shows an evaporation of 9·6 lbs. of water obtained with 1 lb. of coke, while the evaporation of the broad gauge engines is considerably less. He does not comment on his water heating apparatus at Darlington, but since Gooch himself had set the example, in his first experiment, with hot water in the tender, Bidder's silence is perhaps excusable.

[1] (a) This evaporation had already been obtained with Stephenson's broad gauge 'North Star' in 1838, with 66·6 square feet of firebox heating surface. See p. 342, Chapter XXV. ante.

The comparative firebox heating surfaces given by Bidder are for the 'Ixion' and the early long-boiler engines ; the 'A' engine had 58 to 59 square feet of firebox surface. It must be noted that, as in other cases to which we have previously referred, the published and other records of dimensions for these early engines are not always reconcilable. In some cases the surfaces may have been calculated on the fire side, in others on the water side, of tubes and firebox.

(b) D. K. Clark points out that the evaporation of the 'Ixion' class compared unfavourably with that of Stephenson's early six-wheeled engines. *Proc. Inst. Civil Engineers*, Vol. XII., p. 393.

His peculiar turn of arithmetical calculation is evident in the nature and length of his replies and observations, but perusal of the evidence given before the Commission leaves an impression of unreality about the whole of the proceedings, which increases when we come to consider the experiments— an impression which can only be explained by the circumstances in which they had been decided upon and eventually carried out. The railway periodical from which we have already quoted, observes on 3rd January 1846 [1] :—

> The progress of the Gauge Experiments of last week is precisely what we foretold a fortnight ago. The parties are at issue upon the issues; and no sooner do the broad gauge advocates meet the Commissioners at York, than forthwith they begin their experiments by a discussion of the issues.

Commenting on a published report of the first and second day's trials, and in particular on a dispute which took place between the parties as to the suitability of the weather, the same periodical remarks :—

> At 9 o'clock a stiff breeze was blowing from the north-east. . . . . Mr. Bidder objected to make the trial in such weather, and observed that if the experiment were made he should claim a deduction of 12 miles per hour for the retarding power of the wind. (Shrewd, cautious Mr. Bidder!). . . . Mr Gooch urged the propriety of the trip (knowing, clear sighted Mr. Gooch!), stating that the wind prevailing was very little, if any, stronger, than the one against which the broad gauge engine contended with its 80 tons. (Candid Mr. Gooch! he weighs the wind in scales and declares there is no balance). This Mr. Bidder (of course) denied.
>
> The reporter next ushers on the scene the Commissioners themselves—Professor Barlow and Professor (otherwise Royal-Astronomer) Airy. The former is said, shrewdly enough, to have remarked—'that the locomotive had to do its work, as well in unfavourable as in favourable weather, and thought the trip might be undertaken.'

Fortunately for the Commissioners they had not to base their decision either on debating points between Gooch and Bidder, or on the results of the experiments; there were ample other grounds, commercial, economic and strategic, on which to justify their first and vital recommendation :—

> That the gauge of four feet eight inches and a half be declared by the Legislature to be the gauge to be used in all public Railways now under construction or hereafter to be constructed in Great Britain.

In pronouncing judgment on the question whether the gauge should be altered to suit the locomotive, or the locomotive to suit the gauge, they showed, so far as the experiments were concerned, a wisdom worthy of Solomon. Taking Gooch's own experiments on the narrow gauge engines of the South Western Railway they deduced that the broad gauge offered no economy in the locomotive working expenses for passenger trains, observing that the comparisons they had made would have been more in favour of the narrow gauge had they taken into consideration 'one of those engines of whose increased capabilities some of the supporters of the narrow gauge had informed them.'

The question whether it would be possible to design for the narrow gauge such powerful engines as on the broad gauge, they evade by an opinion that, with the then existing permanent way, the limit to engine weights and speeds

---

[1] *Railway Chronicle*, 1846, Vol. I., p. 6.

had been reached on both systems.   Referring particularly to the experiments they discreetly add :—

Towards the close of our enquiry, Mr. Brunel requested on the part of the Broad Gauge Companies, to institute a set of experiments to test the power of their engines; and Mr. Bidder, on the part of the Narrow Gauge Companies, undertook in consequence of such application, to make corresponding experiments on the narrow gauge.   After sanctioning these trials, and being present at the performance of them, a record of which will be found in the Appendix, we may observe, without entering into a minute detail of the results, or the discrepancies between the returns as furnished by the two parties themselves, that we consider them as confirming the statements and results given by Mr. Gooch, in his evidence, proving as they do, that the Broad Gauge Engines possess greater capabilities for speed with equal loads, and, generally speaking, of propelling greater loads with equal speed; and, moreover, that the working, with such engines is economical where very high speeds are required, or where the loads to be conveyed are such as to require the full power of the engine.   They confirm, also, the evidence given by Mr. Bidder as to the possibility of obtaining high evaporative power with long engines for the narrow gauge, but under somewhat peculiar circumstances.   It appears, moreover, that the evaporation thus obtained does not produce a corresponding useful effect in the tractive power of the engine; a circumstance that would probably be differently explained by Mr. Gooch and Mr. Bidder; but as we do not refer to the power of this description of engine in the deductions we have made, it is unnecessary for us to allude further to them.

The immediate influence of the experiments on the principal question at issue—*should there be unity of gauge*—was in fact negligible, but, in spite of the Commissioners' reservations, it appears that the experiments had shown the great economy of evaporation obtained with the long-boiler.

From a consideration of the controversy as to the respective merits of the 'Ixion' and the 'A' engine, a curious aspect of the case emerges, unseen perhaps by those immediately concerned and little noticed since.   The struggle was in effect between an engine of Robert Stephenson's latest design, the rear-driver long-boiler type which had been evolved from his patent of 1841, and an engine, which, though built by another maker, and nominally designed by Gooch, was typical in its general features and identical in much of its detail with Stephenson's previous patent engine of 1833.   The result of the experiments justified Robert Stephenson in the reasons he had put forward for departing from his earlier type—the desire to obtain an economy of fuel by increasing the length of the tubes, and the tube heating surface in proportion to the firebox heating surface.[1]

THE BATTLE OF THE GAUGES Although the Gauge Commissioners' Report in 1846 led eventually to legislation which prevented any extension of the broad gauge system, the controversy did not end with their findings, but found expression later in a keen competition for speed between the engineers of the rival gauges. In 1846 Gooch produced a heavier engine, which he had described to the Commissioners, and had hoped to complete in time to influence their findings. This engine, the 'Great Western,' was an enlargement of the 'Ixion' class, and

[1] The large firebox and grate area in the 'North Star' appear as an exception which may have been due to the fact that this engine had been intended for America and probably to burn wood or coal.   It is clear that for burning coke Robert Stephenson, between 1835 and 1845, had adopted a policy of reducing the grate area in proportion to the tube surface.   See diagrams, p. 401 following.

from a photo in the collection of the Locomotive Publishing Co.
STEPHENSON'S PATENT REAR-DRIVER LONG-BOILER LOCOMOTIVE
built by Jones and Potts for the London and Birmingham Railway, 1846

from a photo by Mr. A. R. Bennett, 1908.
REAR-DRIVER LONG-BOILER ENGINE BUILT BY ROBERT STEPHENSON & CO.
for the West Flanders Railway, 1846, later fitted with a new boiler, and at work in 1908

therefore a development of what we may for the moment call the 'short-boiler' type, and it had the disadvantages peculiar to the type. While in the long-boiler engine the tendency was to have too little weight on the leading wheels, in the short-boiler engine the tendency was to have too much, and Gooch in fact soon found it necessary to add an additional pair of wheels at the front end of the 'Great Western,' which thus became the prototype of the 'Lightning' and the famous 'Lord of the Isles,' the forerunner of the eight-wheeled passenger engine.

So far as Robert Stephenson & Co. were concerned the immediate result of the gauge experiments appears to have been a demand for engines of the 'A' type. The maximum development of this six-wheeled type is to be seen in locomotives built for the southern division of the London and North Western Railway in 1846, having cylinders 15 inches diameter by 24 inches stroke and driving wheels of 7 feet diameter. The total heating surface was about 832 square feet, the grate area about $11\frac{1}{4}$ square feet.

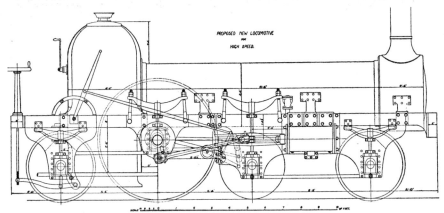

traced from an original drawing in possession of Robert Stephenson & Co., probable date, 1846-1847.

PROPOSED NEW LOCOMOTIVE FOR HIGH SPEED

We have in a contemporary journal a record of an 'extraordinary run' with one of these engines on 7th May 1847 [1] :—

A special train consisting of five carriages, was taken from London to Birmingham, 112 miles yesterday (Wednesday) morning in two hours and thirty minutes. The actual time travelling did not exceed two hours, being an average speed of 56 miles per hour, the train being stopped four times on the journey to allow other trains to be clear of the line, besides stoppage at Wolverton to change engines. The engine which started from London, No. 157, is one of Mr. Stephenson's ordinary patent engines, and the latter part of its journey, 21 miles, was performed in 21 minutes.

The maximum speed over upwards of a mile was 75 miles per hour. The engine from Wolverton to Birmingham was also a patent engine of Mr. Stephenson's having three cylinders, and it performed the first part of the journey, forty-one miles (until it was stopped by another train) in forty-two minutes. Maximum speed in this portion of the journey sixty-four miles per hour. We understand that Lord George Bentinck and several gentlemen going to the

[1] *Newcastle Chronicle*, 7th May 1847. For illustration of the 'ordinary patent engine' see p. 98, Chapter VI. *ante.*

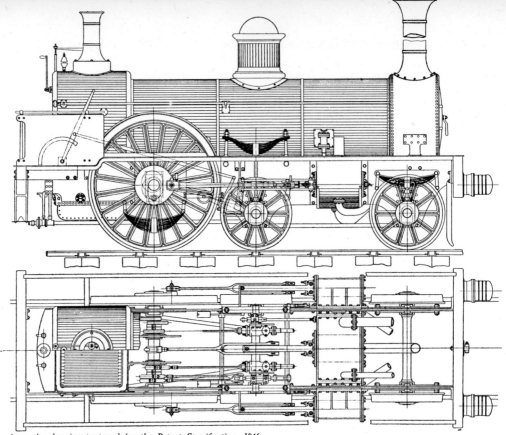

from the drawing prepared for the Patent Specification, 1846.

STEPHENSON AND HOWE'S 3-CYLINDER LOCOMOTIVE

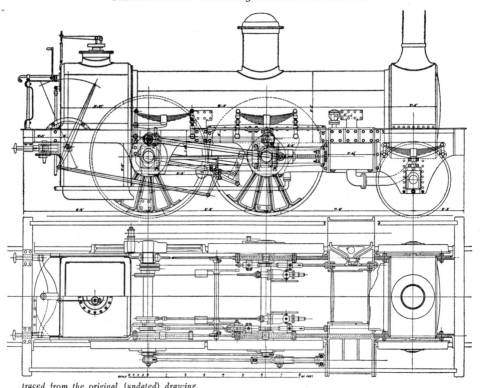

traced from the original (undated) drawing.

STEPHENSON'S FOUR-COUPLED REAR-DRIVER LOCOMOTIVE

Chester Races were in the train. A side wind was blowing throughout the journey. Mr. McConnell (the locomotive superintendent of the London and North Western Railway Company) and Mr. Winter (the Superintendent of Mr. Stephenson's patent engines) were on the engine, and described the motion at the highest velocity as being perfectly steady.

BALANCED
LOCOMOTIVES

The three-cylinder locomotive which hauled the train from Wolverton to Birmingham had been built under the patent taken out by George Stephenson with William Howe.[1] It was fitted with two small outside cylinders and one larger cylinder on the centre line of the engine, having a capacity equal to that of the two outside cylinders. The three cylinders together had a total capacity equal to that of the two-cylinder engines of the 'A' type then in vogue. The cranks of the two outside cylinders were placed on the same dead centre on either side, both cranks being up, or down, simultaneously. The object of the arrangement was elimination of the rocking effect produced in two-cylinder engines by the upward thrust of the connecting rods on the slidebars acting alternately on opposite sides. Incidentally there resulted from the new arrangement an elimination of the swaying motion due to the action of the outside reciprocating masses in two-cylinder engines having the cranks at right angles.

But only two of these three-cylinder engines were built, and one at least was rebuilt about nine years later with a shorter boiler and the firebox placed between the driving and trailing axles.[2] The tendency of the reciprocating masses to cause a 'yawing' motion had been commented on by Robert Stephenson in giving evidence before the Gauge Commission, though he then stated that he had not made up his mind on the question, and he appears to have decided to meet the difficulty for the time by the re-arrangement of cylinders and wheels which he first applied to the 'A' engine. It appears that, whatever may have been done by individuals, there was no general attempt by 1846 to balance reciprocating masses by weights placed in the driving wheels, and we find that Bidder, writing to the secretary of the London and Birmingham Railway Company, on the conclusion of the gauge experiments, recommends the adoption of engines of the 'A' type with certain modifications :—

The same form of engine as tried at York, which possesses several peculiar advantages; the bearings between the extreme wheels of the narrow gauge engine should be extended from 12 feet to 14 or even 15 feet, and the engine connected to the tender by a screw coupling with side buffers, similar to the plan adopted by Mr. Bury on the London and Birmingham Railway; by this arrangement the engine becomes almost a 12-wheeled machine, with a joint in the middle, which though it occasions some increase of resistance in passing round curves, nevertheless gives great steadiness and security to the engine.

We find that, presumably as the result of this recommendation, Robert

[1] Stephenson and Howe's Patent Specification. 1846 (No. 11,086). See p. 101, Chapter VI. *ante*.

[2] D. K. Clark, *Railway Machinery*, 1855, Plate XVI., illustrates the rebuilt engine and refers (p. 211) to it as running on the York, Newcastle and Berwick Railway, 'with very superior steadiness, even when unassisted with balance weights in the wheels; and from its peculiar arrangement it is susceptible of a very perfect equilibration. See p. 401 following.

This was one of the engines usually employed in drawing the Royal trains between York and Berwick when Queen Victoria travelled over the East Coast route. Tomlinson, *The North Eastern Railway*, p. 537.

Stephenson & Co. subsequently built an interesting development of the 'A' type, in which the wheel base was increased to 14 feet, and the centre pair of wheels were coupled to the rear driving wheels. Such engines were supplied in 1848 to the York, Newcastle and Berwick Railway and to one or two continental lines. One original drawing shows the intermediate spring buffers recommended by Bidder, but another drawing shows balance weights in the wheels, the earliest of Robert Stephenson & Co.'s drawings to record such weights, which so late as 1860 were by no means general.

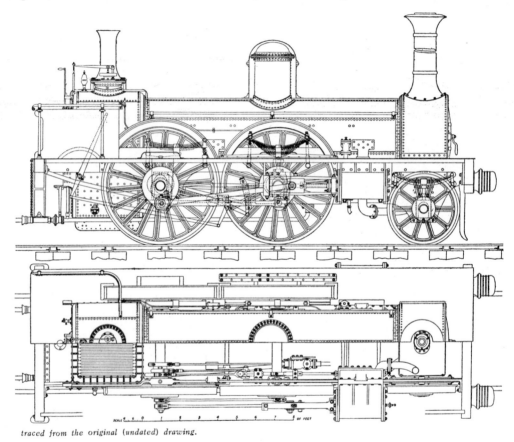

traced from the original (undated) drawing.

FOUR-COUPLED REAR-DRIVER LONG-BOILER LOCOMOTIVE
built for the York, Newcastle and Berwick Railway, 1848

It is interesting to find that towards the end of the nineteenth century locomotives were designed on the continent, in which no attempt was made to balance the reciprocating masses by weights in the driving wheels, but, by means of a special close coupling between the engine and tender, to steady the engine generally in the manner suggested by Bidder.[1]

[1] R. Garbe, for the Prussian State Railways; see (a) *Die Dampflokomotiven der Gegenwart.* (b) *The Application of Highly Superheated Steam to Locomotives,* 1908.

Numbers of two-cylinder long-boiler engines of the 'A' type were ordered for home and foreign railways; some built for Egypt so late as 1855 were at work until 1902; others built in 1846 for the West Flanders Railway were still in service in 1908.[1] These long-boiler engines had a distinct influence on continental design, which is to be seen to this day in the relative positions of the boiler and cylinders on many locomotives running in Europe.

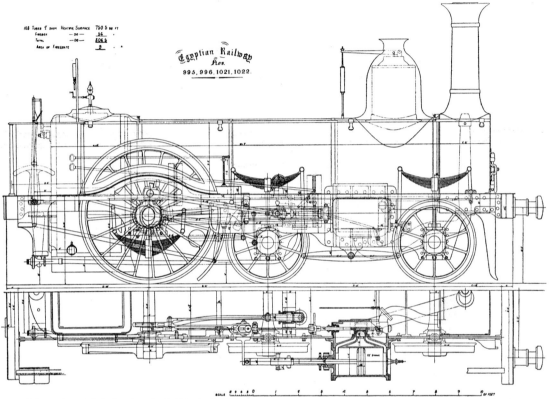

traced from the original drawing dated 28th April 1855.

CRAMPTON'S
PATENT
LOCOMOTIVE

The next rival to Stephenson's 'A' type was designed for the 'narrow gauge' by Thomas R. Crampton, formerly on the Great Western Railway under Gooch. We have referred to the generally prevailing theory that a low centre of gravity was essential to safety, but Robert Stephenson does not appear to have been so much obsessed by this theory as were some other designers.

We find a progressive increase in the height of boiler centre in his engines, and by 1849 at any rate he was in agreement with Brunel himself that 'beyond certain limits a low centre of gravity was not necessarily productive of any

[1] A. R. Bennett, 'The West Flanders Railway Locomotives,' *The Locomotive*, Vol. XIV., p. 142 *et seq.* for a full account, photographs by the writer and reproductions of two original working drawings signed by Robert Stephenson.

beneficial effect, and he denied . . . . that the steadiness of an engine was entirely caused by a low centre of gravity.' [1]   But the idea continued to obsess many engineers, among whom was Crampton.   In order to meet the objections to the long-boiler type with short wheel base, and at the same time keep the centre of the boiler low, he produced a type which had its merits, and subsequently a considerable vogue on the continent.   Engines of his design were in existence in France so late as 1902.   The normal Crampton engine had six wheels, like the ' A ' engine, but the driving wheels were placed behind, instead of in front of, the firebox.   These engines too had long boilers, but with a larger grate area than was obtainable with Stephenson's design.[2]

from Perdonnet's ' Chemins de Fer,' 1865, Vol. III., p. 100.
CRAMPTON LOCOMOTIVE
built by Derosne & Cail for the 'Nord' Railway, France [3]

EIGHT-WHEELED LOCOMOTIVES   We have seen that on the Great Western Railway Gooch had produced an eight-wheeled locomotive, the 'Great Western,' this engine had cylinders 18 inches diameter by 24 inches stroke, and a total heating surface of about 1,952 square feet, far exceeding that of any other engine then at work.   As a challenge to this Crampton designed his famous 'Liverpool' for the London and North Western Railway, with cylinders 18 inches diameter by 24 inches stroke, but with a total heating surface of 2,290 square feet.   Some remarkable performances are recorded, of this engine, but its immense heating surface was rather nominal than effective ; owing to its 'great length of wheel base, well loaded at each end' the engine was very severe on the permanent way in the passage of curves, and the design was not repeated.

[1] *Proceedings Inst. Civil Engineers*, Vol. VIII., p. 242 *et seq.*

[2] See Gaiser, *Die Crampton Lokomotive*, 1909, for an exhaustive monograph on these locomotives.

[3] See Clark, *Railway Machinery*, 1855, p. 208, Plates XIII., XIV.

from the Official Catalogue of the Great Exhibition, 1851, Vol. I., face p. 238.

CRAMPTON'S 'LIVERPOOL' BUILT BY BURY. CURTIS AND KENNEDY, 1848

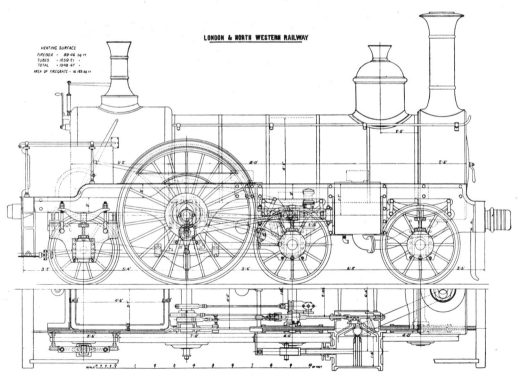

traced from the original drawing dated 24th February 1848.

EXPRESS LOCOMOTIVE FOR THE LONDON AND NORTH WESTERN RAILWAY
built by Robert Stephenson & Co., 1848

Two eight-wheeled engines were built by Robert Stephenson & Co. for the London and North Western Railway in 1848. They were a development of the 'A' type by the addition of hind carrying wheels, which permitted an increase in the grate area to 16 square feet, with a total heating surface of about 1,348 square feet, of which about 89 were in the firebox. The cylinders were 18 inches diameter by 24 inches stroke, the driving wheels 7 feet diameter. The outside bearings for the trailing wheels are worthy of notice, and modern practice has confirmed the desirability of such bearings for carrying wheels placed in close relation to the fire grate.[1]

from Williams' 'Our Iron Roads,' 1852, p. 248.

EIGHT-WHEELED LOCOMOTIVE FOR THE LONDON AND NORTH WESTERN RAILWAY
built by Robert Stephenson & Co., 1848

On the Great Western Railway the large engines designed by Gooch did not produce results in proportion to their nominal capacity. The reasons for this deficiency, and for the greater efficiency of Stephenson's long boiler, as compared with Gooch's boiler of large diameter and short length, have been investigated at great length by the best known English writer on the physiology of the locomotive[2], and his observations are worthy of study. Though primarily applicable to boilers intended for burning coke, they have a practical bearing on some problems of to-day.

INFLUENCE OF GAUGE EXPERIMENTS ON DESIGN

The results obtained in practice with the large engines which we have described showed that the 'Battle of the Gauges' had provoked a demand which was largely artificial, and had been the excuse for a megalomania of which there have been echoes,

[1] See previous page 397.   [2] D. K. Clark, *Railway Machinery*, 1855, Chapter VI., p. 154 *et seq.*

though not for the same causes, at subsequent periods in the history of the locomotive.

We find the writer whom we have just quoted, commenting in 1855 on the 'unsoundness of the policy of getting up heavy engines merely to show what can be done,' for within a few years of the gauge experiments most British railway companies had returned to the use of six-wheeled engines for both passenger and goods traffic. Numbers of this type were built by Robert Stephenson & Co. and for many years they were adequate for the service which was required of them. The 'Battle of the Gauges' appears rather to have stimulated development of the permanent way than led to any profitable innovations in the design of the locomotive. A better road made it possible subsequently to increase the wheel base of the engines, and so place the firebox again between the driving and trailing axle while retaining a greater length of tube than had previously been possible, and Robert Stephenson & Co. resumed the construction of six-wheeled locomotive engines of this type.

from a photo by the Great Western Railway Company.

GOOCH'S EIGHT-WHEELED LOCOMOTIVE 'LIGHTNING,' 1847

In 1848, for engines built for the York, Newcastle and Berwick Railway, they also returned to the use of outside frames and bearings for the leading and trailing wheels.[1] Another interesting feature of these engines is to be seen in the position of the excentrics, outside the driving wheels, but this practice was not generally followed, and eventually Robert Stephenson & Co. returned to the use of outside frames throughout, with inside bearings as well for the driving wheels.[2] This change in their policy, or rather return to a former policy, testifies to the general favour with which such outside frames were regarded.

The engine for the York, Newcastle and Berwick Railway was intended to run the express trains between Newcastle and York 'as soon as the re-laying of the line was completed.' It had a total heating surface of about 1,046 square feet, of which about 82 square feet were in the firebox. The cylinders were 16 inches

[1] See next page. [2] See p. 108, Chapter VI. *ante.*

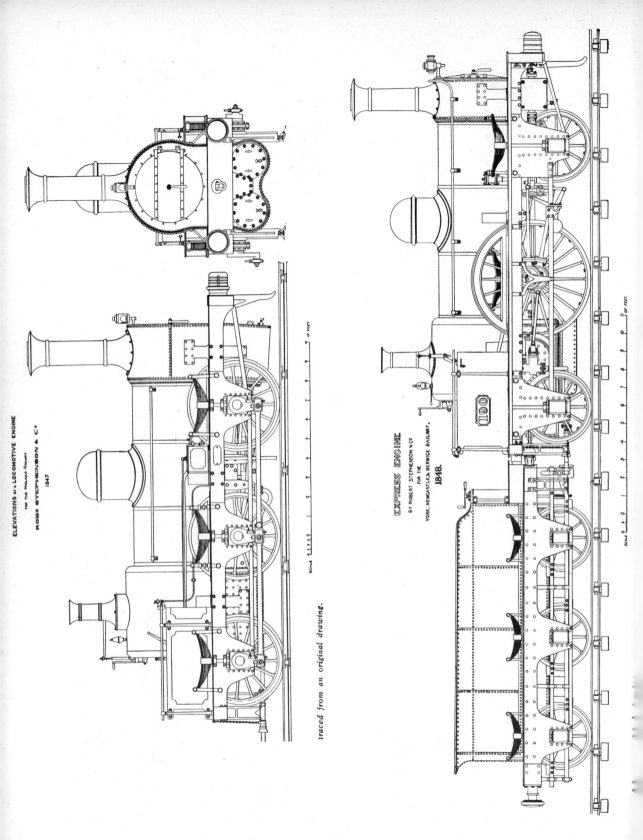

ELEVATIONS OF A LOCOMOTIVE ENGINE
FOR THE MIDLAND RAILWAY
ROBT STEPHENSON & Co
1847

traced from an original drawing.

EXPRESS ENGINE
BY ROBERT STEPHENSON & Co
FOR THE
YORK, NEWCASTLE, & BERWICK RAILWAY,
1848.

190

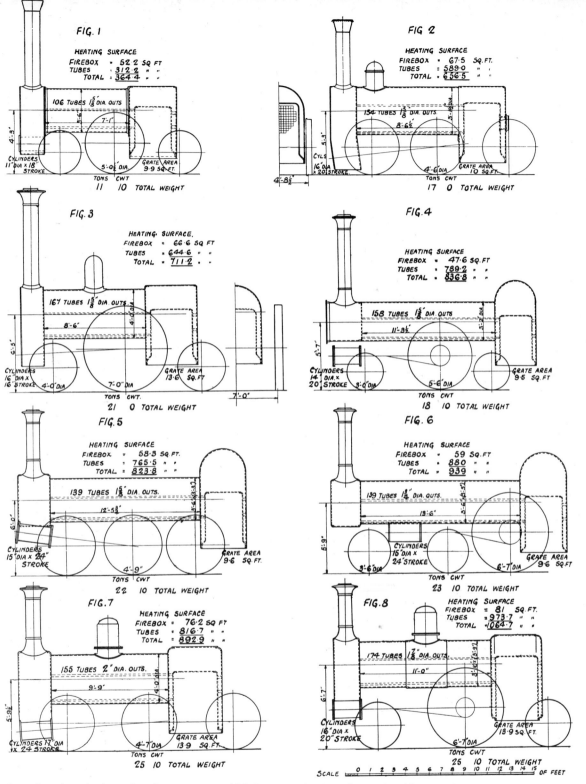

drawn from the makers' records and contemporary published accounts; heating surfaces and weights approximate.

DEVELOPMENT OF THE STEPHENSON SIX-WHEELED LOCOMOTIVE WITH COKE-BURNING BOILER (*ex* Fig. 3, see p. 389 *ante*)

FIG. 1. 'PATENTEE,' 1833 (See p. 310, *ante*). FIG. 2. Leicester and Swannington, 1833 (See p. 314 *ante*).
FIG. 3. 'NORTH STAR,' broad gauge, 1837 (,, pp. 338, 389, ,,). FIG. 4. 'NORTH STAR,' narrow gauge, 1841 (,, p. 348 ,,).
FIG. 5. 'MAMMOTH,' 1844 (,, p. 352, ,,). FIG. 6. 'A,' York and North Midland, 1845 (,, p. 372 ,,).
FIG. 7. Midland, 1847 (,, p. 400, ,,). FIG. 8. York, Newcastle and Berwick, 1848 (,, p. 400 ,,).

diameter by 20 inches stroke ; the driving wheels 6 feet 6 inches diameter.[1]

WORKING
PRESSURES

An examination of many designs of this period shows little increase to the nominal dimensions of the average 'narrow gauge' locomotive between 1840 and 1850. Increased power was being obtained rather by the use of higher pressures, the first notable increases having been made in the 'Ixion' and the 'A' engines, with nominal pressures of 75 lbs per square inch, instead of 50 lbs. as previously in general use. After 1850 there was a rapid increase and by 1860 working pressures had risen to 130 or 140 lbs.

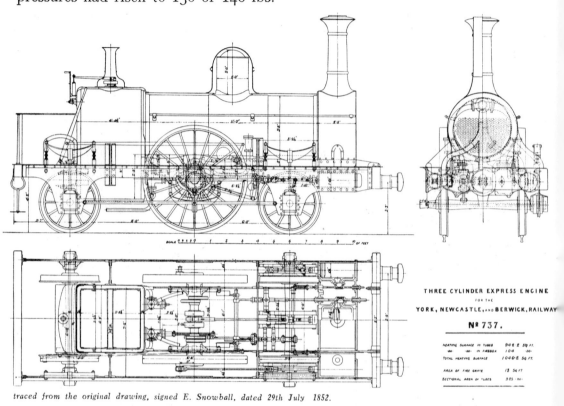

traced from the original drawing, signed E. Snowball, dated 29th July 1852.

THREE-CYLINDER EXPRESS ENGINE FOR THE YORK, NEWCASTLE AND BERWICK RAILWAY, 1853

FOUR-WHEELED
BOGIE

Robert Stephenson & Co.'s records include a design dated 1844 for a four-coupled locomotive with a leading four-wheeled bogie. The engine has a long boiler, but the firebox is placed between the driving and trailing axles. We have no evidence of their having built such an engine. But with the long eight-wheeled engines in use by 1850 some need for flexibility of wheel base no doubt soon became apparent, at any rate on the narrow gauge lines, though the necessity does not

[1] *Proc. Inst. Mechanical Engineers*, 1849, pp. 8, 9. The boiler of this engine, like others built by Robert Stephenson & Co. at this period, was slightly oval, being 3 feet 10 inches in vertical, by 3 feet 9 inches in horizontal section, but the barrel was not stayed across.

appear to have arisen on the broad gauge by 1855, when Robert Stephenson & Co. built for the Great Western Railway some remarkable four-coupled, eight-wheeled engines, with a fixed wheel-base, to Gooch's designs.

In 1854 they built tank engines for the North London Railway, which were remarkable as having inside cylinders, four wheels coupled and a leading four-wheeled bogie [1], and we have a Stephenson design in 1857 for an eight-wheeled tender engine having single driving wheels and a leading bogie. [2] The long boiler barrel, the relation of the smokebox to the wheels, and the outside bearings for the bogie are worthy of notice, but we have no evidence that this engine was built, and the first application of the bogie to an eight-wheeled

from a photo in the collection of Mr. E. L. Ahrons.

THE 'ANTIQUARY' BUILT BY ROBERT STEPHENSON & CO. IN 1855
to the designs of Daniel Gooch, for the Great Western Railway

tender engine by Robert Stephenson & Co. appears to have been on some four-coupled engines for the Ottoman Railway (Smyrna to Aidin) in 1859. [3]

The firm shortly afterwards built engines for the Great North of Scotland Railway having the same wheel arrangement but with bogies of the characteristic Stephenson design with outside bearings. These outside bogie bearings do not appear to have generally found favour on home railways [4]; inside bearings were fitted for subsequent engines of the Great North of Scotland Railway [5] and to some fine four-coupled bogie engines built in 1860 and 1861 for the Stockton and Darlington Railway. [6] The latter engines had the unusually large coupled wheel diameter of 7 feet. In their details generally they were typical of the

[1] See Clark, *Recent Practice in the Locomotive*, 1860, Plate XLIV. One of these engines was at work at Clifton Colliery near Nottingham in 1911.

[2] See next page.   [3] See p. 410 following.

[4] Except on the narrow gauge engines of the Great Western Railway, 1897-1902.

[5] Some of these beautiful little engines were at work until 1920 ; for engines of the same type built by Neilson & Co., see Colburn, *Locomotive Engineering*, Plate XLI.

[6] See p. 110 Chapter VI. *ante* and p. 405 following.

Stephenson design of the period though the driving wheels were of exceptional size for the north.[1]

But in 1860 eight-wheeled engines having leading bogies were exceptional in British practice and the six-wheeled engine was to remain for some time generally sufficient for the normal traffic of most lines, either with four wheels coupled and a single leading wheel, or with single driving wheels in the middle.

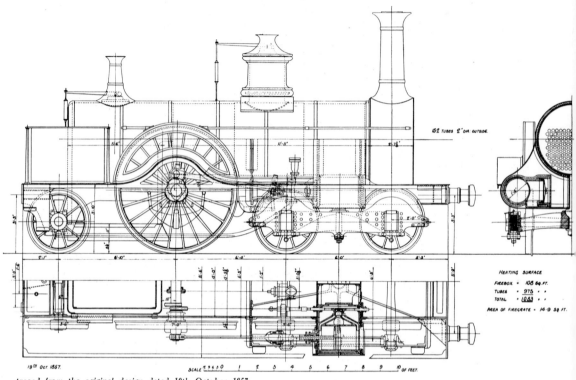

traced from the original design dated 19th October 1857.

PROPOSED SINGLE-DRIVER LOCOMOTIVE WITH FOUR-WHEELED BOGIE

In this state we will leave the Stephenson locomotive as it had become during the life-time of Robert Stephenson, embodying all the essential features which were to distinguish it for the next forty years.

[1] In 1849 Robert Stephenson stated that in the north the diameter of the driving wheels was being reduced with advantage to the speed of travelling on lines where stoppages were frequent—'indeed he was not at all persuaded that large wheels would maintain in the south where light trains and few stoppages were required.' He further remarked that 'at one time an attempt had been made to reduce the speed of the piston as much as possible; it was now found that the utmost speed was desirable—and he did not attach any importance to the size of the wheels.' *Proc. Inst. Civil Engineers*, Vol. VIII., p. 242.

The latest practice of the Great Western Railway Company offers striking confirmation; see p. 435 following.

So early as 1860 Robert Stephenson & Co. built goods engines for Egypt having six coupled wheels 5 feet diam. and cylinders 17 inches diam. by 28 inches stroke. These engines were further remarkable for a total heating surface of 1,612 square feet, with a grate area of 19 square feet.

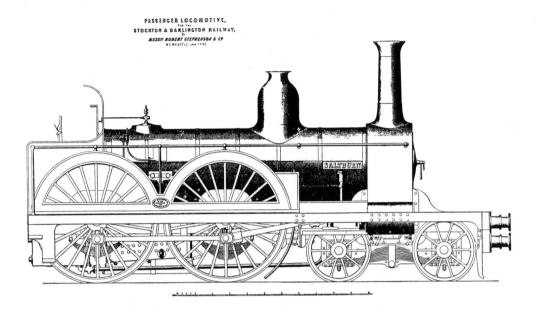

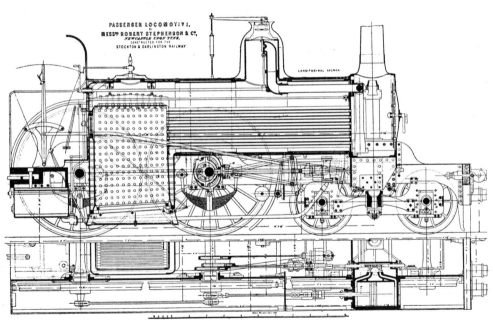

from Colburn's Locomotive Engineering, 1871, Plates XXVI., XXVII.

BOGIE PASSENGER LOCOMOTIVE WITH 7-FOOT DRIVING WHEELS
built for the Stockton and Darlington Railway, 1861

GEORGE ROBERT STEPHENSON

1819—1905

CHAPTER XXIX

THE LATER DEVELOPMENTS OF
ROBERT STEPHENSON & CO.

1859—1923

In a previous chapter we have recorded the foundation of the firm of Robert Stephenson & Co. and its subsequent development from 1823 to 1859—a period of thirty-six years. We have now to trace its history during a period of about sixty-four years, from 1859 to 1923—a period far longer, but in the nature of things bound to offer less material of interest to either the general reader, or to the historian of the locomotive.

With the death of Robert Stephenson one of its greatest figures had passed from the railway world ; another, that of Brunel, passed almost simultaneously, and 'the river of thoughts and events' which had produced and borne forward such men, and George Stephenson before them, could not reverse its course. These men were unique, as their opportunities were unique, and many of the battles they fought were decisive. No man more disliked controversy, and none was more constantly engaged in it, than Robert Stephenson ; but those who succeeded him did not find themselves involved in any of the great fundamental struggles associated with the early development of railways, on the success of which the very existence of their business would directly depend. The subsequent troubles of the firm were to come from other causes, not necessarily connected with the development of the locomotive building industry as a whole—this had been too firmly established, largely as a result of those early endeavours of the Two Stephensons which had hastened the general adoption of the steam locomotive.

So far as the development of the locomotive itself was concerned the death of Robert Stephenson may be said to have coincided with the end of a classical period, during which, principally as the result of his work and that of Robert Stephenson & Co., the design of the locomotive had been stabilised on such lines that for many years subsequently the typical 'Stephenson' locomotive, distinguished for its simplicity and fitness, was to suffice for the ordinary work of the world's railways, and the construction of such locomotives was to offer ample employment to the industry as a whole.

We have devoted many pages to recording the early development of the locomotive and have brought to light links in its history hitherto ignored, or generally unknown. The story of its development during the period of about forty years following the death of Robert Stephenson, is better known ; no such epoch-marking types now appear as George Stephenson's Killingworth engine, and his 'Experiment,'—Hackworth's 'Royal George,'—Robert Stephenson's 'Lancashire Witch,'—'Rocket;'—'Northumbrian,' and 'Planet.'

We shall therefore illustrate only a few of the locomotives built during the period with which we are now dealing, subsequently treating more fully of the productions of the present firm at its new works in Darlington. These works commenced operations at a time when greatly increased demands upon the power of the locomotive had caused a corresponding increase to its size and some inevitable modifications to its design.

On the death of Robert Stephenson his interests in the Newcastle works were inherited by his first cousin, George Robert Stephenson, the only son of Robert, a younger brother of George Stephenson. This Robert, appears to have possessed something of the energy and ability of his famous brother. We have already mentioned that he had constructed the Hetton Colliery Railway which had been laid out by George Stephenson; · for a while he held the position of engineer to the collieries, and his name is recorded on the contemporary print which we have illustrated in an earlier chapter as 'one of those to whom the manager was under obligations for fixing and improving the machinery, and for his skill and attention in the sinking of the pits.'[1] While his brother George was constructing the Liverpool and Manchester Railway, Robert Stephenson was engaged on the Bolton and Leigh line. He was afterwards chief engineer of the Pendleton Collieries, a position which he held at the time of his death.

His son, George Robert, was born at Newcastle-upon-Tyne in 1819, and may be said to have commenced his career when twelve years of age by familiarising himself with the daily underground working of the Pendleton Collieries where his father was engaged, and where the boy himself was usefully employed before his fifteenth year. As a boy too he witnessed the experiments made by De Pambour and Dr. Lardner with the locomotives of the Liverpool and Manchester Railway.[2] He was subsequently sent to King William's College, Castletown, in the Isle of Man, where he remained till he was eighteen ; during this period his father died suddenly, and on leaving college George Robert was placed by his uncle, George Stephenson, in the drawing office of the Manchester and Leeds Railway. Here he remained until 1843 when he was appointed engineer of his uncle's Tapton Collieries. He afterwards became resident engineer for a new line of the South Eastern Railway, then under construction by his cousin Robert Stephenson as engineer-in-chief. He was subsequently engaged in the construction of other railways and works at home and abroad, and as a bridge builder carried out some particularly important work, including a large bridge carrying the railway across the Nile at Kaffr Zeyat.[3]

This bridge had resulted from Robert Stephenson's visit to Egypt in 1850, when he had been commissioned by Abbas Pasha to construct a railway from Alexandria to Cairo. The line was at first carried across the Nile on a

---

[1] See pp. 33, 34, Chapter III. *ante.*

[2] Private Memoir communicated to Robert Stephenson & Co. 1923 by Mr. George Stephenson.

[3] Jeaffreson, *Life of Robert Stephenson*, Vol. II., p. 174. See also *Northern Echo*, 3rd Jan. 1873. Local Industrial Sketches, No. 40.

rail ferry, which was subsequently replaced by the bridge in question, designed by George Robert Stephenson on the tubular system which his cousin had previously adopted for his bridges over the Menai Straits, and the River St. Lawrence in Canada; but in the bridge over the Nile the railway was carried on top of the tube, not through it. The total length of this bridge was 1,607 feet, it had eleven fixed openings each 114 feet wide, and two swing openings each 80 feet wide; it was constructed at Robert Stephenson & Co.'s Newcastle works, the gross weight of the material being about 2,634 tons.

It is recorded that by 1863 the firm had already constructed 38 wrought iron bridges [1], thus continuing the early work of George Stephenson who had built a bridge when in partnership with the Burrells before 1823.[2] Robert Stephenson's own famous High Level Bridge at Newcastle, though so

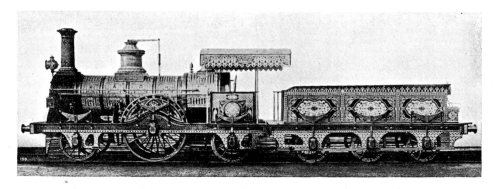

STEPHENSONS' STANDARD EXPRESS PASSENGER LOCOMOTIVE, 1858
specially decorated for the Viceroy of Egypt

near, was not built at his works. This bridge, of which the principal members are in cast iron, was opened by Queen Victoria in 1849, and stands to-day one of the most remarkable monuments to the practical genius of its designer, carrying a traffic which he can have little anticipated.[3] It is well shown on the firm's business card which we have illustrated in our previous chapter on the firm's development.

George Robert Stephenson had been intimately associated since his youth, with the 'Two Stephensons,' his uncle and his cousin, and now that both were gone he benefited by the great inheritance which had resulted from their labours. His other partners were Joseph Pease, M.P., who had succeeded to the interests of Edward Pease, and William Weallens who had succeeded William Hutchinson.

[1] J. F. Tone, *A History of the Trade and Manufactures of the Tyne, Wear and Tees* (British Association 1863). Communicated to Robert Stephenson & Co. 1922 by Mr. Edward Wooler.

[2] See p. 53, Chapter VI. *ante*. The remains of this remarkable bridge are preserved in the Railway Museum of the London and North Eastern Railway at York.

[3] The weight of the heaviest locomotive on the York, Newcastle and Berwick Railway in 1849 was about 26 tons (without tender), the weight of the heaviest locomotive on the London and North Eastern Railway to-day is about four times as great. For illustration of bridge see p. 107, Chapter VI. *ante*.

from a photo in the collection of the Locomotive Publishing Co.

BUILT FOR THE SYDNEY AND GOULBURN RAILWAY, 1854
to the designs of J. E. McConnell
is now preserved at Sydney, New South Wales

BUILT FOR THE OTTOMAN RAILWAY (SMYRNA TO AIDIN), 1859
was in service (rebuilt as shown) in 1910

BUILT FOR THE CEYLON RAILWAYS, 1875

When Robert Stephenson died there were many rivals in the field, but the Newcastle firm still had its own preserves, and was reaping the results of its former chief's labours and friendships. He had told Joseph Pease in 1835 that but for his frequent absences abroad the works would have had to close [1], and a study of the firm's order books amply justifies this assertion. The friendships which Robert Stephenson had formed on his tour on the continent, and in Egypt in particular, were to produce a rich harvest for the Newcastle works in later years, much of it during the period now under review.

SALOON LOCOMOTIVE FOR THE VICEROY OF EGYPT
built by Robert Stephenson & Co. in 1862 and decorated to the designs of Digby Wyatt [2]

Between 1860 and 1870 many of the old names had disappeared for good from the firm's order books, but their places were taken by new names, some representing amalgamations which had embraced the old companies, others showing that new markets had been opened up. For the Australian continent, to which the first locomotives had been sent by Robert Stephenson & Co. in 1854 to the Sydney and Goulburn Railway, we find engines built later for the Melbourne and Hobson's Bay, the Adelaide and Gawler Town, the Victorian, and New South Wales Railways. The firm also supplied locomotives to the Tasmanian Railways, and in 1873 to New Zealand.

For the East, locomotives were sent to Ceylon, and to India for the Calcutta

---

[1] See p. 87, Chapter VI. *ante.*   In December 1861 the firm had one hundred locomotives on order, of a total value of £270,770.

[2] Sir Matthew Digby Wyatt, first 'Slade' Professor of Fine Arts, Cambridge.
We are informed by Mr. J. Stewart, who was at the time a painter in the service of the firm and is now in his ninety-first year, that the colour scheme was in mauve on a white ground.   The dome cover was of bell-metal polished, the hand-rails and other fittings were gilded.   The interior woodwork and upholstery were most elaborate; into the carpet were worked artificial flowers, which after being crushed underfoot opened again by springs.   A door gave access to the footplate for the Viceroy should he desire to drive the engine, which had a spare set of silver handles for the purpose.   Two special coaches accompanied the saloon engine, one for the wives, the other for the body guard of the Viceroy.   (The better known title of 'Khedive' was not granted until 1867.)

STEPHENSON LONG-BOILER LOCOMOTIVE FOR THE NORTH EASTERN RAILWAY, 1866

BUILT FOR THE NORTH EASTERN RAILWAY, 1871
to the designs of E. Fletcher

BUILT FOR THE LONDON AND SOUTH WESTERN RAILWAY, 1886
to the designs of W. Adams

and South Eastern, Great Indian Peninsular, Scinde, Great Southern of India, and Delhi Railways, and in 1882 to Japan.

For South America locomotives were supplied to the Pernambuco and Don Pedro Segundo Railways in Brazil, for the Lima and Callao and Peruvian Railways, the Honduras Railway and the Great Southern Railway of Buenos Ayres.

For Africa engines were sent to the Cape Town Railway, and to the island of Mauritius.

For the European continent Robert Stephenson & Co. built for Holland, Denmark and Norway, and again in large numbers for Italy. For Eastern Europe they sent locomotives to the Riga and Dunaberg, Dunaberg and Witepsk, and to other Russian Railways.

For home lines the firm built during the period 1860 to 1870 for the London Chatham and Dover, London and Brighton, and London and South Western Railways; also for the Great North of Scotland, North British, North Eastern, Eastern Counties, and Great Northern Railways, and again for the Stockton and Darlington line, which still preserved its old identity. The last six of these are now absorbed in the London and North Eastern Railway.

STEPHENSON LONG-BOILER LOCOMOTIVE FOR THE DANISH STATE RAILWAYS, 1868

Many other historic names, including those of the Liverpool and Manchester, Grand Junction, London and Birmingham, and Leicester and Swannington lines, for which Stephenson locomotives have been built in the past, now lose their identity in the London, Midland and Scottish Railway. These great amalgamations will lead to an extension of the policy first adopted in England on a large scale by the Liverpool and Manchester Railway Company—the policy of building their own locomotives. This is indeed to-day the only question, so far as the locomotive building industry is concerned, which corresponds in any degree to the great controversial questions of the past, and on the economic aspects of the case accountants have agreed to differ.

So far as design is concerned, when we consider the varieties of locomotives introduced by individual railway companies between 1850 and 1880, and compare them with the simple 'Stephenson' engine of those times, we may reflect, though we will not attempt to offer an opinion on the question, whether some of those railway companies would not have been better served had they been content with the 'standard' designs of the locomotive builders.

'In the constructive department of locomotives '—says an authority writing in 1855—'engineers have been and are widely at variance, as anyone may judge from the variety of stock now made ; . . . probably five distinct classes of locomotive would afford a variety sufficiently accommodating to suit the varied traffic of railways, whereas I suppose the varieties of locomotives in actual operation in this country and elsewhere are very nearly five hundred in number. Everyone cannot be right, and most of them must be wrong, and it would be for the best interests of railways if the proper authorities could be unanimous in the selection of a good number of classes to uniform patterns to be adopted in future practice. It is doubtful if such an arrangement could be worked out unless there were entire amalgamation of railway interests and the influences of the government, or otherwise it is extremely desirable and is certainly practicable.' [1]

Whether the extraordinary variety, and in some cases the extravagancies of design, examples of which we have described in our last chapter, resulted eventually in any improvement to the locomotive, or assisted its development, has been, and will remain, a matter of opinion. But in considering the question we may bear in mind that the effective development of the locomotive during a most critical period, between 1825 and 1845, was due almost entirely to the locomotive builders, principally to Robert Stephenson & Co., Bury & Co., and, later, Sharp, Roberts & Co.

We must now briefly refer again to the marine work carried on at their Forth Street and South Street works, for though the firm of Robert Stephenson & Co. is to-day solely a locomotive building concern, they did not formerly depend entirely on such work, but while their works remained at Newcastle were in the unique position of constructing both marine engines and locomotives in the same establishment. We have an interesting reference to the marine engines which formed an important part of their output in 1864, during which year the American Civil War was in progress, and blockade running on the American coasts had become a profitable, though risky business. It appears that Robert Stephenson & Co. supplied the engines for two blockade runners, the 'Badger' and the 'Stag,' and we have a contemporary account of a trial run with the first of these steamers. The writer describes 'smashing holes in the paddle boxes to give a good outlet for the water ; cutting apertures in the casing over the engine room to get a good draught for the furnaces ; sails and yards removed out of the way, that not a breath of wind might have a chance for retarding the speed of the slim vessel.' [2]

[1] D. K. Clark, *Railway Machinery*, 1855, Preface, p. vii.
[2] *Liverpool Albion*, 26th March 1864. Communicated to Robert Stephenson & Co. 1923 by Mr. W. G. R. Crow.

A contemporary report [1] describing the trial trip of the 'Stag' states that she was '220 feet long and 26 feet beam, with engines of 180 horse-power, capable of being worked to five times that power, made by the celebrated firm of Robert Stephenson & Co. of Newcastle-on-Tyne.' The 'Stag' did 28 knots in one hour and fifty-three minutes, a speed which the reporter believed 'had never been surpassed by a blockade-runner of her size and power.'

In 1869 the firm built a patent marine engine to a design by their works manager, G. A. Crow, whose appointment in 1845 we have already mentioned.[2] This engine was designed with a view to a reduction of overall length by the use of a return connecting rod, but it differed from previous designs having

PATENT MARINE ENGINES BUILT BY ROBERT STEPHENSON & Co., 1869

the same object, and has a peculiar interest from the obvious similarity of certain parts to those of the locomotive, notably the connecting rod large end. We have already seen that in 1841 Robert Stephenson had fitted a connecting rod of marine type to his long-boiler locomotive.[3]

In 1881 the world was specially reminded of the work of the Stephensons by celebrations held in Newcastle to commemorate the hundredth anniversary of George Stephenson's birth. These celebrations were the occasion for gathering together a remarkable exhibit of locomotives, most of them in working order, showing the development of the Stephenson locomotive from the Killingworth type to the most up-to-date express engine of the day.

[1] *Liverpool Courier*, 19th Oct. 1864.

[2] See p. 109, Chapter VI. *ante*.

[3] See p. 150, Chapter XXVI. *ante*.

B B

In 1882 Robert Stephenson & Co. sent locomotives to China ; ten years previously they had built for the Imperial Railways of Japan ; they had sent across the Atlantic to America in 1828, and the Stephenson locomotive had now completed its journey round the world.

We must now digress to record some changes in the partnership and staff. In 1858 Edward Snowball, then chief draughtsman, had gone to India and his place had been taken by J. D. Wardale. In 1862 William Weallens died suddenly while travelling in Paris. He appears to have been a man of many activities, and was at one time on the Newcastle City Council. He took an active part in the volunteer movement and commanded a company of men from Robert Stephenson & Co.'s works.[1] With his long experience, as chief draughtsman, works manager, and subsequently as managing partner, his death must have been a serious loss to the firm. He was succeeded as general

MARINE BOILER BUILT BY ROBERT STEPHENSON & Co., 1886
the photo shows G. A. Crow, the left of the three figures in front of the boiler

manager by George K. Douglas, who held that position until his death in 1885, being succeeded by G. H. Garrett who died in 1889. In 1872 Joseph Pease died, the last of those who had been partners during the lifetime of Robert Stephenson. His interests were inherited by his son Joseph Whitwell Pease, afterwards created a baronet. In 1873 the late Mr. J. D. Wardale retired, and was succeeded by Mr. A. J. Kitching, who held the position of chief draughtsman until the firm removed their locomotive works to Darlington. In the works G. A. Crow though still known as ' head foreman ' was virtually manager, till his death in 1887, after nearly fifty years service ; his duties afterwards devolved upon his son.[2]

[1] Obituary, *Proc. Inst. Mechanical Engineers.*   [2] The late Mr. W. H. Crow, see p. 417 following.

The firm's activities in marine construction in 1886 are referred to in a contemporary journal [1] :—

Literally moving evidence of the mechanical capabilities of Newcastle was afforded to the gazing surprise of many sightseers this morning. Drawn by a team of fifty-eight horses, a boiler weighing sixty-five tons was removed from the well-known works of Messrs. R. Stephenson & Co., in South Street, and safely deposited under the eighty-ton crane, whence it will, in due course, be transferred to the new steamer 'Dardanus.' The ponderous pile, as it slowly but surely passed through the winding thoroughfares, represented an amount of concentrated labour and mechanical skill, on which the beholders might not unreasonably indulge in a little self-congratulation.

Such difficulties of transport for their heavy productions at this time, and until the removal of their works from Newcastle, were amongst the many which Robert Stephenson & Co. had to face.

In 1886 the partners now representing the original firm decided on a step which was to affect vitally the subsequent history of Robert Stephenson & Co. A private limited company was formed with the intention of extending the firm's activities in both locomotive and marine engine construction and undertaking the building of ships. On 30th December 1886 the lease of a shipyard at Hebburn-on-Tyne was completed, and the building of marine engines and boilers was transferred later to Hebburn, leaving more room for locomotive construction at South Street, but this extension of activities proved to be more apparent than real. Troubles multiplied, and in 1892 we find the directors of the new company and their lately appointed general manager Mr. John Walker [2] facing the question, which, though for different reasons, had troubled the partners in 1827—whether they should not close works which could now no longer be carried on profitably.

In 1899 the private company which had been formed in 1886 was voluntarily wound up, and a new public limited company was formed. Mr. George Robert Stephenson now retired from the concern with which his relatives and himself had been so long associated and lived in retirement until his death a few years later, in 1905, at the age of eighty-six.

One of the most important decisions of the new company was to remove their locomotive works to a more convenient site. The old Forth Street, now known as the South Street works, which had been commenced in 1823 with less than an acre of ground, had been extended to every possible limit. It was decided to dispose of these historic works and lay out a new establishment at Darlington, on a site which should offer ample field for future expansion. With the subsequent vicissitudes of the firm's marine engine and boiler works and the shipyard we need not deal here, since after the removal of the locomotive building works to Darlington this, and the other establishments, became for technical purposes entirely distinct concerns under separate local management.

The new works at Darlington were laid out by Mr. W. Norman, who had been appointed locomotive manager, with the late Mr. W. H. Crow as works

[1] *Newcastle Evening Chronicle*, May 1886. [2] Appointed in 1891.

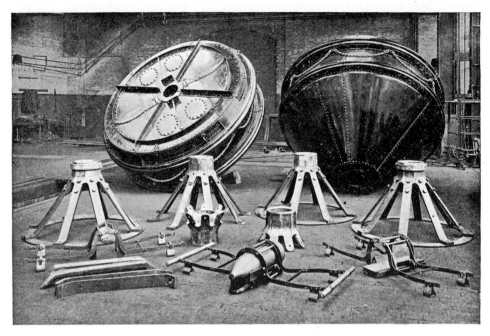

published by permission of the Admiralty.

MOORING BUOYS AND GUN PEDESTALS, 1915-1918

published by permission of the Admiralty.

GUN AND GUN-CARRIAGE PARTS, 1915-1918

manager. Mr. J. M. Galt, who had received his training under the late Edward Snowball[1], was appropriately appointed as chief draughtsman, and Mr. C. Hyde as chief clerk. Constructive operations were commenced in 1900, and though officials and men had to face all the difficulties and troubles incidental to starting a new establishment, the first locomotive built by Robert Stephenson & Co. at Darlington was steamed in October 1902, within a mile of the scene of George Stephenson's early activities on the Stockton and Darlington Railway. In the following year the firm built some remarkable engines for India, which, as in the case of locomotives built by them in earlier days, became the prototype for a large and successful class, and showed that the new establishment could produce engines of the heaviest types then demanded of British locomotive builders.

In 1904 various changes took place; the late Mr. Charles Emmott became chairman[2], Mr. C. N. Goodall, was appointed locomotive manager, and Mr. J. M. Galt works manager. In spite of continued financial difficulties a policy of improving and extending the new works was adopted and consistently pursued, but the company formed in 1899 was to survive little longer than the previous company. In 1914 re-construction took place, the whole of the firm's establishments on Tyneside were disposed of, the locomotive building works alone being retained. This concern was now placed on a sound financial basis under the chairmanship of Sir William B. Peat. The directors of the new company appropriately included a great-grandson of Edward Pease, Mr. Herbert Pike Pease, M.P.[3], who subsequently retired to take government office, but has since rejoined the board as Lord Daryngton. The other directors appointed were Mr. W. Benton Jones, and Mr. William Wingfield; Mr. C. N. Goodall was appointed managing director, and Mr. C. Hyde secretary to the new company.

WAR WORK At the commencement of the World War in 1914, and for some little time after, the firm was fully engaged with large contracts for locomotives for South Africa, India, and elsewhere. But as the need for broadening the basis for the supply of munitions became clear to the British Government, Robert Stephenson & Co., like many other firms, undertook the manufacture of such novelties as gun mountings and sights for the Admiralty, and the supply of gun parts. They adapted their boiler shop flanging plant to the making of 6-inch shell bands, and finally established a complete plant for the manufacture of 18-pounder shrapnel shells, but as military operations progressed on an ever vaster scale the transport engine became more obviously important as an instrument of war; for operating the railways which they had taken over on the Western front alone the British Government required locomotives in ever increasing numbers, and

---

[1] Then chief draughtsman to the well-known firm of Neilson Reid & Co. (now merged in the North British Locomotive Co.) Glasgow. See p. 109 *ante*.

[2] Mr. C. Emmott died in 1910; he is remembered by the firm's present officials for an unfailing courtesy and interest in their work.

[3] Member of Parliament for Darlington, 1898-1923.

BUILT FOR THE MINISTRY OF MUNITIONS
for the Railway Operating Department of the War Office on the Western Front

BUILT FOR THE MINISTRY OF MUNITIONS
for service on the metre gauge lines of the Western Front

during the last two years of the war Robert Stephenson & Co.'s Darlington works were principally employed in the construction of such locomotives for the Ministry of Munitions ; they however continued the manufacture of shells and other war work concurrently until the Armistice in 1918.

When it became possible to command the necessary labour and material the firm made a large extension to their works with a view to considerably increasing their output. It was obvious that quantities of locomotives and material of all kinds would be required to repair the wastage of war, and indeed for a time it appeared that prices would be maintained at the artificial level to which they had been forced by an abnormal demand coincident with a shortage of labour. But such expectations were soon to prove illusory ; many of those who most wanted railway material were unable to pay for it, and those who had ordered and could pay were unable to get it. Constant disputes in the industrial world led eventually to the cancellation of valuable orders for locomotives which had been placed with Robert Stephenson & Co.

published by permission of the Admiralty.

ANTI-AIRCRAFT GUN-MOUNTING AND SIGHT

Although the firm has had for many years such friendly relations between staff and employees as appear to have been a tradition in the lifetime of Robert Stephenson, they cannot escape the effects of disputes in other industries on which they depend for the supply of their materials. The difficulties connected with such disputes are among the most serious of the problems which they, with many others, have to face to-day. Fortunately the foundation of the company on a sound financial basis has enabled it to tide over a period of exceptional difficulty, under conditions to which we can find an equivalent only in the period following the Napoleonic Wars. But their almost empty shops, and the War Memorial unveiled on 15th May 1923, their Centenary year, to the memory of many gallant men, suffice to show the price which Britain has paid for victory in the Great War.

The new extensions, and much new and improved plant, have placed the firm in a position to turn out more, and larger locomotives in the future, but they have to face an unprecedented competition in every market in the world, and, owing to changes in political relationships, less favourable conditions in the Indian market, which had been for some time past a mainstay of the

British locomotive builder. The recent amalgamations of the home railways threaten too to deprive the locomotive manufacturer of a market, which, though it had gradually become more and more restricted still offered them some opportunities.

DARLINGTON
WORKS

|Robert Stephenson & Co.'s new works at Darlington show nothing in common with their old establishment. Though of less extent than the works of many of their competitors to-day, they would in size, and perhaps even more in equipment, be as astonishing to the men of 1823 as the locomotives they produce. The very tools employed are in some cases more complicated than the early locomotives.

PRO PATRIA

LET THOSE WHO COME AFTER SEE TO IT THAT THEIR NAMES BE NOT FORGOTTEN

TO THE MEMORY OF THE MEN FROM THESE WORKS WHO FELL FOR THEIR COUNTRY IN THE GREAT WAR 1914-1918

W. B. ADAMSON — ARTIFICER ROYAL NAVY
W. ARCHBOLD — PTE. 5TH DURHAM LIGHT INF.
S. BAILEY — PTE. 3RD DURHAM LIGHT INF.
R. BAMLETT — CPL. 5TH DURHAM LIGHT INF.
I. F. BENBOW — PTE. 10TH DURHAM LIGHT INF.
A. E. BEXFIELD — PTE. 5TH DURHAM LIGHT INF.
T. D. BOWRAN — PTE. 18TH DURHAM LIGHT INF.
W. COATES — GNR. ROYAL GARRISON ARTY.
R. A. COLLIER — GNR. ROYAL FIELD ARTY.
G. O. S. CURTIS — PTE. 3RD DURHAM LIGHT INF.
D. DALEY — PTE. 5TH DURHAM LIGHT INF.
W. I. DOBSON — PTE. 5TH DURHAM LIGHT INF.
I. FAIRBAIRN — PTE. 5TH DURHAM LIGHT INF.
W. GREER — SAPPER ROYAL ENGINEERS
W. I. HAYES — L. CPL. 5TH DURHAM LIGHT INF.

T. W. HINDMARSH — PTE. 2ND DURHAM LIGHT INF.
C. R. HURWORTH — CAPT. 5TH YORKSHIRE REGT.
D. ICETON — L'CPL. 4TH GREEN HOWARDS
S. LAMBERT — ABLE SEAMAN R. NAVAL DIV'N.
I. N. LUKE — 2 LT. 5TH DURHAM LIGHT INF.
I. MACNICHOL — GNR. ROYAL FIELD ARTY.
W. I. MARTIN — SAPPER ROYAL ENGINEERS
C. MATSON — CPL. 18TH DURHAM LIGHT INF.
P. MOSS — PTE. 5 RD WEST YORKS REGT.
I. MURPHY — PTE. 2ND DURHAM LIGHT INF.
H. NELSON — PTE. 4TH YORKSHIRE REGT.
G. NUTBROWN — PTE. 5TH DURHAM LIGHT INF.
I. T. PEARSON — PTE. COLDSTREAM GUARDS
E. PEIRSON — PTE. 5TH DURHAM LIGHT INF.
T. PEIRSON — GNR. ROYAL FIELD ARTY.

H. RAMSDALE — DRIVER ROYAL ENGINEERS
B. RAMSDEN — PTE. 5TH DURHAM LIGHT INF.
T. W. SMITH — GNR. ROYAL FIELD ARTY.
A. E. SWANNELL — L'CPL. 26TH NORTH'D FUS.
F. TASKER — SERGEANT RIFLE BRIGADE
W. TATE — PTE. COLDSTREAM GUARDS
L. W. TREWHITT — PTE. 19TH NORTH'D FUS.
I. WALLIS — PTE. 5TH DURHAM LIGHT INF.
R. S. WALTON — PTE. 5TH DURHAM LIGHT INF.
H. WARRILOW — SERGT. 5 RD WEST YORKS REGT.
I. WATKINS — LIEUT. ROYAL NAVAL RESERVE
I. W. WATLING — PTE. 5TH DURHAM LIGHT INF.
G. E. WHITE — SERGT. 5 TH DURHAM LIGHT INF.
C. W. WHITFIELD — PTE. 5TH DURHAM LIGHT INF.
W. YOUNG — CPL. 14TH DURHAM LIGHT INF.

THIS TABLET IS DEDICATED BY ROBERT STEPHENSON & Co LIMITED

There are few of the larger machines, even those performing a single operation, which can be bought for the price paid for a locomotive a hundred years ago, or are not in themselves far heavier than the old stationary engine which in 1823, and for many years subsequently, supplied all the motive power required at the Forth Street works at Newcastle, and was in fact in service until those works were abandoned. This old engine, now a centenarian, is still preserved, the only outward and visible link with the original works.

It would be possible to make further comparisons between the tonnage output from the modern works and the output of one hundred years ago, but we shall have failed in one purpose of these notes if we admit that size is in itself a criterion of quality. On such a standard indeed the works of Robert Stephenson & Co. do not attempt comparison with many of the vast locomotive building establishments to-day, and the firm does not claim the attention of modern engineers on account of the quantity, but for the quality of its work, and for its endeavour to maintain the Stephenson traditions which we have recorded in our history.

Association with an historic name has an influence which can be expressed in work. Efficiency with simplicity were the clear ideals, first of George, and then of Robert Stephenson—they may well remain the ideals of those who to-day 'scud with flowing sheet' along a course charted by the work of the Two Stephensons. But each decade, each year, brings new problems, or, to

OLD WORKS ENGINE, 1823

the engine which first supplied the power to the Forth Street Works and was in service until 1899; the cylinders have been renewed and enlarged; the frame, beams and some other parts are original.

speak more exactly, brings the old ones back in new forms. This is one of the great truths which emerges from a study of the past. We have already referred to the struggle for existence against increasing competition, and we speak now of technical problems. The steam locomotive itself is threatened; the fixed engine controversy is revived in a new form by the advocates of electric traction, and just as a hundred years ago there were conditions in which the fixed engine might be more economical, so to-day there are conditions, though of a different kind, which enable the electric to supplant the steam locomotive in certain spheres of work.

We see too the revival of attempts to apply the rotary engine, and the gear drive, and are reminded of Lord Dundonald's experiments with the

Erecting Shop at Robert Stephenson. & Co's. Darlington Works
with Heavy Goods Engines under construction for the Madras and Southern Mahratta Railway

'Rocket,' of George Stephenson's condemnation of the 'rotary fallacy[1],' and of the fact that one of his greatest improvements to the early locomotive was the elimination of a gear drive.[2]   We see the condenser brought into use on the locomotive, and we reflect that it was only Trevithick's abandonment of the condenser which made the steam locomotive possible one hundred and nineteen years ago.   With the condenser we see too a revival of the fan to promote combustion, which failed so signally on the 'William the Fourth' in 1831.[3]

The success of the 'rotary' steam locomotive has yet to be established, though improvements in methods, and improvements in materials, have falsified some of the prophecies which have held good for a century, and may stultify others.   But certain needs must be met for some time by that most successful compromise with realities, the steam locomotive, in all essentials as it was left by Robert Stephenson.   'The consumption of fuel'—he wrote in 1830—'being much greater in Locomotive than Fixed Engines, it becomes a highly interesting, and indeed an essential point to determine the proportion with precision, before a correct comparison can be instituted between the merits of the two systems of conveyance.   It is probable that the consumption of fuel by Locomotive Engines will always be greater than by Fixed Engines. In the latter the heat may, without inconvenience, be applied in the best possible manner, ... but lightness, compactness, and simplicity being absolutely necessary in Locomotives, we are compelled to adopt less economical methods of applying the fuel.'[4]

We may remember moreover that certain principles are immutable; that simple design and good workmanship are worth striving for, and worth paying for, are we believe, such principles, and so far as is humanly possible Robert Stephenson & Co. still strive to-day after such design and such work, and offer them to those who want the locomotive of the future, whether operated by steam or other power.   They do not claim to-day that they can teach to build locomotives, but they do claim that they are not unmindful of the lessons which their predecessors taught the world.

ROBERT STEPHENSON & CO'S DARLINGTON WORKS.

[1] See p. 290, Chapter XXI. *ante.*   [2] See p. 22, Chapter III. *ante.*
[3] See p. 210, Chapter XIII. *ante,* p. 243, Chapter XVIII. *ante.*
[4] *Observations on the Comparative Merits of Locomotive and Fixed Engines.*

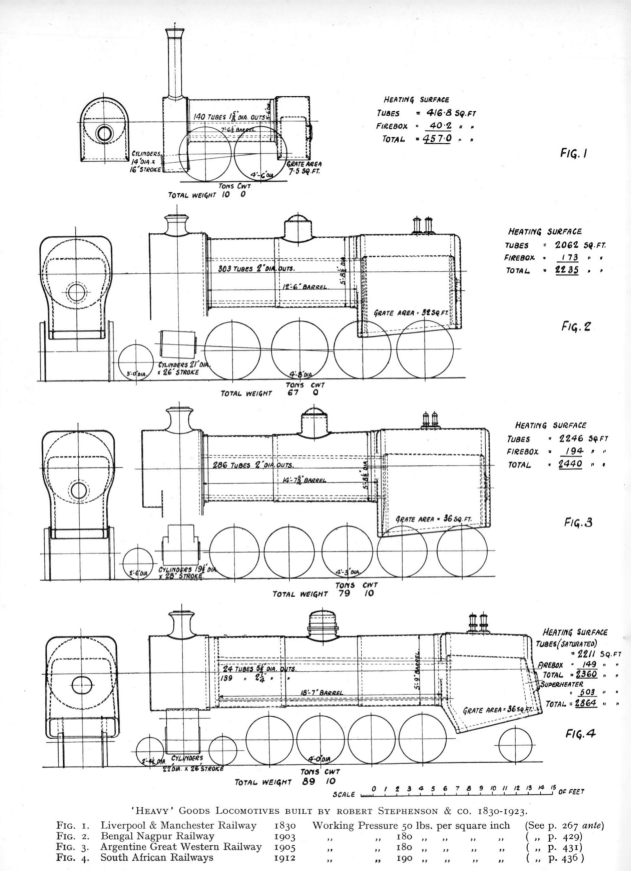

HEATING SURFACE
TUBES = 416·8 SQ.FT
FIREBOX = 40·2 „ „
TOTAL = 457·0 „ „

FIG. 1

140 TUBES 1⅝" DIA. OUTS
7'-6½" BARREL
CYLINDERS
14" DIA. x
16" STROKE
4'-6" DIA
GRATE AREA
7·5 SQ. FT.
TOTAL WEIGHT 10 0
TONS CWT

HEATING SURFACE
TUBES = 2062 SQ. FT.
FIREBOX = 173 „ „
TOTAL = 2235 „ „

FIG. 2

303 TUBES 2" DIA. OUTS.
12'-6" BARREL
5'-8½" DIA
GRATE AREA = 32 SQ. FT.
CYLINDERS 21" DIA.
x 26" STROKE
3'-0" DIA
4'-8" DIA
TOTAL WEIGHT 67 0
TONS CWT

HEATING SURFACE
TUBES = 2246 SQ. FT
FIREBOX = 194 „ „
TOTAL = 2440 „ „

FIG. 3

286 TUBES 2" DIA. OUTS.
14'-7½" BARREL
5'-8½" DIA
GRATE AREA = 36 SQ. FT.
CYLINDERS 19½" DIA.
x 28" STROKE
2'-6" DIA
4'-5" DIA
TOTAL WEIGHT 79 10
TONS CWT

HEATING SURFACE (SATURATED)
TUBES (SATURATED)
= 2211 SQ. FT.
FIREBOX = 149 „ „
TOTAL = 2360 „ „
SUPERHEATER
= 503 „ „
TOTAL = 2864 „ „

FIG. 4

24 TUBES 5½" DIA. OUTS.
139 „ 2¼" „
18'-7" BARREL
5'-9" BARREL
GRATE AREA = 36 SQ. FT.
CYLINDERS
22" DIA. x 26" STROKE
3'-4½" DIA
4'-0" DIA
TOTAL WEIGHT 89 10
TONS CWT

SCALE 0 1 2 3 4 5 6 7 8 9 10 11 12 13 14 15 OF FEET

'HEAVY' GOODS LOCOMOTIVES BUILT BY ROBERT STEPHENSON & CO. 1830–1923.

FIG. 1. Liverpool & Manchester Railway   1830   Working Pressure 50 lbs. per square inch   (See p. 267 *ante*)
FIG. 2. Bengal Nagpur Railway   1903   „   „ 180 „ „ „ „   („ p. 429)
FIG. 3. Argentine Great Western Railway   1905   „   „ 180 „ „ „ „   („ p. 431)
FIG. 4. South African Railways   1912   „   „ 190 „ „ „ „   („ p. 436)

CHAPTER XXX

THE MODERN STEAM LOCOMOTIVE

1903—1923

Steam is almost an Englishman.—*Emerson.*

Voilà la plus merveilleuse de toutes les Machines ; le Mécanisme ressemble à celui des animaux. . . . .
Cette Machine a pris sa naissance en Angleterre.—*Belidor.*

The latter words were written nearly two hundred years ago, of the Newcomen pumping engines at work in the early years of the eighteenth century, the first engines in which the power of steam was applied to a piston in order to produce a reciprocating motion. Later, Watt accomplished the translation of a reciprocating into a rotative motion, and finally Trevithick successfully made the steam engine loco-motive, so completing the analogy to a living organism which had impressed the French engineer, and adding that remarkable suggestion of personality which has made the steam locomotive so attractive to mankind.

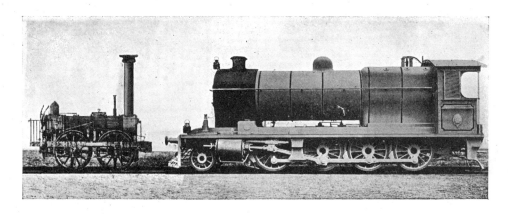

1830   'HEAVY' STEPHENSON GOODS ENGINES   1903

We shall conclude our 'Century of Locomotive Building' with a few examples of the modern locomotives constructed by Robert Stephenson & Co. during the past twenty years ; but although the productions of their Darlington works are in a broad sense 'Stephenson' locomotives, they are not necessarily all designed by the firm which bears that name to-day. Some are literally so, others are built to designs and drawings supplied by the various railway companies. From the general interchange and publication of drawings which now prevails there results an increasing tendency ·towards the disappearance of those individual characteristics which have distinguished the productions of the various locomotive builders in the past. Survivals of

427

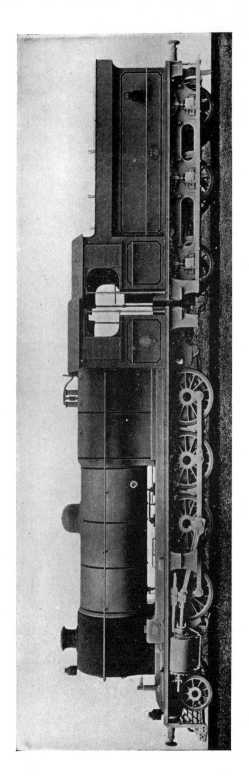

from a photo in the collection of the Locomotive Publishing Co., see 'The Locomotive,' Vol. XI., p. 180.

'H' CLASS HEAVY GOODS ENGINE BUILT FOR THE BENGAL NAGPUR RAILWAY, 1903

for dimensions, heating surface, and weight, see diagram p. 426 *ante*

individual practice may however be detected in the design of details, for the preparation of working drawings is still frequently left to the builders, especially when they are required to produce that '*multum in parvo*'—an engine of maximum power and minimum weight.

This was the fundamental problem which faced the designer of the first rail locomotive nearly one hundred and twenty years ago, and it remains the fundamental problem to-day; though the question to be decided now is, not whether to use four, or six, wheels, but whether ten, twelve, fourteen, or more will be required. For those who are not immediately behind the scenes, and for the many who are interested in the locomotive though not concerned with its construction, it may be worth while to describe the conditions under which the designs for new classes or types are prepared when the builders are not supplied with complete drawings. In such cases they are usually provided with a 'sketch' design, in which the locomotive is represented by a rectangular figure suggesting the boiler, and a series of circles representing the wheels ; a heating surface is indicated of the ample proportions desired by the locomotive superintendent to satisfy the running department of the railway company, and the weight is specified as the maximum allowed by the permanent way department. Such designs frequently represent an optimistic attempt to squeeze a quart into a pint pot, and the builders who, with equal optimism, accept this presentation of the case, and undertake to supply locomotives accordingly, are likely to find themselves involved in serious difficulties, and with engines on their hands weighing some tons in excess of the weight recorded on the sketch design.

BROAD GAUGE LOCOMOTIVES   Such a problem quickly presented itself on a large scale to Robert Stephenson & Co. in their new establishment, in 1902, in a contract for heavy goods engines required by the Bengal-Nagpur Railway Company for the Indian Standard gauge of 5 feet 6 inches. In this case neither the Consulting Engineer [1] nor the builders had any illusions as to the difficulty of the task before them, and when the engines had been successfully built to the specified weight, about 67 tons in working order, all concerned had cause for gratification.

These engines, the 'H' class of the Bengal-Nagpur Railway, have cylinders 21 inches diameter by 26 inches stroke, coupled wheels 4 feet 8 inches diameter, a working pressure of 180 lbs. per square inch, with a total saturated heating surface of about 2,000 square feet, and a grate area of 32 square feet. The tractive effort at low speeds is estimated at about 31,000 lbs. on the basis of a mean effective cylinder pressure of 85 per cent. of the boiler working pressure. Soon after they had been put into service these engines were operating coal trains having a gross total weight of 1,200 tons, and tests made with 1,600 tons behind the tender showed that it was not the engines, but the train couplings, which must be improved before the higher loads could be hauled in normal service.[2]

[1] Sir John Wolfe Barry, K.C.B.
[2] *The Locomotive*, 1905, Vol. XI., p. 180.

The subsequent adoption of couplings made of special alloy steel has made such loads practicable, and the engines are now, after twenty years, regularly employed on the heaviest traffic of the Bengal-Nagpur Railway, 'handling with ease the standard load of 1,500 tons over gradients of 1 in 200, with a coal consumption of 95 lbs. to 100 lbs. per train mile, and an average mileage of 80,000 miles between shop repairs. Trials made early in 1908 showed that an engine of this class could haul a load of 2,287 tons, starting at the foot of a 1 in 200 grade on a 2° curve, the whole of the load being on the grade and on the curve.' On the occasion of a heavy block of traffic one of these engines has worked a load of 1,914 tons behind the tender from Khargpur to Shalimar, a distance of 72½ miles, keeping the scheduled time at ten miles per hour, and generally speaking their actual performances exceed what might be expected on the basis of a theoretical tractive effort rated by the formulæ in general use. The original engines are still working with saturated steam, none of the class having been equipped with superheaters.[1]

BUILT FOR THE MADRAS AND SOUTHERN MAHRATTA RAILWAY
to the modified designs of the Indian Standard Locomotives Committee,

It is worth noting that they have the 'Stephenson' link motion, and in simplicity of design generally are typical of the practice to which the firm of Robert Stephenson & Co. have endeavoured to adhere for one hundred years. The production of this engine of at least double the weight of any locomotive built by the firm at their Newcastle works, showed at once the capacity of their new establishment at Darlington, and its performances gave sufficient evidence that they had not forgotten the technical traditions of their earlier days.

So immediately successful were the 'H' class engines of the Bengal-Nagpur Railway that the type was adopted by the Standards Committee for the Indian State Railways, though with some slight modification in the design of details. Subsequently, in accordance with the tendency of the time, the Stephenson valve gear was abandoned, and Walschaerts gear adopted for the Standard

---

[1] Letter to Robert Stephenson & Co. from Mr. A. C. Carr, former Chief Mechanical Engineer, now of Sir John Wolfe Barry & Partners, Consulting Engineers.

Indian designs. This had the advantage of enabling a drive on to the third axle, but it involved an increase to the weight of the engine. In 1907 engines of the modified type were built at Darlington for the Madras and Southern Mahratta Railway Company, being the first locomotives for India to be equipped with superheaters; the necessary additions and modifications involved a further increase to the weight.

BUILT FOR THE ARGENTINE GREAT WESTERN RAILWAY,
see diagram p. 426 *ante*

In 1905 a heavy 'Decapod' experimental engine was built by Robert Stephenson & Co. for the 5 foot 6 inch gauge of the Argentine Great Western Railway, for working a section of that railway on which light axle loads only were permissible. This engine was the first of its type to be constructed in Great Britain; like most of the heavy engines built at the time it was fitted with Walschaerts valve motion. Some others of the class were subsequently built, but generally speaking the policy pursued by most railway companies of improving the permanent way so as to permit of higher axle loads rather than multiply the number of coupled wheels, has postponed the necessity for such wheel arrangements and comparatively few other ten-coupled engines have been built by British locomotive builders.

EXPRESS PASSENGER LOCOMOTIVE BUILT FOR THE BENGAL NAGPUR RAILWAY

BUILT FOR THE BENGAL NAGPUR RAILWAY, 5 FOOT 6 INCH GAUGE

BUILT FOR THE OTTOMAN RAILWAY (SMYRNA TO AIDIN), 4 FOOT 8½ INCH GAUGE

BROAD GAUGE TANK ENGINES As in the case of engines with tenders, such as we have described, there has been during the past twenty years a notable increase in the weight of tank engines, many of which are now built with eight wheels coupled, and leading and trailing bogies, or radial axleboxes. Engines of this type, supplied by Robert Stephenson & Co. for the 5 foot 6 inch gauge lines of the Bengal-Nagpur Railway[1], have been the proto-type for a new and useful class recently adopted by the Indian Standards Committee.

For mixed and passenger traffic the firm has built, for the Argentine Great Western, and for the Buenos Ayres Great Southern, Railways, tank engines having six wheels coupled and leading and trailing 'Bissell' trucks, a wheel arrangement well fitted for running in either direction as required.

BUILT FOR THE BRECON AND MERTHYR RAILWAY

STANDARD GAUGE TANK ENGINES Among the early productions of the Darlington works were six-coupled tank engines with trailing radial axlebox, designed for the severe gradients and curves of the Rhymney Railway, South Wales. Many others of the same type have since been supplied by Robert Stephenson & Co. for other Welsh railways, though with various modifications to suit the requirements of different companies. These engines, though by modern standards they would be considered 'light,' are typical of the simple 'Stephenson' locomotive which has done useful work on British railways for many years.

A modern 'heavy' tank engine is represented by the locomotive built for the Ottoman Railway (Smyrna to Aidin).

[1] To the designs of Mr. A. S. Bailey, then Chief Mechanical Engineer.

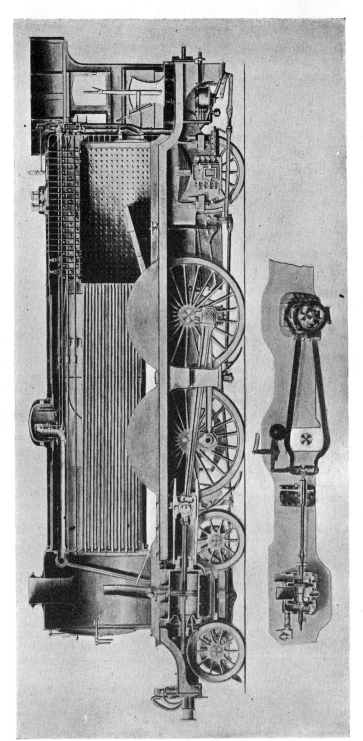

'ATLANTIC' EXPRESS LOCOMOTIVE BUILT BY ROBERT STEPHENSON & CO. FOR THE NORTH BRITISH RAILWAY

Heating Surface, tubes	..	2071·5 square feet		
,, ,, firebox	,,	184·5 ,, ,,		
,, ,, total	,,	2256·0 ,, ,,		
Grate Area,	,,	28·5 ,,		
Working Pressure,	200 lbs. per square inch			
Cylinders, diameter	..	..	20 inches	
,, stroke	..	..	28 ,,	
Coupled Wheels, diameter	..	6 feet 9 inches		
Weight on Coupled Wheels,	..	40 tons 10 cwt.		
Weight of Engine, Total	..	74 ,, 15 ,,		

STANDARD GAUGE ENGINES WITH TENDERS For the 'Standard' 4 foot 8½ inch gauge many tender engines of various types have been built by the firm at its Darlington works for both home and foreign railways. Among these have been four-coupled bogie passenger engines, and six-coupled goods engines, of the types defined during the lifetime of Robert Stephenson. The four-coupled heavy express passenger engine has developed logically by the addition of trailing carrying wheels into the 'Atlantic' type[1], of which some notable examples are in service on the North British Railway, on which they have been remarkably successful in performance; their essential simplicity of design is shown by the sectional drawing opposite.[2]

BUILT FOR THE OTTOMAN RAILWAY (SMYRNA TO AIDIN)

In recent years the majority of engines built for express work have had six, and for goods traffic, eight wheels coupled. We illustrate as typical an eight-coupled goods engine for the Ottoman Railway (Smyrna to Aidin).

Robert Stephenson & Co. have also built some remarkable six-coupled locomotives with a leading truck, a type now in general use for mixed traffic.[3] These engines, built to the designs of the Great Western Railway Company, have cylinders 18½ inches diameter by 30 inches stroke; the coupled wheels are 5 feet 8 inches diameter; the boiler provides a total tube surface of about 1,478 square feet, with a firebox heating surface of about 128 square feet and a grate area of about 20½ square feet. The boilers are fitted with the 'Swindon' superheater, having a surface of about 186 square feet. The working pressure is 200 lbs. per square inch; the total weight in working order is 64 tons, of which about 53 tons 14 cwt. are on the coupled wheels.

[1] For a similar evolution, see pp. 397, 398 *ante*.

[2] The first engines of this class, to the designs of Mr. W. P. Reid, late Locomotive Superintendent, were built by the North British Locomotive Company; later engines have been equipped with superheaters. For an account of the performances of both classes, see *Journal Institution Locomotive Engineers*, Vol. XVIII., p. 189.

[3] One of the standard types designed by Mr. G. J. Churchward when Chief Mechanical Engineer; for others see *The Engineer*, Vol. CX., Supplement, 16th December, p. xii.

BUILT FOR THE NATAL SECTION OF THE SOUTH AFRICAN RAILWAYS, 3 FOOT 6 INCH GAUGE

BUILT FOR THE SUDAN GOVERNMENT RAILWAYS, 3 FOOT 6 INCH GAUGE

Engines of this type are chiefly employed on long distance freight trains fitted with a vacuum brake, and timed at speeds of from 40 to 45 miles per hour with loads of 60 wagons, giving a total weight of about 600 tons. The ordinary freight trains which they work are composed of 70 to 80 wagons giving a gross weight of 700 to 800 tons, and are timed at from 30 to 35 miles per hour. Engines of this type are also employed on semi-fast passenger trains having speeds between stations of from 45 to 50 miles per hour, and are most useful for sections where the gradients are severe. The trains are composed of from 9 to 11 coaches and have approximate total weights of from 240 to 350 tons.[1]

BUILT FOR THE GREAT WESTERN RAILWAY

The engines built by the firm at Darlington take their place with others of the same class built at the Swindon works of the Great Western Railway Company, whose standard of attainment on the narrow gauge to day remains as it was set in 1837 for the broad gauge. Whether, like the 'North Star' then, the engine of 1923 would be 'a beautiful ornament for a lady's drawing room' is for modern taste to decide.[2] Economic considerations to-day prohibit the finish and decoration which were at one time considered essential, but if fitness be a test of beauty, the standard engines of the Great Western Railway to-day will satisfy the standard laid down by Brunel.

NARROW GAUGE LOCOMOTIVES During the past twenty years Robert Stephenson & Co. have built many hundreds of locomotives, varying in weight between 10 and 140 tons, for narrow gauges of from 2 feet $5\frac{1}{2}$ inches to 3 feet 6 inches; for the metre gauge lines of India they have built to the well-known 'Standard' designs.[3]

For the South African Government Railways with a gauge of 3 feet 6 inches they have supplied large numbers of heavy goods engines[4] to operate on the

---

[1] Communicated to Robert Stephenson & Co. by Mr. C. B. Collett, now Chief Mechanical Engineer.

[2] See Brunel's letter to T. E. Harrison, pp. 338, 441.

[3] *British Engineering Standards Association. Report* No. 50; also *Proc. Inst. Mech. Engineers*, 1910.

[4] These engines form one of several successful classes designed by Mr. D. A. Hendrie, late Chief Mechanical Engineer. See opposite page.

lines of the Natal section, where curves and gradients are of unusual severity; these engines afford striking evidence of the fact that load gauge, rather than rail gauge, is the limit to the capacity of the modern locomotive.

'MIKADO' TYPE LOCOMOTIVE FOR THE KASSALA RAILWAY
3 foot 6 inch gauge.

BAR FRAME FOR 'MIKADO' TYPE LOCOMOTIVE 1923

Among other noteworthy engines for the 3 foot 6 inch gauge are those of the 'Atlantic' type built for the Sudan Government Railways, on which this class has been remarkably successful for all services; these engines, shown on a previous page, embody many interesting features.[1]

[1] See *The Engineer*, Vol. CX., p. 95. These, and the 'Mikado' type engines shown above, are to the designs of Mr. C. G. Hodgson, Consulting Mechanical Engineer to the Sudan Government Railways.
The design of the trailing truck for the latter engines is due to the late W. S. Hodges; see *Engineering*, Vol. XCIX., p. 651.

In its Centenary year the firm is building, for the Kassala line extension of the same railways, locomotives of the 'Mikado' type, in which, though they embody the latest American designs, we find echoes of a Stephenson practice of nearly ninety years ago.

Little as may be the external resemblance, it would indeed be difficult to find the steam locomotive to-day which does not embody in either an identical, or some highly developed form, one or more of the many devices which have been originally applied by Robert Stephenson & Co. at some time during the Century of locomotive building which they have just completed.

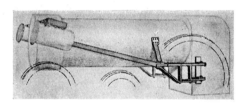

STEPHENSON BAR FRAME FOR AMERICA
1835

APPENDIX

The following letters (from the collection of Mr. Isaac Briggs) were received too late for inclusion in the text :—

(*a*)

LIVERPOOL RAILWAY OFFICE,
March 17, 1829.

DEAR SIR,

When I had the pleasure of meeting you at Durham you stated that you had made some observations with deflexion of the Rails caused by the different Locomotive Engines on the Darlington & Stockton Railway. You mentioned that the six wheel engine made at Newcastle with springs caused less deflexion than any of the 4 wheeled engines though much heavier.

In the present discussion going on amongst the Directors of the Company this would be an interesting and important fact to lay before them. May I therefore beg the favour of your writing me a letter containing the results of your experiments and observations on this point.

The weight of the engine I allude to is stated by Raistrick & Walker at 10 Tons & some odd weight—I don't remember. Your early attention to this will oblige,

Yours very truly

ROBT. STEPHENSON.

Mr. Thomas Storey
    Engineer
        Railway Office
           Darlington.

NOTE.—The locomotive referred to is the 'Experiment' on the Stockton and Darlington Railway (*see* page 123). The letter is important as showing that the question of six-wheeled *v.* four-wheeled locomotives raised in George Stephenson's report to the Directors of the Liverpool and Manchester Railway (*see* page 169) must have been fully considered by them in the light of experience obtained with the Stephenson six-wheeled engine on the Stockton and Darlington Railway. This appears to have been the first locomotive having such a wheel arrangement combined with the complete and efficient application of springs which was made possible by the use of horizontal cylinders.

(*b*)

18 DUKE STREET, WESTMINSTER,
March 6th, 1838.

Great Western Railway.

MY DEAR SIR,

I congratulate you upon the success which has attended the trials of your engines. I am effectually puzzled as to the name—I am much obliged to you for the offer of naming it after me but it is quite inadmissible.

I do take considerable merit to myself for having at once adopted what I believe will prove a most important change in the construction—and I shall be very much gratified if hereafter—when the success becomes equally evident to all—my early 'patronage' as you call it, is remembered—but I have no pretension to anything beyond this and my name might mislead—I should prefer a distinct class of names—which if possible should in some way have reference to their peculiar character, and at the same time if possible which wᵈ admit of the addition of your name in speaking of them—I should propose then this first should bear your name simply but then I think as we have others making & which will I hope soon follow—it would be a pity to fix your name untill we determine which is the best of the three—at present therefore perhaps we had better postpone this by no means unimportant question—and in the mean time it will be called 'Harrison's Engine.'

You ought to have sent me more details—does the gearing make much noise—how does the boiler work? I am very sorry that you have no reversing motion as it will prevent my venturing upon so great a speed as I otherwise should at all events until I have 10 miles clear run which will not be much before the opening of the whole—I trust you have applied good breaks and that there will be *plenty of steam*.

I imagine there must be some screen to protect the engine man or he will be cut to pieces with the wind—have you arranged anything—and lastly let me call your attention to the appearance—we have a splendid engine of Stephenson's it would be a beautyfull ornament in the most elegant drawing room and we have another of Quaker-like simplicity carried even to shabbyness but very possibly as good an engine but the difference in the care bestowed by the engine man the favour in which it is held by others and even oneself not to mention the public—is striking—a *plain* young lady however amiable is apt to be neglected—now your engine is capable of being made very handsome—and *it ought to be so*.

Yours very truly
I. K. Brunel

Thos. E. Harrison, Esq.
Stanhope & Tyne Railway
South Shields.

Note.—This letter has reference to the geared engines built by R. & W. Hawthorn for the Great Western Railway Company to the designs of T. E. Harrison (*see* p. 337), and is evidence that Brunel himself approved of the attempt to return to the use of gears. These engines appear to have been complete failures.

For a quotation of the concluding paragraph, *see* p. 338; the correct transcription of the original is as given above.

INDEX

Abbreviations of railway titles have been used in the following cases : G.W.R., for Great Western Railway ; L. & M.R., for Liverpool and Manchester Railway ; S. & D.R., for Stockton and Darlington Railway. A bibliography of Authorities quoted will be found in the footnotes to the references. Drawings or illustrations are indicated by the figures in heavy type. Names of particular locomotives are given in italics. Titles of published engravings, etchings, and prints are given in italics ; the artist's name, date, and publisher's name are given under each illustration.

'A' Engine, The, **372**, 375, 377, 379 ; Gooch's opinion of, 385 ; performance in Gauge Experiments, 385 *et seq.* ; diagram, **401**.

'A' Type Locomotives, adoption of, 391 ; for Egypt, **395** ; for Flanders, **390**, 395 ; influence on Continental design, 395.

Aalen, locomotive building at, 321.

Abbas Pasha, Saloon engine for, **104**, **409**.

Accidents, due to broken crank axles, 312 ; to high speed, 373 ; to light weight, 386.

Adams, W., locomotives designed by, **412**.

Adams, C. F., on early railroads in America, 299[2].

Adamson, James, secretary to Geo. Stephenson & Son, 64.

Adelaide and Gawler Town Railway, 411.

'*Adelaide*,' The (S. & D.R.), 295 ; boiler of, 297.

Adhesion, sufficiency of smooth wheels for, 13, 15, 20 ; experiments to prove, 17 ; with smooth wheels and edge rails, 22 ; with six wheels, 24 ; with cast iron wheels, 30.

Admiralty, The, work for, **418**, 419.

Africa, locomotives for, 413, **436**, **438**.

Airy, G. B., Professor, Gauge Commissioner, 374[2] ; opinion on 'A' Engine, 386 ; on weather, 388.

Alais and Beaucaire Railway, 93 ; locomotive for, **324**.

Alexandria to Cairo, proposed railway from, 104 ; bridge for, 408.

Allcard William, proposed appointment of, 64.

Allen, Horatio, visits England, 150 ; orders locomotives, 151.

'*America*,' The, 150.

America, United States of, visit of engineers from, 72 ; first locomotive for, 150 *et seq.* ; cylinder of first Stephenson locomotive for, **159** ; locomotives sent to, by English builders, 309[3] ; 'Planet' type in, 299 *et seq.* ; railway progress in, 299 ; condition of permanent way, 303 ; financial panic in, 376.

American Design, characteristics of, 152, 309 ; influences on, 305, 309 ; modern example of, **438**, **439**.

Anderson, T., 64 ; purchase of ground from, for Forth Street Works, 59, 60, 74.

'*Antiquary*,' The (G.W.R.), **403**.

Apprentices, Premium, Robert Stephenson's opinion of, T. Whitwell on, 89.

Argentine Great Western Railway, Decapod locomotive for, **426**, **431**, 433.

'*Arrow*,' The, L. & M.R., **232** ; original drawing for, **233** ; performance, 234, 266 ; weight, 234.

Artificial Draught, by exhaust steam, 13, 27, 139, 200 ; by bellows, 142, 147, 195, 201, **205**, 208, 245 ; by fan, **136**, 138, 210, 425 ; in fireplace, 141, 147, by stationary engine, 385.

Ashbox, **212**, 237, 276.

Ashes, ejection of when running, 351.

Ashpan, 276, **267**, **283**.

'*Atlas*,' The, (L. & M.R.), mileage of, 274.

'Atlantic' type locomotive, **434** ; evolution of, 435 ; for 3 foot 6 inch gauge, **436**, 438.

Atmospheric Railway, 6, **99** ; proposed from Newcastle-on-Tyne to Berwick-on-Tweed, opposed by the Stephensons, supported by Brunel, 99 ; failure of, in South Devon, 335[1].

Auckland, St. Helens, winding engine for, 74.

Austen, Jane, 185.

Australia, locomotive for, **410**, 411.

Avignon-Marseilles Railway, medal, **96**. *See also* Marseilles-Avignon.

Axle, 118 ; adjustable brasses for, **280** ; chairs for, 24 ; of 'Rocket,' 182 ; experiment with fractured, 328 ; swivelling, **114**.

Axle, Cranked. *See* Crank Axle.

Axlebox, 'Planet' type, **287** ; wear of, with outside cylinders, 380.

Axlebox Bearings, outside wheels, adopted by George Stephenson, 181, **333** ; advantages of, **398** ; above frame, 255, 339 ; bogie, 403, **404**.

Axlebox Horns, or Guides, 281 ; above frame, **254**, 255, **338**, 339 ; bolted on, **257** ; continuous plate, **282** ; forged solid, **280**.

Axle Rods, to support crank axle, **280**, 281.

Backhouse, Jonathan, 42, 46, 50.

'*Badger*,' The, steamship, 414.

Balance Weights, 377, 378, **392**, 393.

Balanced Locomotives, 393.

Balancing, proposal for, 377.

Baldwin, Matthias W., his first locomotive, 301 ; half crank, 307 ; practice in design, 309 ; use of Carmichael's valve gear, 307, 359[2].

Ball Valves, for pumps, 279, **287**.

Baltimore and Ohio Railroad, curves on, 305 ; gauge of, 331.

Baltimore and Susquehanna Railroad, 301 ; locomotive on, 304 ; cast iron crank axles on, 309 ; gauge of, 331.

Bandon and Wideopen Railway, 166.

Bangor, Old Town and Milford Railroad (Bangor & Piscataquis Canal and Railroad), locomotives, on, **304**.

Bank Engines, on L. & M.R., 266.

Bar Frame, introduced to America, 152 ; of 'Rocket,' 183 ; developed by Bury, 262, 309, **327** ; as made by Stephensons, 1835, **308**, **438** ; modern, **438**.

Barlow, Professor Peter, experiments with rails, 332[1] ; Gauge Commissioner, 374[2].

Barry, Sir John Wolfe, 429[1].

Battle of the Gauges, 100, 346, 373, 389 *et seq.* ; influence of, on design of locomotive, 399.